INTRODUCTORY ALGEBRA AND TRIGONOMETRY

by

ABRAHAM SPITZBART

and

ROSS H. BARDELL

University of Wisconsin—Milwaukee

ADDISON-WESLEY PUBLISHING COMPANY, INC.
READING, MASSACHUSETTS
PALO ALTO · LONDON

This book is in the
ADDISON-WESLEY SERIES
IN INTRODUCTORY MATHEMATICS

RICHARD S. PIETERS AND GEORGE B. THOMAS, JR.
Consulting Editors

Printed in the United States of America

Library of Congress Catalog Card No. 62–9397

PREFACE

With the needs of modern society in mind, educators are making an increasing effort to have students continue their mathematical education beyond the usual year of algebra and year of plane geometry. Those students who choose to continue may desire either to prepare for further work in mathematics, including the calculus, or to have an additional terminal course or courses.

The student for whom algebra and trigonometry is the terminal mathematics course should attempt to achieve some feeling for mathematics as a cultural subject and some knowledge of the concepts contained therein that can persist when the special skills may be forgotten. The continuing student must, of course, obtain a firm foundation in the many skills required, and at the same time must acquire a regard for mathematics as more than a mere collection of skills.

It was with the awareness of the needs of both types of student with minimal preparation, and the goal of satisfying both kinds of need with the same presentation, that the present book was undertaken. It is felt that the book is sufficiently broad to be useful for terminal mathematics, and at the same time sufficiently detailed to serve as an introduction to higher mathematics.

The first four chapters include some review of arithmetic, together with the fundamental operations as applied to algebraic quantities, and an elementary approach to factoring. The function concept is introduced in Chapter 5 as a set of ordered pairs of numbers and, insofar as possible, is used throughout the remainder of the text as a unifying idea relating to many of the usual topics in algebra and trigonometry.

The use of the radian measure of an angle is introduced early, in conjunction with the degree measure, and continuous use is made of it in the following treatment. The distinction between the idea of angle and the measure of an angle is clearly made.

The choice of four-place tables on which to base the numerical aspects of the presentation was made with the idea that such tables involve the same principles as do more accurate tables and have an advantage in the economy of time involved in their use.

There is adequate material for a course of up to eight semester hours. For the better prepared student, much of the first three chapters can be omitted and then the text can be adapted to a five or six semester hour course.

The integration of algebra and trigonometry has been effected where feasible, but artificial attempts at integration have been avoided. In many cases the exercises to be worked by the student have been designed so as to make use of common principles. For the reader, answers for odd-numbered exercises are provided at the back of the book. For the teacher, the answers to even-numbered exercises are available in a separate booklet.

A. S.
R. H. B.

January, 1962

CONTENTS

USEFUL ITEMS FROM PLANE GEOMETRY

1. Two angles are complementary if their sum is 90°.
2. Two angles are supplementary if their sum is 180°.
3. The sum of the angles of any triangle is 180°.
4. *Theorem of Pythagoras.* In a right triangle the square of the hypotenuse is equal to the sum of the squares of the legs.
5. If a right triangle has a 30° angle, the side opposite that angle is equal to one-half of the hypotenuse.
6. If two angles of a triangle are equal, the opposite sides are equal, and conversely.
7. Two triangles are similar if the angles of one are equal, respectively, to the angles of the other.
8. If two triangles are similar, corresponding sides of the triangles are proportional.
9. If the sides of an angle are perpendicular, respectively, to the sides of another angle, the angles are either equal or supplementary.
10. The area of any triangle is equal to one-half the product of any side and the altitude drawn to that side.
11. The angle bisectors of a triangle intersect in a point, which is the center of the inscribed circle.
12. The perpendicular bisectors of the sides of a triangle meet in a point, which is the center of the circumscribed circle.

Greek Alphabet

α alpha	β beta	γ gamma	δ delta	ϵ epsilon	ζ zeta
η eta	θ theta	ι iota	κ kappa	λ lambda	μ mu
ν nu	ξ xi	o omicron	π pi	ρ rho	σ sigma
τ tau	υ upsilon	ϕ phi	χ chi	ψ psi	ω omega

CHAPTER 1

THE REAL NUMBER SYSTEM AND FUNDAMENTAL OPERATIONS

1–1 The positive integers. The most elementary experience with numbers occurs in the process of learning to count. This use of numbers involves only the *positive integers* 1, 2, 3, 4, etc., or the *natural numbers*, as they are also called. We shall be concerned, initially, with the positive integers.

Addition of the positive integers is familiar from the study of arithmetic. For example, $3 + 4 = 7$, $19 + 12 = 31$, and so on. The next step in the operations with positive integers is the operation of multiplication. It is again familiar that the *multiplication* of positive integers is defined in terms of the addition of positive integers. Thus, the *product* of 3 and 7 means that 7 is to be used 3 times in an operation of addition, so that

$$3 \times 7 = 7 + 7 + 7 = 21.$$

1–2 The use of letters as numbers. One of the benefits to be derived from a study of algebra is that one learns to think of the processes of arithmetic with greater generality than was possible in arithmetic. Some of this generality is attained by the use of letters to represent numbers, in cases where we wish to talk about different numbers in the same sort of way. For example, we may wish to consider two integers whose sum is 7. If these integers are designated by the letters a and b, we write

$$a + b = 7.$$

We may then have $a = 3$ and $b = 4$, or $a = 6$ and $b = 1$, or several other possibilities. (What are all the possibilities if a and b are positive integers?)

With this idea in mind we may define multiplication of positive integers as follows:

DEFINITION 1–1. *If b and c are positive integers, the product of b and c means the sum $c + c + c + \cdots + c$, where there are b numbers c in the sum. The product of b and c is designated by bc, or $b \cdot c$, or $b \times c$.*

EXAMPLES. $4 \cdot 6 = 6 + 6 + 6 + 6 = 24;$

$6 \cdot 4 = 4 + 4 + 4 + 4 + 4 + 4 = 24.$

1–3 Parentheses or grouping symbols. Where a succession of arithmetic operations is involved, it is frequently necessary to use appropriate grouping symbols to indicate clearly how these operations are to be performed. What is the meaning of the expression $2 \cdot 3 + 4$? By historical agreement among the developers and users of algebra, it means that 3 is multiplied by 2 to give 6, and then 6 and 4 are added to give 10 as the final result. Now suppose we wish to indicate that 3 and 4 are to be added, to give 7, and then 7 is to be multiplied by 2 to give 14 as the final result. We would indicate this by enclosing $3 + 4$ in *parentheses*, ( ), and write the expression as

$$2 \cdot (3 + 4).$$

Such an expression is taken to mean precisely what we wish, that the operations within the parentheses are to be performed before other operations. We then have

$$2 \cdot (3 + 4) = 2 \cdot 7 = 14.$$

Other grouping symbols in more or less common use are *brackets*, [ ], *braces*, { }, and the vinculum, ——, the last one being placed above the expression to be considered as a group.

EXAMPLE. $2 + 3(4 + 5) + \overline{2 + 9} = 2 + 3 \cdot 9 + 11 = 2 + 27 + 11 = 40.$

As the expressions with which we deal become more complicated, it becomes necessary at times to have grouping symbols within grouping symbols. In the expression

$$7 + 3 \cdot [8 + 2 \cdot (10 + 4)]$$

the number 3 multiplies everything within the brackets, while the number 2 multiplies the numbers within the parentheses. Thus we evaluate the above expression as follows:

$$\begin{aligned} 7 + 3 \cdot [8 + 2 \cdot (10 + 4)] &= 7 + 3 \cdot [8 + 2 \cdot 14] = 7 + 3 \cdot [8 + 28] \\ &= 7 + 3 \cdot 36 = 7 + 108 = 115. \end{aligned}$$

EXAMPLE. Evaluate the expression

$$a(b + c) + xy$$

if $a = 2$, $b = 2$, $c = 7$, $x = 5$, and $y = 6$.

Solution. In such an evaluation, we may substitute the given values, and then proceed. Thus,

$$a(b + c) + xy = 2(2 + 7) + 5 \cdot 6 = 2 \cdot 9 + 30 = 18 + 30 = 48.$$

It is convenient at this point to introduce the minus sign (—) and to indicate the difference between a and b as $a - b$. Thus we have $9 - 2 = 7$. We note that it is not always possible to find the difference between two positive integers as a positive integer (for example, $3 - 5$ is not a positive integer). In order to have a system of numbers in which subtraction is always possible, it is necessary to define *zero* and *negative integers*, and to enlarge the system of positive integers by adjoining these new numbers. We shall define the number *zero* as the difference between any positive integer and itself,

$$0 = a - a,$$

so that if the previous definition of subtraction is to hold, we must have the property

$$a + 0 = a.$$

A *negative integer* $(-a)$, where a is a positive integer, is then defined as the number which, when added to a, gives zero,

$$a + (-a) = 0.$$

(In the discussion of zero and negative integers we have made the assumption that the difference $a - b$ between two integers a and b is unique, that is, that there cannot be more than one integer c such that $a = b + c$.)

By adjoining the negative integers and zero to the positive integers, we obtain, simply, the system of integers. (Note that zero is included in the system of integers.) We shall consider the arithmetic operations of the system of integers in the next section.

1–6 Operations with positive and negative integers. The generality with which we are concerned in algebra requires that we deal with both positive and negative numbers. The rules for operating with negative numbers can be derived from those for the positive integers, plus the definitions of the preceding section, and the requirement that the system of all integers obey the same laws as the positive integers (given in Section 1–4).

Addition. The addition of two positive integers is familiar. What shall be meant by the addition of two negative integers? Let the negative integers be $(-a)$ and $(-b)$, where a and b are positive integers. By the definition we have

$$a + (-a) = 0, \qquad b + (-b) = 0.$$

By adding the two quantities which are zero, we again have zero; hence

$$a + b + (-a) + (-b) = 0.$$

Since we may introduce grouping symbols, we may write this equation as

$$(a + b) + [(-a) + (-b)] = 0.$$

Now, since $a + b$ is a positive integer, the equation just obtained defines the negative of $a + b$, and we have

$$(-a) + (-b) = -(a + b).$$

The rule for the addition of positive numbers, or for the addition of negative numbers, may now be written as follows:

When two numbers of the same sign are to be added, proceed as though both numbers are positive, and attach the sign of the given numbers to the result.

EXAMPLES. $3 + 5 = 8$; $-3 + (-5) = -8$.

It is not our intention to prove all the properties of the operations with negative integers; some of these properties will merely be stated.

It is convenient at times, when talking about numbers, to refer only to the numerical value of the number, apart from its sign. For example, the *numerical value* of 3, as well as of -3, is taken to be 3. Another name for numerical value is *absolute value*. A more formal definition need not be given here.

When two numbers of opposite sign are to be added, subtract the smaller numerical value from the larger numerical value, and attach the sign of the number with the larger numerical value.

EXAMPLES. $3 + (-5) = -2$; $5 + (-3) = 2$;
$(-7) + 9 = 2$; $-9 + 5 = -4$.

Subtraction. Subtraction which involves negative numbers is defined in precisely the same manner as the subtraction of positive integers. *To subtract a positive number from a positive number, subtract the smaller number from the larger one, and attach the sign of the larger number.*

EXAMPLES. $(7) - (9) = -2$; $(6) - (2) = 4$; $12 - 13 = -1$.

To subtract a positive number from a negative number, add the positive number to the numerical value of the negative number, and place a minus sign before the result.

EXAMPLES. $(-3) - (8) = -(3 + 8) = -11$;
$(-5) - (12) = -(5 + 12) = -17$.

To subtract a negative number, simply add the numerical value of the negative number.

EXAMPLES. $(19) - (-12) = 19 + 12 = 31;$
$(-8) - (-3) = -8 + 3 = -5.$

We shall indicate a proof of the latter rule. Let

$$N = a - (-b).$$

By the above definition of subtraction this means that

$$a = N + (-b).$$

We now add b to the two equal numbers and obtain

$$a + b = N + (-b) + b = N + [(-b) + b] = N.$$

Hence $a - (-b) = a + b$, which is precisely what the rule states.

EXERCISE GROUP 1–2

In Exercises 1–16, (a) add the two numbers, (b) subtract the second from the first.

1. 27, −19	2. 33, −26	3. 13, −71	4. −17, 26
5. −39, 47	6. −27, 84	7. −19, −7	8. −13, −78
9. −26, −35	10. 28, −38	11. −72, 39	12. −81, −18
13. 37, −22	14. −43, 37	15. −16, −62	16. 105, 217

In Exercises 17–36, evaluate the given expression if $a = -3, b = 7, c = -12, d = -19, x = 5$, and $y = -43$.

17. $x - a$
18. $y - b$
19. $x - a + b$
20. $x + a - c$
21. $a + b - c$
22. $a - x - y$
23. $(a + b) + (x + y)$
24. $(a + b) - (x + y)$
25. $a - b + c - d$
26. $a - x - b + y$
27. $(a + b) - (c + d + x)$
28. $(a - b) + (c - d + x)$
29. $(a + x) + (b - x - y)$
30. $(x + y - d) - (a - b)$
31. $(a + b + d) - (x + y - c)$
32. $(x - a + c) + (d - b - y)$
33. $(a + c + y) - (b - d - x)$
34. $(b + c - x) - (a + d - y)$
35. $-(a + b) - (c - d) + (x - y)$
36. $(a - b) - (c - d) - (x - y)$

1–7 Multiplication of integers. In the development of the operation of multiplication in which negative integers are involved, we impose the requirement, as with addition and subtraction, that the same properties are satisfied as are satisfied in the multiplication of positive integers. For example, by the product $4 \cdot (-3)$ is meant

$$4 \cdot (-3) = (-3) + (-3) + (-3) + (-3) = -12.$$

Since the commutative law is to hold for multiplication, the same value, -12, is obtained for the product $(-3) \cdot 4$. We state the rule of which we have just seen an example.

To multiply a positive integer and a negative integer (in either order), multiply the positive integer by the numerical value of the negative integer, and prefix a minus sign.

There remains the consideration of the product of two negative integers. Let a and b be positive integers. Then

$$a + (-a) = 0.$$

It can be shown that the product of any integer and zero is again zero. If we now multiply both members of the preceding equation by $(-b)$, we have

$$a(-b) + (-a)(-b) = 0. \tag{1}$$

We also have

$$b + (-b) = 0,$$

so that, on multiplying by a,

$$ab + a(-b) = 0. \tag{2}$$

Now (1) says that $(-a)(-b)$ is the negative of $a(-b)$, and (2) says that ab is the negative of $a(-b)$. Hence

$$(-a)(-b) = ab,$$

and we have the rule:

The product of two negative integers is equal to the product of their numerical values, and is positive.

EXAMPLE 1. $(-2)(-3) = 6$; $(-2)(-3)(4) = [(-2)(-3)](4) = 6 \cdot 4 = 24$; $(-2)(-3)(-4) = [(-2)(-3)](-4) = 6(-4) = -24$.

From these examples, we are led to the following result, for which a formal proof could be given.

The product of any number of nonzero integers is positive if an even number of the integers are negative, and is negative if an odd number of the integers are negative.

It follows from the above development that *Properties A, B, C, D, and E of Section* 1–4 *now hold for the system of all integers.*

EXAMPLE 2. $2 \cdot 3 \cdot (-2)(-4) = 48$; $(-1)(-3)(-7) = -21$;
$(-2)(-4)(3)(-2) + (-2)(-3) = -48 + 6 = -42$.

EXAMPLE 3. Evaluate the following expression:

$$9 - 2[3 + 2(8 - 14) - 7\{9 - 3(-2 - 8)\}].$$

Solution. Calling the desired value N, we have

$$\begin{aligned} N &= 9 - 2[3 + 2(-6) - 7\{9 - 3(-10)\}] \\ &= 9 - 2[3 - 12 - 7\{9 + 30\}] \\ &= 9 - 2[-9 - 7(39)] = 9 - 2[-9 - 273] \\ &= 9 - 2[-282] = 9 + 564 = 573. \end{aligned}$$

EXERCISE GROUP 1–3

In Exercises 1–24, evaluate the given expression.

1. $(-3)(-5)$
2. $(-5)(7)$
3. $(-9)(-7)$
4. $(17)(-13)$
5. $(-2)(-6)(7)$
6. $(-5)(-7)(-9)$
7. $(-4)(6)(-7)$
8. $(2)(-4)(-6)(8)$
9. $(-4)(-7)(3)(-9)$
10. $(3)(5)(7)(-9)$
11. $(-3)(-6)(-9)(-12)$
12. $(31)(-27)(-19)(-11)$
13. $(23)(-15)(-17)(33)$
14. $3 - 7(2 - 5)$
15. $-4 + 3(2 - 7)$
16. $(3 - 7)(2 - 5)$
17. $(-4 + 3)(2 - 7)$
18. $5 - 2[4 - 3(1 - 3)]$
19. $-5 - 3[(4 - 3)(1 - 3)]$
20. $7 - 3[2(7 - 4) - 3(8 - 2)]$
21. $5 - 2[-3(-2 - 7) - 5(-3 + 7)]$
22. $(-7 + 3)(-13 + 5) + (5 - 8)(26 - 11)$
23. $3 - (13 - 5) - 14(11 - 7)$
24. $8 - 3(5 + 9) + 9(3 - 5)$

In Exercises 25–36, evaluate the given expression after setting $x = 2$, $y = -3$, and $z = 5$.

25. $-2(4x - 5y)$
26. $z(x - 3y)$
27. $(x - y)(x + 2z)$
28. $(x - 7)(2y + 4)$
29. $(2x - y) - (3x + 7y)$
30. $(x + 2z) - 3(x - y)$
31. $2(x + 3y) - 4(y - z)$
32. $x(y + z) - y(x + z)$
33. $x + 3(2x - 3y) - 4(3z - 7x)$
34. $(x + 2)(y - 7) - (2x - 1)(y + 2)$
35. $(x + y + z)(x + y - z)$
36. $3x - 4(2y - 3x) - 3[2y - 2(2y + x)]$

1–8 Algebraic sums. In Section 1–2 the use of letters was introduced to represent integers. This idea will be carried further here. For example, the expression ax means the product of the integers represented by a and x. We may also have more involved expressions, such as $ax + by - c$, in which five letters are used to represent integers. Such an expression is an example of an *algebraic sum*. In an algebraic sum each part, together with the sign which is present or implied before it, is called a *term* of the expression.

Terms such as $2ax$ and $5ax$, which are identical in the literal part, and differ only in the multiplier, are called *similar*. They may be combined as follows:

$$\begin{aligned} 2ax + 5ax &= (ax) \cdot 2 + (ax) \cdot 5 && \text{(commutative law of multiplication)} \\ &= (ax)(2 + 5) && \text{(distributive law)} \\ &= (ax) \cdot 7 = 7ax && \text{(commutative law of multiplication).} \end{aligned}$$

This suggests the general law by which similar terms may be combined. Similarly, we have

$$2ax - 5ax = (2 - 5)ax = -3ax.$$

The sign associated with the expression ax is plus, since no specific sign precedes ax. However, as a number, ax is a product, and may be positive or negative, depending on the signs of the values represented by a and x. For a single letter we have $a = -(-a)$, if a is a positive integer. If a is a negative integer, the same rule holds; for example, if $a = -3$, we have $-(-a) = -(-[-3]) = -(+3) = -3$, which is the same as a.

We also write $ax = -(-ax)$, in a similar manner as with a single letter, since if a and x are integers, then ax is also an integer. As an illustration, suppose that $a = -3$, $x = -7$. Then

$$ax = (-3)(-7) = 21.$$

On the other hand, we have

$$-(-ax) = -(-[-3][-7]) = -(-[21]) = 21,$$

and we see that for the given values $ax = -(-ax)$.

What we have seen in the last two paragraphs are illustrations of a most important principle. If we think of ax, $-ax$, by, and so on, as *signed expressions* (the sign of the expression, and the sign of the number represented by the expression for given values of the letters may or may not be the same), this principle may be stated as follows.

The rules of signs as developed earlier for integers are equally valid for signed expressions.

EXAMPLES. $2ax - (-3ax) = 2ax + 3ax = 5ax;$
$-ay + 3(-ay) = -ay - 3ay = -4ay;$
$bx - 3(-4bx) = bx + 12bx = 13bx.$

We shall further illustrate the above principle in the following examples.

EXAMPLES. The sum of $(3x + 2y - 5)$ and $(2x - 3y + 7)$ is

$$\begin{aligned}(3x + 2y - 5) + (2x - 3y + 7) &= 3x + 2y - 5 + 2x - 3y + 7 \\ &= (3x + 2x) + (2y - 3y) + (-5 + 7) \\ &= 5x - y + 2.\end{aligned}$$

The difference between $(3x + 2y - 5)$ and $(2x - 3y + 7)$ is

$$\begin{aligned}(3x + 2y - 5) - (2x - 3y + 7) &= 3x + 2y - 5 - 2x + 3y - 7 \\ &= (3x - 2x) + (2y + 3y) + (-5 - 7) \\ &= x + 5y - 12.\end{aligned}$$

The last example illustrates the rule: *the removal of parentheses (or other grouping symbols) preceded by a minus sign necessitates a change in sign of each term within the parentheses.*

EXAMPLE.

$$\begin{aligned}3x - [2x + (x - 5) - (3x - 1)] &= 3x - [2x + x - 5 - 3x + 1] \\ &= 3x - [-4] = 3x + 4.\end{aligned}$$

The name *algebraic sum* is used even though some of the signs of the terms may be minus; thus $ax - by$ is a sum of the two terms ax and $(-by)$.

EXERCISE GROUP 1-4

In Exercises 1-8, determine the sum of the two expressions, and also the difference of the first expression minus the second.

1. $8x - 3y$ and $-5x + 2y$
2. $31 - 4a$ and $17 + 8a$
3. $21x + 13y$ and $9y + 11z$
4. $13a + 5x$ and $11y - 9x$
5. $26ab - 8abc - 15bc$ and $-12ab + 15abc - 20bc$
6. $19ab + 17bc - 14ac$ and $17ab + 19bc + 14ac$
7. $26m + 10x + 14v + z$ and $-12m + 15x - 20z$
8. $3x - 2y - 5z + 7w$ and $-2x - 3y - 7z + 5w$

In Exercises 9-24, remove all signs of grouping and combine similar terms.

9. $3x - (2x + 5y)$
10. $-2(4x - 5y) + 3x$
11. $(2x - y) - (4x - 7y)$
12. $3a - 3b - (4b - 4a)$
13. $-(m - 3n + 4p) + (-3m + 4n - 3p)$
14. $(4x - 20z) - (5z - 3y) + (8x + 9y)$

15. $5(a - 2b) - 7(2a - b)$
16. $-2(3x - 4y) - 4(2x + 7y)$
17. $a(b - c) - b(a - c)$
18. $x(y - z) + 2y(x - z) + 3z(x - y)$
19. $a + b - [(b + d) - (a - b)]$
20. $-[m - (m + n) - (m - n) - (n - m)]$
21. $x + y - [-(x - y) + \{x - (x - y) - x\}]$
22. $3x - [2(x - y) - 3(2x - y + z)]$
23. $-5(2x - 3y) + [3x - (2y - z)] - [(x - 2y) + (3x - 2z + y)]$
24. $-3 - \{2 - [5 + (7 - 4x - 3y) + 2(x - 3y)] + 3\}$

In Exercises 25–36, determine what expression must be added to the first quantity to obtain the second quantity.

25. $a, \quad b$
26. $a + 2, \quad 2a - 3$
27. $2a - 3b, \quad -a + b$
28. $-4b + 6c, \quad -10b + 3c$
29. $2x + 3y, \quad z$
30. $y - x, \quad 2a$
31. $2x - 7z, \quad x + 3z$
32. $2x + 3c, \quad 4x - 2c$
33. $a - 2b - c, \quad a - b + 2c$
34. $2x - 3w + 4, \quad 5x - 2w - 7$
35. $3x - 2y - 2z - 4w, \quad 3x + 4y - 5z - 6w$
36. $15a - 17b + 13x - 15y, \quad 9a - 7b + 11x - 19y$

In Exercises 37–46, enclose the last two terms of each expression in parentheses preceded by a minus sign.

37. $ax + bx - ay - by$
38. $ah - ak - bh + bk$
39. $cx - dx - dy + cy$
40. $ux - uy + vy - vx$
41. $3au + 3bu + bv - av$
42. $3cw - 3cx + 4kx - 4kw$
43. $3ax - 5bx + 6ay - 10by$
44. $cx + 3dx - 2cy - 6dy$
45. $bu - bv + 2hu - 2hv$
46. $-2ax + 2ah - abh + abx$

1–9 Exponents. We have earlier defined the product of positive and negative integers. Suppose we have the product of an integer by itself, as $3 \cdot 3$. We write that as 3^2, where the number 2, used in this manner, is called an *exponent*, and indicates that 3 is multiplied by itself; thus, $3^2 = 3 \cdot 3 = 9$. Similarly, we write

$$3^4 = 3 \cdot 3 \cdot 3 \cdot 3 = 81,$$

in which 4 is the exponent of 3^4 and indicates that 3 is used as a multiplier 4 times. In the same manner we write

$$b^2 = b \cdot b, \qquad b^3 = b \cdot b \cdot b, \qquad b^5 = b \cdot b \cdot b \cdot b \cdot b,$$

and analogously for any exponent which is a positive integer. The quantity 3^2 is called the second power, or *square* of 3, while b^3 is called the third power, or *cube* of b.

DEFINITION 1-2. *If n is a positive integer, the quantity b^n, the nth power of b, is defined as the product of n numbers each equal to b. In symbols, $b^n = b \cdot b \cdot b \cdots b$, where there are n numbers b in the product on the right.*

In particular, the first power of any number b is the number itself,

$$b^1 = b.$$

The following result is easily established, with n a positive integer:

b^n *is positive if* b *is positive,*

b^n *is positive if* b *is negative and* n *is even,*

b^n *is negative if* b *is negative and* n *is odd.*

EXAMPLES. $3^4 = 81$, $(-3)^4 = 81$, $(-4)^3 = -64$, $(-b)^3 = -b^3$, $(-b)^4 = b^4$.

The distinction between $(-b)^4$ and $-b^4$ should be noted. The two quantities are not equal. In particular, we may write $-b^4 = -(b^4)$, but in practice the parentheses are omitted.

By making use of the definition of the power b^n, we may derive important properties or laws of exponents. Thus b^pb^q means a product in which p numbers b are followed by q numbers b to give a product of $p + q$ numbers each equal to b; by Definition 1-2, this is equal to b^{p+q}. In condensed form we have

$$b^pb^q = \underbrace{(b \cdot b \cdots b)}_{p \text{ numbers } b} \cdot \underbrace{(b \cdot b \cdots b)}_{q \text{ numbers } b} = \underbrace{b \cdot b \cdots b}_{p+q \text{ numbers } b} = b^{p+q}.$$

The relevant properties are:

LAWS OF EXPONENTS		ILLUSTRATIONS
A.	$b^pb^q = b^{p+q}$	$a^2a^3 = a^{2+3} = a^5$
B.	$(b^p)^q = b^{pq}$	$(b^2)^3 = b^{2\cdot 3} = b^6$
C.	$(bc)^p = b^pc^p$	$(2a)^5 = 2^5a^5 = 32a^5$

Property B may be proved as follows (and Property C similarly):

$$(b^p)^q = \underbrace{b^p \cdot b^p \cdots b^p}_{q \text{ numbers } b^p} = \underbrace{\underbrace{(b \cdot b \cdots b)}_{p \text{ numbers } b} \cdots \underbrace{(b \cdot b \cdots b)}_{p \text{ numbers } b}}_{q \text{ products } (b \cdot b \cdots b)} = \underbrace{b \cdot b \cdots b}_{pq \text{ numbers } b} = b^{pq}.$$

The student should give the reason for each of the equals signs in the following examples.

EXAMPLES. $(a^2b^3)(a^4b^2) = (a^2a^4)(b^3b^2) = a^{2+4}b^{3+2} = a^6b^5$;
$(-2ab^2)^3 = (-2)^3a^3(b^2)^3 = -8a^3b^6$.

EXERCISE GROUP 1-5

In each of the following exercises, perform the indicated operations.

1. 3^2
2. 2^4
3. 4^3
4. 5^3
5. 6^3
6. 7^3
7. 3^5
8. $2^3 \cdot 2^5$
9. $3^2 \cdot 3^3$
10. $2^9 \cdot 2^{17}$
11. $10^5 \cdot 10^8$
12. $5^7 \cdot 5^8 \cdot 5^2$
13. $7^2 \cdot 7^9 \cdot 7^4$
14. $2^3 \cdot 5^3$
15. $(2 \cdot 5)^3$
16. $(2^4 \cdot 5^3)^3$
17. $(2^3 \cdot 3^2)^5$
18. $(3^2 \cdot 5^3)^4$
19. $(2^5 \cdot 7^2)^3$
20. $(2^3 \cdot 5^4)^2$
21. $(2^3 \cdot 3^2)^2(2^2 \cdot 3^3)^4$
22. $(3^2 \cdot 5^3)^2(3^4 \cdot 5^2)^3$
23. $(2^5 \cdot 3^2 \cdot 5^3)(2^3 \cdot 5^2)^2$
24. $2a^3 \cdot a^4$
25. $3x^3 \cdot x^2 \cdot x^4$
26. $(2x^3)(3x^2)^2$
27. $(2^2a^3)^2(3^2b^4)^3$
28. $(2^2a^5)^3(5^3a^2)^2$
29. $(a^2b^3)^2(a^3b^2)^3$
30. $(-2a^2)^3(-3a^3)^2$
31. $(-2ab^2)^5(-5a^3)^4$
32. $(-3ab^2)^2(-2a^2b)^3$
33. $(2a^h)^2(3a^h)^3$
34. $(2a^2b)^h(2^2b)^h$
35. $(a^2b)^k(ab^2)^k$
36. $(2a^2)^k(b^3)^k$
37. $(a^2b^3)^k(a^3b)^k$
38. $(a^3b^2c)^k(b^3c^2)^k$
39. $(3a^{2b}c^x)^d(3c^x)^d$
40. $(2a^xb^{2y})^k(2a^x)^k$
41. $(3a^{2h}b^k)^n(b^n)^k$
42. $(a^2)^k(a^h)^2$
43. $(2a^2)^k(2a^h)^3$
44. $(2a^k)^h(3a^h)^2$

1-10 Multiplication of algebraic expressions. By employing the properties developed in Section 1-7, in conjunction with the properties of exponents, we may multiply algebraic expressions. For example, by the distributive law of multiplication with respect to addition we have

$$\begin{aligned} 2x(3x - 4y) &= (2x)(3x) - (2x)(4y) \\ &= 6x^2 - 8xy. \end{aligned}$$

As another example, again by the use of the distributive law, with $3x + 2y$ considered initially as a single number, we have

$$\begin{aligned} (3x + 2y)(2x - 5y) &= (3x + 2y)(2x) + (3x + 2y)(-5y) \\ &= 6x^2 + 4xy - 15xy - 10y^2 \\ &= 6x^2 - 11xy - 10y^2. \end{aligned}$$

We observe that the technique of multiplication is equivalent to multiplying each term of the first expression by each term of the second expression, and then combining similar terms. This observation permits us to use the arrangement of the following example for certain multiplications.

EXAMPLE. Expand and simplify the expression

$$(2x^3 - 3x^2y - xy^2 + 3y^3)(x^2 + xy - 2y^2).$$

Solution. Write one expression under the other, and multiply the first expression by each term of the second expression, placing similar product terms in the same vertical column.

$$\begin{array}{llllll}
2x^3 - 3x^2y - xy^2 + 3y^3 & & & & & \\
x^2 + xy - 2y^2 & & & & & \\
\hline
2x^5 & - 3x^4y & - x^3y^2 & + 3x^2y^3 & & \\
 & 2x^4y & - 3x^3y^2 & - x^2y^3 & + 3xy^4 & \\
 & & - 4x^3y^2 & + 6x^2y^3 & + 2xy^4 & - 6y^5 \\
\hline
2x^5 & - x^4y & - 8x^3y^2 & + 8x^2y^3 & + 5xy^4 & - 6y^5
\end{array} \quad \text{(answer)}$$

The answer, which appears in the last row, is obtained by adding the three previous rows.

A useful aid in checking an algebraic operation is the substitution of particular numbers for the letters involved.

EXAMPLE. Check the following multiplication:

$$(3x + 2y)(2x - 5y) = 6x^2 - 11xy - 10y^2.$$

Solution. Let $x = 2$ and $y = 3$. Then,

$$\begin{aligned}
3x + 2y &= 3 \cdot 2 + 2 \cdot 3 = 6 + 6 = 12, \\
2x - 5y &= 2 \cdot 2 - 5 \cdot 3 = 4 - 15 = -11, \\
6x^2 - 11xy - 10y^2 &= 6 \cdot 4 - 11 \cdot 2 \cdot 3 - 10 \cdot 9 \\
&= 24 - 66 - 90 = -132.
\end{aligned}$$

We should have

$$12 \cdot (-11) = -132,$$

which is correct.

It is important to note that a check as just carried out is not a proof. As an illustration, suppose that in some manner one obtained $9x^2 - 13xy - 10y^2$ for the product in the above example. Substitution of $x = 2$ and $y = 3$ gives

$$9x^2 - 13xy - 10y^2 = 9 \cdot 4 - 13 \cdot 2 \cdot 3 - 10 \cdot 9 = 36 - 78 - 90 = -132,$$

which provides a "check" although the result is incorrect. However, if such a check does not work, the relation must be false.

Exercise Group 1–6

In Exercises 1–47, perform the indicated multiplications and collect similar terms. Check as directed by the instructor.

1. $3x(2x - 5)$
2. $2a(3 - 4a)$
3. $-a(2x - ay)$
4. $-3a(-2x + 3y)$
5. $-3y(a - 2y)$
6. $-5y(2ay^2 - y^4 - 6y)$
7. $-3xy(x^2 - y^2 - 1)$
8. $-5a^2(-5a^2 - 5a - 5)$
9. $\frac{3}{2}a^2(4a^4 - 2ab - 4b^4)$
10. $6xy^2(2x^2 - 2xy - y^3 - 1)$
11. $-5x^4y(7xyz - 5xy^2z^2 - 2z^3)$
12. $-4xz(5x^2z - 3xz^2 + 2xz)$
13. $3x(2 - 3x + 4x^2)$
14. $(x - 2)^2$
15. $(x - 4)(x + 5)$
16. $(x + 3)^2$
17. $(2x - 5)^2$
18. $(3x + 7)(2x - 5)$
19. $(3x - 4y)(5x + 7y)$
20. $(3x + 5y)^2$
21. $(2y - 3z)^2$
22. $(x + 5)(x^2 - 5x + 25)$
23. $(2x - b)(2x + b)$
24. $(x - 5)(x + 5)$
25. $(x - 2y)(x^2 + 2xy + 4y^2)$
26. $(x^2 + 5x + 6)(x + 4)$
27. $(x + 1)(x + 2)(x + 3)$
28. $(x - 3)(x + 4)(x - 5)$
29. $(2x - 3y)(2x + 3y)$
30. $(3x + 5y)(7x + 9y)$
31. $(2x - 3y)(3x - 4y)$
32. $(3x - 7y)^2$
33. $(ax^2 + by^3)^2$
34. $(ax + y)^3$
35. $(x^4 - 3x^3 - 4x^2 + 5x + 3)(x - 7)$
36. $(a^4 - 4a^3b + 6a^2b^2 - 4ab^3 + b^4)(a^2 - 2ab + b^2)$
37. $(x^7 + x^3 + x + 1)(x^3 - 3x - 1)$
38. $(x^2 + y^2)(x^2 - y^2)(x^4 + y^4)$
39. $(a + 1)(a - 1)(a^2 + 1)(a^4 + 1)(a^8 + 1)$
40. $(\frac{1}{2}a^2 + \frac{1}{3}a - 1)(2a - 4)(6a - 3)$
41. $(a^m - 3a^{m-1} + 4a^{m-2})(a^2 + a + 1)$
42. $(x^7 + x^6 + x^5 + x^4 + x^3 + x^2 + x + 1)(x - 1)$
43. $(x^n + y^k)(x^{2n} - x^ny^k + y^{2k})$
44. $(x^{2a} - 2x^ay^a + y^{2a})(x^{2a} + 2x^ay^a + y^{2a})$
45. $(x^n - y^k)(x^{2n} + x^ny^k + y^{2k})$
46. $(x + 1)(x + 2)(x + 3) - (x + 2)(x + 3)(x + 4) + 3(x + 2)(x + 3)$
47. $(x^3 + x^2 + x + 1)(x - 1) - (x^2 + 1)(x + 1)(x - 1)$

1–11 Division of integers; rational numbers. Further investigation of the properties of numbers leads to the following problem: given two integers b and c, with $c \neq 0$ (this means c is not equal to zero), find a number Q such that $b = cQ$. The number Q, if it exists, is called the *quotient* in the division of b by c. The process of finding Q is called *division*, and if

Q exists it may be designated by

$$b/c \quad \text{or} \quad \frac{b}{c} \quad \text{or} \quad b \div c.$$

In the division, b is called the *dividend* and c the *divisor*. We shall assume that Q as defined can be proved unique if it exists.

For example, $156 \div 12 = 13$ since $156 = 12 \cdot 13$. In this indicated division the dividend is 156, the divisor is 12, and the quotient is 13.

Why is division by zero excluded from the definition? Since the product of zero by any integer is equal to zero, we cannot have

$$0 \cdot Q = b$$

unless $b = 0$. On the other hand, if $b = 0$ any integer Q would suffice and the quotient would not fulfill the uniqueness requirement.

A simple problem such as the division of 3 by 2 shows that division is not always possible if the quotient is to be an integer, and we must again expand the number system if we are to have a system in which division is always possible (*except, of course, when the divisor is zero*). This expansion of the number system is accomplished by including all numbers of the form p/q, where p and q are integers, with $q \neq 0$. These numbers are called *rational numbers,* and include all the integers as special cases.

It should be emphasized that *division by zero is impossible, in fact undefined;* hence a divisor must always be different from zero. For example, $(x + 5)/(x - 2)$ has no meaning for $x = 2$.

We have seen that a rational number may be thought of as an indicated quotient of one integer by another, whether the result is an integer or not. Such an indicated quotient is called a *fraction,* the dividend being the *numerator,* and the divisor the *denominator* of the fraction.

It follows that the sum, difference, product, and quotient of two rational numbers can be obtained from the rules for performing these operations on fractions. These will be presented in Chapter 3. It will appear in that presentation that the result of each such operation on rational numbers is again a rational number.

Moreover, since addition and multiplication of rational numbers ultimately involves these operations with integers, it follows that *for rational numbers these arithmetic operations continue to have the commutative, associative, and distributive properties.*

THEOREM 1-1. *The quotient of two integers of like sign is positive; the quotient of two integers of opposite sign is negative.*

The proof is based on the definition of division. Let $Q = a/b$, then $a = bQ$. If a and b are both negative, Q must be positive since the product of b and Q is negative. Similar considerations apply to the other possible signs for a and b.

In Section 1–8 we stated an important principle for signed expressions. We state here, without proof, that this principle is valid also when the letters represent rational numbers.

1–12 Division of powers. It can be shown that the properties of exponents as given in Section 1–9 hold also for rational numbers. At this point we give a property of exponents, in addition to those of Section 1–9.

Property D.

$$\text{If } x \neq 0, \quad \frac{x^p}{x^q} = \begin{cases} 1 & \text{if } p = q, \\ x^{p-q} & \text{if } p \text{ is larger than } q, \\ \dfrac{1}{x^{q-p}} & \text{if } q \text{ is larger than } p. \end{cases}$$

Proof. If $p = q$ then $x^p = x^q$, and the quotient of two equal numbers is 1.

If $p \neq q$, we have, by Definition 1–2,

$$\frac{x^p}{x^q} = \frac{\overbrace{x \cdot x \cdots x}^{p \text{ numbers } x}}{\underbrace{x \cdot x \cdots x}_{q \text{ numbers } x}}.$$

Let $x^p/x^q = Q$. Then $Q \cdot x^q = x^p$. If p is larger than q, then $p - q$ is positive and, by Property A of exponents,

$$x^{p-q} \cdot x^q = x^p, \qquad \text{and} \qquad Q = x^{p-q}.$$

If q is larger than p, then $q - p$ is positive; moreover, q is larger than $q - p$. Hence by the second part of the proof,

$$\frac{x^q}{x^{q-p}} = x^{q-(q-p)} = x^p.$$

But

$$\frac{1}{x^{q-p}} \cdot x^q = \frac{x^q}{x^{q-p}}.$$

Hence, this time we have $Q = 1/x^{q-p}$ and the property is proved.

EXAMPLES.

$$\frac{x^3}{x} = x^{3-1} = x^2; \qquad \frac{x^3}{x^7} = \frac{1}{x^{7-3}} = \frac{1}{x^4}.$$

THEOREM 1-2.

$$\frac{a}{b} \cdot \frac{c}{d} = \frac{ac}{bd}.$$

Proof. Let $a/b = q$, $c/d = r$. Then, by the definition of division, $bq = a$, $dr = c$. Since the products of equal quantities are equal, we get

$$bq \cdot dr = bd \cdot qr = ac.$$

But by the definition of division again, this means that

$$qr = \frac{ac}{bd}.$$

Hence, with the meanings of q and r, the theorem is proved.

EXAMPLES.

$$\frac{2}{5} \cdot \frac{3}{7} = \frac{2 \cdot 3}{5 \cdot 7} = \frac{6}{35},$$

$$\frac{3x^3}{2x^2} = \frac{3}{2} \cdot \frac{x^3}{x^2} = \frac{3}{2} \cdot x = \frac{3x}{2},$$

$$\frac{5x}{7x^3} = \frac{5}{7} \cdot \frac{x}{x^3} = \frac{5}{7} \cdot \frac{1}{x^2} = \frac{5}{7x^2}.$$

EXERCISE GROUP 1-7

In Exercises 1-23, perform the indicated operations.

1. $\frac{2^7}{2^2}$
2. $\frac{3^9}{3^4}$
3. $\frac{5^3}{5^8}$
4. $\frac{7^4}{7^7}$
5. $\frac{2^7 \cdot 3^3}{2^3 \cdot 3^8}$
6. $\frac{2^9 \cdot 5^8}{2^4 \cdot 5^4}$
7. $\frac{10^2 \cdot 10^6}{10^7 \cdot 10^5}$
8. $\frac{7^{11} \cdot 10^{12}}{7^6 \cdot 10^8}$
9. $\frac{3^4 \cdot 10^2}{3^9 \cdot 10^7}$
10. $\frac{2^7 \cdot 3^4 \cdot 5^8}{2^2 \cdot 3^9 \cdot 5}$
11. $\frac{2x^{10}}{6x^2}$
12. $\frac{6x^4}{3x^{10}}$
13. $\frac{2^3x^9}{6^3x^2}$
14. $\frac{10^8x^2}{5^8x^8}$
15. $\frac{x^3y^7}{x^8y^2}$
16. $\frac{a^7b^2c}{ab^8c^7}$
17. $\frac{2x^3y^7z^8}{3x^7yz^2}$
18. $\frac{2^3x^2y^7}{3^2x^7y^3}$
19. $\frac{5^7a^6bx^8}{10^5a^2b^7x}$
20. $\frac{2^5 \cdot 5^8a^4b^9x^3}{2^4 \cdot 5^7a^7b^5x}$

21. $\dfrac{a^3b^5c^7x^9y^{11}}{a^{10}b^8c^9x^5y}$ 22. $\dfrac{2^3x^4y^5z^{10}}{2^8x^9y^2z^7}$ 23. $\dfrac{3^5a^7b^3c^9x}{3^9a^5b^9cx^7}$

In Exercises 24–32, perform the indicated operations, assuming that the letters x, y, and z represent positive integers each less than 10 and also that x is less than y, which in turn is less than z.

24. $\dfrac{2^xa^yb^z}{2^za^xb^y}$ 25. $\dfrac{2^9a^8b^{10}}{2^ya^xb^z}$ 26. $\dfrac{a^xa^zb^y}{a^yb^x}$

27. $\dfrac{2^y2^za^xb^{10}}{2^xa^yb^z}$ 28. $\dfrac{2^x3^ya^7b^z}{2^y3^za^2b^x}$ 29. $\dfrac{2^92^xa^yb^z}{2^za^8a^xb^y}$

30. $\dfrac{a^9a^yb^xb^{10}}{a^zb^y}$ 31. $\dfrac{2^x5^xa^yb^z}{10^za^xb^y}$ 32. $\dfrac{a^xa^yb^zc^{10}}{ab^{10}b^xc^z}$

Using the above definition of division, prove each of the following statements.

33. $\dfrac{a+b}{c} = \dfrac{a}{c} + \dfrac{b}{c}$ 34. $\dfrac{a+b}{c} \cdot \dfrac{d}{e} = \dfrac{d(a+b)}{ce}$

1–13 Division of polynomials. If each term of an algebraic sum is either a number or of the form ax^n, where n is a positive integer, the expression is called a *polynomial in* x, and will be designated by a symbol such as $P(x)$. The largest exponent of x in the sum is the *degree* of the polynomial, provided the terms with that exponent do not drop out.

EXAMPLE 1. $P(x) = 3x^3 - 7x^2 + 2x - 5$ is a polynomial of degree 3 in x, the *terms* being $3x^3$, $-7x^2$, $2x$, -5.

EXAMPLE 2. $P(x) = ax^5 - bx^3 + cx + d$ is a polynomial of degree 5 in x, if $a \neq 0$, where it is understood that the letters a, b, c, and d represent numbers.

The multiplier of x^m in any term is called the *coefficient* of x^m. For example, the coefficient of x^3 in Example 2 is $-b$.

If a polynomial contains only one term it is called a *monomial;* a polynomial of two terms is a *binomial.*

The division of a polynomial by a monomial consists of dividing each term of the polynomial by the monomial, and adding the results. The proof of this is similar to that of Exercise 33 of Exercise Group 1–7 and involves principally the definition of division.

EXAMPLE 3. By the rule just given we obtain

$$\frac{3x^3 + 5x^2 + 7}{2x^2} = \frac{3x^3}{2x^2} + \frac{5x^2}{2x^2} + \frac{7}{2x^2}.$$

By the theorem of the preceding section, we then obtain

$$\frac{3x^3 + 5x^2 + 7}{2x^2} = \frac{3x}{2} + \frac{5}{2} + \frac{7}{2x^2}.$$

At this point it is appropriate to say something about the long-division algorithm in arithmetic. If 297 is divided by 19, the quotient is 15 and the remainder is 12. We may then write

$$\tfrac{297}{19} = 15 + \tfrac{12}{19}.$$

We may also write

$$297 = 19 \cdot 15 + 12.$$

In either form the dividend is 297, the divisor is 19, the quotient is 15, and the remainder is 12.

Similar definitions apply to the division of two polynomials.

Definition 1–3. *To divide a polynomial $P(x)$ by a polynomial $D(x)$, where the degree of $P(x)$ is larger than or equal to that of $D(x)$, means to find polynomials $Q(x)$ and $R(x)$ such that*

$$P(x) = D(x) \cdot Q(x) + R(x),$$

where the degree of $R(x)$ is less than that of $D(x)$, or $R(x) = 0$.

$P(x)$ is called the *dividend,* $D(x)$ the *divisor,* $Q(x)$ the *quotient,* and $R(x)$ the *remainder.*

If the remainder $R(x)$ is zero, the division of $P(x)$ by $D(x)$ is said to be *exact.* Let us consider a special example of this type.

Example 4. If $Q(x) = 3x + 2$, $D(x) = 2x^2 - 3x + 5$, then

$$P(x) = D(x) \cdot Q(x) = (2x^2 - 3x + 5) \cdot (3x + 2) = 6x^3 - 5x^2 + 9x + 10.$$

This means that the division of $6x^3 - 5x^2 + 9x + 10$ by $2x^2 - 3x + 5$ is exact, and the quotient is $3x + 2$. Let us try to see how the division can actually be performed. The product $D(x) \cdot Q(x)$ can be written as

$$3x(2x^2 - 3x + 5) + 2(2x^2 - 3x + 5) = (6x^3 - 9x^2 + 15x) + (4x^2 - 6x + 10).$$

This equation gives a clue to the process of division; we see that the first term $6x^3$ of the dividend is the product of $2x^2$, the first term of the divisor, and $3x$, the first term of the quotient. Hence the first term of the quotient can be determined by dividing the first term of the dividend by the first term of the divisor, where the terms in each are written in order of decreasing exponents.

The next step is to multiply the divisor by the first term of the quotient, and to subtract the result from the dividend. The process is then repeated. A convenient arrangement for the work is the following:

$$
\begin{array}{lr@{\,}l l}
 & & \underline{3x + 2 \qquad\qquad\qquad\quad} & \text{(quotient)} \\
\text{(Divisor)} & 2x^2 - 3x + 5 & \big)\, 6x^3 - 5x^2 + 9x + 10 & \text{(dividend)} \\
 & & \underline{6x^3 - 9x^2 + 15x} & \\
 & & \qquad\quad 4x^2 - 6x + 10 & \\
 & & \qquad\quad \underline{4x^2 - 6x + 10} & \\
\end{array}
$$

The procedure just employed is known as the *long-division algorithm.* Of course, we do not know in advance whether $R(x)$ is zero or not. The work is the same in either case.

EXAMPLE 5. Divide $2x^3 - 3x^2 + 8x + 3$ by $x^2 - x + 2$.

$$
\begin{array}{lr@{\,}l}
 & & \underline{2x - 1 \qquad\qquad\qquad} \\
\textit{Solution.} & x^2 - x + 2 & \big)\, 2x^3 - 3x^2 + 8x + 3 \\
 & & \underline{2x^3 - 2x^2 + 4x} \\
 & & \qquad - x^2 + 4x + 3 \\
 & & \qquad \underline{- x^2 + x - 2} \\
 & & \qquad\qquad\quad 3x + 5 \quad \text{(remainder)} \\
\end{array}
$$

The division is continued until the degree of the remainder is less than the degree of the divisor. The result can also be expressed as follows:

$$\frac{2x^3 - 3x^2 + 8x + 3}{x^2 - x + 2} = 2x - 1 + \frac{3x + 5}{x^2 - x + 2}.$$

In general, if A is the number of any step in the process of long division, Step A can be described as the multiplication of $D(x)$ by a suitable term ax^m and the subtraction of the resulting product from what remained after Step A–1, that is, from the *intermediate remainder* after Step A–1 [the intermediate remainder before the first step is $P(x)$ itself]. As long as the degree of the intermediate remainder is not less than that of $D(x)$, the process continues. At each step the degree of the intermediate remainder is decreased. Hence the process ends when the degree of the intermediate remainder is less than the degree of $D(x)$, and this final remainder is called *the remainder.* We have now proved

THEOREM 1–3. *The long division as specified in Definition 1–3 can always be performed.*

The discussion preceding Theorem 1–3 shows that *the equation* $P(x) = D(x) \cdot Q(x) + R(x)$ *holds for every value of* x. An alternative form of this equation, obtained by dividing both sides by $D(x)$, is

$$\frac{P(x)}{D(x)} = Q(x) + \frac{R(x)}{D(x)}.$$

This equation, however, holds only for values of x for which $D(x)$ is not zero.

Exercise Group 1-8

In each of the following, determine the quotient and the remainder.

1. $67 \div 13$ 2. $79 \div 15$ 3. $103 \div 12$ 4. $214 \div 17$
5. $376 \div 19$ 6. $613 \div 23$ 7. $569 \div 21$ 8. $798 \div 27$
9. $879 \div 37$ 10. $987 \div 29$
11. $(x^2 - 5x + 6) \div (x - 2)$
12. $(x^2 - 5x - 14) \div (x + 2)$
13. $(x^2 - 2x - 15) \div (x - 5)$
14. $(x^3 - 8x^2 + x + 42) \div (x - 7)$
15. $(21a^2 + 13ab - 20b^2) \div (7a - 5b)$
16. $(16r^2 - 46rs + 15s^2) \div (2r - 5s)$
17. $(2a^3 - 9a^2 + 11a - 3) \div (2a - 3)$
18. $(2a^3 + 17 - 5a - 7a^2) \div (2a + 3)$
19. $(5x - 2x^2 + 3x^3 - 26) \div (x - 2)$
20. $(5b^2 - 2ab + 2a^3 - 5a^2b) \div (2a - 5b)$
21. $(7 - 8x^2 + 4x^3 - 9x) \div (2x - 3)$
22. $(a^4 - 16) \div (a - 2)$ 23. $(x^5 + 243) \div (x + 3)$
24. $(81b^4 - 256) \div (3b + 4)$ 25. $(32 - x^5) \div (x - 2)$
26. $(15x^4 + 9x + 7x^3 + 15x^2 + 7) \div (3x^2 + 2x + 1)$
27. $(25a^2 + 40a + 16 - 49a^4) \div (5a + 4 - 7a^2)$
28. $(6a^3 - 3 + 8a^4 + 6a) \div (2a - 1 + 2a^2)$
29. $(9b^2 - 7 + 2b^3 + 8b) \div (3b - 2 + b^2)$
30. $(p^2 + 1 + p + 2p^4) \div (1 + 2p^2 - 2p)$
31. $(216a^3 + 126) \div (36a^2 - 30a + 25)$
32. $(7x^3 - 2x^4 + 82x^2 + 143x + 75) \div (9 + 8x - x^2)$
33. $(a^4 + a^2b^2 + b^4) \div (a^2 - ab + b^2)$
34. $(x^{3m} + y^{3n}) \div (x^m + y^n)$
35. $(x^{4m} - y^{4n}) \div (x^m + y^n)$
36. $(x^{4m} + x^{2m}y^{2n} + y^{4n}) \div (x^{2m} - x^my^n + y^{2n})$
37. $(6x^{3n} + 5x^{2n} - 18x^n + 8) \div (3x^n - 2)$
38. $(10x^{2n} - 18x^n + 3x^{3n} + 35) \div (x^n + 5)$

1–14 Irrational numbers and the real number system. The rational number system defined in Section 1–11 has the property that the sum of any two rational numbers is again rational; the same is true for the difference, the product, and the quotient of any two rational numbers (division by zero excluded, of course). We then say that *the rational number system is closed under the four arithmetic operations of addition, subtraction, multiplication, and division by nonzero rational numbers.*

However, this system is still inadequate for our needs. There are entire classes of numbers which cannot be expressed as the quotient of two integers. For example, in a square of which the length of each side is unity, the length of a diagonal is not a rational number, for, the theorem of Pythagoras states: *In a right triangle the square of the length of the hypotenuse is equal to the sum of the squares of the lengths of the other two sides.* Hence, if x is the length of the diagonal (Fig. 1–1), it follows by the theorem of Pythagoras that $x^2 = 1 + 1 = 2$, and it can be proved that such a value of x is not rational.

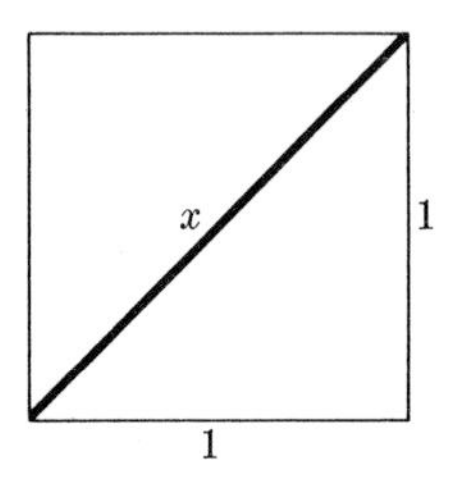

FIGURE 1–1

If we simply seek values of x for which $x^2 = 2$, there will actually be two such values, one positive and one negative, since the square of either a positive or a negative number is positive. These numbers are called *square roots* of 2; the positive one is written as $\sqrt{2} = 1.414\ldots$, and the negative one as $-\sqrt{2}$.

Another example of a familiar number which is not rational is π, the ratio of the circumference of any circle to its diameter, and there are many others.

Any positive or negative number which is not rational is called an *irrational number.*

If the irrational numbers are adjoined to the rational numbers defined in Section 1–11 there results the *real number system.* It follows that this system includes the positive and negative integers, zero, all fractions of the form p/q where p and q are integers with q not zero, and the irrational numbers.

It can be shown that the system of real numbers is closed under the four arithmetic operations of addition, subtraction, multiplication, and division by nonzero real numbers, and that in this system addition and multiplication have the commutative, associative, and distributive properties described in Section 1–4.

The system of real numbers is adequate for much of elementary mathematics, but one further extension is necessary for our purpose; this concerns complex numbers, and will be considered in Section 4–11.

Review Exercises

In Exercises 1–6, evaluate the given expressions if $x = -5$, $y = 13$, $z = -37$, $u = 7$, and $v = -139$.

1. $(u + x - y) - (y - x + v)$
2. $(2x - 3y + z) + (v - u + 13)$
3. $(3x - 2z) - (5u + 4v - y)$
4. $5z - 17x - (v - 7y) + 17u$
5. $3v - (y - 3z) + (15u - 9x)$
6. $v - [z - (3x - 2y) - (3u + v)]$

In Exercises 7–10, remove all signs of grouping and combine similar terms.

7. $3x - (2y - 3x) - [2y - (2y + x)]$
8. $(6x - 2y) - [2x - \{2(y - 3x) - (x - 5y)\}]$
9. $-\{(4a - b) - [5a - b - (3x - 2y) - 3b]\}$
10. $6x - 2[2 - 3(2x - 3 - a) - 5\{a - (2x - 2a) - 4\}]$

In Exercises 11–26, perform the indicated operations, and collect similar terms, where applicable.

11. $a^5 \cdot b^3 \cdot a^2 \cdot b^7$
12. $(2^3 \cdot 3^5)^3(3^2 \cdot 2^7)^2$
13. $(2^2a^3b^4)^2(2a^4b^3)^3$
14. $(3^2a^3b^4)^h(3^4a^2b^3)^h$
15. $5a^2(4ab + 3a^2b - 2a^3b^2)$
16. $3ab(3a^2b^2 - 2ab^2 + 3a^2b)$
17. $(2a^2 + 3ay)(3a^2 - 2ay)$
18. $(a^2 + 2ab - 3b^2)(2a - ab + 3b)$
19. $(3x^2 - 2ax + a^2)(x - a)$
20. $(4x - 3y + z)(2x + 5y - 2z)$
21. $(a^3b^2)^2 \div (a^2b^3)^3$
22. $(2^2a^3b^5)^3 \div (2^3a^5b^2)^2$
23. $\dfrac{36x^8y^5z^2}{48x^9yu^3}$
24. $\dfrac{-36p^5q^4r}{9p^7q^2}$
25. $\dfrac{(x - 1)^{2n}(x + 1)^{n+1}}{(x - 1)^n(x + 1)^n}$
26. $\dfrac{(x - y)^{n+10}(x + y)^{n+7}}{(x - y)^{n+6}(x + y)^{n+5}}$

In Exercises 27–30, find the quotient and remainder.

27. $(10a^3 + 3a^2 - 2a - 7) \div (2a - 5a^2 + 3)$
28. $(4x^4 + 7a^2x^2 + 16a^4) \div (2x^2 + 4a^2 + 3ax)$
29. $(7x^2 + 6x - 5x^3 + 3x^5 - 21) \div (7 - 2x + 3x^3)$
30. $(20x^3y^2 - 26x^2y^3 + 3x^5 - 13x^4y + 26xy^4 - 7y^5) \div (y^2 - 3xy + x^2)$

CHAPTER 2

SPECIAL PRODUCTS AND FACTORING

2–1 Introduction. In Chapter 1 we were introduced to various properties of the positive integers. It was then pointed out that these properties can be extended to the real numbers, and also to algebraic expressions in which letters are used to represent numbers. These properties were then used to obtain products of algebraic expressions. It turns out that certain special products occur so frequently that they should be memorized (just as it is necessary in arithmetic to learn a multiplication table). These will be considered shortly.

The reverse problem is also of considerable importance, that is, to be able to represent a given algebraic expression as a product of other expressions, called its *factors*. At the same time, it is often necessary that these factors be such that they cannot be factored further.

We consider first the corresponding question for integers, that is, the question of representing an integer as a product of other integers. For example, $42 = 6 \cdot 7$, in which case 6 and 7 are called *factors* of 42. However, $6 = 2 \cdot 3$ so that we have $42 = 2 \cdot 3 \cdot 7$. In this form we see that 2, 3, and 7 are factors of 42; in particular, they are factors which cannot be factored further, and because of this property the integers 2, 3, and 7 are examples of *prime factors.*

DEFINITION 2–1. *An integer n is called prime if the only factors of n are $\pm n$ and ± 1. An integer which is not prime is called a composite integer.*

For example, 7 is a prime number since it is divisible by $+7$, -7, $+1$, and -1, and by no other integer. We now state a fundamental principle of integers.

FUNDAMENTAL PRINCIPLE. *An integer can be factored into prime factors in only one way (apart from sign and the order of the factors).*

Thus, 42 can be factored in no way which is essentially different from $2 \cdot 3 \cdot 7$.

EXAMPLES. The following represent factorizations into prime factors, as may be easily verified:

$$\begin{aligned} 1155 &= 3 \cdot 5 \cdot 7 \cdot 11; \\ 121{,}275 &= 3^2 \cdot 5^2 \cdot 7^2 \cdot 11; \\ 1188 &= 2^2 \cdot 3^3 \cdot 11. \end{aligned}$$

It should be noted that a prime integer may occur more than once in the factorization of a composite integer. Once a prime factor has been found, the same integer should be tried again as a factor.

Exercise Group 2–1

In Exercises 1–25, factor each of the integers into prime factors. The numbers have been chosen so that there is at most one distinct prime factor greater than 11.

1. 462	2. 3990	3. 6790	4. 1136	5. 1692
6. 3087	7. 1848	8. 44100	9. 1715	10. 1650
11. 2304	12. 46656	13. 1089	14. 2541	15. 78408
16. 169785	17. 326095	18. 5733	19. 100548	20. 91287
21. 437325	22. 191884	23. 47775	24. 32291	25. 13941

26. Determine the prime integers between 1 and 50, inclusive.

27. Determine the prime integers between 51 and 100, inclusive.

2–2 A common factor. The first multiplication formula, or *type form*, to be considered is obtained by multiplying a quantity u by the quantity $x + y$, giving, directly by the distributive law of multiplication with respect to addition,

$$u(x + y) = ux + uy. \tag{1}$$

The letters appearing in (1) may represent any quantity whatever. For example, u may be a, x may be b, and y may be $3c$. We then have

$$\begin{aligned} a(b + 3c) &= ab + a(3c) \qquad \text{[by (1)]} \\ &= ab + 3ac. \end{aligned}$$

On the other hand, u may be $3a$, x may be $2b$, and y may be $c + d$. We then have

$$\begin{aligned} 3a[2b + (c + d)] &= 6ab + 3a(c + d) \qquad \text{[by (1)]} \\ &= 6ab + 3ac + 3ad \qquad \text{[using (1) again].} \end{aligned}$$

Such generality is indeed characteristic of all the type forms to be presented, and should be borne in mind at all times.

Example 1. To expand

$$7z[a + b + 3c - 4d]$$

we may introduce parentheses within the brackets, and then apply Eq. (1). Thus, we may enclose $a + b$ in parentheses, and also $3c - 4d$, and then apply

(1) with $u = 7z$, $x = a + b$, and $y = 3c - 4d$. We get

$$\begin{aligned} 7z[(a + b) + (3c - 4d)] &= 7z(a + b) + 7z(3c - 4d) \\ &= 7az + 7bz + 21cz - 28dz. \end{aligned}$$

EXAMPLE 2. To expand $(2a + 3b)(c + 3d)$ we may apply (1) first with $u = 2a + 3b$, $x = c$, and $y = 3d$ to give

$$(2a + 3b)(c + 3d) = (2a + 3b)c + (2a + 3b)(3d).$$

The expressions on the right are then expanded by the commutative law of multiplication, and then (1) again:

$$\begin{aligned} (2a + 3b)(c + 3d) &= (2a + 3b)c + (2a + 3b)(3d) \\ &= c(2a + 3b) + 3d(2a + 3b) \\ &= 2ac + 3bc + 6ad + 9bd. \end{aligned}$$

The type form (1) may also be written as

$$\boxed{ux + uy = u(x + y).} \tag{2}$$

In this form the algebraic quantity $ux + uy$ has been expressed as the product of the *factor* u and the *factor* $x + y$, and we say that $ux + uy$ has been factored by *extracting a common factor*.

EXAMPLE 3. Factor $9ax + 12ay$.

Solution. The terms $9ax$ and $12ay$ have a common factor $3a$, and no larger factor. Moreover, $3a$ divides into $9ax$ (exactly) with a quotient $3x$ and into $12ay$ with a quotient $4y$. Hence, by (2),

$$9ax + 12ay = 3a(3x + 4y).$$

The formula (2) can be extended to a sum of more than two terms, all of which have a common factor.

EXAMPLE 4. Factor $4x^3 + 6x^2y + 8xy^2$.

Solution. The greatest common factor of $4x^3$, $6x^2y$, and $8xy^2$ is $2x$; hence

$$4x^3 + 6x^2y + 8xy^2 = 2x(2x^2 + 3xy + 4y^2).$$

The common factor u of (2) may be a *binomial*, a sum of two terms, or even a *polynomial*, a sum of any number of terms. (A sum of three terms is called a *trinomial*).

EXAMPLE 5. Factor $(3a - 5b)x + (3a - 5b)(2y)$.

Solution. The given expression conforms to the type form (2) with $u = 3a - 5b$; hence

$$(3a - 5b)x + (3a - 5b)(2y) = (3a - 5b)(x + 2y).$$

We note in this example that the method is very similar if the given expression is

$$x(3a - 5b) + 2y(3a - 5b),$$

and the final result is the same.

EXAMPLE 6. Factor $ax + ay - bx - by$.

Solution. It should be noted that the first two terms have a common factor of a and the last two terms have a common factor of $-b$. Hence

$$\begin{aligned} ax + ay - bx - by &= a(x + y) - b(x + y) \\ &= (x + y)(a - b). \end{aligned}$$

EXERCISE GROUP 2-2

In Exercises 1–21, expand each of the indicated products by using type form (1).

1. $3(2a - 5b)$
2. $-3(5a - 2b + 3c)$
3. $2a(3b - 5c)$
4. $3x(x - y)$
5. $x^2(a - 2b + 3c)$
6. $4a(x^2 - y^2 - a^2)$
7. $(x + y)a$
8. $(x^2 - 3x - 1)x^4$
9. $(2a^2 - 3b^2)(3b)$
10. $(2x^2 + 3y^2)3xy$
11. $3a^2b^3(5a^3 - 7b^3)$
12. $5x^3y^2(3x^3 - 2xy^3)$
13. $(2x + 3y)(x - y)$
14. $(3x + 2y)(3x + 2y)$
15. $(ax + by)(ax + by)$
16. $(x + 5)(x + 3)$
17. $(x + a)(x + b)$
18. $(x + 5)(x - 7)$
19. $(x + a)(x - b)$
20. $(3x + 5)(2x - 7)$
21. $(2x + 5)(5x - 3)$

Factor each of the expressions in Exercises 22–46.

22. $bu + bv$
23. $3ax - 6a^2y$
24. $-20abc + 15b^2x$
25. $10ab^2 - 6a^2bx$
26. $ax - 3a^2y + 5az^2$
27. $-4bx + x^2 - ax^3$
28. $5xy - 3y + 7y^2$
29. $x^4 - 3x^3 - 2x^2$
30. $27x^2y - 36xy^2$
31. $54axy^2 - 81a^2xy$
32. $a^6 - a^4x^2 + a^2x^4$
33. $3a(u - v) + 5b(u - v)$
34. $2a(x^2 + 1) + 3x(x^2 + 1)$
35. $x^2(a + b) + y^2(a + b)$
36. $3x^2(m + n) - 2y^3(m + n)$
37. $(a + b + c)(2x - y) + 2(a + b + c)(y - x)$
38. $(x + y)(3a - b) - (x + y)(a - 2b)$
39. $xm + ym + xn + yn$
40. $6am - 3bm - 6an + 3bn$
41. $2an - 3bn + 2ay - 3by$
42. $2y^4 - y^3 + 14y - 7$
43. $6x^4 - 13x^3 - 42x + 91$
44. $x^2 + mxy - 4xy - 4my^2$
45. $ax + by + az + bx + ay + bz$
46. $ax - cy + cx - ay - bx + by$

2–3 The difference of two squares. The methods of multiplication developed in Chapter 1 give, when applied to the product of $u + v$ and $u - v$,

$$\boxed{(u + v)(u - v) = u^2 - v^2.} \tag{3}$$

Again it should be remembered that the letters u and v in (3) may represent any algebraic quantities.

EXAMPLES. 1. $(2x + 3y)(2x - 3y) = (2x)^2 - (3y)^2 = 4x^2 - 9y^2$.
2. $(ab + cd)(ab - cd) = (ab)^2 - (cd)^2 = a^2b^2 - c^2d^2$.
3. $(3ax - 5by)(3ax + 5by) = (3ax)^2 - (5by)^2 = 9a^2x^2 - 25b^2y^2$.

A useful application of (3) is in the multiplication of certain integers.

EXAMPLES. 4. $81 \cdot 79 = (80 + 1)(80 - 1) = (80)^2 - 1^2 = 6400 - 1 = 6399$.
5. $122 \cdot 118 = (120 + 2)(120 - 2)$
$= (120)^2 - (2)^2 = 14400 - 4 = 14396$.

If the type form (3) is written in the reverse order, we have the formula for the factorization of the difference of two squares:

$$\boxed{u^2 - v^2 = (u + v)(u - v).} \tag{4}$$

The quantities $u - v$ and $u + v$ are, accordingly, factors of $u^2 - v^2$.

EXAMPLES. 6. $9x^2 - 16y^2 = (3x)^2 - (4y)^2 = (3x + 4y)(3x - 4y)$.
7. $a^2b^2 - c^2d^2 = (ab)^2 - (cd)^2 = (ab + cd)(ab - cd)$.
8. $4a^2x^2 - 25b^2y^2 = (2ax)^2 - (5by)^2 = (2ax + 5by)(2ax - 5by)$.
9. $4(a + b)^2 - (a - b)^2 = [2(a + b)]^2 - (a - b)^2$
$= [2(a + b) + (a - b)][2(a + b) - (a - b)]$
$= (3a + b)(a + 3b)$.

EXERCISE GROUP 2–3

In Exercises 1–21, expand each of the indicated products.

1. $(c + b)(c - b)$
2. $(3x + y)(3x - y)$
3. $(ax - y)(ax + y)$
4. $(a^3x - y^2)(a^3x + y^2)$
5. $(2 - 5x)(2 + 5x)$
6. $(2a - 3b)(2a + 3b)$
7. $(-bu - v)(bu - v)$
8. $(x^2y^2 - 4z)(x^2y^2 + 4z)$
9. $(x^a - y^b)(x^a + y^b)$
10. $(x^u + y^v)(x^u - y^v)$
11. $(x^{2a} + 1)(x^{2a} - 1)$
12. $(u^{2k} + v^h)(u^{2k} - v^h)$
13. $(y^3 - y^2)(y^3 + y^2)$
14. $(c^3 - 3^2d)(c^3 + 3^2d)$

15. $(3a^2 + 7k)(3a^2 - 7k)$
16. $[2(a + b) + 3d][2(a + b) - 3d]$
17. $[3x - 5(y + z)][3x + 5(y + z)]$
18. $[a + b - c][a - (b - c)]$
19. $[x + (y + z)][x - y - z]$
20. $[(a + c) + (b + d)][a - b + c - d]$
21. $[a - b + c - d][(a - d) + (b - c)]$

Perform the multiplications in Exercises 22–29 by the method of Examples 4 and 5.

22. $25 \cdot 15$
23. $77 \cdot 83$
24. $115 \cdot 125$
25. $195 \cdot 205$
26. $63 \cdot 57$
27. $97 \cdot 83$
28. $1002 \cdot 998$
29. $2009 \cdot 1991$

Factor the expression in each of the following exercises.

30. $9 - x^2$
31. $16 - 9y^2$
32. $4x^2 - y^2$
33. $9a^2 - 16b^2$
34. $4a^2x^2 - 81b^4y^2$
35. $25u^2 - 64v^2$
36. $49p^2 - 100q^2$
37. $-36x^2 + 1$
38. $a^2b^2 - 25c^2$
39. $144 - 25c^2$
40. $121a^2 - 36b^2$
41. $9y^2 - \frac{1}{9}$
42. $a^2u^4 - 49$
43. $a^6b^2 - 4c^8$
44. $4 - 169b^4$
45. $64a^2 - 81b^4$
46. $(2x - 1)^2 - 4$
47. $(3x - 2y)^2 - y^2$
48. $9a^2 - (b - c)^2$
49. $49x^4 - (2a + b)^2$
50. $(a + 2b)^2 - 16b^2$
51. $(a + b)^2 - (a - b)^2$
52. $(2x + 3y)^2 - (2x - 3y)^2$
53. $(7x - y)^2 - (2a - b)^2$
54. $(3x - y)^2 - (u - 3v)^2$
55. $16(y - 3x)^2 - (x + 2y)^2$

2–4 The square of a binomial. From the definition of exponents given in Section 1–9 it follows that the expression $(u + v)^2$ represents the product of the two equal factors $u + v$ and $u + v$, and similarly for the expression $(u - v)^2$. If the indicated multiplications are carried out in accordance with the methods of Section 1–10, we obtain the type forms

$$(u + v)^2 = u^2 + 2uv + v^2, \tag{5a}$$

$$(u - v)^2 = u^2 - 2uv + v^2. \tag{5b}$$

With the general nature of u and v, the following examples readily follow.

EXAMPLES. 1. $(2x + 3y)^2 = (2x)^2 + 2(2x)(3y) + (3y)^2$
$= 4x^2 + 12xy + 9y^2.$

2. $(ax^2 + by^3)^2 = (ax^2)^2 + 2(ax^2)(by^3) + (by^3)^2$
$= a^2x^4 + 2abx^2y^3 + b^2y^6.$

EXAMPLES. 3.
$$(a+b-c)^2 = [(a+b)-c]^2 = (a+b)^2 - 2(a+b)c + c^2 = a^2 + 2ab + b^2 - 2ac - 2bc + c^2.$$

4.
$$(2x-y+3c)^2 = [(2x-y)+3c]^2 = (2x-y)^2 + 2(2x-y)(3c) + (3c)^2 = 4x^2 - 4xy + y^2 + 12cx - 6cy + 9c^2.$$

The squaring of integers can often be conveniently performed by using the above type forms.

EXAMPLES. 5.
$$(81)^2 = (80+1)^2 = (80)^2 + 2(80)(1) + (1)^2 = 6400 + 160 + 1 = 6561.$$

6.
$$(1196)^2 = (1200-4)^2 = (1200)^2 - 2(1200)(4) + (4)^2 = 1440000 - 9600 + 16 = 1430416.$$

Rewriting type forms (5a) and (5b) in the following forms

$$u^2 + 2uv + v^2 = (u+v)^2, \tag{6a}$$

$$u^2 - 2uv + v^2 = (u-v)^2, \tag{6b}$$

we have two additional formulas for factoring. Each formula expresses a type of trinomial expression as the square of a binomial. The characteristics of these trinomials are that two of the terms are squares of quantities and the third, or middle term is (plus or minus) twice the product of the quantities of which the other terms are squares.

EXAMPLE 7. Factor $9x^2 + 24xy + 16y^2$.

Solution. We note that $9x^2$ is the square of $3x$ and $16y^2$ is the square of $4y$. Moreover $24xy = 2(3x)(4y)$. Hence (6a) applies with $u = 3x$ and $v = 4y$, so that

$$9x^2 + 24xy + 16y^2 = (3x+4y)^2.$$

EXAMPLE 8. Factor $36a^2 - 4ab + \frac{1}{9}b^2$.

Solution. The expression can be written in the form $(6a)^2 - 2(6a)(\frac{1}{3}b) + (\frac{1}{3}b)^2$, from which it follows from (6a) that

$$36a^2 - 4ab + \tfrac{1}{9}b^2 = (6a - \tfrac{1}{3}b)^2.$$

EXAMPLE 9. Factor $(a+b)^2 - 4(a+b)(a-b) + 4(a-b)^2$.

Solution. The given expression conforms to the left side of (6b) with $u = a + b$, and $v = 2(a - b)$. Hence,

$$(a + b)^2 - 4(a + b)(a - b) + 4(a - b)^2 = [(a + b) - 2(a - b)]^2$$
$$= (3b - a)^2 \quad \text{or} \quad (a - 3b)^2.$$

Exercise Group 2-4

Expand the expressions in Exercises 1-22 by the use of an appropriate type form.

1. $(a + b)^2$
2. $(3x + 2y)^2$
3. $(x + cy)^2$
4. $(ax + by)^2$
5. $(b - c)^2$
6. $(5x - 2y)^2$
7. $(ax - by)^2$
8. $(\frac{1}{2}x - \frac{1}{3}y^2)^2$
9. $(0.2u + 0.3v)^2$
10. $[(x + y) + z]^2$
11. $[(a - b) - c]^2$
12. $[a + (b - c)]^2$
13. $[a - (b - c)]^2$
14. $[2(a - b) - 3]^2$
15. $[x - (2 - a)]^2$
16. $[5 - (x + y)]^2$
17. $[x - (3y - z)]^2$
18. $[y^2 + (y + 1)]^2$
19. $[(a + b) + (c + d)]^2$
20. $[2(x - y) - 3(u - v)]^2$
21. $[(2x - 3y) + (2y - 3x)]^2$
22. $[(x - 2y) - (3z + 4w)]^2$

Use the type forms for the square of a binomial to evaluate the numbers in Exercises 23-30.

23. $(79)^2$
24. $(101)^2$
25. $(99)^2$
26. $(202)^2$
27. $(299)^2$
28. $(999)^2$
29. $(1002)^2$
30. $(8999)^2$

Factor each of the following expressions.

31. $4x^2 + 20xy + 25y^2$
32. $9a^2 + 42a + 49$
33. $36u^2 + 60uv + 25v^2$
34. $16b^2 - 56bx + 49x^2$
35. $9x^2 - 12xy + 4y^2$
36. $25p^2 - 70pq + 49q^2$
37. $121y^2 - 44yz + 4z^2$
38. $a^2x^2 + 2abxy + b^2y^2$
39. $\frac{1}{4}a^2 - \frac{1}{3}ax + \frac{1}{9}x^2$
40. $0.64m^2 + 0.48mn + 0.09n^2$
41. $\frac{1}{16}c^2 + \frac{3}{2}cd + 9d^2$
42. $121x^2 - 220xy + 100y^2$
43. $289y^2 - 442xy + 169x^2$
44. $729a^2 + 54ab + b^2$
45. $4u^2 - 60uv + 225v^2$
46. $9 + 6(x + y) + (x + y)^2$
47. $(x - y)^2 - 10(x - y) + 25$
48. $49(a - 2b)^2 + 42(a - 2b) + 9$
49. $16(3a - 4b)^2 + 40a(3a - 4b) + 25a^2$
50. $9z^2 + 42(x + 2y)z + 49(x + 2y)^2$
51. $64(3x - y)^2 - 80(3x - y)z + 25z^2$
52. $49(2a - 3b)^2 + 42(2a - 3b)(2b - 3a) + 9(2b - 3a)^2$
53. $25(2a + 5b)^2 - 20(2a + 5b)(5b - 3a) + 4(5b - 3a)^2$
54. $4(2 - a)^2 - 12(2 - a)(2 + a) + 9(2 + a)^2$

2–5 The product of two binomials. Type forms (5a) and (5b) may be thought of as expressing the product of two *equal* binomials. A natural extension is a formula expressing the product of two different binomials:

$$\boxed{(au + b)(cu + d) = acu^2 + (ad + bc)u + bd.} \tag{7a}$$

The first term on the right is the product of au and cu, the last term is the product of b and d, and the middle term is the sum of the products $(au)d$ and $b(cu)$.

It is helpful to consider separately formula (7a) in which $a = 1$ and $c = 1$. We then have

$$\boxed{(u + b)(u + d) = u^2 + (b + d)u + bd.} \tag{7b}$$

EXAMPLE 1. By formula (7b) we have

$$\begin{aligned}(x + 3)(x + 5) &= x^2 + (3 + 5)x + 3 \cdot 5 \\ &= x^2 + 8x + 15.\end{aligned}$$

Formula (7b) applies equally well if either b or d, or both, is negative.

EXAMPLE 2. Applying (7b) with $b = -7$ and $d = 3$, we have

$$\begin{aligned}(x - 7)(x + 3) &= x^2 + [(-7) + 3]x + (-7)(3) \\ &= x^2 - 4x - 21.\end{aligned}$$

As in previous formulas, u may represent more general quantities.

EXAMPLE 3. $\begin{aligned}(2x - 5)(2x + 7) &= (2x)^2 + [7 + (-5)](2x) + (-5)(7) \\ &= 4x^2 + 4x - 35.\end{aligned}$

EXAMPLE 4. $[(a + 3) + 2y][(a + 3) - 5y]$ may be expanded by formula (7b) with u taken as $a + 3$, thus

$$\begin{aligned}[(a + 3) + 2y][(a + 3) - 5y] &= (a + 3)^2 + (2y - 5y)(a + 3) + (2y)(-5y) \\ &= (a + 3)^2 - 3y(a + 3) - 10y^2 \\ &= a^2 + 6a + 9 - 3ay - 9y - 10y^2.\end{aligned}$$

We now consider the more general formula (7a), in which, again, each letter may represent any quantity whatever.

EXAMPLE 5. $\begin{aligned}(3x + 2)(4x + 1) &= (3x)(4x) + (3 \cdot 1 + 2 \cdot 4)x + 2 \cdot 1 \\ &= 12x^2 + 11x + 2.\end{aligned}$

EXAMPLE 6.
$$\begin{aligned}(3x - 2)(4x + 1) &= [3x + (-2)][4x + 1]\\ &= (3x)(4x) + [3 \cdot 1 + (-2)4]x + (-2)1\\ &= 12x^2 - 5x - 2.\end{aligned}$$

EXAMPLE 7. $[(a + 3) + 2y][3(a + 3) - 2y]$ may be expanded by (7a) with $u = a + 3$, thus:

$$\begin{aligned}&[(a + 3) + 2y][3(a + 3) - 2y]\\ &\quad = 1 \cdot 3(a + 3)^2 + [1 \cdot (-2) + 2 \cdot 3](a + 3)y + (2y)(-2y)\\ &\quad = 3(a + 3)^2 + 4(a + 3)y - 4y^2\\ &\quad = 3(a^2 + 6a + 9) + 4ay + 12y - 4y^2\\ &\quad = 3a^2 + 18a + 27 + 4ay + 12y - 4y^2.\end{aligned}$$

We may rewrite both (7a) and (7b) as factorization formulas:

$$\boxed{acu^2 + (ad + bc)u + bd = (au + b)(cu + d),} \tag{8a}$$

$$\boxed{u^2 + (b + d)u + bd = (u + b)(u + d).} \tag{8b}$$

The application of type forms (8a) and (8b) usually requires a certain amount of trial and error, to be illustrated in the following examples.

EXAMPLE 8. Factor $x^2 - 3x - 10$.

Solution. If the expression can be factored, it is of the form (8b). We must then have $bd = -10$, so that b and d are of opposite sign. Moreover, $b + d = -3$ and we find that $b = 2$, $d = -5$ will satisfy the requirements. Hence

$$x^2 - 3x - 10 = (x + 2)(x - 5)$$

is the desired factorization, which may be verified by multiplication.

EXAMPLE 9. Factor $7x^2 + 19x - 6$.

Solution. This is of the form (8a) and we must have

$$ac = 7, \qquad bd = -6, \qquad ad + bc = 19.$$

We may take $a = 7$, $c = 1$. Then b and d must be chosen so that $b + 7d = 19$ and $bd = -6$. Clearly b and d have opposite signs, since their product is negative. Since $b + 7d = +19$, it is likely that d is positive and b is negative. It turns out that $b = -2$ and $d = 3$ satisfy the requirements, giving

$$7x^2 + 19x - 6 = (7x - 2)(x + 3)$$

as the desired factorization.

EXAMPLE 10. Factor $31x - 5x^2 - 6$.

Solution. Applying (8a), we may take $a = 1$, $c = -5$; then b and d are to be determined. We must have

$$31x - 5x^2 - 6 = (x + b)(-5x + d),$$

and hence

$$-5b + d = 31, \qquad bd = -6.$$

Obviously b and d must be of opposite sign and one possibility is that $b = -3$ and $d = 2$. This gives $-5(-3) + 2 = 17$ and not 31. Another possibility is $b = -2$ and $d = 3$, which gives $-5(-2) + 3 = 13$ instead of 31. We try next $b = -6$ and $d = 1$, which gives $-5(-6) + 1 = 31$, the desired value. Hence the desired result is

$$31x - 5x^2 - 6 = (x - 6)(-5x + 1).$$

It is easily verified that two other factorizations are

$$-(x - 6)(5x - 1) \qquad \text{and} \qquad (-x + 6)(5x - 1).$$

EXAMPLE 11. Factor $5(x + y)^2 - 27(x + y) + 10$.

Solution. Applying (8a), we may take $a = 1$, $c = 5$ and then b and d must be determined so that

$$[1(x + y) + b][5(x + y) + d] = 5(x + y)^2 - 27(x + y) + 10.$$

Obviously $bd = 10$ and $5b + d = -27$ from which it follows that b and d are both negative. Try $b = -2$ and $d = -5$, which gives $5b + d = -15$ instead of -27. Next try $b = -5$ and $d = -2$, which gives $5b + d = -27$, and we have the desired factorization:

$$\begin{aligned} 5(x + y)^2 - 27(x + y) + 10 &= [(x + y) - 5][5(x + y) - 2] \\ &= (x + y - 5)(5x + 5y - 2). \end{aligned}$$

EXERCISE GROUP 2–5

In Exercises 1–28, perform the indicated multiplications.

1. $(x + 5)(x + 7)$
2. $(x + 4)(x + 9)$
3. $(x - 5)(x + 11)$
4. $(x + 9)(x - 6)$
5. $(x + 2y)(x + 7y)$
6. $(x + 3y)(x + 8y)$
7. $(x - 3y)(x + 5y)$
8. $(x + 6y)(x - 11y)$
9. $(2x + 3y)(2x - 7y)$
10. $(2x - 11y)(2x + 13y)$
11. $(3x - 8y)(3x - 7y)$
12. $(3x - 11y)(3x + 7y)$
13. $(ax - 3y)(ax + 7y)$
14. $(bx + 2y)(bx - 9y)$
15. $(2u - 3v)(5u + v)$
16. $(5a + 2b)(3a - 7b)$
17. $(3a^2 - 7b)(2a^2 + 5b)$
18. $(4x^2 - 11y)(5x^2 + 7y)$

19. $(7a - 5b^2)(3a - 11b^2)$
20. $(2a^2 + 3b^2)(4a^2 + 5b^2)$
21. $[(a + b) + 3][2(a + b) + 7]$
22. $[2(x - y) - 5][3(x - y) + 11]$
23. $[2x + 3(y + z)][5x + 2(y + z)]$
24. $[5x - 7(u + v)][9x + 5(u + v)]$
25. $[11a - 4(b + c)][3a + 13(b + c)]$
26. $[2a + b(x - y)][7a - c(x - y)]$
27. $[2a + 3(b + c)][7a - 11(b + c)]$
28. $[5(x + y) - 7c][9(x + y) + 11c]$

Factor each of the following expressions.

29. $x^2 + 9x + 14$
30. $x^2 - 5x - 14$
31. $a^2 - 3a - 10$
32. $p^2 + 9p + 18$
33. $p^2 - 7p - 18$
34. $x^2 - 3x - 18$
35. $15 - 2x - x^2$
36. $20 + x - x^2$
37. $21 - 4x - x^2$
38. $30 + x - x^2$
39. $14 - 5x - x^2$
40. $36 - 5x - x^2$
41. $4x^2 + 11x - 20$
42. $3x^2 - 17x + 20$
43. $-2x^2 + 7x + 15$
44. $-6x^2 + 12 + x$
45. $10x^2 - 29x + 10$
46. $14x^2 - 53x + 14$
47. $14x^2 + 45x - 14$
48. $3m^2 - 10m + 3$
49. $10x^2 - 21x - 10$
50. $3c^2 + 8c - 3$
51. $8y^2 + 9y - 14$
52. $7a^2b^2 - 24ab + 9$
53. $14r^2 + 11r - 15$
54. $7a^2 - 27a + 18$
55. $48x^2 + 16x - 15$
56. $121s^2 - 55s + 6$
57. $14 + y - 30y^2$
58. $14 + 23u + 8u^2$
59. $7t^2 - 19t + 10$
60. $168x^2y^2 + 10axy - 25a^2$
61. $6a^2 - ab - 35b^2$
62. $3 + 23c + 14c^2$
63. $12 - a - 35a^2$
64. $2c^2 - 3cy - 14y^2$

2–6 The sum and difference of two cubes. By direct multiplication we may obtain the following formulas:

$$(u + v)(u^2 - uv + v^2) = u^3 + v^3, \tag{9a}$$

$$(u - v)(u^2 + uv + v^2) = u^3 - v^3. \tag{9b}$$

Their use will now be illustrated.

EXAMPLE 1. Multiply $(3a + 2b)(9a^2 - 6ab + 4b^2)$.

Solution. The given expression conforms to the left side of (9a) with $u = 3a$ and $v = 2b$. We note particularly that the middle term in the second factor is $-uv$. By formula (9a) we obtain

$$(3a + 2b)(9a^2 - 6ab + 4b^2) = (3a)^3 + (2b)^3 = 27a^3 + 8b^3.$$

If the signs between the terms in the binomial, and the sign of the middle term in the trinomial are reversed, formula (9b) applies, and we have

$$(3a - 2b)(9a^2 + 6ab + 4b^2) = (3a)^3 - (2b)^3 = 27a^3 - 8b^3.$$

As we have noted before, reversing of a multiplication formula leads to a factorization formula. The reversal of (9a) and (9b) leads to the important formulas

$$u^3 + v^3 = (u + v)(u^2 - uv + v^2), \tag{10a}$$

$$u^3 - v^3 = (u - v)(u^2 + uv + v^2), \tag{10b}$$

the *formulas for factoring the sum and the difference of two cubes, respectively.*

EXAMPLE 2. Factor $8a^3 - b^3$.

Solution. The expression conforms to the left side of (10b), with $u = 2a$ and $v = b$. Hence

$$\begin{aligned} 8a^3 - b^3 &= (2a - b)([2a]^2 + [2a][b] + b^2) \\ &= (2a - b)(4a^2 + 2ab + b^2). \end{aligned}$$

If the expression to be factored is $8a^3 + b^3$, formula (10a) applies, and we have

$$8a^3 + b^3 = (2a + b)(4a^2 - 2ab + b^2).$$

EXERCISE GROUP 2-6

Apply type forms (9a) and (9b) to obtain the products in Exercises 1-14.

1. $(a + 2)(a^2 - 2a + 4)$
2. $(2a + b)(4a^2 - 2ab + b^2)$
3. $(a - 2b)(a^2 + 2ab + 4b^2)$
4. $(2x - 3y)(4x^2 + 6xy + 9y^2)$
5. $(2u + \frac{1}{2})(4u^2 - u + \frac{1}{4})$
6. $(\frac{1}{2}c + \frac{1}{3}d)(\frac{1}{4}c^2 - \frac{1}{6}cd + \frac{1}{9}d^2)$
7. $(2x^2 + 3)(4x^4 - 6x^2 + 9)$
8. $(3a^2 - 5y^2)(9a^4 + 15a^2y^2 + 25y^4)$
9. $(ax^3 + b^3y)(a^2x^6 - ab^3x^3y + b^6y^2)$
10. $(c^2x - dy^2)(c^4x^2 + c^2dxy^2 + d^2y^4)$
11. $[a + (b + c)][a^2 - a(b + c) + (b + c)^2]$
12. $[(a + b) - c][(a + b)^2 + (a + b)c + c^2]$
13. $[a - 2(b - c)][a^2 + 2a(b - c) + 4(b - c)^2]$
14. $[(2a + b) + 3c][(2a + b)^2 - 3c(2a + b) + 9c^2]$

Factor each of the following expressions.

15. $a^3 + 8b^3$
16. $27b^3 - a^3$
17. $8x^3 + 27y^3$

18. $x^3 - 27y^3$
19. $t^3 - \frac{1}{8}s^3$
20. $8u^3 + \frac{1}{8}v^3$
21. $64x^3 - 27a^3b^3$
22. $125c^3 + d^3$
23. $\frac{1}{27}a^3 - c^3$
24. $\frac{1}{125} - 27a^3b^3$
25. $\frac{1}{8}a^3 + \frac{1}{27}x^3$
26. $\frac{1}{64} + \frac{1}{27}a^3x^3$
27. $0.001 - x^3$
28. $0.125y^3 + 0.001$
29. $\frac{1}{1000}a^3x^3 + 8u^3$
30. $a^3b^6 + c^6d^3$
31. $(a + b)^3 - c^3$
32. $8x^3 - 27(y + z)^3$
33. $27(u + v)^3 + 125w^3$
34. $8a^3 - (3b - c)^3$
35. $0.008u^3 + (v - 0.1w)^3$
36. $8(a + b)^3 + 27(c + d)^3$
37. $125(a - b)^3 - (2c - 3d)^3$

2–7 Multiplication by type forms. For additional emphasis of the usefulness of the type forms of multiplication, we list them again:

1. $$u(x + y) = ux + uy,$$

2. $$(u + v)(u - v) = u^2 - v^2,$$

3a. $$(u + v)^2 = u^2 + 2uv + v^2,$$

3b. $$(u - v)^2 = u^2 - 2uv + v^2,$$

4. $$(au + b)(cu + d) = acu^2 + (ad + bc)u + bd,$$

5a. $$(u + v)(u^2 - uv + v^2) = u^3 + v^3,$$

5b. $$(u - v)(u^2 + uv + v^2) = u^3 - v^3.$$

Examples of the use of these type forms have been given in the earlier sections. We reiterate the generality of these formulas, which lies in the fact that each letter in each of the formulas may represent any quantity whatsoever.

It often happens that the proper insertion of parentheses permits the use of one of the type forms and thus greatly simplifies a given multiplication. In other instances it may be necessary to rearrange the terms before inserting the parentheses. The following examples will illustrate these techniques.

EXAMPLE 1. Expand $(a + b - 2)^2$.

Solution. Upon enclosing $a + b$ in parentheses we may write

$$\begin{aligned} (a + b - 2)^2 &= [(a + b) - 2]^2 \\ &= (a + b)^2 - 4(a + b) + 4 && \text{[by type form 3b]} \\ &= a^2 + 2ab + b^2 - 4a - 4b + 4 && \text{[by types 3a and 1].} \end{aligned}$$

EXAMPLE 2. Expand $(x + 2y + 3)(x - 2y + 3)$.

Solution. By rearranging within the parentheses we have

$$\begin{aligned} (x + 2y + 3)(x - 2y + 3) &= [(x + 3) + 2y][(x + 3) - 2y] \\ &= (x + 3)^2 - 4y^2 && \text{[by type form 2]} \\ &= x^2 + 6x + 9 - 4y^2 && \text{[by type 3a].} \end{aligned}$$

EXERCISE GROUP 2–7

Use one or more of the type forms listed in Section 2–7 to perform the indicated multiplications in the following exercises.

1. $-3xy(x^2 - y^2 - 1)$
2. $-4xz(5x^2z - 3xz^2 + 2xz)$
3. $2xyz(7x^2y + 2yz^2 - 3x^2z)$
4. $\frac{3}{2}a^2(4a^4 - 2ab - 4b^4)$
5. $b^m(1 + b^n - b^m)$
6. $-a^n(1 - a^{2n} + a^{3n} - a^{4n})$
7. $(2a - 3b)(2a + 3b)$
8. $(6p - 9q)(2p + 3q)$
9. $(-bu - v)(bu - v)$
10. $(x^2y^2 - 4z)(x^2y^2 + 4z)$
11. $(x^m - y^m)(x^m + y^m)$
12. $[(a + b) + c][(a + b) - c]$
13. $(2a + 9b)^2$
14. $(4m - 3n)^2$
15. $(4d^2e^2 + 3f^2)^2$
16. $(6x^2y^2 - 3y^2z^2)^2$
17. $[(a + b) + c]^2$
18. $[(a + b) - c]^2$
19. $(3x + 5y)(2x + 7y)$
20. $(a^2 - 7b^2)(2a^2 - 3b^2)$
21. $(2x^2 + 3y^3)(2x^2 + 5y^3)$
22. $(-x^3 + 2ab)(2x^3 - 3ab)$
23. $[(a + b) + 2c][(a + b) - c]$
24. $[a - (b - c)]^2$
25. $[a + (x + y)][a - (x + y)]$
26. $[(x + y) + 7z][(x + y) - 3z]$
27. $[x + (2y + 3z)]^2$
28. $(\frac{1}{2}x - \frac{1}{3}y)(\frac{1}{4}x^2 + \frac{1}{6}xy + \frac{1}{9}y^2)$
29. $(2x + 3y)(4x^2 - 6xy + 9y^2)$
30. $(2a - b)(4a^2 + 2ab + b^2)$
31. $[(x + y) - z][x + y + z]$
32. $[(2x - 3y) + 4z]^2$
33. $[(a + b) - 3]^2$
34. $[(u + 3x) + v][u + 3x - v]$
35. $[(2x + 3y) - 5z]^2$
36. $[(u + x) + (v + y)][u - v + x - y]$
37. $[(2u + 7y) + (3v + 5x)][2u - 3v - 5x + 7y]$
38. $(2a - 3b + 4c)^2$

2–8 Complete factorization. We list here the formulas for factoring which have been used in the earlier sections of this chapter:

1. $$\boxed{ux + uy = u(x + y),}$$

2. $$\boxed{u^2 - v^2 = (u + v)(u - v),}$$

3a. $$\boxed{u^2 + 2uv + v^2 = (u + v)^2,}$$

3b. $$\boxed{u^2 - 2uv + v^2 = (u - v)^2,}$$

4. $$\boxed{acu^2 + (ad + bc)u + bd = (au + b)(cu + d),}$$

5a. $$\boxed{u^3 + v^3 = (u + v)(u^2 - uv + v^2),}$$

5b. $$\boxed{u^3 - v^3 = (u - v)(u^2 + uv + v^2).}$$

Example 1. Factor $3x^2 + 8x - 3$.

Solution. If the given expression can be factored, it appears that formula 4 above, which factors a trinomial as a product of two binomials, must apply. Upon consideration of the relatively few possibilities, we obtain the result

$$3x^2 + 8x - 3 = (3x - 1)(x + 3).$$

In Section 2–1 the main concern in the factoring of integers was to obtain *prime* factors, that is, integers which could not be factored further. In the factorization of algebraic expressions it is also desirable to obtain factors such that, in some sense, none of them can be factored further. In particular, we shall mean by this a factorization in which no factor can be further broken down into expressions containing only rational numbers, except for a numerical factor.

Definition 2–2. *To factor completely an expression containing only rational numbers shall mean to factor it as far as possible in the rational number system (in other words, in the sense described above).*

The effect of this discussion on the technique of factoring is that any factor which is obtained must be examined to see whether it can be factored further.

EXAMPLE 2. Factor $4x^2y^2 - 36x^2z^2$ completely.

Solution. Formula 1 above applies, with $u = 4x^2$. We obtain

$$4x^2y^2 - 36x^2z^2 = 4x^2(y^2 - 9z^2).$$

However, we now recognize that the factor $y^2 - 9z^2$ is a difference of two squares and can also be factored. The final result is then

$$4x^2y^2 - 36x^2z^2 = 4x^2(y + 3z)(y - 3z).$$

In Example 2 the factor 4 can be written as 2^2, but it is customary in this connection not to factor an integral factor further.

EXAMPLE 3. Factor $a^4 - a^2 - 12$ completely.

Solution. Form 4 applies, with $u = a^2$, and we obtain

$$a^4 - a^2 - 12 = (a^2 + 3)(a^2 - 4).$$

The first factor on the right does not factor further, but the second factor, $a^2 - 4$, is a difference of two squares. Completion of the factorization gives

$$a^4 - a^2 - 12 = (a^2 + 3)(a + 2)(a - 2).$$

EXERCISE GROUP 2–8

Factor each of the following expressions completely.

1. $x^4 - 9x^2$
2. $x^3 - 4x$
3. $x^4 - 5x^3$
4. $3x^2 - 27x + 54$
5. $2a^2 + 10ax - 12x^2$
6. $a^2b^2 - 25c^2$
7. $9x^2y^2z^2 - 9x^2y^2$
8. $1 - 3b - 10b^2$
9. $15 + 2x - x^2$
10. $x + 12 - x^2$
11. $6 + x^2 - 7x$
12. $16 - 17y^2 + y^4$
13. $2 - 72x^2$
14. $x^2y + 9xy + 14y$
15. $(a + 5)(x - y) + (b - 3)(x - y)$
16. $x^2(a + b) + 4x(a + b) + 4(a + b)$
17. $72xy - 4x^3y - 12x^2y$
18. $4(x + y)^2 + 24(x + y) + 36$
19. $6(a + b)^2 - 24(a + b) + 24$
20. $(x^2 + 5x)^2 - 8(x^2 + 5x) - 84$
21. $30x^3y + 95x^2y^2 - 35xy^3$
22. $x^2(x - 3) - 4(x - 3)$
23. $x^4(x^2 - 1) - 16(x^2 - 1)$
24. $(a + 2b)^2 - 14(a + 2b) + 40$
25. $(x^2 - 3x)^2 - 8(x^2 - 3x) - 20$
26. $(a^2 + 2ab)^2 - 2b^2(a^2 + 2ab) - 3b^4$
27. $98x^4y^2 - 56x^3y^3 + 8x^2y^4$
28. $4a^6 - 52a^4 + 144a^2$

29. $17a^4 - 59a^2b^2 - 36b^4$
30. $28x^4 - 19x^2y^2 - 99y^4$
31. $25x^4 - 101x^2y^2 + 4y^4$
32. $8a^3 - x^3$
33. $x^6 + 5x^3 + 4$
34. $m^6 - 2m^3n^3 + n^6$

2–9 Factoring by grouping of terms. There are many problems in factoring which do not conform directly to the above forms but can be made to do so by properly grouping the terms. This is usually accomplished through the use of parentheses or other grouping symbols. We seek a grouping of some of the terms in such a way that the group which is formed can be factored while at the same time the new form of the expression conforms to one of the standard type forms.

We will illustrate the procedure by some examples. The reference numbers employed to identify the type forms involved are used in accordance with the listing of forms in Section 2–8.

EXAMPLE 1. Factor $ax + by + ay + bx$ completely.

Solution. The first and last terms have the factor x in common, while the second and third terms have the factor y in common. Hence we may rewrite the expression and we have

$$\begin{aligned} ax + bx + ay + by &= x(a + b) + y(a + b) \\ &= (a + b)(x + y) \qquad [\text{by 1 with } u = a + b]. \end{aligned}$$

EXAMPLE 2. Factor $2ax - 3by - 2ay + 3bx$ completely.

Solution. As in Example 1, x is a common factor of the first and last terms while y is a common factor of the second and third terms. Upon rewriting we have

$$\begin{aligned} 2ax + 3bx - 2ay - 3by &= x(2a + 3b) - y(2a + 3b) \\ &= (2a + 3b)(x - y). \end{aligned}$$

The same result may be obtained by noting that $2a$ is a common factor of the first and third terms, and that $3b$ is a common factor of the second and last terms. Hence a different grouping gives

$$\begin{aligned} 2ax - 2ay + 3bx - 3by &= 2a(x - y) + 3b(x - y) \\ &= (x - y)(2a + 3b). \end{aligned}$$

EXAMPLE 3. Factor $xy - 3y + y^2 - 3x$ completely.

Solution. $$\begin{aligned} xy - 3y + y^2 - 3x &= (xy + y^2) - (3x + 3y) \\ &= y(x + y) - 3(x + y) = (x + y)(y - 3). \end{aligned}$$

EXAMPLE 4. Factor $x^2 + 2xy + y^2 - 9$ completely.

Solution. The appearance of the trinomial $x^2 + 2xy + y^2$, which is the square of the binomial $(x + y)$, suggests the grouping.

We obtain

$$\begin{aligned}(x^2 + 2xy + y^2) - 9 &= (x + y)^2 - 9 && \text{[by 3a]}\\ &= [(x + y) + 3][(x + y) - 3] && \text{[by 2]}\\ &= (x + y + 3)(x + y - 3).\end{aligned}$$

EXAMPLE 5. Factor $a^2 - 2ab + b^2 - x^2 - 2xy - y^2$ completely.

Solution. Familiarity with type forms 3a and 3b suggests the following grouping:

$$\begin{aligned}(a^2 - 2ab + b^2) - (x^2 + 2xy + y^2) &= (a - b)^2 - (x + y)^2\\ &= [(a - b) + (x + y)][(a - b) - (x + y)]\\ &= (a - b + x + y)(a - b - x - y).\end{aligned}$$

EXERCISE GROUP 2–9

By inserting parentheses (rearranging terms where necessary), reduce each of the following to a type form and then factor completely.

1. $x - y - 3z(x - y)$
2. $bx + by + ax + ay$
3. $ax - by - bx + ay$
4. $ux + vy - vx - uy$
5. $3ax - 5bx + 6ay - 10by$
6. $3au - 3ay - 5bu + 5by$
7. $bu + bv + 2hu + 2hv$
8. $3au + 3bu + av + bv$
9. $3cw - 3cx - 4kw + 4kx$
10. $-2ax - 2ah - abx - abh$
11. $(a^3 - 2a^2) - (a - 2)$
12. $(ab^3 + cb^2) - (ab + c)$
13. $u^3 + 2u^2 + u + 2$
14. $av^3 + 2v^2 - av - 2$
15. $u^2 - (2x - y)^2$
16. $(3x - y)^2 - 9u^2$
17. $xm + ym + xn + yn$
18. $6am - 3bm - 6an + 3bn$
19. $2ax - 3bx + 2ay - 3by$
20. $x^2 + mxy - 4xy - 4my^2$
21. $ax + by + az + bx + ay + bz$
22. $x^2 - y^2 - x + y$
23. $9u^2 - 9x^2 + 6x - 1$
24. $25v^2 - 2ab - a^2 - b^2$
25. $16a^2 + 8ab + b^2 - 25c^2$
26. $x^2(a - b) + y^2(b - a)$
27. $x^2 + 2xy - 16z^2 + y^2$
28. $u^2 - 4b^2 + 2uv + v^2$
29. $ax + 6by + 3bx + 2ay$
30. $a^3 - 3a^2 - a + 3$
31. $(a + 3) + 3a^2 + a^3$
32. $bx^2 + x^3 - by^2 - xy^2$
33. $4u^2 - 12uv + 9v^2 - 2ab - a^2 - b^2$
34. $u^2 + 2uv + v^2 - a^2 + 2ab - b^2$
35. $3x^2 - 6xy + 3y^2 - 10x + 10y + 3$
36. $4x^2 - 12xy + 9y^2 - 2x + 3y$
37. $x^2 - 3xy + 2y^2 - 2x + 4y$
38. $x^2 - 6xy + 9y^2 - 7x + 21y + 12$
39. $ax^2 + bx^2 + 4ax + 4bx + 4a + 4b$
40. $(x^2 + 4x - 6)^2 - 14x(x^2 + 4x - 6) + 45x^2$
41. $(x^2 + 4x + 8)^2 + 3x(x^2 + 4x + 8) + 2x^2$

Review Exercises

In each of Exercises 1–24, perform the indicated multiplication.

1. $(3a + 2b)(3a - 2b)$
2. $(ax^2 - by^2)(ax^2 + by^2)$
3. $(ax + by)^2$
4. $(3a^2 + 4b^2)^2$
5. $(2ax + 3by^2)^2$
6. $(a + b + c)(a + b - c)$
7. $(2x + 3y - 4z)(2x + 3y + 4z)$
8. $(a + 2b - 3c)(a - 2b + 3c)$
9. $(ax + by + c)^2$
10. $(3x + 4y - 5z)^2$
11. $(2ax - 3by + cz)^2$
12. $(a - b - c)^2$
13. $(2a + 3b - 4c)^2$
14. $(-a + 2b - 3c)^2$
15. $(a + 2b - 3c)(2a + 2b - 3c)$
16. $(3x - 4y + 5z)(5x - 4y + 5z)$
17. $(x + 2)^3$
18. $(a - 3)^3$
19. $(2x + 3y)^3$
20. $(3x - 2y)^3$
21. $(2x - 3y)(4x^2 + 6xy + 9y^2)$
22. $(3x + 2y)(9x^2 - 6xy + 4y^2)$
23. $(x - 5)(x^2 + 5x + 25)$
24. $(a + 7)(a^2 - 7a + 49)$

In each of the following exercises, factor completely.

25. $9x^2 - 25y^2$
26. $a^2x^2 - b^2$
27. $(a - b)^2 - (x + y)^2$
28. $a^2 - (2x - y)^2$
29. $49a^2 + 28ab + 4b^2$
30. $9x^2 - 30xy + 25y^2$
31. $25 - 10(x - y) + (x - y)^2$
32. $(a + b)^2 + 6(a + b) + 9$
33. $a^2 - b^2 - 4a + 4b$
34. $27 - 27y - 9y^2 + y^3$
35. $x^2 - y^2 + 6y - 9$
36. $y^2 - a^2 - 10a - 25$
37. $p^2 - 2pq + q^2 - r^2$
38. $-15 + 46a - 24a^2$
39. $-21a^2 + 92ab - 55b^2$
40. $-6x^2 - xy + 15y^2$
41. $-15x^2 + 29xy + 14y^2$
42. $a^2 + b^2 + 9 + 6a - 2ab - 6b$
43. $36 + 9a^2 + 9b^2 - 36a + 36b - 18ab$
44. $a^3 - 2a^2 - a + 2$
45. $9u^2 - 16x^2 + 4v^2 - 25y^2 - 12uv + 40xy$
46. $a^3 - 8b^3$
47. $27x^3 - 8y^3$
48. $x^4 - y^4 + 2x^3y - 2xy^3$
49. $a^2 + b^2 + 5a + 2ab + 5b + 4$
50. $x^2 + 4y^2 + 3x - 4xy - 6y - 4$

CHAPTER 3

FRACTIONS

3–1 Fractions. In Section 1–11 it was pointed out that the indicated quotient of an integer by a nonzero integer is called a fraction, and, accordingly, that any rational number may be considered to be a fraction. More generally, we may give the following definition, to apply to all real numbers.

DEFINITION 3–1. *A* fraction *shall mean the indicated quotient of any number by any nonzero number. The dividend in the division is called the* numerator *of the fraction, and the divisor is called the* denominator *of the fraction.*

For example, $\frac{5}{7}$ is a fraction in which 5 is the numerator and 7 is the denominator.

As was pointed out in Section 1–2 it is frequently advantageous to represent integers, in fact all types of numbers, by letters. Thus, a/b is also a fraction, and so also is any quotient in which the numerator and denominator are algebraic expressions, provided the denominator is not zero. The expressions

$$\frac{3ab}{a^2 - b^2} \quad \text{and} \quad \frac{x^2 - 4xy - 5y^2}{x^2 + 5xy + 6y^2}$$

are, accordingly, fractions.

It is assumed, in what follows, that the numerical values of all letters appearing in any fraction are such that the denominator does not vanish, that is, such that the denominator is not zero.

3–2 Equality of fractions. In this and later sections we shall present the important properties of fractions.

PROPERTY I. $a/b = c/d$ *if and only if* $ad = bc$.

We shall omit a proof of this criterion for the equality of two fractions.

EXAMPLE 1. Is $\frac{2}{9}$ equal to $\frac{98}{441}$?

Solution. By Property I we must determine whether $2 \cdot 441$ and $9 \cdot 98$ are equal. By direct multiplication each product is equal to 882, and the two given fractions are equal.

EXAMPLE 2. Are $\frac{4}{7}$ and $\frac{3}{5}$ equal fractions?

Solution. By Property I the products to be compared are $4 \cdot 5 = 20$, and $7 \cdot 3 = 21$; the fractions are therefore not equal.

Property I leads directly to a most useful principle, stated as follows:

FUNDAMENTAL PRINCIPLE. *The value of a fraction is unaltered if both numerator and denominator are multiplied or divided by the same number (not zero).*

Proof. Both parts of the principle are verified if we prove that

$$\frac{ac}{bc} = \frac{a}{b}, \qquad (c \neq 0).$$

By Property I we must then show that $(ac)b = (bc)a$, which holds since each product is equal to abc, so that the *fundamental principle* is established.

EXAMPLE 3. $\frac{2}{3} = \frac{2 \cdot 4}{3 \cdot 4} = \frac{8}{12}; \quad \frac{15}{36} = \frac{15 \div 3}{36 \div 3} = \frac{5}{12}.$

EXAMPLE 4. $\frac{3x}{5y} = \frac{3x(xy)}{5y(xy)} = \frac{3x^2y}{5xy^2}.$

EXAMPLE 5. $\frac{24a^2bx^3}{60ab^3x} = \frac{24a^2bx^3 \div (12abx)}{60ab^3x \div (12abx)} = \frac{2ax^2}{5b^2}.$

3–3 The signs of a fraction. There are three signs associated with a fraction: the sign of the numerator, the sign of the denominator, and the sign preceding the fraction.

From Theorem 1–1 of Section 1–11 and the discussion following that theorem, it follows that

$$\frac{-a}{b} = -\frac{a}{b} \quad \text{and} \quad \frac{a}{-b} = -\frac{a}{b}.$$

Combining these relations, we have

$$\frac{-a}{b} = \frac{a}{-b} = -\frac{a}{b},$$

and we note the rule:

Any two of the three signs of a fraction may be changed without changing the value of the fraction.

EXAMPLE 1. $\frac{-3}{7} = \frac{3}{-7} = -\frac{3}{7}.$

EXAMPLE 2. $+\frac{(-3)(-a)(-b)}{(-2)(-c)} = +\frac{-3ab}{2c} = -\frac{3ab}{2c}.$

3–4 Simplest form of a fraction. By the Fundamental Principle, a fraction in which the numerator and denominator have a factor in common may be simplified, or reduced, by dividing out that factor.

For a fraction to be in *simplest form* or *lowest terms* the numerator and denominator may have no common factor other than $+1$ and -1. *One may eliminate any common factors by*

1. *factoring both numerator and denominator completely,*
2. *dividing out all common factors.*

The following examples illustrate the reduction of a fraction to simplest form.

EXAMPLE 1. $$\frac{-36}{20} = \frac{(-1)\cdot 2^2 \cdot 3^2}{2^2 \cdot 5} = \frac{(-1)\cdot 3^2}{5} = -\frac{9}{5}.$$

EXAMPLE 2. $$\frac{a^4x^2y^3}{a^7xy^2} = \frac{a^4xy^2(xy)}{a^4xy^2(a^3)} = \frac{xy}{a^3}.$$

EXAMPLE 3. $$\frac{a^2 + 5ab}{a^2 + 3ab} = \frac{a(a + 5b)}{a(a + 3b)} = \frac{a + 5b}{a + 3b}.$$

EXAMPLE 4. $$\frac{b^2 - 9}{b^2 - 6b + 9} = \frac{(b + 3)(b - 3)}{(b - 3)(b - 3)} = \frac{b + 3}{b - 3}.$$

EXAMPLE 5. $$\frac{ax - by + bx - ay}{3ax - 5by + 5bx - 3ay} = \frac{x(a + b) - y(a + b)}{x(3a + 5b) - y(3a + 5b)}$$
$$= \frac{(a + b)(x - y)}{(3a + 5b)(x - y)} = \frac{a + b}{3a + 5b}.$$

In order to simplify a fraction it is not actually necessary to factor both numerator and denominator completely. If, for example, the numerator has been factored completely, it is sufficient to test whether each factor obtained is or is not a factor of the denominator.

EXAMPLE 6. Simplify $\frac{84}{4551}$.

Solution. We factor 84 as $84 = 2^2 \cdot 3 \cdot 7$. Of these factors only 3 is a factor of 4551. Thus, we have

$$\frac{84}{4551} = \frac{2^2 \cdot 3 \cdot 7}{3 \cdot 1517} = \frac{28}{1517},$$

and no further simplification is possible.

Exercise Group 3-1

In Exercises 1–9, use Property I to determine whether the two given fractions are equal.

1. $\frac{2}{3}, \frac{57}{85}$
2. $\frac{18}{19}, \frac{126}{133}$
3. $\frac{1.7}{0.32}, \frac{85}{16}$
4. $\frac{2}{56}, \frac{9}{252}$
5. $\frac{2.7}{0.06}, \frac{2.25}{0.05}$
6. $\frac{8801}{5932}, \frac{756}{509}$
7. $\frac{3}{84}, \frac{14}{392}$
8. $\frac{0.67}{2}, \frac{29.15}{87}$
9. $\frac{293}{814}, \frac{576}{1601}$

In the following exercises, reduce the given fraction to simplest form.

10. $\frac{52}{91}$
11. $\frac{102}{85}$
12. $\frac{165}{308}$
13. $\frac{-147}{231}$
14. $\frac{2^3 \cdot 7^2 \cdot 5}{192}$
15. $\frac{(-3)^5 \cdot 4^2}{2^5 \cdot 21}$
16. $\frac{15 \cdot 14}{36 \cdot 35}$
17. $\frac{93(-55)}{(-87)(-155)}$
18. $\frac{21}{770}$
19. $\frac{324}{84}$
20. $\frac{798}{1197}$
21. $\frac{963}{243}$
22. $\frac{30x}{75x^2}$
23. $\frac{12x^2y}{42xy^3}$
24. $\frac{a^4x^2y^3}{a^7xy^2}$
25. $\frac{a(3a + b)}{a^2 + 3ab}$
26. $\frac{ax^2 - ay^2}{a^2x + a^2y}$
27. $\frac{a^2(x + y)^2}{ax^2 - ay^2}$
28. $\frac{a^2 - 4}{2a - 4}$
29. $\frac{y^2 - x^2}{a(x - y)}$
30. $\frac{4a^2 - 9b^2}{2a + 3b}$
31. $\frac{9a^2b + 12ab^2}{9a^3b - 15ab^3}$
32. $\frac{a^2 - 3a - 4}{a^2 - 8a + 16}$
33. $\frac{-y^2 + x^2}{xy - 2x^2 + y^2}$
34. $\frac{x^2 - 3xy + 2y^2}{2y^2 - xy - x^2}$
35. $\frac{x^2 - x - 6}{x^2 + x - 12}$
36. $\frac{3x^4 - 21x^3 + 36x^2}{x^2 - 8x + 15}$
37. $\frac{81y^4 - x^4}{(x^2 - 9y^2)(x + 3y)}$
38. $\frac{cx^2 - dy^2 - cy^2 + dx^2}{dx + cy + dy + cx}$
39. $\frac{x^2 + ax - ab - bx}{(x + a)(b - x)}$
40. $\frac{ax - by + bx - ay}{3ax - 5by + 5bx - 3ay}$
41. $\frac{a + b - c}{ac - bc - a^2 + b^2}$
42. $\frac{x^4 - y^4 + 2xy(x^2 - y^2)}{x^4 - y^4}$

43. $\dfrac{a^2x^2 + x^3 - a^2y^2 - xy^2}{ax - ay + by - bx}$

44. $\dfrac{(x - y)^2}{y^2 - xy}$

45. $\dfrac{a^2c - a^2d + b^2d - b^2c}{c^2a - c^2b + d^2b - d^2a}$

46. $\dfrac{3x^2 - 17x + 20}{6x^2 - 7x - 5}$

47. $\dfrac{a^2 - b^2 + c^2 + 2ac}{a^2 - c^2 + b^2 + 2ab}$

48. $\dfrac{-2x^2 + 7x + 15}{3x^2 - 13x - 10}$

49. $\dfrac{3x^2 + 5x - 22}{3x^2 - x - 10}$

50. $\dfrac{x^3 - 8}{x^3 - 2x^2 + 4x - 8}$

51. $\dfrac{a^3 + 8b^3}{a^3 + 2a^2b - 4a - 8b}$

52. $\dfrac{5ab^3 - 5ab}{15ab^4 - 15ab}$

53. $\dfrac{8x^3 - 27b^3}{9b^2 + 4x^2 - 12bx}$

54. $\dfrac{81 - 3x^3}{-6 + x^2 - x}$

55. $\dfrac{3a^3 - 13a^2 + 23a - 21}{9a^2 - 36a + 35}$

3–5 Lowest common multiple. Lowest common denominator. The *lowest common multiple* of two or more integers is the smallest integer which is exactly divisible by each of the given integers, and the following procedure applies.

RULE. To find the lowest common multiple, or LCM, of two or more integers:

1. *Express each number as a product of its prime factors.*
2. *Form the product of all the different prime factors which appear in the given integers, each with an exponent which is the largest exponent of that prime in all the factorizations.*

EXAMPLE 1. Find the LCM of 18, 108, and 40.

Solution. Expressing each given number as a product of its prime factors we have

$$18 = 3^2 \cdot 2, \qquad 108 = 3^3 \cdot 2^2, \qquad 40 = 2^3 \cdot 5.$$

The LCM will contain the prime factors 2, 3, and 5; the highest exponent of 2 is 3, the highest exponent of 3 is also 3, and the highest exponent of 5 is 1. Hence the LCM of 18, 108, and 40 is

$$2^3 \cdot 3^3 \cdot 5 = 8 \cdot 27 \cdot 5 = 1080.$$

In an entirely analogous manner we define and determine the lowest common multiple, or LCM, of algebraic expressions.

EXAMPLE 2. Find the LCM of $12(x^2 - 1)$, $2x^2 + x - 3$, $2x^2 + 5x + 3$, and $15(x^2 + 2x + 1)$.

Solution. The factorizations of the given expressions are as follows:

$$12(x^2 - 1) = 2^2 \cdot 3(x + 1)(x - 1), \qquad 2x^2 + x - 3 = (2x + 3)(x - 1),$$
$$2x^2 + 5x + 3 = (2x + 3)(x + 1), \qquad 15(x^2 + 2x + 1) = 3 \cdot 5(x + 1)^2.$$

The desired LCM is then seen to be

$$2^2 \cdot 3 \cdot 5(x + 1)^2(x - 1)(2x + 3) = 60(x + 1)^2(x - 1)(2x + 3).$$

EXAMPLE 3. Find the LCM of $x^2 + 3x + 2$, $6 + x - x^2$, and $x^2 - 2x - 3$.

Solution. The given expressions are factored as follows:

$$x^2 + 3x + 2 = (x + 2)(x + 1),$$
$$6 + x - x^2 = (3 - x)(x + 2) = -(x - 3)(x + 2),$$
$$x^2 - 2x - 3 = (x - 3)(x + 1).$$

The LCM is then seen to be $(x + 2)(x + 1)(x - 3)$.

The application of lowest common multiple to fractions is in finding the lowest common denominator.

DEFINITION 3–2. *The lowest common denominator* (LCD) *of two or more fractions is the lowest common multiple of the denominators of the fractions.*

Since this definition involves nothing more than a new name, all the above examples apply equally well to illustrate how to find the LCD. In general there is no fixed rule as to whether the LCM or LCD should be multiplied out or left in factored form.

EXERCISE GROUP 3–2

Find the LCM of the given set of quantities in Exercises 1–25.

1. 32, 40
2. 20, 14, 30
3. 24, 32, 36
4. 15, 25, 35
5. 21, 28, 49
6. 42, 70, 98
7. 66, 110, 154
8. 63, 105, 147
9. $6ab$, $15ab^2$, $21a^2b$
10. $15a^2b$, $25a^3b^2$, $35ab^3$
11. $8x^2y^3$, $18x^3y^5$, $30y^4z^2$
12. $21a^2b^3c$, $30a^3bc^2$, $70ab^2c^3$
13. $66a^3b^2c^4$, $63a^4b^3c^2$, $40c^3d^2$
14. $52a^4x^3$, $55b^3y^4$, $56a^3x^2b$
15. $9x^2 - 9$, $12x^2 - 24x + 12$
16. $35(x^2 - y^2)$, $x^2 + 3xy - 4y^2$, $21(x - y)^2$
17. $3x - 6$, $6x + 18$, $15(x^2 + x - 6)$
18. $6a + 18$, $5a - 55$, $60(a^2 - 8a - 33)$

19. $x^2 - x - 6,\ x^2 + x - 12,\ x^2 + 6x + 8$
20. $54a^2 - 24b^2,\ 81a^4 - 16b^4,\ 27a^3b + 12ab^3$
21. $-(3 + a - 2a^2),\ 12 + a - 6a^2,\ 4 + 7a + 3a^2$
22. $4x - 12,\ 3x + 12,\ 2x^2 + 2x - 24$
23. $15x^2 - 19x - 10,\ 25x^2 - 4,\ 3x^2 + 4x - 15$
24. $2x^2 - 5x + 2,\ 6x^2 + x - 2,\ 3x^2 - 4x - 4$
25. $a^2 - b^2,\ a^3 + b^3,\ a^3 - b^3$

Find the LCD of each of the following groups of fractions.

26. $\dfrac{a}{a^2 - 4a + 4},\ \dfrac{5}{7a - 14}$

27. $\dfrac{x + 2}{x^2 + 3x - 10},\ \dfrac{x - 3}{x^2 + x - 6},\ \dfrac{1}{x + 5}$

28. $\dfrac{3x - 7}{x^2 - 2x - 15},\ \dfrac{7x + 5}{6 - x - x^2},\ \dfrac{5x - 3}{x^2 - 7x + 10}$

29. $\dfrac{2x - 3}{20 + x - x^2},\ \dfrac{-2x + 5}{12 - x - x^2},\ \dfrac{7x + 3}{x^2 - 8x + 15}$

30. $\dfrac{3x + 2}{4x^2 - 1},\ \dfrac{x + 3}{4x^2 + 6x + 2},\ \dfrac{x - 2}{4x^2 + 2x - 2}$

31. $\dfrac{3x + 2}{15x^2 - 4x - 4},\ \dfrac{7x - 3}{6x^2 + 11x - 10},\ \dfrac{1}{5x + 2}$

32. $\dfrac{3x - 7}{3x^2 + 4x - 15},\ \dfrac{7x + 5}{6 - x - x^2},\ \dfrac{5x - 3}{10 - 11x + 3x^2}$

33. $\dfrac{x + y}{x^2 + y^2},\ \dfrac{2}{x^3 + y^3},\ \dfrac{3}{x^4 - y^4}$

3–6 Addition and subtraction of fractions. In Exercise 33 of Exercise Group 1–7, it was stated that

$$\frac{a + b}{c} = \frac{a}{c} + \frac{b}{c}.$$

The proof, which is not difficult, may be extended to a sum or difference of more than two fractions with the same denominator; the result applies as well where algebraic expressions are involved, and may be stated as follows:

To add or subtract two or more fractions with the same denominator, form the corresponding sum or difference of the numerators as the numerator of the resulting fraction with the common denominator as denominator.

EXAMPLE 1. Find the sum $\frac{1}{9} + \frac{7}{9} + \frac{4}{9}$.

Solution. Following the above instructions we get

$$\frac{1}{9}+\frac{7}{9}+\frac{4}{9}=\frac{1+7+4}{9}=\frac{12}{9}=\frac{4}{3}.$$

It should be noted that application of the rule gave the fraction $\frac{12}{9}$; this was then simplified to get the equivalent fraction $\frac{4}{3}$, which is in simplest form.

EXAMPLE 2. By applying the rule, we have

$$\frac{2}{3x-2}-\frac{3x}{3x-2}+\frac{7x^2}{3x-2}=\frac{2-3x+7x^2}{3x-2}.$$

Since the numerator cannot be factored, the fraction cannot be simplified further.

If fractions with different denominators are to be added, the first step is to change each fraction to an equivalent fraction, in such a way that all the new fractions have the same denominator. This common denominator will be the lowest common denominator, or LCD, *defined in Section* 3–5. *After all the fractions have the same denominator, the above rule for addition and subtraction of fractions may be applied.*

EXAMPLE 3. Find the sum $\frac{1}{5}+\frac{2}{3}+\frac{3}{7}$.

Solution. The LCD is $5\cdot 3\cdot 7 = 105$. To change $\frac{1}{5}$, for example, to an equivalent fraction with denominator 105, we must multiply both numerator and denominator by 21, and get $\frac{21}{105}$. In this manner we get

$$\frac{1}{5}+\frac{2}{3}+\frac{3}{7}=\frac{1\times 21}{105}+\frac{2\times 35}{105}+\frac{3\times 15}{105}=\frac{21+70+45}{105}=\frac{136}{105}.$$

EXAMPLE 4. Reduce to a single fraction in lowest terms

$$\frac{3}{x^2-1}+\frac{4x}{2x^2+x-3}-\frac{3x+2}{2x^2+5x+3}.$$

Solution. The denominators factor as

$$x^2-1=(x+1)(x-1),\qquad 2x^2+x-3=(2x+3)(x-1),$$
$$2x^2+5x+3=(2x+3)(x+1).$$

Hence, LCD $=(x+1)(x-1)(2x+3)$. Changing each fraction to an equivalent fraction with the LCD as the denominator, we get

$$\frac{3(2x+3)}{(x+1)(x-1)(2x+3)}$$
$$+\frac{4x(x+1)}{(x+1)(x-1)(2x+3)}-\frac{(3x+2)(x-1)}{(x+1)(x-1)(2x+3)}$$
$$=\frac{6x+9+4x^2+4x-3x^2+x+2}{(x+1)(x-1)(2x+3)}=\frac{x^2+11x+11}{(x+1)(x-1)(2x+3)}.$$

Since $x^2 + 11x + 11$ cannot be factored, the last fraction is in simplest form, and hence is the answer.

EXAMPLE 5. Express as a single fraction in simplest form

$$\frac{2-x}{x^2-1} + \frac{8}{1-x^2} - \frac{5+x}{1-x^2}.$$

Solution. Since $1 - x^2 = -(x^2 - 1)$, the LCD may be taken as $x^2 - 1$. The sum can then be written as

$$\frac{(2-x) + 8(-1) - (5+x)(-1)}{x^2-1} = \frac{-1}{x^2-1} = \frac{1}{1-x^2}.$$

Note: The LCD may also be taken as $1 - x^2$.

EXERCISE GROUP 3-3

In each of the following exercises, reduce the given expression to a single fraction in simplest form.

1. $\frac{3}{7} + \frac{5}{7} - \frac{2}{7}$
2. $\frac{5}{11} + \frac{7}{11} - \frac{3}{11}$
3. $\frac{4}{15} + \frac{7}{15} - \frac{1}{15}$
4. $\frac{23}{70} + \frac{37}{70} - \frac{4}{70}$
5. $\frac{29}{33} - \frac{17}{22} + \frac{5}{66}$
6. $\frac{31}{35} - \frac{19}{21} + \frac{2}{5}$
7. $\frac{3}{a} + \frac{a-6}{a} + \frac{3-2a}{a}$
8. $\frac{x-y}{x+y} - \frac{y-2x}{x+y} - \frac{x-4y}{x+y}$
9. $\frac{a^2}{a^2-b^2} + \frac{2b^2}{a^2-b^2} - \frac{b^2+2a^2}{a^2-b^2}$
10. $\frac{a}{3(a-b)} + \frac{b}{2(a-b)} - \frac{a+4b}{6(a-b)}$
11. $\frac{x}{5(x+y)} - \frac{y}{7(x+y)} + \frac{10y-2x}{35(x+y)}$
12. $\frac{1}{x+3} + \frac{1}{x+4}$
13. $\frac{x}{x+y} + \frac{y}{x-y}$
14. $\frac{1+x}{1-x} - \frac{1-x}{1+x}$
15. $\frac{x+y}{x-y} + \frac{x-2y}{x+y} + \frac{x^2+3y^2}{y^2-x^2}$
16. $\frac{x}{x^2+xy} + \frac{x+y}{xy-y^2} - \frac{y}{x^2-y^2}$
17. $\frac{a}{ab-bc} - \frac{b}{ac-a^2}$
18. $\frac{x-2}{x-1} - \frac{3}{1-x} + \frac{x}{1-x}$

19. $\dfrac{a-4}{a-2}+\dfrac{2-11a}{2-a}$

20. $a+x+\dfrac{x^2}{a-x}$

21. $3x+1-\dfrac{2-7x}{2x-3}$

22. $ax-2+\dfrac{1}{ax}$

23. $\dfrac{x-1}{x-2}-\dfrac{x+1}{x+3}$

24. $\dfrac{x-1}{x+3}-\dfrac{x+3}{x-1}$

25. $\dfrac{x+3}{x^2+5x+6}+\dfrac{x+2}{x^2+8x+12}$

26. $\dfrac{1}{x-1}+\dfrac{2}{x-2}-\dfrac{3}{x-3}$

27. $\dfrac{a}{4b^2-a^2}-\dfrac{2b}{a^2+ab-6b^2}$

28. $\dfrac{x(3y-x)}{y^2-x^2}+\dfrac{3x}{x-y}$

29. $\dfrac{3}{2a-3}-\dfrac{2}{3-2a}+\dfrac{15}{9-4a^2}$

30. $\dfrac{1}{a-2}+\dfrac{1}{a+2}+\dfrac{4}{a^2+4}-\dfrac{8a^2}{a^4-16}$

31. $\dfrac{x^2}{x^2-1}+\dfrac{x}{x+1}-\dfrac{x}{x-1}$

32. $\dfrac{a}{3+a}-\dfrac{a}{3-a}-\dfrac{a^2}{a^2-9}$

33. $\dfrac{x^2+1}{x-1}-(x-1)-\dfrac{x^2-1}{1-x}+\dfrac{x^3}{x^2-1}$

34. $a^2+a+1+\dfrac{a^3}{1-a}-\dfrac{3}{a-1}$

35. $\dfrac{x+3}{x^2+3x+2}-\dfrac{x-2}{3+2x-x^2}$

36. $2a+1-\dfrac{3a^3+2a^2-1}{2a-1}$

37. $2a+\dfrac{3a^4-8a^3+1}{4a^2-4a+1}-1$

38. $\dfrac{5-4a}{7-2a}-\dfrac{12a^2-48a-6}{4a^2-16a+7}+1$

39. $\dfrac{2a}{a^2-b^2}+\dfrac{1}{b-a}+\dfrac{1}{a+b}$

40. $\dfrac{2x+3}{x^2-4x-5}-\dfrac{2x-3}{x^2-3x-10}$

41. $\dfrac{a-6}{a^2+3a-4}+\dfrac{1}{1-a}-\dfrac{2}{4+a}$

42. $\dfrac{x+2}{x^2+x}-\dfrac{1}{x}-\dfrac{x-3}{x^2+2x+1}$

43. $\dfrac{2}{1-3x}-\dfrac{3}{1-2x}+\dfrac{3}{x}-\dfrac{x}{1-5x+6x^2}$

44. $\dfrac{y^2}{x^3+xy^2}+\dfrac{x^2}{x^2y+y^3}-\dfrac{1}{x+y}$

45. $\dfrac{x-1}{x^2+3x+2}+\dfrac{x+1}{6+x-x^2}-\dfrac{x-2}{x^2-2x-3}$

3–7 Multiplication and division of fractions. It can be shown from the definitions that

$$\frac{a}{b} \cdot \frac{c}{d} = \frac{ac}{bd},$$

so that we may state the following:

The product of two or more fractions is a fraction whose numerator is the product of all the numerators and whose denominator is the product of all the denominators.

EXAMPLE 1. $\dfrac{2}{3} \cdot \dfrac{3}{5} \cdot \dfrac{5}{7} = \dfrac{2 \cdot 3 \cdot 5}{3 \cdot 5 \cdot 7} = \dfrac{2}{7}$

It should be noted that the product was reduced to simplest form. Moreover, the process is such that *a common factor in any numerator and any denominator may be divided out* before combining into a single fraction, as in the following.

EXAMPLE 1a. $\frac{2}{3} \cdot \frac{3}{5} \cdot \frac{5}{7} = \frac{2}{1} \cdot \frac{1}{1} \cdot \frac{1}{7} = \frac{2}{7}$, since the common factors 3 and 5 may be divided out.

The most convenient procedure in multiplying fractions is, thus, to factor each numerator and denominator, and to divide out common factors.

EXAMPLE 2. Perform the multiplication and simplify:

$$\frac{9y^2 - 1}{y^2 - 16} \cdot \frac{y^2 + 4y}{6y + 2}.$$

Solution. Factor each numerator and denominator to obtain,

$$\frac{9y^2 - 1}{y^2 - 16} \cdot \frac{y^2 + 4y}{6y + 2} = \frac{(3y + 1)(3y - 1)}{(y + 4)(y - 4)} \cdot \frac{y(y + 4)}{2(3y + 1)}$$
$$= \frac{3y - 1}{y - 4} \cdot \frac{y}{2} = \frac{y(3y - 1)}{2(y - 4)}.$$

To determine the rule for dividing fractions, we recall that in Section 1–11 the quotient of two integers a and b was defined by the relation

$$a = bq.$$

The same definition applies to all numbers, and in particular to fractions. Thus, we have

$$\frac{x}{y} = \frac{u}{v} \cdot q,$$

where q is the quotient when x/y is divided by u/v. If both members of the above relation are multiplied by v/u, we obtain

$$q = \frac{x}{y} \cdot \frac{v}{u}.$$

In obtaining the last relation we made use of the fact that

$$\frac{u}{v} \cdot \frac{v}{u} = 1,$$

from which it follows that

$$\frac{u}{v} = 1 \div \frac{v}{u}.$$

The fraction v/u is called the *reciprocal* of u/v, so that we have the rule:

To find the quotient of two fractions, multiply the dividend by the reciprocal of the divisor; or, briefly, invert the divisor and multiply the resulting fractions.

Note: The product of any nonzero number and its reciprocal is unity.

EXAMPLE 3. $\frac{3}{5} \div \frac{2}{7} = \frac{3}{5} \cdot \frac{7}{2} = \frac{21}{10}$.

EXAMPLE 4.
$$\frac{3x - 1}{\dfrac{9x^2 - 1}{4x + 5}} = \frac{3x - 1}{1} \cdot \frac{4x + 5}{9x^2 - 1} = \frac{(3x - 1)(4x + 5)}{(3x + 1)(3x - 1)}$$
$$= \frac{4x + 5}{3x + 1}.$$

EXAMPLE 5. Simplify the expression

$$\frac{x^2 + 14x - 15}{x^2 + 4x - 5} \div \frac{x^2 + 12x - 45}{x^2 + 6x - 27}.$$

Solution. Inverting the second fraction we obtain

$$\frac{x^2 + 14x - 15}{x^2 + 4x - 5} \cdot \frac{x^2 + 6x - 27}{x^2 + 12x - 45} = \frac{(x + 15)(x - 1)}{(x + 5)(x - 1)} \cdot \frac{(x + 9)(x - 3)}{(x + 15)(x - 3)}$$
$$= \frac{x + 9}{x + 5}.$$

EXERCISE GROUP 3–4

In each of the following exercises, perform the indicated operations and express the result in simplest form.

1. $\frac{5}{8} \cdot \frac{2}{3}$
2. $\frac{3}{16} \cdot \frac{4}{9}$
3. $\left(\frac{-5}{16}\right)\left(\frac{-4}{15}\right)$

4. $\left(\frac{8}{-3}\right)\left(\frac{9}{-12}\right)$ 5. $\left(\frac{-5}{-12}\right)\left(\frac{3}{-25}\right)$ 6. $\left(\frac{30}{-14}\right)\left(-\frac{7}{12}\right)$

7. $\left(\frac{-15}{-14}\right) \div \left(\frac{10}{-21}\right)$ 8. $\left(\frac{9}{-16}\right) \div \left(\frac{-72}{56}\right)$

9. $\left(-\frac{13}{51}\right) \div (-26)$ 10. $\left(\frac{39}{-14}\right) \div \left(\frac{-13}{7}\right)$

11. $(-17) \div \left(\frac{13}{-7}\right)$ 12. $\frac{5}{21} \div 35$

13. $\frac{3ax}{4by} \cdot \frac{2ay}{5bx}$ 14. $\frac{3ax^2}{4by^2} \div \frac{9b^2y}{12a^2x}$

15. $\frac{ax - ay}{2x + 4y} \cdot \frac{2y + x}{y - x}$ 16. $\frac{a + 1}{a + 2} \cdot \frac{a + 2}{a + 3}$

17. $\frac{a^2 - 5a + 4}{a^2 - 3a - 4} \cdot \frac{a^2 + 3a - 4}{a^2 + 5a + 4}$ 18. $\frac{a^2 + ab}{a^2 - ab} \div \frac{a^3 + a^2b}{ab^2 + b^3}$

19. $\frac{x^2 - 3x + 2}{(x - 2)^2} \div \frac{(x - 1)^2}{x^2 - 5x + 4}$ 20. $\frac{(x - 1)^2}{(x + 2)^2} \cdot \frac{x^2 - 4}{x^2 - 1}$

21. $\frac{a + 5b}{a^2 + 6ab} \div \frac{ab + 5b^2}{a^3 + 6a^2b}$ 22. $\frac{a^2 - b^2}{(a + b)^2} \div \frac{(a - b)^2}{a^2 - b^2}$

23. $\frac{3a - 3b}{x^2 - y^2} \div \frac{2b - 2a}{x - y}$ 24. $\frac{ax + bx}{ay - by} \cdot \frac{az - bz}{aw + bw}$

25. $(x^2 - y^2) \cdot \frac{ab}{cx - cy}$ 26. $\frac{xy^2 - y^3}{x^3 + x^2y} \div \frac{x^2 - 2xy + y^2}{x^2 - xy - 2y^2}$

27. $\frac{x^2 - 13x + 22}{x^2 - 9x + 8} \div \frac{x^2 - 5x + 6}{x^2 - 6x - 16}$

28. $\frac{a^4 - b^4}{(a - b)^2} \cdot \frac{a - b}{a^2 + ab} \cdot \frac{a^2}{a^2 + b^2}$ 29. $\left[\frac{y^2}{1 - y^2} + \frac{2y}{1 - y}\right] \div \frac{1 - y}{y + 1}$

30. $\frac{x^2 + 18x + 80}{x^2 + 15x + 56} \cdot \frac{x^2 + 6x - 7}{x - 1} \cdot \frac{x - 6}{x^2 + 5x - 50}$

31. $\frac{x^2 + 14x - 15}{x^2 + 4x - 5} \div \frac{x^2 + 12x - 45}{x^2 + 6x - 27}$

32. $\frac{x^2 - 5x}{x - 1} \div \left[\frac{x^2 - 25}{x^2 + x - 20} \cdot \frac{x^2 - 2x - 8}{x^2 + x - 2}\right]$

33. $\frac{2x^2 - 13x + 15}{4x^2 - 9} \div \left[\frac{2x - 1}{2x + 1} \div \frac{2x - 1}{x - 5}\right]$

34. $\frac{x^2 - 5x - 24}{x^2 - 5x + 6} \cdot \frac{x^2 - 2x - 8}{x^2 - 4x - 21} \cdot \frac{x^2 - 9x + 14}{x^2 - 6x - 16}$

35. $\dfrac{16a+4}{5a+5}\cdot\dfrac{a^2-1}{6a-6}\cdot\dfrac{a^2-2a+1}{16a^2-1}$

36. $(r+s)\div\left[\dfrac{r^2-s^2}{1+y}\div\dfrac{r-s}{1-y^2}\right]$

37. $\dfrac{7+6a-a^2}{3a-2}\cdot\dfrac{2a-3}{a^2-8a+7}\div\dfrac{1-a^2}{a^2-2a+1}$

38. $\left[\dfrac{x^2+xy}{x^2-xy}\div\dfrac{x^3+x^2y+xy^2}{x-y}\right]\cdot\dfrac{x^2+xy+y^2}{x+y}$

39. $\left[3x-2-\dfrac{8(2x+3)}{x+3}\right]\div\left[3(x+2)-\dfrac{2(x^2-4)}{x-3}\right]$

40. $\left[9a+\dfrac{17a^3+9a^2b}{b^2-ab-2a^2}\right]\div\left[3+\dfrac{5a}{b-2a}\right]$

41. $\left[a-\dfrac{2a^2b}{b^2+ab-6a^2}\right]\cdot\left[1+\dfrac{2ab}{b^2-ab-6a^2}\right]$

42. $\dfrac{a^4-b^4}{a^2-2ab+b^2}\div\dfrac{a^2+b^2}{a^2-ab}$

3-8 Complex fractions. A complex fraction is any fraction in which the numerator or denominator or both contain fractions. (Of course, an expression such as $a - b$ can be considered as a fraction with denominator equal to 1.) *Two methods are given for simplifying a complex fraction.*

I. *Multiply numerator and denominator of the principal fraction by the* LCD *of all the secondary fractions.*

II. *Express the principal numerator as a single fraction, and also the principal denominator.*

EXAMPLE 1. Simplify $\dfrac{1+\frac{2}{3}}{3-\frac{2}{5}}$.

Solution I. If we multiply numerator and denominator by $3\cdot 5 = 15$, we obtain

$$\frac{1+\frac{2}{3}}{3-\frac{2}{5}}\cdot\frac{15}{15}=\frac{15+10}{45-6}=\frac{25}{39}.$$

Solution II. $\dfrac{1+\frac{2}{3}}{3-\frac{2}{5}}=\dfrac{\frac{5}{3}}{\frac{13}{5}}=\dfrac{5}{3}\cdot\dfrac{5}{13}=\dfrac{25}{39}$.

EXAMPLE 2. Simplify $\dfrac{3-\dfrac{2a}{5a-1}}{4a-\dfrac{a}{1+2a}}$.

Solution I. Multiplying numerator and denominator by $(5a - 1)(1 + 2a)$, we obtain

$$\frac{3 - \dfrac{2a}{5a-1}}{4a - \dfrac{a}{1+2a}} \cdot \frac{(5a-1)(1+2a)}{(5a-1)(1+2a)} = \frac{3(5a-1)(1+2a) - 2a(1+2a)}{4a(5a-1)(1+2a) - a(5a-1)}$$
$$= \frac{(1+2a)(15a-3-2a)}{a(5a-1)(4+8a-1)}$$
$$= \frac{(1+2a)(13a-3)}{a(5a-1)(8a+3)}.$$

Solution II.
$$\frac{3 - \dfrac{2a}{5a-1}}{4a - \dfrac{a}{1+2a}} = \frac{\dfrac{15a-3-2a}{5a-1}}{\dfrac{4a+8a^2-a}{1+2a}} = \frac{13a-3}{5a-1} \cdot \frac{1+2a}{a(8a+3)}$$
$$= \frac{(13a-3)(1+2a)}{a(5a-1)(8a+3)}.$$

Exercise Group 3–5

In each of the following exercises, reduce the given complex fraction to a fraction in simplest form.

1. $\dfrac{3 - \frac{1}{2}}{5 + \frac{2}{3}}$
2. $\dfrac{2 + \frac{3}{5}}{7 - \frac{3}{2}}$
3. $\dfrac{\frac{2}{3} - \frac{3}{5}}{\frac{4}{7} + \frac{5}{9}}$
4. $\dfrac{\frac{3}{7} - 1}{2 - \frac{7}{5}}$
5. $\dfrac{\frac{5}{8} - 7}{\frac{9}{16} + \frac{2}{7}}$
6. $\dfrac{15 - \frac{3}{11}}{\frac{7}{13} + 5}$
7. $\dfrac{x - y}{x + 2y}$ for (a) $x = \frac{1}{3}$, $y = \frac{1}{6}$, (b) $x = -\frac{3}{5}$, $y = \frac{7}{10}$, (c) $x = -\frac{5}{7}$, $y = -\frac{7}{3}$
8. $\dfrac{5\frac{3}{7} - 2\frac{2}{3}}{3\frac{7}{9} + 5\frac{3}{7}}$
9. $\dfrac{4}{4 + \dfrac{3}{3 + \frac{2}{3}}}$
10. $\dfrac{2}{2 - \dfrac{3}{3 - \frac{24}{19}}}$
11. $\dfrac{5}{\frac{3}{8} - \dfrac{1}{\frac{2}{3} - \frac{21}{2}}}$
12. $\dfrac{\dfrac{1}{x} - \dfrac{1}{y}}{\dfrac{a}{x} - \dfrac{a}{y}}$
13. $\dfrac{a - \dfrac{a}{b}}{c - \dfrac{c}{b}}$
14. $\dfrac{\dfrac{u^2}{v^2} - 1}{\dfrac{u}{v} - 1}$
15. $\dfrac{a + 1 - \dfrac{6}{a}}{a + 5 + \dfrac{6}{a}}$
16. $\dfrac{\dfrac{2a+b}{a+b} + 1}{\dfrac{2a+b}{a+b} - 1}$

17. $\dfrac{1+\dfrac{2}{x^2}+\dfrac{1}{x^4}}{1+\dfrac{2}{x}+\dfrac{1}{x^2}}$

18. $\dfrac{4-\dfrac{1}{1-x}}{16+\dfrac{7}{x^2-1}}$

19. $\dfrac{1+\dfrac{2}{x-1}}{\dfrac{x^2+x}{x^2+x-2}}$

20. $\dfrac{1-\dfrac{1}{x+2}}{2x-2-\dfrac{12}{x-2}}$

21. $\dfrac{a^2-\dfrac{1}{a}}{a+\dfrac{1}{a}+1}$

22. $\dfrac{\dfrac{1}{x+1}-\dfrac{1}{x-1}}{\dfrac{1}{x-1}+\dfrac{1}{x+1}}$

23. $\dfrac{\dfrac{a}{b}-\dfrac{b}{a}}{\dfrac{a}{b}+\dfrac{b}{a}+2}$

24. $\dfrac{\dfrac{a+1}{a-1}-\dfrac{a-1}{a+1}}{\dfrac{a+1}{a-1}+\dfrac{a-1}{a+1}}$

25. $\dfrac{\dfrac{1}{x-2}-\dfrac{1}{x-3}}{1+\dfrac{1}{x^2-5x+6}}$

26. $\dfrac{\dfrac{a-x}{x}-\dfrac{x-1}{x-a}}{x(x-a)}$

27. $\dfrac{\dfrac{x+3}{x-1}-\dfrac{x-1}{x+3}}{(x+3)^2}$

28. $\dfrac{\dfrac{1}{x}+\dfrac{1}{y+z}}{\dfrac{1}{x}-\dfrac{1}{y+z}}\left[1+\dfrac{y^2+z^2-x^2}{2yz}\right]$

Review Exercises

In each of the following exercises, reduce the given expression to a single fraction in simplest form.

1. $3a-\dfrac{3-7a}{2a-3}+1$

2. $\dfrac{2a-1}{2a+3}-\dfrac{a+2}{2-3a}$

3. $\dfrac{u-v}{uv-uy}+\dfrac{x-y}{cy-cv}$

4. $\dfrac{3}{x}+2-\dfrac{x-3}{x^2+5x}$

5. $\dfrac{x-y}{x-3y}-\dfrac{2x-y}{x+3y}+3$

6. $\dfrac{2}{x+3}-\dfrac{5}{x^2-x-12}-\dfrac{x+3}{4-x}$

7. $\dfrac{7-a}{3-a}-\dfrac{3a^2-16a+17}{a^2-5a+6}+2$

8. $\dfrac{3a-5}{2-3a}-\dfrac{17-18a^2}{9a^2-3a-2}-1$

9. $\dfrac{-2}{x^2+x-6}-\dfrac{3}{x^2+3x-10}+\dfrac{5}{x^2-9}$

10. $\dfrac{3}{4x^2-1}-\dfrac{4x}{4x^2+4x-3}-\dfrac{3x+2}{4x^2+8x+3}$

11. $\dfrac{16x - 4}{7x - 7} \cdot \dfrac{x^2 - 1}{6x + 6} \cdot \dfrac{x^2 + 2x + 1}{16x^2 - 1}$

12. $\dfrac{6a^2 + ab - 15b^2}{9a^2 - 25b^2} \div \dfrac{6a^2 - 7ab - 3b^2}{3a^2 - 2ab - 5b^2}$

13. $\dfrac{a^2 - 2ab + b^2}{a^2 + 2ab + b^2} \div \dfrac{a^2 + ab - 2b^2}{a^2 - ab - 2b^2}$

14. $\left[a - 2 + \dfrac{1}{a}\right] \div \left[1 - \dfrac{1}{a^2}\right]$

15. $\left[\dfrac{1}{1 - x} - \dfrac{1}{1 + x}\right] \div \left[\dfrac{1}{1 - x} + \dfrac{1}{1 + x}\right]$

16. $\left[3 + \dfrac{3a}{a + 2b}\right] \div \left[2 - \dfrac{a^2 - 7b^2}{a^2 - 4b^2}\right]$

17. $\left[\dfrac{a}{a - b} - \dfrac{b}{a + b}\right] \div \dfrac{ab}{a^2 - b^2}$

18. $\left[1 + \dfrac{3}{x - 2}\right] \div \left[2(x - 1) - \dfrac{12}{x - 2}\right]$

19. $\left[\dfrac{1}{1 - \dfrac{1}{1 + a}} - \dfrac{1}{\dfrac{1}{1 - a} - 1}\right] \div \left[1 + \dfrac{1}{1 - 2a}\right]$

20. $\dfrac{\dfrac{1}{(4 + \frac{2}{3}) - (3 + \frac{1}{2})} - (2 + \frac{3}{4})}{(1 - \frac{1}{8}) \div 2}$

21. $\dfrac{x - y}{a} \div \left[\dfrac{y^3 - x^3}{a^3} \div \dfrac{x^2 + xy + y^2}{a^2}\right]$

22. $\dfrac{8a^3 - b^3}{2a + 3b} \cdot \dfrac{2a^2 + 5ab + 3b^2}{4a^2 - b^2} \cdot \dfrac{4a^2 + 4ab + b^2}{4a^2 + 2ab + b^2}$

23. $\dfrac{\dfrac{2}{(3 - \frac{2}{5}) - (5 + \frac{1}{3})} - (3 - \frac{3}{7})}{(2 - \frac{3}{5}) \div 49}$

CHAPTER 4

EXPONENTS AND RADICALS

4–1 Negative integral and zero exponents. In Section 1–9 the quantity x^n, when n is a positive integer, was defined as follows:

DEFINITION 4–1. *If n is a positive integer, the quantity x^n, the nth power of x, is defined as the product $x \cdot x \cdot x \cdots x$, where there are n numbers x in the product.*

As an immediate consequence of this definition the following *laws of exponents* were developed in Sections 1–9 and 1–12.

LAWS OF EXPONENTS	ILLUSTRATIONS
1. $x^p x^q = x^{p+q}$	$a^2 a^3 = a^{2+3} = a^5$
2. $(x^p)^q = x^{pq}$	$(b^2)^3 = b^{2\cdot 3} = b^6$
3. $(xy)^p = x^p y^p$	$(2b)^5 = 2^5 b^5 = 32b^5$
4. $\left[\frac{x}{y}\right]^p = \frac{x^p}{y^p}$, if $y \neq 0$	$\left[\frac{a}{b}\right]^7 = \frac{a^7}{b^7}$
5. $\frac{x^p}{x^q} = x^{p-q}$, if $x \neq 0$	$\frac{a^5}{a^2} = a^{5-2} = a^3$

Since only positive integral exponents have been defined, Law 5 is valid only when p is larger than q. It would be desirable to have Law 5 hold for all values of p and q. The remainder of this section will be devoted to accomplishing this goal and then to the application of the five laws.

If $p = q$, the application of Law 5 gives $x^p/x^p = x^0$, which is meaningless in terms of Definition 4–1. However, any quantity such as x^p divided by itself gives 1 as a quotient if $x \neq 0$. Thus Law 5 will hold when $p = q$ if we define x^0 as follows:

DEFINITION 4–2.

If $x \neq 0$, then $x^0 = 1$.

EXAMPLES. $2^0 = 1$, $3x^0 = 3 \cdot 1 = 3$, $(3x)^0 = 1$.

It should be noted in the above examples that in $3x^0$ the exponent applies *only* to the x while in $(3x)^0$ the exponent applies to the entire quantity

$3x$. Thus great care must be exercised in using mathematical symbols to *express exactly* what is intended.

If p is less than q, then from Law 5 we have $x^p/x^q = x^{p-q}$, which is meaningless in terms of Definition 4–1 since $p - q$ is a negative number. However, in Section 1–12 the quotient x^p/x^q, when p is less than q, was shown to be $1/x^{q-p}$. Thus we see that Law 5 can be applied when p is less than q if we define x^{p-q} as $1/x^{q-p}$, or in general if we define x^{-n}, when n is a positive integer, as follows:

DEFINITION 4–3.

If n is a positive integer and $x \neq 0$, then $x^{-n} = 1/x^n$.

EXAMPLES.

$$x^{-3} = \frac{1}{x^3}, \qquad 2x^{-5} = 2 \cdot \frac{1}{x^5} = \frac{2}{x^5},$$

$$(2x)^{-5} = \frac{1}{(2x)^5} = \frac{1}{2^5x^5} = \frac{1}{32x^5},$$

$$\frac{x^3}{x^7} = x^{3-7} = x^{-4} = \frac{1}{x^4}.$$

With the addition of Definitions 4–2 and 4–3, Law 5 becomes valid for all integral values of p and q. In fact all operations with exponents are accomplished by using the five laws stated in Section 4–1.

EXAMPLE 1. Write $5x^{-3}y^0$ without zero or negative exponents.

Solution. $y^0 = 1$ and $x^{-3} = 1/x^3$. Therefore

$$5x^{-3}y^0 = 5 \cdot \frac{1}{x^3} \cdot 1 = \frac{5}{x^3}.$$

EXAMPLE 2. Use the laws of exponents to perform the indicated operations in

$$(2^3x^45^2y^7)^5.$$

Solution. Application of Law 3 gives

$$(2^3x^45^2y^7)^5 = (2^3)^5(x^4)^5(5^2)^5(y^7)^5.$$

If we now apply Law 2 to each power of the right member we obtain

$$(2^3x^45^2y^7)^5 = (2^3)^5(x^4)^5(5^2)^5(y^7)^5 = 2^{15}x^{20}5^{10}y^{35}.$$

EXAMPLE 3. Perform the indicated operations:

$$(7 \cdot 10^5)^3 \cdot (3 \cdot 10^{-3})^4.$$

Solution.

$$\begin{aligned}(7\cdot 10^5)^3\cdot(3\cdot 10^{-3})^4 &= (7^3 10^{15})\cdot(3^4 10^{-12}) &&\text{[by Law 3 and Law 2]}\\ &= 3^4\cdot 7^3\cdot 10^{15}\cdot 10^{-12}\\ &= 3^4\cdot 7^3\cdot 10^3 &&\text{[by Law 1].}\end{aligned}$$

EXAMPLE 4. Perform the indicated operations and simplify:

$$\left[\frac{-5b^y}{3^2x^5}\right]^3\left[\frac{3x^7}{5b^y}\right]^2.$$

Solution.

$$\begin{aligned}\left[\frac{-5b^y}{3^2x^5}\right]^3\left[\frac{3x^7}{5b^y}\right]^2 &= \frac{(-5b^y)^3}{(3^2x^5)^3}\cdot\frac{(3x^7)^2}{(5b^y)^2} &&\text{[by Law 4]}\\ &= \frac{(-5)^3(b^y)^3}{(3^2)^3(x^5)^3}\cdot\frac{3^2(x^7)^2}{5^2(b^y)^2} &&\text{[by Law 3]}\\ &= \frac{-5^3b^{3y}}{3^6x^{15}}\cdot\frac{3^2x^{14}}{5^2b^{2y}} &&\text{[by Law 2]}\\ &= \frac{-5b^y}{3^4x} = -\frac{5b^y}{81x} &&\text{[by Law 5].}\end{aligned}$$

EXAMPLE 5. Express $\left[\dfrac{3x^{-1}-y^{-2}}{x^{-2}+2y^{-1}}\right]^{-2}$ without negative exponents.

Solution.

$$\begin{aligned}\frac{3x^{-1}-y^{-2}}{x^{-2}+2y^{-1}} &= \frac{\dfrac{3}{x}-\dfrac{1}{y^2}}{\dfrac{1}{x^2}+\dfrac{2}{y}} = \frac{\dfrac{3y^2-x}{xy^2}}{\dfrac{y+2x^2}{x^2y}}\\ &= \frac{3y^2-x}{xy^2}\cdot\frac{x^2y}{y+2x^2}\\ &= \frac{x(3y^2-x)}{y(y+2x^2)}.\end{aligned}$$

Therefore

$$\left[\frac{3x^{-1}-y^{-2}}{x^{-2}+2y^{-1}}\right]^{-2} = \left[\frac{x(3y^2-x)}{y(y+2x^2)}\right]^{-2} = \frac{1}{\left[\dfrac{x(3y^2-x)}{y(y+2x^2)}\right]^2} = \frac{y^2(y+2x^2)^2}{x^2(3y^2-x)^2}.$$

EXERCISE GROUP 4–1

In each of Exercises 1–10, find the value of the given quantity.

1. 4^{-3}
2. 1^{-9}
3. 2^{-4}
4. 2^{-3}
5. 4^0
6. 10^0
7. 2^{-5}
8. $(\frac{1}{3})^0$
9. $\dfrac{1}{2^{-2}}$
10. $\dfrac{1}{3^{-1}}$

In each of Exercises 11–38, write the given expression without zero or negative exponents.

11. $3x^{-5}$ 12. $5x^{-2}$ 13. $(2x)^{-3}$ 14. $(3x)^{-2}$
15. $2x^0$ 16. $7x^0$ 17. $(3x)^0$ 18. $(3x)^0y^{-2}$
19. $5x^0y^{-3}$ 20. $2x^{-2}y^0$ 21. $2^0x^0y^{-2}$ 22. $3x^{-3}y^4$
23. $4x^{-5}y^0$ 24. $5x^{-3}y^{-2}$ 25. $5x^{-3}y^2$ 26. $2^{-2}x^3y^{-1}$
27. $2x^{-2}y^{-3}$ 28. $3^{-1}x^0y^2$
29. $3x^0 + y^{-2}$ 30. $x^{-1} + (2^0x)^{-2} + 3x^{-3}$

31. $\dfrac{x^{-1} + y^{-1}}{x^{-1}y^{-1}}$ 32. $\dfrac{5x^{-1} + y^{-2}}{x^{-2} - 3y^{-1}}$

33. $\dfrac{x^{-2} - y^{-2}}{x^{-2}y^{-2}}$ 34. $\dfrac{3x^{-1}}{x^{-1} - 2y^{-1}}$

35. $\dfrac{x^{-1} - y^{-1}}{x^{-2} - y^{-2}}$ 36. $\dfrac{x^{2} + y^{-2}}{x^{-2} - y^2}$

37. $\left[\dfrac{3x^{-1} + y^{-1}}{x^{-1} - y^{-1}}\right]^0$ 38. $\left[\dfrac{2x^{-2} - 3y^{2}}{4x^2 + 5y^{-2}}\right]^0$

In Exercises 39–50, write each quantity without a denominator (use negative exponents).

39. $\dfrac{12a^2b^3}{c^3d}$ 40. $\dfrac{a^2b^3c^4}{x^3y^4z^5}$ 41. $\dfrac{x^{-2}y^3}{a^2b^{-3}}$ 42. $\dfrac{3a^2b^3}{5x^{-6}y^8}$

43. $\dfrac{1}{5x^2y^3z^0}$ 44. $\dfrac{5}{x^0y^{-2}z^7}$ 45. $\dfrac{2}{3x^7y^3z^{-4}}$ 46. $\dfrac{3}{2^0x^2y^3z^5}$

47. $\dfrac{1}{3x + 2y}$ 48. $\dfrac{3}{(x + 3y)^2}$ 49. $\dfrac{2x + y}{x - 5y}$ 50. $\dfrac{3x^2 + 4y^2}{2x^2 - 5y^3}$

In each of the following exercises, use the laws of exponents to perform the indicated operations and then simplify the result by expressing without zero or negative exponents.

51. a^3a^5 52. x^4x^7 53. $y^{2x}y^x$ 54. $b^{3a}b^{2a}$
55. $c^{2b}c^{5b}$ 56. $d^xd^{2x}d^{3x}$ 57. x^7x^{-3} 58. y^ay^{-b}
59. z^xz^{3-x} 60. b^2b^{-3x} 61. $5^25^35^{-4}$ 62. $3^73^{-2}3^5$
63. 5^x5^{2-x} 64. $3^2x^3x^y$ 65. $(x^5)^4$ 66. $(y^3)^7$
67. $(a^6)^3$ 68. $(b^7)^5$ 69. $(x^{2a})^3$ 70. $(5^{2x})^3$
71. $(x^{3a})^{2b}$ 72. $(x^2y^3)^7$ 73. $(a^5b^3)^6$ 74. $(c^3z^5)^7$
75. $(2^33^2)^5$ 76. $(3^45^3)^x$ 77. $(a^{2bc})^{5c}$ 78. $(a^{3x}b^{4y})^z$

79. $(2^x a^2 3^y b^3)^z$ 80. $(3^a b^3 5^c c^2)^5$ 81. $(2^3 a^{2x} 3^2 b^{3y})^c$ 82. $\left[\frac{x}{y}\right]^5$

83. $\left[\frac{a}{b}\right]^7$ 84. $\left[\frac{2a}{3y}\right]^4$ 85. $\left[\frac{a^2}{b^3}\right]^6$ 86. $\left[\frac{x^3}{y^2}\right]^7$

87. $\left[\frac{2x^2}{3y^4}\right]^5$ 88. $\left[\frac{2^3 a^4}{3^2 b^3}\right]^7$ 89. $\left[\frac{-2a}{3b^2}\right]^5$ 90. $\left[\frac{-3x^2}{5y^a}\right]^6$

91. $\left[\frac{-1}{3b^2}\right]^a$ 92. $\left[\frac{-a^3}{b^2 c^7}\right]^b$ 93. $\frac{a^2 b^3}{a^3 b^2}$ 94. $\frac{x^7 y^8}{x^{10} y^3}$

95. $\frac{2^5 a^7}{2^3 a}$ 96. $\frac{5^7 x^8}{5^3 x^2}$

97. $\frac{10^2 10^7}{10^5}$ 98 $\frac{(4 \cdot 10^7)(3 \cdot 10^{12})}{6 \cdot 10^8}$

99. $\frac{(2 \cdot 10^3)^2 (3 \cdot 10^5)}{5 \cdot 10^7}$ 100. $(2 \cdot 10^7)^2 (3 \cdot 10^4)^3 (2 \cdot 10^5)$

101. $\left[\frac{3x^2}{4y^3}\right]^2 \left[\frac{2y}{9x}\right]^5$ 102. $\left[\frac{-2a^3}{3b^2}\right]^7 \left[\frac{-a^2}{5b^4}\right]^3$ 103. $\left[\frac{-3b^2}{2c^3}\right]^4 \left[\frac{-2b^3}{c^2}\right]^6$

104. $\left[\frac{-2x}{5y^2}\right]^3 \left[\frac{3y}{4x}\right]^5$ 105. $\left[\frac{-2a^7}{3b^3}\right]^4 \left[\frac{3b^5}{2a^4}\right]^3$ 106. $\left[\frac{a^x b^y}{x^a y^b}\right]^2 \left[\frac{x^{2a} y^{3b}}{a^{3x} b^{2y}}\right]^3$

107. $(3a^{-5} - 4a^{-4} + 5a^{-3})(2a^{-2} - a^{-1})$

108. $(2x^2 - 3x^{-1} + 2x - 3)(2x - 1)$

4–2 Fractional exponents. In Section 4–1 the idea of exponents was extended to include zero and negative integers. In making the extension, we were careful to define the new exponents so that *they would obey the same rules which hold for positive integral exponents.* In this section we shall further extend the concept of exponents to include fractional exponents. As in the previous section, we wish to have the new exponents obey the five rules stated above in Section 4–1.

The symbol $x^{1/3}$, for example, has no meaning under Definitions 4–1, 4–2, or 4–3. It is then our privilege to define it in any manner that suits our purpose, which is that the previously established properties for exponents hold also for fractional exponents. Thus if Law 2 in Section 4–1 is to hold, we must have

$$(x^{1/3})^3 = x^{(1/3) \cdot 3} = x,$$

so that $x^{1/3}$ must be a number, if it exists, such that its third power equals x. This will be the definition of $x^{1/3}$. In general, we have

DEFINITION 4–4. *If there exists a number y such that $y^p = x$, where p is a positive integer greater than* 1, *then y is called a pth root of x.*

The number (or numbers) y just defined can be shown to exist if x is any complex number. However, such generality is not needed here. *For the remainder of this chapter, we shall adopt the convention that all letters represent real positive numbers.* Then x has a positive pth root; henceforth *the symbols* $x^{1/p}$ *and* $\sqrt[p]{x}$ *will be used to designate the* positive *pth root if x is positive.*

EXAMPLE 1. If $x^2 = 5$, then one value of x is $x = 5^{1/2} = \sqrt{5}$ (the square root).

EXAMPLE 2. If $x^3 = 8$, then one value of x is $x = 8^{1/3} = \sqrt[3]{8} = 2$ (the cube root).

DEFINITION 4–5. *If p is an integer and q is a positive integer, then*

$$\boxed{x^{p/q} = (x^{1/q})^p = (\sqrt[q]{x})^p;}$$

also

$$\boxed{x^{p/q} = (x^p)^{1/q} = \sqrt[q]{x^p}.}$$

It can be shown that the two parts of the definition are consistent, and that Laws 1–5 of Section 4–1 hold.

EXAMPLE 3. $(x^6)^{2/3} = x^{6(2/3)} = x^4$.

EXAMPLE 4. $27^{-2/3} = [27^{1/3}]^{-2} = 3^{-2} = \dfrac{1}{3^2} = \dfrac{1}{9}$.

EXAMPLE 5. $x^{3/7} \cdot x^{5/2} = x^{(3/7)+(5/2)}$ (Law 1) $= x^{41/14}$.

EXAMPLE 6. $x^{3/5} \div x^{2/3} = x^{(3/5)-(2/3)}$ (Law 5) $= x^{-1/15} = \dfrac{1}{x^{1/15}}$.

EXAMPLE 7. Determine the value of $(0.0081)^{-3/4}$.

Solution. $(0.0081)^{-3/4} = [(0.3)^4]^{-3/4} = (0.3)^{-3} = \dfrac{1}{(0.3)^3} = \dfrac{1}{0.027} = \dfrac{1000}{27}$.

EXAMPLE 8. Determine the value of $(5^{3/4}5^{2/3}5^{-5/2}5^{5/3})/(5^{1/3}5^{-5/2}5^{7/4})$.

Solution. Law 1 of Section 4–1 gives

$$\frac{5^{(9+8-30+20)/12}}{5^{(4-30+21)/12}} = \frac{5^{7/12}}{5^{-5/12}}.$$

Now applying Law 5 we obtain

$$5^{(7/12)-(-5/12)} = 5^{12/12} = 5.$$

EXAMPLE 9. Perform the indicated operations in the following expression and write the final result without negative or zero exponents:

$$\left(\frac{64a^{-3}b^{4/3}}{27a^{-9}b^{-14/3}}\right)^{-2/3}.$$

Solution. Applying Laws 4 and 3 in that order we have

$$\frac{(64)^{-2/3}a^2b^{-8/9}}{(27)^{-2/3}a^6b^{28/9}} = \frac{(4^3)^{-2/3}}{(3^3)^{-2/3}a^4b^{36/9}} = \frac{4^{-2}}{3^{-2}a^4b^4} = \frac{\frac{1}{16}}{\frac{1}{9}a^4b^4} = \frac{9}{16a^4b^4}.$$

EXAMPLE 10. Determine the value of

$$\frac{[25^{-3/2} + 7x^0 + 8^{2/3}]^{-1}}{[5y^0 + 0.5(-2.5)^{-1} + 3(81)^{-0.75}]^{-1}}.$$

Solution. Using Definitions 8–2 and 8–3, together with the five laws of exponents, we have

$$[25^{-3/2} + 7x^0 + 8^{2/3}]^{-1} = \left[\frac{1}{125} + 7 + 4\right]^{-1} = \left[\frac{1 + 1375}{125}\right]^{-1} = \frac{125}{1376},$$

and

$$\begin{aligned}[5y^0 + 0.5(-2.5)^{-1} + 3(81)^{-0.75}]^{-1} &= [5 - 0.2 + 3(\tfrac{1}{27})]^{-1}\\ &= [5 - \tfrac{1}{5} + \tfrac{1}{9}]^{-1}\\ &= \left[\frac{225 - 9 + 5}{45}\right]^{-1} = \frac{45}{221}.\end{aligned}$$

Therefore

$$\frac{[25^{-3/2} + 7x^0 + 8^{2/3}]^{-1}}{[5y^0 + 0.5(-2.5)^{-1} + 3(81)^{-0.75}]^{-1}} = \frac{125}{1376} \div \frac{45}{221} = \frac{125}{1376}\cdot\frac{221}{45} = \frac{5525}{12384}.$$

A negative number may be raised to a power with a fractional exponent p/q if q is odd. The value will be negative if p is odd, and positive if p is even. Definition 4–5 still applies.

EXAMPLE 11.

$$\begin{aligned}(-8)^{1/3} &= -2;\\ (-32)^{2/5} &= [(-32)^{1/5}]^2 = (-2)^2 = 4;\\ (-32)^{3/5} &= [(-32)^{1/5}]^3 = (-2)^3 = -8.\end{aligned}$$

EXERCISE GROUP 4-2

Determine a simple value of the expression in each of Exercises 1–35.

1. $4^{1/2}$
2. $81^{1/2}$
3. $27^{1/3}$
4. $8^{1/3}$
5. $16^{-1/2}$
6. $25^{-1/2}$
7. $16^{1/4}$
8. $81^{1/4}$

9. $(\frac{1}{4})^{1/2}$ 10. $(\frac{1}{9})^{1/2}$ 11. $(\frac{1}{16})^{1/2}$ 12. $(\frac{1}{25})^{1/2}$

13. $(8)^{-1/3}$ 14. $(27)^{-1/3}$ 15. $(49)^{-1/2}$ 16. $(64)^{-1/3}$

17. $(-1)^{-1/5}$ 18. $(-8)^{-1/3}$ 19. $(-27)^{-1/3}$ 20. $(-32)^{-1/5}$

21. $(0.01)^{1/2}$ 22. $(0.0016)^{1/4}$ 23. $9^{3/2}$ 24. $8^{5/3}$

25. $125^{2/3}$ 26. $25^{-3/2}$ 27. $4^{-5/2}$ 28. $27^{-4/3}$

29. $(-64)^{-4/3}$ 30. $2^{3/2}2^{5/2}$ 31. $5^{5/3}5^{4/3}$ 32. $10^{7/5}10^{8/5}$

33. $(3^{10})^{-2/5}$ 34. $(4^{8})^{-3/16}$ 35. $\dfrac{10^{2/3}10^{3/5}10^{-5/4}}{10^{-7/12}10^{-2/5}}$

Simplify each of the following by performing the indicated operations and removing negative and zero exponents. (In each case express *without* radicals.)

36. $(9a^{-2}b^{6})^{1/2}$ 37. $\left[\dfrac{9x^{-2}}{4y^{4}}\right]^{1/2}$ 38. $(2x^{1/3}y^{5/6})^{6}$

39. $(8a^{-9}b^{6})^{1/3}$ 40. $(2a^{-3}b^{2})^{-5}$ 41. $(8x^{6}y^{-3})^{2/3}$

42. $\left(\dfrac{27a^{-3}}{64b^{-3}}\right)^{-1/3}$ 43. $\left(\dfrac{2a^{1/2}b^{1/3}}{3a^{1/6}b^{1/2}}\right)^{6}$ 44. $\left(\dfrac{a^{2}b}{3a^{4}x^{2}}\right)^{3/2}$

45. $\left[\dfrac{4a^{3}b^{5}}{25a^{-1}b}\right]^{1/2}$ 46. $\left\{\dfrac{[a^{3/5}(a^{3/5})^{1/3}]^{5}}{a^{2}}\right\}^{5/2}$ 47. $\left[x^{2/3}\left\{\left(\dfrac{x^{2/3}}{x^{1/4}}\right)^{6}\right\}^{1/3}\right]^{2}$

48. $\left(\dfrac{8y^{2}z^{5}}{27x^{6}y^{-4}z^{-1}}\right)^{1/3}$ 49. $\left(\dfrac{9a^{0}b^{-5}c^{3}}{16b^{3}c^{-7}}\right)^{-1/2}$ 50. $\dfrac{10^{1/2}\cdot 10^{5/2}\cdot 10^{-3}}{10^{2/3}\cdot 10^{1/3}}$

51. $\left[\dfrac{9a^{-5}b^{3}}{25ab^{-7}}\right]^{3/2}$ 52. $\left(\dfrac{81x^{-8}y^{6}}{25a^{4}b^{-10}}\right)^{-3/2}$ 53. $\left(\dfrac{24b^{3/4}a^{3/2}}{16a^{3/4}b^{5/2}}\right)^{4/3}$

54. $(a^{1/3}b^{1/3} - a^{1/2}b^{1/2})(a^{1/3}b^{1/3} + a^{1/2}b^{1/2})$

55. $(a^{1/5}b^{1/7} - a^{2/5}b^{3/7})(a^{1/5}b^{1/7} + a^{2/5}b^{3/7})$

56. $(a^{1/3} - b^{1/5}c^{1/7})^{2}$ 57. $(a^{2/3} + 2a^{1/3}b^{1/3} + b^{2/3})^{1/2}$

58. $\sqrt[3]{a}\cdot\sqrt[4]{a}$ 59. $\sqrt[3]{a^{2}}\cdot\sqrt[4]{a^{3}}$ 60. $\dfrac{\sqrt[4]{a}}{\sqrt[3]{a}}$ 61. $\dfrac{16}{\sqrt[3]{16}}$

62. $\dfrac{\sqrt[4]{3}}{\sqrt[8]{81}}$ 63. $\dfrac{\sqrt{x^{4}}\sqrt[4]{x^{2}}}{\sqrt[3]{x}\cdot x^{3/4}}$ 64. $\sqrt[5]{x^{2}y}\cdot\sqrt[5]{x^{3}y^{4}}$ 65. $\dfrac{(\sqrt[3]{a^{2}b})^{8}}{\sqrt[3]{ab^{2}}}$

66. $\sqrt{16\sqrt[3]{a^{6}b^{12}}}$ 67. $\sqrt[3]{\sqrt{a^{-12}b^{0}}}$ 68. $\left(\dfrac{27^{-2/3} + (5a)^{0}}{3(a^{2})^{0} + 9^{3/2}}\right)^{-1/3}$

69. $8^{-2/3} + 5(25)^{-1/2} + 16^{1/2}(16)^{0}$

70. $(16)^{-3/4} + 5x^{0} - (25^{-1})^{-1/2} - (-8)^{5/3}$

71. $\dfrac{0.0016^{-0.75} - 4^{-0.5}}{25^{-0.5} - 8^{-1/3}}$ 72. $\dfrac{(0.25)^{-2/3} - (0.008)^{-3/2}}{(0.00032)^{-0.6} - 6x^{0}}$

4–3 Radicals and their properties. A pth root of x, where p is an integer greater than 1, has been defined as any value of y for which $y^p = x$. It is clear that if $y^2 = x$ there are two values of y, namely,

$$y_1 = \sqrt{x} \quad \text{and} \quad y_2 = -\sqrt{x}.$$

There are four values of y for which $y^4 = x$. In general, there are p pth roots* of x, that is, p numbers y such that $y^p = x$. To avoid confusion, one of the pth roots of x is designated as the *principal pth root* and is defined as follows:

DEFINITION 4–6. *If x is a positive real number, the principal pth root of x is the real positive pth root of x. If p is an odd integer and x is a positive real number, the principal pth root of $(-x)$ is the negative real pth root of $(-x)$.*

EXAMPLE. The principal square root of 25 is $+5$, and will be written as $\sqrt{25} = 5$. If the other root is desired, it will be designated as $-\sqrt{25} = -5$. The principal cube root of -27 is $\sqrt[3]{-27} = -3$.

The *radical* $\sqrt[p]{x}$ will be used to designate the principal pth root of x. The number x is called the *radicand* and the number p the *index of the radical.* It is customary to omit the index 2 in the case of a square root, so that $\sqrt[2]{x}$ is usually written $\sqrt{x}$.

Since, as we have seen, radicals can be expressed in terms of fractional exponents, the rules stated in Section 4–1 yield rules for working with radicals. To avoid any difficulties which might arise from roots of negative numbers, we assume here and throughout the remainder of this chapter that all literal radicands represent real numbers and, in the case of radicals with even index, are also positive. The *laws* for radicals are then as follows:

1. $\boxed{(\sqrt[n]{x})^n = x}$ (by definition).

2. $$\boxed{\sqrt[n]{x} \cdot \sqrt[n]{y} = x^{1/n} \cdot y^{1/n} = (xy)^{1/n} = \sqrt[n]{xy}.}$$

3. $$\boxed{\frac{\sqrt[n]{x}}{\sqrt[n]{y}} = \frac{x^{1/n}}{y^{1/n}} = \left(\frac{x}{y}\right)^{1/n} = \sqrt[n]{\frac{x}{y}}\cdot}$$

---

* See Chrystal, *College Algebra*, p. 238. London: A. & C. Black, Ltd. (1926).

4. $$\sqrt[p]{\sqrt[n]{x}} = [x^{1/n}]^{1/p} = x^{1/np} = \sqrt[np]{x}.$$

5. $$\sqrt[p]{x^n} = (\sqrt[p]{x})^n = x^{n/p}$$ (by definition).

Some applications of these laws can be seen in the following illustrations:

EXAMPLE 1. $\sqrt{27} = \sqrt{9 \cdot 3} = \sqrt{9} \cdot \sqrt{3} = 3\sqrt{3}$ (Law 2).

EXAMPLE 2. $\dfrac{\sqrt[3]{32}}{\sqrt[3]{4}} = \sqrt[3]{\dfrac{32}{4}} = \sqrt[3]{8} = 2$ (Law 3).

EXAMPLE 3. $\sqrt[3]{\sqrt{27}} = \sqrt[6]{27} = \sqrt{\sqrt[3]{27}} = \sqrt{3}$ (Law 4).

4–4 Removal of factors from the radicand. The above illustrations serve as examples of the operations usually employed in simplifying a radical. Thus, in Example 1 the factor 9 was removed from the radicand. In this connection we speak of 9 as a *perfect square,* since it is the square of 3. In general, a rational expression is called a *perfect nth power* if it is the nth power of some rational expression. *One step in simplifying a radical of index n is the removal from the radicand of all perfect nth powers.*

EXAMPLE 1. $\sqrt{50ab^3} = \sqrt{25b^2 \cdot 2ab} = \sqrt{25b^2} \cdot \sqrt{2ab} = 5b\sqrt{2ab}.$

EXAMPLE 2. $\sqrt[5]{-64x^{11}} = \sqrt[5]{(-1)32x^{10} \cdot 2x} = \sqrt[5]{(-1)32x^{10}} \cdot \sqrt[5]{2x}$
$= -2x^2 \cdot \sqrt[5]{2x}.$

EXAMPLE 3. $\sqrt[n]{a^{3n+2}b^{2n+1}} = \sqrt[n]{a^{3n}b^{2n}a^2b} = a^3b^2\sqrt[n]{a^2b}.$

EXAMPLE 4. $\sqrt{75a^3 + 50a^2b} = \sqrt{25a^2(3a + 2b)} = 5a\sqrt{3a + 2b}.$

EXAMPLE 5. $\sqrt{2a^2c + 4abc + 2b^2c} = \sqrt{(a + b)^2 \cdot 2c} = (a + b)\sqrt{2c}.$

EXAMPLE 6. $\sqrt[3]{54x^4 - 81x^3y} = \sqrt[3]{27x^3(2x - 3y)} = 3x\sqrt[3]{2x - 3y}.$

EXAMPLE 7. $\sqrt[3]{32a^3 + 48a^2b + 24ab^2 + 4b^3} = \sqrt[3]{(2a + b)^3 \cdot 4}$
$= (2a + b)\sqrt[3]{4}.$

EXERCISE GROUP 4–3

In each of the following exercises, remove all possible factors from under the radical sign.

1. $\sqrt{50}$
2. $\sqrt{98}$
3. $\sqrt[3]{54}$
4. $\sqrt[3]{250}$
5. $\sqrt[4]{32}$
6. $\sqrt[4]{162}$

7. $\sqrt[3]{-375}$ 8. $\sqrt[4]{48}$ 9. $\sqrt[3]{-16}$

10. $\sqrt[3]{-81a^3}$ 11. $\sqrt{72ab^3}$ 12. $\sqrt[3]{24a^4b^2}$

13. $\sqrt[4]{16a^5b^6}$ 14. $\sqrt[5]{a^{10}b^{11}c^{12}}$ 15. $\sqrt[5]{64a^6b^6c^{10}}$

16. $\sqrt[4]{32a^5b^9c^{13}}$ 17. $\sqrt{a^2b^2 + b^2c^2}$ 18. $\sqrt{9x^2 - 18x^3}$

19. $\sqrt[3]{16x^3 + 24x^5}$ 20. $\sqrt[3]{27x^3 - 81}$ 21. $\sqrt[3]{27x^3 + 64x^3y^3}$

22. $\sqrt{9x^2 + 81y^2}$ 23. $\sqrt[4]{16a^4 + 256b^4}$

24. $\sqrt[3]{16a^4 + 64a^3b^3}$ 25. $\sqrt[4]{32a^5 - 16a^4b^4}$

26. $\sqrt{(a+1)^2(a-3)^3}$ 27. $\sqrt{(a-2)^2(a+2)^2(a+3)}$

28. $\sqrt[3]{2^5(a-5)^4 3^2(a+4)}$ 29. $\sqrt{2a^2 + 4ab + 2b^2}$

30. $\sqrt{3x^2 - 18xy + 27y^2}$ 31. $\sqrt{a^3b + 6a^2b^2 + 9ab^3}$

32. $\sqrt[3]{8a^4 + 12a^3b + 6a^2b^2 + ab^3}$ 33. $\sqrt{(a^3 - b^3)(a^2 - b^2)}$

34. $\sqrt{(a^3 + b^3)(a + b)}$ 35. $\sqrt{(a^2 - 4)(a^2 + a - 2)}$

36. $\sqrt{(4a^2 - 9)(2a^2 + a - 3)}$ 37. $\sqrt{(a^6 + b^6)(a^4 - b^4)}$

38. $\sqrt[n]{a^{2n}b^{3n+2} + a^{2n+3}b^{3n}}$ 39. $\sqrt[k]{2^k x^{2k+1} y^{3k-1} - 2^{k+2} x^{2k} y^{2k}}$

40. $\sqrt[k]{2^{2k}3^{3k}x^{k+1} + 2^{2k+1}3^k x^k}$ 41. $\sqrt{3^{10k}5^{8k}x^{2k+1} + 3^{8k}5^{6k}x^{2k}}$

4-5 Rationalizing the denominator. In Example 2 of Section 4-3 we were successful in removing the denominator completely by dividing it into the numerator. In general, this will not be possible, but it will always be possible to remove the denominator from a radicand by a process called *rationalizing the denominator.* To rationalize a denominator, multiply the numerator and denominator by the simplest expression which will make the denominator a perfect nth power. Thus, *a second step in simplifying a radical is to rationalize any denominator.*

EXAMPLE 1. $\sqrt{\frac{3}{2}} = \sqrt{\frac{3 \cdot 2}{2 \cdot 2}} = \frac{\sqrt{6}}{2}.$

EXAMPLE 2.
$$\sqrt{ax - 2 + \frac{1}{ax}} = \sqrt{\frac{(ax)^2 - 2ax + 1}{ax}}$$
$$= \sqrt{\frac{(ax-1)^2}{ax} \cdot \frac{ax}{ax}} = \frac{\pm(ax-1)\sqrt{ax}}{ax},$$

the minus sign being used if $ax - 1$ is negative.

EXAMPLE 3. $\frac{\sqrt[3]{7}}{\sqrt[3]{3x^2}} = \sqrt[3]{\frac{7}{3x^2}} = \sqrt[3]{\frac{7 \cdot 3^2 \cdot x}{3x^2 \cdot 3^2 \cdot x}} = \frac{\sqrt[3]{63x}}{3x}.$

EXERCISE GROUP 4–4

In each of the following exercises, reduce the given expression to one without fractions in the radicand, and with all possible perfect powers removed from the radicand.

1. $\sqrt{\frac{5}{14}}$ 2. $\sqrt{\frac{2a^2}{3b^2}}$ 3. $\sqrt{\frac{13a^7}{18x}}$ 4. $\sqrt[5]{\frac{a^5b^6}{27c^4}}$

5. $\frac{\sqrt[3]{16}}{\sqrt[3]{54}}$ 6. $\frac{\sqrt{75}}{\sqrt{27}}$ 7. $\frac{\sqrt[4]{162}}{\sqrt[4]{2}}$ 8. $\sqrt{\frac{1}{5}}$

9. $\sqrt{\frac{2}{3}}$ 10. $\sqrt{\frac{5}{8}}$ 11. $\sqrt[3]{\frac{3}{4}}$ 12. $\sqrt[3]{\frac{5}{9}}$

13. $\sqrt[3]{\frac{3}{40}}$ 14. $\sqrt[5]{\frac{-32a^{10}}{b^4}}$ 15. $\sqrt[7]{\frac{a^8b^6}{c^3}}$ 16. $\sqrt[3]{\frac{4a^2}{5}}$

17. $\frac{2a}{b}\sqrt[3]{\frac{27b^4}{2a}}$ 18. $\sqrt[m]{\frac{b^{m+1}}{a^{m-1}}}$ 19. $\sqrt[k]{\frac{x^{2k+2}}{2y^{k-3}}}$ 20. $\sqrt[n]{\frac{2a^{3n-1}}{3b^{2n+1}}}$

21. $\sqrt{\frac{1}{2}+\frac{1}{3}}$ 22. $\sqrt{\frac{1}{a}-\frac{1}{b}}$ 23. $\sqrt[3]{\frac{1}{a^2}+\frac{1}{b^2}}$ 24. $\sqrt{5a-2+\frac{1}{5a}}$

25. $\sqrt{\frac{3a}{4b}-2+\frac{4b}{3a}}$ 26. $\sqrt[3]{\frac{a}{8}-\frac{3}{y^3}}$

27. $\sqrt[3]{\frac{27}{8a^3}-\frac{27}{4b^3}}$ 28. $\sqrt{\frac{1}{x^2}+\frac{1}{y^2}}$

29. $\sqrt{\frac{1}{a^2}-\frac{1}{b}}$ 30. $\sqrt{2x+2+\frac{1}{2x}}$

4–6 Lowering the index of a radical. In Example 3 of Section 4–3 a sixth root of 27 was reduced to the square root of 3; the index of the radical was lowered from 6 to 2. Thus we see that a third step in simplifying a radical is to lower the index of the radical. This is accomplished by expressing the radicand in powers of its prime factors and using Law 5.

EXAMPLE 1. $\sqrt[8]{16x^2} = \sqrt[8]{2^4x^2} = (2^4x^2)^{1/8} = ([2^2x]^2)^{1/8} = (2^2x)^{1/4} = \sqrt[4]{4x}.$

EXAMPLE 2. $\sqrt[10]{243a^5} = (3^5a^5)^{1/10} = ([3a]^5)^{1/10} = (3a)^{1/2} = \sqrt{3a}.$

EXAMPLE 3. $\sqrt[4]{9x^2+2+\frac{1}{9x^2}} = \sqrt[4]{\frac{(9x^2)^2+2(9x^2)+1}{9x^2}} = \sqrt[4]{\frac{(9x^2+1)^2}{9x^2}}$

$$= \sqrt{\frac{9x^2+1}{3x}} = \frac{\sqrt{(9x^2+1)3x}}{3x}.$$

Exercise Group 4–5

In each of the following exercises, reduce the index of the radical as far as possible and where possible remove factors from the radicand; express the result without fractions in the radicand.

1. $\sqrt[4]{4}$
2. $\sqrt[6]{8}$
3. $\sqrt[6]{25}$
4. $\sqrt[10]{32}$
5. $\sqrt[8]{16}$
6. $\sqrt[4]{49}$
7. $\sqrt[12]{64}$
8. $\sqrt[9]{27}$
9. $\sqrt[4]{64a^6b^2}$
10. $\sqrt[6]{16x^8y^2}$
11. $\sqrt[8]{81x^4y^6}$
12. $\sqrt[12]{64a^6b^{18}}$
13. $\sqrt[10]{32a^{15}b^{20}}$
14. $\sqrt[6]{125a^9b^{12}}$
15. $\sqrt[8]{36x^6y^8}$
16. $\sqrt[4]{49a^4b^6c^2}$
17. $\sqrt[6]{\dfrac{8a^3b^9}{27c^3}}$
18. $\sqrt[4]{\dfrac{25x^6y^2}{49z^2}}$
19. $\sqrt[8]{\dfrac{16a^4b^4}{81c^{12}d^4}}$
20. $\sqrt[9]{\dfrac{27x^6y^3}{64z^{12}u^9}}$
21. $\sqrt[4]{(a+b)^2}$
22. $\sqrt[6]{(a+b)^3}$
23. $\sqrt[8]{16(a+b)^4c^{10}}$
24. $\sqrt[10]{\dfrac{(a+b)^5}{32}}$
25. $\sqrt[4]{x^2+\dfrac{1}{x^2}-2}$
26. $\sqrt[6]{x^2+\dfrac{4}{x^2}+4}$
27. $\sqrt[8]{16\left(a^2+\dfrac{9}{a^2}+6\right)^2}$
28. $\sqrt[6]{27\left(x+\dfrac{16}{x}-8\right)^3}$
29. $\sqrt[9]{8\left(u-10+\dfrac{25}{u}\right)^3}$
30. $\sqrt[4]{36\left(u^2-12+\dfrac{36}{u^2}\right)^3}$

4–7 The standard form of a radical. We shall now adopt the following criterion for a standard form of a radical.

A radical is in standard form *if the following conditions are satisfied:*

(1) *the radicand contains no fractions,*

(2) *the radicand contains no factors which are perfect nth powers, where n is the index of the radical,*

(3) *the index of the radical is as low as possible.*

The methods developed in Sections 4–4, 4–5, and 4–6 are the procedures to be followed in reducing a radical to standard form. It is suggested that the student supply the reasons for the steps in the following examples.

Example 1. $\sqrt[6]{\frac{4}{9}} = \sqrt[6]{(\frac{2}{3})^2} = \sqrt[3]{\frac{2}{3}} = \frac{1}{3}\sqrt[3]{18}.$

Example 2. $\sqrt{\sqrt[3]{128x^5}} = \sqrt[6]{128x^5} = 2\sqrt[6]{2x^5}.$

Example 3. $\sqrt[4]{1+\dfrac{4}{x^2}+\dfrac{4}{x^4}} = \sqrt[4]{\dfrac{x^4+4x^2+4}{x^4}}$

$$= \sqrt[4]{\frac{(x^2+2)^2}{x^4}} = \frac{1}{x}\sqrt[4]{(x^2+2)^2} = \frac{1}{x}\sqrt{x^2+2}.$$

EXAMPLE 4. $\sqrt[4]{16\left(\dfrac{9x^2}{4y^2}+2+\dfrac{4y^2}{9x^2}\right)}$

$$= \sqrt[4]{\frac{4(81x^4+72x^2y^2+16y^4)}{9x^2y^2}} = \sqrt[4]{\left[\frac{2(9x^2+4y^2)}{3xy}\right]^2}$$

$$= \sqrt{\frac{2(9x^2+4y^2)}{3xy}} = \frac{1}{3xy}\sqrt{6xy(9x^2+4y^2)}.$$

It should be stated that there is an element of arbitrariness in the above criterion for the standard form of a radical. To illustrate this, we use the following example:

$$\sqrt{\frac{1}{3}} = \frac{1}{\sqrt{3}} \quad \text{[by Law 3 of Section 4–3]}$$

$$= \frac{\sqrt{3}}{3} \quad \text{[by the above criterion].}$$

The question arises as to whether $\sqrt{3}/3$ is simpler than $1/\sqrt{3}$. Good reasons can be presented for the contention that the latter form is simpler. In the last analysis, however, the determination of what is simpler is governed by the use to which the result is to be put. Whatever criterion is established, the principles employed in achieving a certain form are essentially the same. The above criterion should be considered in this light.

EXERCISE GROUP 4–6

Reduce each of the following radicals to standard form.

1. $\sqrt{\frac{2}{3}}$ 2. $\sqrt{\frac{3}{4}}$ 3. $\sqrt[3]{\frac{2}{3}}$ 4. $\sqrt[3]{\frac{3}{4}}$

5. $\sqrt{\frac{a}{b}}$ 6. $\sqrt{\frac{a}{b^2}}$ 7. $\sqrt[3]{\frac{a}{b}}$ 8. $\sqrt[3]{\frac{a}{b^2}}$

9. $\sqrt[4]{\frac{ax^4}{32}}$ 10. $\sqrt[3]{\frac{x^7}{9}}$ 11. $\sqrt[5]{\frac{64}{a^4}}$ 12. $\sqrt[6]{\frac{64}{a^4}}$

13. $\sqrt{\frac{uv^2}{wz^2}}$ 14. $\sqrt[3]{\frac{54x^7}{25yz^4}}$ 15. $\sqrt[10]{\frac{x^{15}y^{25}}{z^5}}$ 16. $\frac{x}{y}\sqrt[n]{\frac{x^{n+1}}{y^{n-1}}}$

17. $\sqrt{\frac{xy^2}{x+y}}$ 18. $\sqrt{\frac{1}{u^2}+\frac{1}{v^2}}$

19. $\sqrt[3]{\frac{a}{b}-\frac{b}{a}}$ 20. $\sqrt{\frac{a-b}{b}+\frac{b-a}{a}}$

21. $\sqrt{\dfrac{(x-y)^2}{y} - \dfrac{(x-y)^2}{x}}$

22. $\sqrt[4]{\dfrac{2x^2}{3y^2} - 2 + \dfrac{3y^2}{2x^2}}$

23. $\sqrt[6]{u^6 - 2u^5v + u^4v^2}$

24. $\sqrt{\dfrac{16}{81a^4} - \dfrac{16}{81b^4}}$

25. $\sqrt[3]{\dfrac{27}{8x^3} + \dfrac{27}{64y^4}}$

26. $\sqrt{\sqrt[3]{16x^4}}$

27. $\sqrt[3]{\sqrt[4]{64(a+b)^6}}$

28. $\sqrt[5]{\sqrt[4]{\sqrt[3]{32x^{10}y^{15}}}}$

29. $\sqrt[n]{\dfrac{x^{2n+1}y^{3n+5}}{z^{2n-2}}}$

30. $\sqrt{x^{k^2+k}y^{5k}(u+v)^{2k+1}}$

31. $\sqrt[6]{(a^3+b^3)^2}$

32. $\sqrt[6]{(a^3+b^3)^2(a+b)^4}$

33. $\sqrt{32x^3 + 48x^2y^2}$

34. $\sqrt{x + \dfrac{2y}{x} + \dfrac{y^2}{x^3}}$

35. $\sqrt[3]{27x - \dfrac{54}{y^3}}$

36. $\sqrt{36 - 36y^2}$

37. $\sqrt[3]{\dfrac{x^2}{y} - \dfrac{27y^2}{x}}$

38. $\sqrt[3]{\dfrac{1}{a^3} - \dfrac{1}{b^2}}$

39. $\sqrt[6]{4x^2 + 8xy + 4y^2}$

40. $\sqrt[4]{16a^2 + 32ab + 16b^2}$

41. $\sqrt[4]{9 + \dfrac{18y}{x^2} + \dfrac{9y^2}{x^4}}$

42. $\sqrt[4]{(x-y)^2\sqrt[3]{(a+b)^6}}$

43. $\sqrt[3]{\dfrac{32a^4b^{6k}}{81c^2}}$

44. $\sqrt{\dfrac{32a^3}{3b} - \dfrac{64a^2b}{c}}$

4-8 Addition and subtraction of radicals. In an algebraic expression such as $3x - x + 5y$, the x terms are combined to obtain $2x + 5y$. If x is replaced by $\sqrt{2}$ and y by $\sqrt{3}$, we have

$$3\sqrt{2} - \sqrt{2} + 5\sqrt{3} = 2\sqrt{2} + 5\sqrt{3}.$$

In general, *in adding or subtracting radicals those with the same index and radicand are combined in a single term.* Radicals with the same index and radicand are said to be *similar*, so that we may speak of collecting similar radicals. Thus, to simplify an algebraic sum (which may include addition and subtraction) of terms involving radicals, we reduce each radical to standard form and collect similar radicals.

EXAMPLE 1. $\sqrt[3]{16} - \sqrt[3]{54} + \sqrt[3]{250} = 2\sqrt[3]{2} - 3\sqrt[3]{2} + 5\sqrt[3]{2} = 4\sqrt[3]{2}.$

EXAMPLE 2. $\sqrt{12} + \sqrt{75} - \sqrt{18} = 2\sqrt{3} + 5\sqrt{3} - 3\sqrt{2}$
$= 7\sqrt{3} - 3\sqrt{2}.$

EXAMPLE 3. $\sqrt{3\frac{3}{5}} - \sqrt{6\frac{2}{5}} + \sqrt{19\frac{3}{5}} = \sqrt{\frac{18}{5}} - \sqrt{\frac{32}{5}} + \sqrt{\frac{98}{5}}$

$$= 3\sqrt{\frac{2}{5}} - 4\sqrt{\frac{2}{5}} + 7\sqrt{\frac{2}{5}}$$

$$= \frac{3\sqrt{10}}{5} - \frac{4\sqrt{10}}{5} + \frac{7\sqrt{10}}{5} = \frac{6\sqrt{10}}{5}.$$

EXAMPLE 4. $\frac{x-y}{xy}\sqrt{\frac{x-y}{x+y}} - \frac{x}{x+y}\sqrt{\left(\frac{x}{y} - \frac{y}{x}\right)\frac{1}{xy}}$

$$= \frac{(x-y)\sqrt{x^2-y^2}}{xy(x+y)} - \frac{x\sqrt{x^2-y^2}}{xy(x+y)}$$

$$= \frac{\sqrt{x^2-y^2}}{xy(x+y)}(x-y-x)$$

$$= \frac{-y\sqrt{x^2-y^2}}{xy(x+y)} = -\frac{\sqrt{x^2-y^2}}{x(x+y)}.$$

EXAMPLE 5. $\sqrt{\frac{a-b}{a+b}} - \sqrt{\frac{a+b}{a-b}} = \frac{\sqrt{a^2-b^2}}{a+b} - \frac{\sqrt{a^2-b^2}}{a-b}$

$$= \sqrt{a^2-b^2}\left[\frac{a-b-(a+b)}{a^2-b^2}\right]$$

$$= -\frac{2b\sqrt{a^2-b^2}}{a^2-b^2}.$$

EXERCISE GROUP 4-7

In each of Exercises 1–34, perform the indicated operations and reduce the result to standard form.

1. $2\sqrt{5} + 3\sqrt{5}$
2. $3\sqrt{2} + \sqrt{8}$
3. $2\sqrt[3]{3} - 3\sqrt[3]{3} + \sqrt[3]{81}$
4. $\sqrt{12} - \sqrt{27} + \sqrt{48}$
5. $\sqrt{8} + \sqrt{50} - \sqrt{18}$
6. $\sqrt{72} - \sqrt{32} + \sqrt{98}$
7. $\sqrt{\frac{1}{2}} - \sqrt{\frac{9}{2}} + \sqrt{50}$
8. $\sqrt{75} - \sqrt{\frac{4}{3}} + \sqrt{\frac{50}{6}}$
9. $\sqrt[3]{3} - \sqrt[3]{-375} + \sqrt[3]{-81}$
10. $2\sqrt[3]{-16} + 3\sqrt[3]{250} - 4\sqrt[3]{128}$
11. $\frac{1}{2}\sqrt{\frac{5}{8}} + 3\sqrt{\frac{5}{2}} - \sqrt{\frac{125}{8}}$
12. $\sqrt[3]{54} - 2\sqrt[3]{16} + 3\sqrt[3]{\frac{125}{4}}$
13. $\sqrt{1\frac{1}{3}} + 5\sqrt{5\frac{1}{3}} - 3\sqrt{8\frac{1}{3}}$
14. $\frac{3}{5}\sqrt[3]{1\frac{7}{9}} - \frac{1}{2}\sqrt[3]{14\frac{2}{9}} + \frac{2}{3}\sqrt[3]{6}$
15. $\sqrt[3]{\frac{32}{9}} - \frac{2}{3}\sqrt[3]{\frac{250}{18}} + \frac{3}{5}\sqrt[3]{\frac{1280}{45}}$
16. $\sqrt{49ax^3} - \sqrt{16a^3x}$
17. $\sqrt{18a} + \sqrt{72ab^2}$
18. $\sqrt[3]{54a^3b} - \sqrt[3]{16ab^4}$

19. $\sqrt[3]{24a^2b^5} + \sqrt[3]{81a^5b^2}$

20. $\sqrt{4 + 4x^2} + \sqrt{9 + 9x^2}$

21. $\sqrt{\dfrac{a^4c}{b^3}} + \sqrt{\dfrac{a^2c^2}{bx^2}} + \sqrt{\dfrac{a^2cx^2}{by^2}}$

22. $\sqrt[4]{81a^5} + 2\sqrt[4]{16a^5} - \sqrt[4]{256a^9}$

23. $\sqrt[3]{\dfrac{a^4b}{c^2}} - \sqrt[3]{\dfrac{ab^4}{c^5}} + \sqrt[3]{\dfrac{c^4}{a^2b^2}}$

24. $\sqrt{\dfrac{2}{3a}} - 3\sqrt{\dfrac{3}{2a}}$

25. $\sqrt{xy^3z^3} + \dfrac{\sqrt{x^3y^5z^7}}{xyz^2} - \sqrt{x^3y^7z^5}$

26. $\sqrt{\dfrac{x+y}{x-y}} - \sqrt{\dfrac{x-y}{x+y}}$

27. $2\sqrt{\dfrac{3}{5a}} + 3\sqrt{\dfrac{5}{3a}}$

28. $\dfrac{-4 + \sqrt{16 - 4 \cdot 2 \cdot 1}}{2}$

29. $\dfrac{-6 + \sqrt{12}}{6}$

30. $\dfrac{-5a + \sqrt{25a^2 + 4(5a)(3a)}}{10a}$

31. $\dfrac{-8 - \sqrt{64 - 4 \cdot 3 \cdot 2}}{6}$

32. $\dfrac{-10 - \sqrt{100 - 4 \cdot 5 \cdot 3}}{10}$

33. $\dfrac{-3b - \sqrt{9b^2 - 4(2)(-9b)}}{4}$

34. $\dfrac{-q + \sqrt{q^2 - 4pr}}{2r} + \dfrac{-q - \sqrt{q^2 - 4pr}}{2r}$

4–9 Multiplication of radicals. Multiplication of *radicals of the same index* is accomplished by use of Law 2 of Section 4–3, together with the ordinary rules for multiplying algebraic expressions.

EXAMPLE 1. $\sqrt[3]{3ab^2} \cdot \sqrt[3]{18a^3b} = \sqrt[3]{54a^4b^3} = \sqrt[3]{27a^3b^3 \cdot 2a} = 3ab\sqrt[3]{2a}.$

EXAMPLE 2. Multiply $(2\sqrt{3} + 3\sqrt{2})$ by $(3\sqrt{3} - 2\sqrt{2})$.

Solution. By type (4) of the special products in Section 2–7, we have

$$\begin{aligned}(2\sqrt{3} + 3\sqrt{2})(3\sqrt{3} - 2\sqrt{2}) &= 6(\sqrt{3})^2 + 5\sqrt{2}\sqrt{3} - 6(\sqrt{2})^2 \\ &= 18 + 5\sqrt{6} - 12 = 6 + 5\sqrt{6}.\end{aligned}$$

EXAMPLE 3. Multiply $(a\sqrt{b} + b\sqrt{c})$ by $(b\sqrt{b} - a\sqrt{c})$.

Solution. Proceeding as in Example 2, we have

$$\begin{aligned}(a\sqrt{b} + b\sqrt{c})(b\sqrt{b} - a\sqrt{c}) &= ab(\sqrt{b})^2 + (b^2 - a^2)\sqrt{b}\sqrt{c} - ab(\sqrt{c})^2 \\ &= ab^2 + (b^2 - a^2)\sqrt{bc} - abc \\ &= ab(b - c) + (b^2 - a^2)\sqrt{bc}.\end{aligned}$$

To multiply two *radicals with different indices* we convert each radical to a fractional power of the radicand by Law 5 of Section 4–3. The exponents of these fractional powers are then changed to equivalent fractions with the same denominator (the LCD), the fractional powers are then converted back to radical form, and the result is put in standard form. Some examples will clarify the method.

EXAMPLE 4. $\sqrt[3]{4}\sqrt[4]{8} = 4^{1/3}8^{1/4} = 4^{4/12}8^{3/12} = (4^4 8^3)^{1/12} = \sqrt[12]{4^4 8^3}$
$= \sqrt[12]{(2^2)^4(2^3)^3} = \sqrt[12]{2^8 2^9} = \sqrt[12]{2^{17}} = 2\sqrt[12]{2^5} = 2\sqrt[12]{32}.$

EXAMPLE 5. $\sqrt[5]{8a^3}\sqrt{2ab^2} = (2^3a^3)^{1/5}(2ab^2)^{1/2} = (2^3a^3)^{2/10}(2ab^2)^{5/10}$
$= (2^6a^6 2^5a^5b^{10})^{1/10} = \sqrt[10]{2^{11}a^{11}b^{10}} = 2ab\sqrt[10]{2a}.$

EXERCISE GROUP 4-8

In each of Exercises 1-42, perform the indicated operations and reduce the result to standard radical form.

1. $\sqrt{3}\sqrt{5}$
2. $\sqrt{15}\sqrt{5}$
3. $\sqrt{27}\sqrt{18}$
4. $2\sqrt{28}\sqrt{7}$
5. $\sqrt[3]{25}\sqrt[3]{10}$
6. $(\sqrt{3} + \sqrt{4} + \sqrt{5})\sqrt{5}$
7. $\sqrt[3]{-18}\sqrt[3]{-12}$
8. $\sqrt[3]{25}\sqrt[3]{40}$
9. $\sqrt[3]{16}\sqrt[3]{36}$
10. $\sqrt{3ax^3}\sqrt{2a^3x}$
11. $\sqrt[3]{4a^2b}\sqrt[3]{6a^2b^5}$
12. $\sqrt{x}\sqrt{2x}\sqrt{6x^3}$
13. $6x\sqrt[6]{x^7y}\sqrt[6]{x^2y}$
14. $3a\sqrt[4]{a^3}\sqrt[4]{a^7}$
15. $(3\sqrt{2x^5})^2$
16. $(2x\sqrt[3]{3x^2})^3$
17. $(\sqrt{a^2 + b^2})^2$
18. $\sqrt{3}(\sqrt{6} - \sqrt{30})$
19. $\sqrt{a}(\sqrt{b} - \sqrt{c})$
20. $(\sqrt{2} + \sqrt{3})(3\sqrt{2} - \sqrt{3})$
21. $(\sqrt{2} - 2\sqrt{3})(\sqrt{3} + 3\sqrt{2})$
22. $(3\sqrt{5} - 2\sqrt{3})^2$
23. $(2\sqrt{7} - \sqrt{3})^2$
24. $(\sqrt{5} - \sqrt{3})(\sqrt{5} + \sqrt{3})$
25. $(\sqrt{a} + 2\sqrt{b})(\sqrt{a} - 2\sqrt{b})$
26. $(2\sqrt{x} - 5\sqrt{x + 1})(3\sqrt{x} - \sqrt{x + 1})$
27. $(\sqrt{2} + \sqrt{3} + \sqrt{5})(2\sqrt{3} - 3\sqrt{5})$
28. $(2\sqrt{2} - 3\sqrt{3} + 5\sqrt{5})(3\sqrt{2} - 2\sqrt{5})$
29. $(a\sqrt{b} + b\sqrt{c} - c\sqrt{a})(b\sqrt{c} - c\sqrt{b})$
30. $\left(\dfrac{-5 + \sqrt{7}}{3}\right)\left(\dfrac{-5 - \sqrt{7}}{3}\right)$
31. $\left(\dfrac{-2 + 3\sqrt{5}}{7}\right)\left(\dfrac{-2 - 3\sqrt{5}}{7}\right)$
32. $\left(\dfrac{-3 + \sqrt{5}}{2}\right)^2$
33. $\left(\dfrac{-3 + \sqrt{3}}{3}\right)^2$
34. $\left(\dfrac{-3 + \sqrt{3}}{3}\right)\left(\dfrac{-3 - \sqrt{3}}{3}\right)$
35. $\left[\dfrac{-q + \sqrt{q^2 - 4pr}}{2r}\right]\left[\dfrac{-q - \sqrt{q^2 - 4pr}}{2r}\right]$

36. $\sqrt[6]{(x-y)^3} + y\sqrt[6]{x^2 - 2xy + y^2} - (x-y)\sqrt[3]{x-y}$

37. $(2 - \sqrt{x^2 - 3})^2$

38. $(\sqrt{x-1} - \sqrt{x+1})^2$

39. $(\sqrt{x} + \sqrt{3-x})^2$

40. $\sqrt{2}\sqrt[3]{3}$

41. $\sqrt[3]{4}\sqrt{6}$

42. $\sqrt[6]{x^2y}\sqrt{y^3}$

Determine the value in each of the following exercises.

43. $3x^2 + 2x - 3$, when $x = -1 + \sqrt{10}$

44. $x^2 + 2x - 5$, when $x = -1 + \sqrt{6}$

45. $x^2 - 2xy + y^2$, when $x = 1 + \sqrt{2}$ and $y = 1 - \sqrt{2}$

46. $x^2 - 4x - 1$, when $x = 2 - \sqrt{15}$

47. $x^2 - x - 3$, when $x = \frac{1}{2}(1 - \sqrt{13})$

48. $2x^2 - x - 5$, when $x = \frac{1}{4}(1 + \sqrt{41})$

49. $3x^2 + 2x - 5$, when $x = 2 + \sqrt{3}$

50. $2x^2 - x - 5$, when $x = 1 - \sqrt{41}$

51. $3x^2 + 2x - 5$, when $x = \frac{1}{3}(-1 + \sqrt{14})$

52. $3x^2 - 2xy - 4y^2$, when $x = 2 - \sqrt{3}$ and $y = 2 + \sqrt{3}$

4–10 Division with radicals, and rationalizing denominators. Two radicals with the same index can be divided by applying Law 3 of Section 4–3 and then reducing the result to standard form.

EXAMPLE 1. $$\frac{\sqrt{5}}{\sqrt{3}} = \sqrt{\frac{5}{3}} = \sqrt{\frac{5}{3}\cdot\frac{3}{3}} = \frac{\sqrt{15}}{3}.$$

If the denominator of a fraction is of the form $\sqrt{a} + \sqrt{b}$, it can be rationalized by multiplying it by $\sqrt{a} - \sqrt{b}$. This follows from type form (2) of Section 2–7. The numerator of the fraction must then be multiplied by the same quantity.

EXAMPLE 2. $$\frac{3}{\sqrt{2} - \sqrt{3}} = \frac{3}{\sqrt{2} - \sqrt{3}}\cdot\frac{\sqrt{2} + \sqrt{3}}{\sqrt{2} + \sqrt{3}} = \frac{3(\sqrt{2} + \sqrt{3})}{2 - 3}$$
$$= -3\sqrt{2} - 3\sqrt{3}.$$

To divide two radicals with different indices, we may indicate the quotient as a fraction, then rationalize the denominator, and perform the resulting multiplication in the numerator as described in Section 4–9.

EXAMPLE 3. $$\frac{\sqrt[4]{8}}{\sqrt[3]{4}} = \frac{\sqrt[4]{8}}{\sqrt[3]{4}}\cdot\frac{\sqrt[3]{2}}{\sqrt[3]{2}} = \frac{(2^3)^{1/4}\cdot 2^{1/3}}{2} = \frac{2^{13/12}}{2} = 2^{1/12} = \sqrt[12]{2}.$$

Exercise Group 4–9

In each of the following exercises, rationalize the denominator and reduce the result to standard radical form.

1. $\dfrac{\sqrt{5}}{\sqrt{3}}$
2. $\dfrac{3\sqrt{7}}{\sqrt{2}}$
3. $\dfrac{\sqrt{15}}{\sqrt{3x}}$
4. $\dfrac{\sqrt{12x^3}}{\sqrt{3x^5}}$
5. $\dfrac{\sqrt{12}}{\sqrt{6}}$
6. $\dfrac{\sqrt[3]{54}}{\sqrt[3]{9}}$
7. $\dfrac{\sqrt{14}}{\sqrt{3}}$
8. $\dfrac{\sqrt[3]{15}}{\sqrt[3]{4}}$
9. $\dfrac{3x\sqrt{2x}}{\sqrt{5x}}$
10. $\dfrac{3\sqrt{5x}}{\sqrt{2x^3}}$
11. $\dfrac{2\sqrt[3]{6x}}{\sqrt[3]{3x^2}}$
12. $\dfrac{\sqrt{2x^3}}{\sqrt{9x}}$
13. $\dfrac{2x\sqrt{3}}{\sqrt{18x}}$
14. $\dfrac{3\sqrt{2x}}{\sqrt{32x^3}}$
15. $\dfrac{2\sqrt[3]{x^2}}{\sqrt[3]{24}}$
16. $\dfrac{\sqrt{3x^2}}{\sqrt[3]{25x}}$
17. $\dfrac{\sqrt[3]{3x}}{\sqrt{2x^3}}$
18. $\dfrac{\sqrt{6}}{4-2\sqrt{3}}$
19. $\dfrac{9\sqrt{10}}{4+2\sqrt{5}}$
20. $\dfrac{3\sqrt{7}-5\sqrt{3}}{5\sqrt{7}+3\sqrt{3}}$
21. $\dfrac{1}{2+\sqrt{3}}$
22. $\dfrac{\sqrt{2}}{\sqrt{3}+2}$
23. $\dfrac{\sqrt{3}}{\sqrt{5}+\sqrt{7}}$
24. $\dfrac{\sqrt{3}-\sqrt{5}}{\sqrt{7}}$
25. $\dfrac{\sqrt{3}-\sqrt{2}}{\sqrt{3}+\sqrt{2}}$
26. $\dfrac{2\sqrt{3}+3\sqrt{2}}{3\sqrt{2}-2\sqrt{3}}$
27. $\dfrac{2\sqrt{5}-\sqrt{3}}{3\sqrt{5}+2\sqrt{3}}$
28. $\dfrac{2\sqrt{5}-7\sqrt{2}}{7\sqrt{2}-3\sqrt{7}}$
29. $\dfrac{x\sqrt{y}-y\sqrt{x}}{a\sqrt{x}+y\sqrt{y}}$
30. $\dfrac{x-\sqrt{x^2-1}}{x+\sqrt{x^2-1}}$
31. $\dfrac{\sqrt{a-1}}{1+\sqrt{a-1}}$
32. $\dfrac{\sqrt{a-b}}{c-\sqrt{a-b}}$
33. $\dfrac{\sqrt{10}}{\sqrt[3]{2}}$
34. $\dfrac{\sqrt{8}}{\sqrt[3]{4}}$
35. $\dfrac{\sqrt[4]{6}}{\sqrt[3]{4}}$
36. $\dfrac{\sqrt[3]{x^2}}{\sqrt{3xy}}$
37. $\sqrt[3]{\frac{1}{2}} \div \sqrt{\frac{1}{3}}$
38. $\sqrt[3]{\frac{2}{3}} \div \sqrt[4]{\frac{6}{7}}$

4–11 Imaginary numbers. If one attempts to apply Definition 4–4 with $x = -1$ and $p = 2$, the number y would have to be such that $y^2 = -1$. Since the square of either a positive or a negative number is positive, the values of y must be some new kind of number. If we continue to use the same notation as above then we must have

$$y = \pm\sqrt{-1},$$

and this new number $\sqrt{-1}$ is called an *imaginary number* and is designated by i. From the definition of i we have

$$i = \sqrt{-1} \qquad \text{and} \qquad i^2 = -1.$$

If we assume that the laws for radicals still apply, we may express the square root of any negative number $-A$, where A is positive, as follows:

$$\sqrt{-A} = \sqrt{-1}\sqrt{A} = i\sqrt{A}.$$

Thus, $\sqrt{-4} = i\sqrt{4} = 2i$, and $\sqrt{-3} = i\sqrt{3}$.

EXAMPLE 1. Simplify $\sqrt{-50}$.

Solution. $\sqrt{-50} = \sqrt{(-1)(25)(2)} = \sqrt{-1}\sqrt{25}\sqrt{2} = i \cdot 5 \cdot \sqrt{2} = 5i\sqrt{2}$.

A number of the form $a + bi$, where a and b are real numbers and $i = \sqrt{-1}$, is called a *complex number;* a is called the *real part* of the complex number, and b is the *imaginary part.* In a number of ways complex numbers behave like real numbers containing square roots. In particular, the imaginary parts of complex numbers are similar terms and may be combined. Thus

$$\begin{aligned}(2 + 3i) - (4 + 2i) &= (2 - 4) + (3 - 2)i = -2 + i;\\ (2 + 3i)(4 + 2i) &= 2 \cdot 4 + (2 \cdot 2 + 3 \cdot 4)i + 3 \cdot 2i^2\\ &= 8 + 16i - 6 \qquad [\text{since } i^2 = -1]\\ &= 2 + 16i.\end{aligned}$$

EXAMPLE 2. Evaluate $x^2 - 2x + 6$ for $x = 3 + 2i$.

Solution. Substituting the given value, we get

$$\begin{aligned}x^2 - 2x + 6 &= (3 + 2i)^2 - 2(3 + 2i) + 6\\ &= 9 + 12i + (2i)^2 - 6 - 4i + 6\\ &= 9 + 12i - 4 - 6 - 4i + 6 \qquad [\text{since } (2i)^2 = 4i^2 = -4]\\ &= 5 + 8i.\end{aligned}$$

It is true that the operations of addition, subtraction, multiplication, and division (other than by zero) with complex numbers lead to complex numbers. We may then say that the system of complex numbers is closed under these four operations. The elaboration of this idea is left for Chapter 16.

We may consider the system of real numbers as a subset of the system of complex numbers by associating the real number a with the complex number $a + 0i$, that is, a complex number with the imaginary part zero.

Exercise Group 4–10

In Exercises 1–19, express the given quantity in the form $a + bi$.

1. i^3
2. i^4
3. i^5
4. i^6
5. i^7
6. $\sqrt{-9}$
7. $\sqrt{-49}$
8. $\sqrt{-25}$
9. $\sqrt{-121}$
10. $\sqrt{-75}$
11. $\sqrt{-8}$
12. $\sqrt{-242}$
13. $\sqrt{-147}$
14. $\sqrt{-162}$
15. $\sqrt{-98}$
16. $\sqrt{8^2 - 4(1)(25)}$
17. $\sqrt{5^2 - 4(3)(7)}$
18. $\sqrt{3^2 - 4(2)(5)}$
19. $\sqrt{4^2 - 4(2)(13)}$

In Exercises 20–23, simplify the given expression and write it in terms of i.

20. $\sqrt{-12} - \sqrt{-27} + \sqrt{-48}$
21. $\sqrt{-72} - \sqrt{-32} + \sqrt{-98}$
22. $\sqrt{-63} + \sqrt{-700} - \sqrt{-175}$
23. $\sqrt{-120} + \sqrt{-\frac{5}{6}} + \frac{1}{2}\sqrt{-\frac{6}{5}}$

In the following exercises, evaluate the given expression for the given value of x.

24. $x^2 + 2x + 3$ for $x = -1 - i\sqrt{2}$
25. $x^2 - 4x + 6$ for $x = 2 - i\sqrt{2}$
26. $2x^2 - 13x + 17$ for $x = 3 + i\sqrt{23}$
27. $x^2 + 6x + 7$ for $x = -3 - i\sqrt{19}$
28. $3x^2 - 5x + 7$ for $x = \dfrac{5 + i\sqrt{59}}{6}$
29. $2x^2 + 3x + 5$ for $x = \dfrac{-3 - i\sqrt{31}}{4}$

Review Exercises

In Exercises 1–6, find the value of each of the given quantities.

1. $\dfrac{2^{-3}}{3^{-2}}$
2. $\dfrac{3^{-1}x^0}{(5y)^0}$
3. $\dfrac{(2^3)(2^{5/2})(2^{-7/2})}{2(2^{-2})(2^0)}$
4. $\dfrac{(10^2)(10^{3/5})(10^{-4/3})}{(10^{-2/5})(10^{2/3})}$
5. $(8^{-2/3} + 3x^0 + 9^{3/2})^{-1}$
6. $(16^{-3/4} + 27^{2/3} - 8x^0)^{-2}$

In Exercises 7–18, write each of the given expressions without zero or negative exponents and reduce to simplest form (without radicals).

7. $\left[\dfrac{2a^2y}{5a^{-3}y^{-2}b^{-1/2}}\right]^{-2}$
8. $\left\{\dfrac{[a^{2/3}(a^{5/7})^{1/5}]^7}{a^2}\right\}^{3/5}$

9. $\left[\frac{a^2}{a^3}\right]^5 \div \left\{\left[\frac{a^4}{a^5}\right]^9 \cdot \left[\frac{a^2}{a^4}\right]^{-6}\right\}$

10. $\frac{x^{5n+1}5^{-2n}a^{2n}}{5^{3n+2}a^{-6}5^{-2}}$

11. $\left\{\left[x^{-3/5}\left(\frac{x^{1/2}}{x^{1/3}}\right)^9\right]^{1/5}\right\}^{1/3}$

12. $[x^{-2} + 3^0x^{-1} + 5x^{-3}]^{-1}$

13. $\frac{3x^{-1} + 2y^{-1}}{xy^{-1}}$

14. $\left[\frac{3x^{-1} - 2y^{-1}}{x^{-1}y^{-1}}\right]^{-1}$

15. $\left[\frac{8^{-2/3} + (7x)^0}{2(x^2)^0 + 4^{1.5}}\right]^{-5/3}$

16. $\frac{3^{n+5} - 3(3)^{n+2}}{3(3)^{n+1}}$

17. $\frac{2(5)^{n-1} + 3(5)^{n+1}}{5(5)^n}$

18. $\frac{(0.25)^{-3/2} - (0.008)^{-2/3}}{(0.00032)^{-0.6} - 6a^0}$

In Exercises 19–36, perform the indicated operations and in each case reduce the final result to standard radical form.

19. $\sqrt{9x^2 + 27x^3}$

20. $\sqrt{8a^3 + 64a^3b^3}$

21. $\sqrt{\frac{y}{x} + 4 + \frac{4x}{y}}$

22. $\sqrt{-72} - \sqrt{-50} + \sqrt{-18}$

23. $\sqrt{50} - \sqrt{8} + \sqrt{72}$

24. $\sqrt[3]{24} + \sqrt[3]{81} + \sqrt[3]{\frac{64}{3}}$

25. $\sqrt{3}\sqrt[3]{2a^3}$

26. $\sqrt[4]{4x^2y}\sqrt[3]{8xy^2}$

27. $\sqrt{\sqrt[3]{64a^3b^2}}$

28. $\sqrt[3]{3a^2} \div \sqrt{2a}$

29. $\sqrt{2a} \div \sqrt[3]{3a^2}$

30. $\sqrt[6]{8(a + b)^3c^6}$

31. $\sqrt[4]{16x^2(y + z)^6}$

32. $\frac{\sqrt{2a} + \sqrt{3b}}{\sqrt{5c}}$

33. $\frac{\sqrt{3a}}{\sqrt{2b} - 5\sqrt{c}}$

34. $\frac{\sqrt[3]{4a^2} + \sqrt[3]{8b^2}}{\sqrt[3]{9c}}$

35. $(\sqrt{8} + \sqrt{-12})(\sqrt{18} - \sqrt{-48})$

36. $\frac{\sqrt{2a} + \sqrt[3]{4ab^2}}{\sqrt[3]{4a^2b}}$

CHAPTER 5

COORDINATE GEOMETRY AND FUNCTIONS

5–1 Introduction. A better understanding of many problems in algebra can often be obtained by a geometrical interpretation, and many geometrical problems are facilitated when algebraic methods can be applied to their solution. The means by which this interplay of algebra and geometry can be accomplished will be introduced in the following sections.

5–2 Geometrical representation of real numbers. Directed distances. If use is made of the familiar concept of length on a straight line, together with direction on the line, a very useful geometrical representation of the real numbers may be given. On a straight line which extends indefinitely in both directions, a point O is chosen as *origin* (Fig. 5–1). One of the two possible directions on the line is chosen as the *positive* direction, and the opposite direction as *negative.* In the figure the direction to the right was chosen as positive. Further, a unit of length is chosen on the line. A positive number a is then represented by a point on the line to the right of O at a distance of a units from O; a negative number $(-a)$ is represented by a point to the left of O, the same distance from O. Several illustrations are indicated in Fig. 5–1.

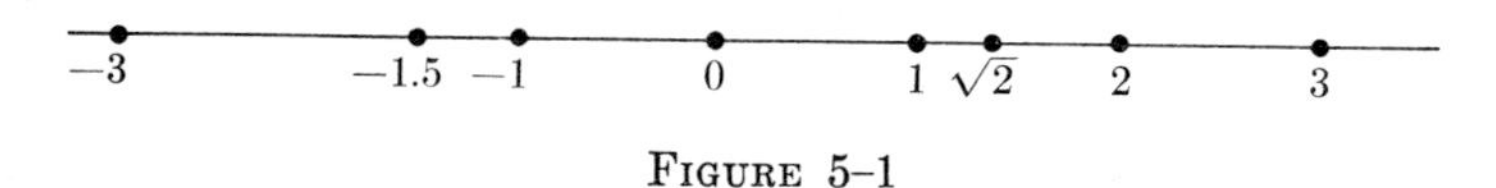

FIGURE 5–1

The line as set up in this manner is called a *coordinate line* or *axis,* and the number associated with a point on this line is the *linear coordinate* or simply *coordinate* of the point.

The important property should be noted that *to any real number there corresponds precisely one point on the line, and to any point on the line there corresponds precisely one real number.*

Let P_1 and P_2 be two points on a coordinate line. The *directed line segment* P_1P_2 is defined as the line segment in the direction from P_1 to P_2. The *directed distance* $\overline{P_1P_2}$ is defined as the length of P_1P_2 if the direction from P_1 to P_2 is the positive direction along the coordinate line, and as the negative of the length of P_1P_2 if the direction from P_1 to P_2 is the negative direction along the line. It follows that

$$\overline{P_1P_2} = -\overline{P_2P_1}.$$

If O is the origin on a coordinate line, and P is a point on this line with coordinate x, then $\overline{OP} = x$.

If A, B, C are any three points on a coordinate line, it can be shown that

$$\overline{AB} + \overline{BC} = \overline{AC} \tag{1}$$

regardless of the relative positions of the points.

Let P_1 and P_2 be points on a line with coordinates x_1 and x_2. Then by (1) we have

$$\overline{P_1P_2} = \overline{P_1O} + \overline{OP_2} = \overline{OP_2} - \overline{OP_1} = x_2 - x_1.$$

Thus the directed distance $\overline{P_1P_2}$ is the coordinate of the second point minus the coordinate of the first point.

EXAMPLE. Verify (1) if A, B, C have the coordinates $-3, 4, -7$, respectively.

Solution. $\overline{AB} = 4 - (-3) = 7$, $\overline{BC} = -7 - 4 = -11$, $\overline{AC} = -7 - (-3) = -4$, and $7 + (-11) = -4$.

5-3 Rectangular coordinates. We may extend the idea of a coordinate line, by which the real numbers were represented graphically, to a *coordinate plane*, by which pairs of real numbers are represented graphically. This is accomplished by constructing a line perpendicular to the line in Fig. 5-1 at the origin O. These lines are called *axes*, and are generally drawn in such a way that one may be designated as horizontal, the other as vertical. The horizontal axis is commonly called the x-axis, and the vertical axis the y-axis. A unit of measurement, and a positive direction, usually upward, are chosen on the y-axis. Generally the same unit of measure is applied to the x-axis, and the positive direction is to the right. Negative numbers are assigned to the points on the x-axis to the left of the origin and on the y-axis below the origin.

A point P in the plane is designated by the number pair (x, y), where x indicates the perpendicular distance of the point P from the y-axis, and y the perpendicular distance of P from the x-axis. The number x is called the *abscissa*, or *x-coordinate*, of the point P, and y is the *ordinate*, or *y-coordinate*, of P, while x and y together are the *coordinates* of P.

This representation of points in a plane by pairs of numbers is called *the rectangular Cartesian coordinate system*, the name Cartesian being used in recognition of René Descartes (1596–1650), who is usually credited with the discovery of the method.

EXAMPLE. The location of the points A, B, C, D, whose coordinates are the number pairs $(3, 1)$, $(-8, 2)$, $(5, -3)$, and $(-8, -3)$ respectively, is given in Fig. 5-2.

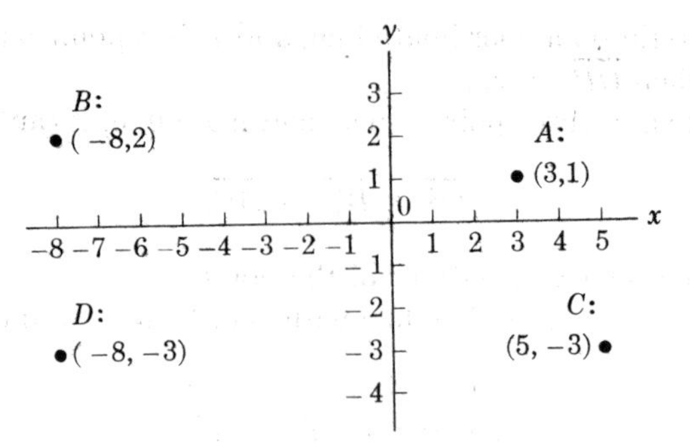

FIGURE 5–2

Note that the correspondence between points in the plane and pairs of numbers is reciprocal, in the sense that for each point there is one and only one pair of numbers, and for each pair of numbers there is exactly one point.

The idea of directed distance between two points on a line parallel to the x-axis or on a line parallel to the y-axis is now defined as in Section 5–2. For example, if P_1 is (2, 3), and P_2 is (2, —7), then

$$\overline{P_1P_2} = -7 - 3 = -10.$$

In general, for $P_1(x_1, y_1)$ and $P_2(x_1, y_2)$ we have

$$\overline{P_1P_2} = y_2 - y_1$$

and similarly for a line segment parallel to the x-axis.

In general we do not use direction on a line not parallel to one of the coordinate axes.

EXERCISE GROUP 5–1

1. Plot the points $A(-2, 3)$; $B(-\frac{3}{2}, -\frac{2}{3})$; $C(7, -\frac{5}{2})$.
2. Plot the points $A(2, -3)$; $B(5, -\frac{3}{2})$; $C(-\frac{3}{5}, -\frac{10}{9})$.
3. Plot the points $(-5, 3)$; $(-4, 4)$; $(-3, 2)$; $(-2, 0)$; $(-1, -1)$; $(0, 0)$; $(1, 2)$; $(3, -2)$; and $(5, 1)$. Join consecutive points with straight line segments.
4. Plot the points $(-3, -5)$; $(-2, -2)$; $(-1, 5)$; $(0, -3)$; $(1, 2)$; $(2, 4)$; $(3, -2)$; $(4, -7)$; and $(5, 3)$. Join consecutive points with straight line segments.
5. Where are all the points whose abscissas are -3? whose ordinates are 2?
6. Where are all the points whose abscissas are a? whose ordinates are b?
7. What is the directed distance from $(2, -3)$ to $(2, 6)$?
8. What is the directed distance from $(-1, 4)$ to $(5, 4)$?
9. What is the directed distance from $(5, -3)$ to $(-8, -3)$?
10. What is the directed distance from $(-8, 2)$ to $(-8, -3)$?
11. Where are all the points which are equidistant from $(2, -3)$ and $(2, 6)$?

12. Where are all the points which are equidistant from (—1, 4) and (5, 4)?

13. The ends of the base of an isosceles triangle are at (3, 0), (8, 0), and the altitude to the base is of length 4. Find the coordinates of the third vertex.

14. Three vertices of a parallelogram are (—3, 2); (1, 0); and (0, 3). Locate the fourth vertex. Is there more than one solution?

15. Three vertices of a rectangle are (—8, —3); (5, —3); and (—8, 2). Locate the fourth vertex. Is there more than one solution?

16. The legs of a right triangle are on the coordinate axes, and the hypotenuse is of length a. If (x, y) are the coordinates of the midpoint of the hypotenuse, show that $4x^2 + 4y^2 = a^2$.

17. Two vertices of an isosceles right triangle are at (1, 3) and (6, 3), and the line segment joining these points is one of the equal sides. Find the coordinates of a third vertex.

18. Verify Eq. (1) if the points have coordinates, respectively,

(a) —5, —7, 2; (b) 1.5, —2, 3.5; (c) —4, 0, —2.

5–4 The distance formula and midpoint formula. We shall now obtain a formula for the (undirected) distance between two points. Let the points be $P_1(x_1, y_1)$ and $P_2(x_2, y_2)$ as in Fig. 5–3. If $y_1 = y_2$, then, as in Section 5–3, we have $\overline{P_1P_2} = x_2 - x_1$. The actual length of the line segment, which we designate by $|P_1P_2|$, is either $x_2 - x_1$, or $x_1 - x_2$, whichever is non-negative, and we may write

$$|P_1P_2| = \pm(x_2 - x_1), \qquad \text{or,} \qquad |P_1P_2| = |x_2 - x_1|. \tag{2}$$

Similarly, if $x_1 = x_2$, we have

$$|P_1P_2| = \pm(y_2 - y_1), \qquad \text{or,} \qquad |P_1P_2| = |y_2 - y_1|.$$

We now assume that $x_1 \neq x_2$ and $y_1 \neq y_2$. Draw a line through P_1 parallel to the x-axis, and a line through P_2 parallel to the y-axis. These lines are perpendicular and their intersection may be taken as $M(x_2, y_1)$. By the above we have

$$|P_1M| = |x_2 - x_1|, \qquad |MP_2| = |y_2 - y_1|,$$

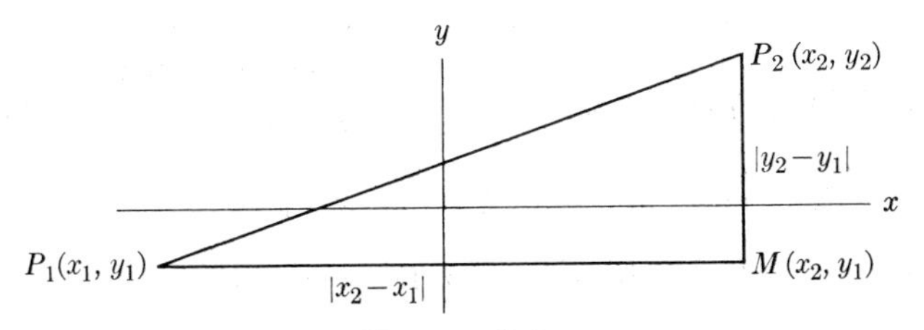

FIGURE 5–3

and hence, by the Theorem of Pythagoras applied to triangle P_1MP_2,

$$\boxed{d = |P_1P_2| = \sqrt{(x_2 - x_1)^2 + (y_2 - y_1)^2},} \tag{3}$$

since $(x_2 - x_1)^2 = |x_2 - x_1|^2$ and $(y_2 - y_1)^2 = |y_2 - y_1|^2$. Equation (3) is known as the *distance formula.*

It should be noted that formula (3) still holds if $x_1 = x_2$ or if $y_1 = y_2$. For example, if $y_1 = y_2$, (3) becomes

$$d = \sqrt{(x_1 - x_2)^2} = |x_2 - x_1|,$$

which is consistent with (2), and similarly if $x_1 = x_2$. Moreover, since $(x_2 - x_1)^2 = (x_1 - x_2)^2$ and $(y_2 - y_1)^2 = (y_1 - y_2)^2$, it is immaterial, when two points are given, which is designated as P_1 and which as P_2.

EXAMPLE 1. Find the distance between the points $(-2, 5)$ and $(3, -7)$.

Solution. By formula (3) we have

$$d = \sqrt{[-2 - 3]^2 + [5 - (-7)]^2} = \sqrt{25 + 144} = \sqrt{169} = 13.$$

EXAMPLE 2. Show that the triangle with $(-3, 2)$, $(1, 1)$, and $(-4, -2)$ as vertices is an isosceles triangle.

Solution. Let the points be designated as A, B, and C respectively. Then

$$|AB| = \sqrt{(1 + 3)^2 + (1 - 2)^2} = \sqrt{17},$$
$$|AC| = \sqrt{(-4 + 3)^2 + (-2 - 2)^2} = \sqrt{17}.$$

Hence $|AB| = |AC|$, and the triangle is isosceles. Furthermore,

$$|BC| = \sqrt{(-4 - 1)^2 + (-2 - 1)^2} = \sqrt{34}.$$

Since $|BC|^2 = |AB|^2 + |AC|^2$, the Theorem of Pythagoras holds, and ABC is a right triangle, with the right angle at A.

Let $P(x, y)$ be the midpoint of the line segment joining $P_1(x_1, y_1)$ and $P_2(x_2, y_2)$. Through P_1, P, and P_2 draw lines perpendicular to the x-axis. These lines intersect the x-axis in the points shown in Fig. 5–4. We must have $\overline{AB} = \overline{BC}$; hence $x - x_1 = x_2 - x$, and it then follows that

$$x = \tfrac{1}{2}(x_1 + x_2).$$

In a similar manner, by drawing lines perpendicular to the y-axis we get

$$y = \tfrac{1}{2}(y_1 + y_2).$$

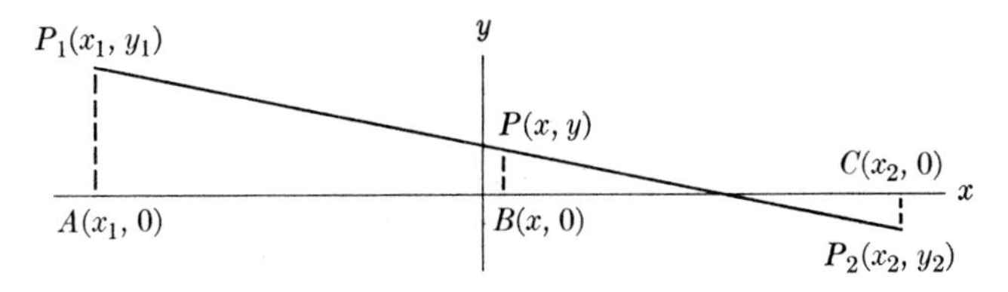

FIGURE 5-4

We combine these in the statement: *The midpoint of the line segment joining $P_1(x_1, y_1)$ and $P_2(x_2, y_2)$ is given by*

$$\boxed{P[\tfrac{1}{2}(x_1 + x_2),\ \tfrac{1}{2}(y_1 + y_2)].} \tag{4}$$

This formula expresses the coordinates of the midpoint of a line segment in terms of the coordinates of its endpoints.

EXAMPLE 3. Determine the coordinates of the midpoint of the line segment joining the points (3, —8) and (—7, 5).

Solution. The coordinates of the desired midpoint are given by formula (4) as

$$x = \tfrac{1}{2}[3 + (-7)] = -2, \qquad y = \tfrac{1}{2}(-8 + 5) = -\tfrac{3}{2}.$$

EXERCISE GROUP 5-2

In Exercises 1-9, determine the coordinates of the point midway between the two given points and also the distance between them.

1. (—5, 2), (3, —7)
2. (—6, —2), (5, 7)
3. (—3, 5), (7, 10)
4. (5, —3), (8, 11)
5. (—3, —8), (—8, 9)
6. (—7, —5), (6, —9)
7. (a, b), (c, d)
8. $(a, -a)$, (c, c)
9. $(a, -c)$, $(-c, a)$

10. Find the distance from the point (3, 5) to the midpoint of the line segment joining the points (5, —3) and (—3, —7).

11. Show that the points (0, 0), (a, c), (b, d), and $(a + b, c + d)$ are the vertices of a parallelogram. (*Hint:* Show that opposite sides are equal.)

12. Find the coordinates of the midpoint of the diagonals of the rectangle with vertices at the points (0, 0), $(a, 0)$, $(0, b)$, (a, b).

13. Show that the triangle with vertices at (6, —2), (—2, 2), and (1, —2) is isosceles.

14. Show that the triangle with vertices at (5, —1), (1, —3), and (8, —7) is a right triangle.

15. Show that the quadrilateral with vertices at (5, —1), (1, —3), (—2, 3), and (2, 5) is a rectangle.

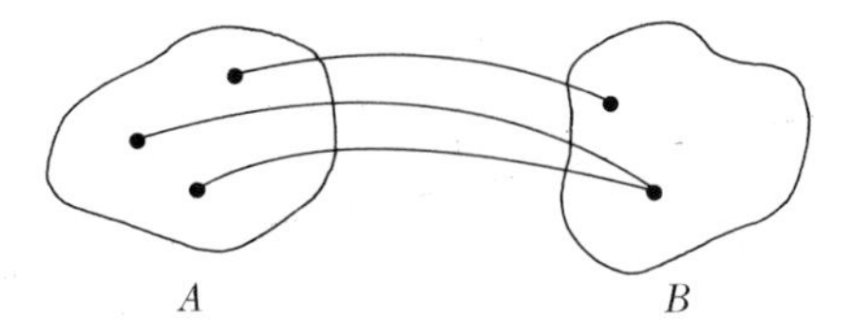

FIGURE 5–5

5–5 Functions. Many mathematical concepts that play an important role in modern mathematics have developed slowly over periods of many years. Among these is the mathematical idea of correspondence between objects, or, more specifically, the mathematical concept of function, which is the subject of the present chapter.

Many familiar experiences of everyday living reflect the idea of correspondence, or relationship, as we wish to use it. In a given day the temperature bears a definite relation to the time. The yield of an acre of wheat clearly depends on the amount of rainfall. The speed of an airplane certainly depends on the amount of fuel fed to the engines. The strength of a wooden beam corresponds to the thickness of the beam. Such examples can be multiplied indefinitely—each of them exhibits the correspondence between two specific quantities.

The concept can be extended to include a correspondence among three or more quantities. Thus, the yield of an acre of wheat depends on temperature as well as rainfall. The speed of an airplane depends on altitude as well as fuel consumed. In large part, however, we shall be concerned with relations or correspondences between two quantities.

We shall mean by a set of numbers any collection of numbers under discussion. Let A and B be two sets of numbers, shown symbolically in Fig. 5–5, such that exactly one number in B corresponds to each number in A, and each number in B corresponds to at least one number in A. This correspondence determines *pairs* of numbers (a, b) where a is in A and b is in B. The collection of all such pairs of numbers defines a *function* whose *domain* is the set of numbers in A, and whose *range* is the set of numbers in B.

EXAMPLE 1. The number pairs

$$(2, 3), \quad (-1, 4), \quad (3, -5), \quad (4, 3)$$

define a function with the numbers 2, -1, 3, 4 as the domain, and the numbers 3, 4, -5 as the range. Note that a number in the range may correspond to more than one number in the domain.

The second number of any pair in a function is called the *value of the function* corresponding to the first number of the pair. If the function is denoted by f, the value of the function corresponding to any number x in the domain is written as $f(x)$.

If f denotes the function in Example 1, we have

$$f(2) = 3, \quad f(-1) = 4, \quad f(3) = -5, \quad f(4) = 3.$$

The value of a function may be given by an algebraic expression. If we write

$$f(x) = 2x - 3,$$

then for any value of x, the value of the function is $2x - 3$. In particular,

$$f(3) = 2 \cdot 3 - 3 = 3, \quad f(-4) = 2(-4) - 3 = -11,$$

and so on.

Many familiar equations define functions, as in the following examples.

EXAMPLE 2. The perimeter P of a square is given by the formula $P = 4s$, where s is the length of a side. This relation defines the function $(s, 4s)$, with a domain, in this case, consisting of all positive numbers. We also say that P is a function of s.

EXAMPLE 3. In the relation $A = lw$, where A is the area of a rectangle and l and w are the lengths of the sides, A is a function of w if l is held fixed in value, and A is a function of l if w is held fixed in value.

Letters other than f are also used to designate a function. If a function is defined by a mathematical expression and no domain is specified, it is assumed that the domain consists of all numbers for which the expression has a value.

EXAMPLE 4. Let $f(x) = 3x^3 + 7x - 5$; then

$$f(2) = 3(2)^3 + 7(2) - 5 = 33, \quad f(0) = -5, \quad f(-1) = -15, \quad f(1) = 5.$$

The student should verify these values for $f(0)$, $f(-1)$, and $f(1)$.

EXERCISE GROUP 5-3

In Exercises 1–6, express each of the functional relations as an explicit algebraic equation.

1. The area A of a square in terms of the length of a side s.
2. The circumference C of a circle in terms of the radius r of the circle.
3. The area A of a circle in terms of the diameter d of the circle.
4. The area A of a rectangle in terms of the width w when the length of the rectangle is twice the width.
5. The hypotenuse y of a right triangle in terms of the shorter leg x when the longer leg of the triangle is twice the shorter leg.

6. The perimeter P of the rectangle of Exercise 4 in terms of the width w.

7. Given $f(x) = x^2 - 3x + 6$, find $f(0)$, $f(-2)$, $f(3)$, $f(a)$.

8. Given $G(x) = \dfrac{x+2}{3-x}$, find $G(0)$, $G(1)$, $G(-1)$, $G(z)$. Does $G(3)$ have a value?

9. Given $H(y) = \dfrac{3y^2+2}{y}$, find $H(2)$, $[H(-1)]^2$, $H\left(\dfrac{x}{z}\right)$.

10. If $f(x) = (x-2)/(x+2)$, compute $f(x+2)$, $f(x-2)$.
11. Find $f(x) - f(x-1)$ if $f(x) = 2x + 3$.
12. Find $f(a) - f(a-1)$ if $f(x) = mx + b$.
13. Find $f(x) - f(x+2)$ if $f(x) = 2x^2 + 3x - 3$.
14. Find $f(2x) - 2f(x)$ if $f(x) = 2x - 5$.

In Exercises 15–18, compute $f(-x)$, $f(x+1)$, $f(x+h)$, $\dfrac{1}{h}[f(x+h) - f(x)]$.

15. $f(x) = 2x - 1$
16. $f(x) = x^2$
17. $f(x) = x^3 - x$
18. $f(x) = \dfrac{x^2}{x+1}$

If $f(x) = 3x^2 - 4x + 1$ and $F(x) = x^2 + 6x - 7$, prove that:

19. $f(4) = F(4)$
20. $f(0) = 8 + F(0)$
21. $F(-7) + f(x) = f(x)$
22. $F(x) + f(1) = F(x)$

Determine the functions in Exercises 23–26 if $f(x) = x^2 + x$, and $g(x) = x - 1$.

23. $f[g(1)]$
24. $g[f(1)]$
25. $f[g(x)]$
26. $g[f(x)]$

27. If a right triangle has a 30° angle, express the length of the altitude drawn to the hypotenuse as a function of the length of the hypotenuse c.

28. Express the number of degrees F on the Fahrenheit scale as a function of the number of degrees C on the Centigrade scale, if the freezing point of water is given by 0°C and 32°F, while the boiling point is 100°C and 212°F.

29. A window is in the form of a semicircle mounted on a rectangle. If the height of the rectangle is twice the width, express the total area of the window as a function of the width w.

30. A ball thrown into the air with a velocity of 32 ft/sec will be above the ground s ft at any time t (measured in seconds from the instant when it is thrown), where s is given by the function $s = -16t^2 + 32t$. Compute the values of s for every quarter-second from $t = 0$ to $t = 2$. Explain the results.

31. Express the area A of an equilateral triangle as a function of the length of one side s.

32. If city property is worth \$300 a front foot, express the value of a lot as a function of its width, x ft.

33. Express the altitude H of an equilateral triangle as a function of the base x.

34. The volume of a cube is given by the formula $V = x^3$, where x is the length of a side. If the length of each side is taken as a and then increased

by the amount h, express the corresponding increase in the volume as a function of h.

35. The following number pairs define a function g:

$$(1, 2),\quad (2, 3),\quad (3, 4),\quad (4, 5)$$

(a) Find $g(1)$ and $g(3)$. (b) Find x if $g(x) = 3$.

In each of the following, the number pairs define a function f with domain consisting of all real numbers. Find $f(2)$ and $f(4)$.

36. $(x, 2x)$ 37. $(x, 3x^2)$ 38. $\left(x, \dfrac{x}{x^2+1}\right)$ 39. $(x, x^2 - x)$

5–6 Graphical representation of functions. With a means for representing pairs of real numbers geometrically now at hand, we can devise an effective way of representing a function $y = f(x)$ graphically. To each value of x there corresponds a value y as determined by the function. The pair of numbers (x, y) may be represented graphically as a point in a rectangular coordinate system. We then say that the aggregate of all points (x, y) as determined by the function $f(x)$ constitutes the *graph of the function*, or the graph of the equation $y = f(x)$.

When a function is given by means of an algebraic expression in x, for example, the simplest method of graphing the function is to assign values to x, compute the corresponding values of y, plot the pairs of numbers thus obtained, and join them with a smooth curve.

EXAMPLE 1. Graph the function $3x - 5$.

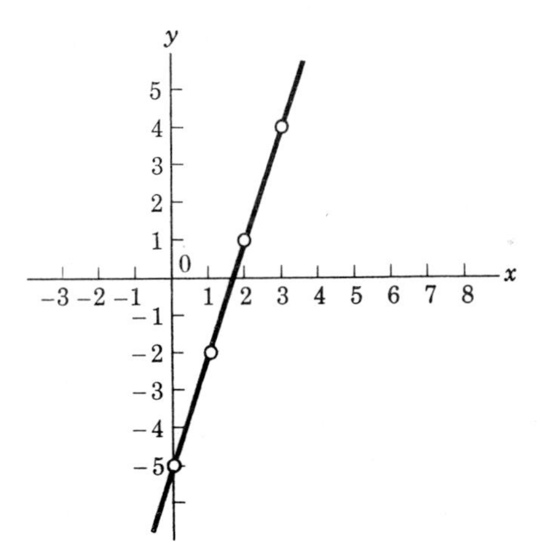

FIGURE 5–6

Solution. Let $y = 3x - 5$; then assign values to x and compute the corresponding values of y, the results being conveniently arranged in a table.

x:	0	1	2	3
y:	-5	-2	1	4

The various points (x, y) are then plotted and joined by a smooth curve, which turns out to be a straight line (Fig. 5–6).

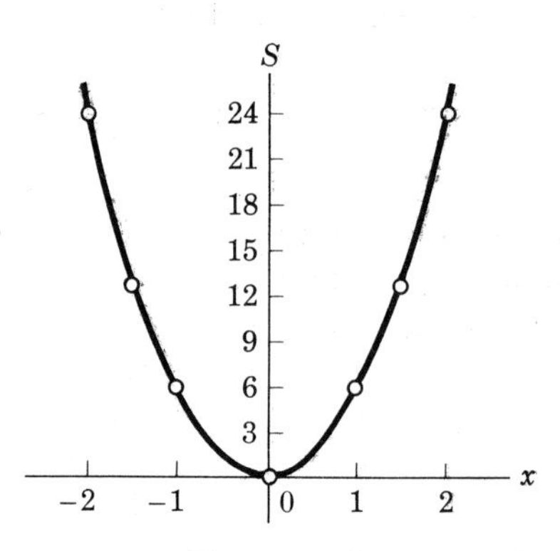

FIGURE 5–7

EXAMPLE 2. The surface S of a cube is given by the formula $S = 6x^2$, where x represents the length of an edge. Graph S as a function of x.

Solution. In the formula $S = 6x^2$ negative values of x may be used as well as positive ones. The points determined by these negative values of x belong to the graph of $S = 6x^2$, although they have no meaning in relation to the cube. The table of values from which the graph in Fig. 5–7 was constructed follows:

x:	-2	$-\frac{3}{2}$	-1	0	1	$\frac{3}{2}$	2
S:	24	$\frac{27}{2}$	6	0	6	$\frac{27}{2}$	24

Note that the axis of ordinates is labeled S. Moreover, units of different size are used on the two axes; this may be done if convenient, but should be avoided where possible.

EXERCISE GROUP 5–4

Draw the graph of the given function in Exercises 1–20.

1. $x - 3$
2. $2x + 5$
3. $-3x + 7$
4. $-2x - 5$
5. $\dfrac{-4x + 3}{5}$
6. x^2
7. $-x^2$
8. $4x^2$

9. $4x^2 - 4x$ 10. $-4x^2 + 4x$ 11. $2x^2 - 3x + 1$

12. x^3 13. $-x^3 + 2x + 1$ 14. $2x^3 - x$

15. $\dfrac{1}{x}$ 16. $x + \dfrac{1}{x}$ 17. $\dfrac{2x + 9}{3x}$

18. $\dfrac{x}{x + 1}$ 19. $\dfrac{x}{x^2 + 1}$ 20. $-x^3$

21. If $f(x) = 2x - 3$, draw the graph of each of the following functions, on the same set of axes: $f(2x)$, $f(\frac{1}{2}x)$, $f(x + 2)$, $f(x^2)$.

22. If $f(x) = x^2 - 3x$, draw the graph of each of the following functions, on the same set of axes: $f(x - 3)$, $f(3x)$, $f(x/3)$.

5–7 Graphical representation of empirical data. The functions considered thus far have been defined by means of formulas. It is possible, however, for one variable to be a function of another, although it may not be possible to express the relation between them by a formula. For example, let us agree that when x is positive, y is equal to -5; when $x = 0$, $y = 2$; when x is negative, $y = -1$. A value of y is determined for each value of x; it follows from the definition of function that y is a function of x. The graph of this function, shown in Fig. 5–8, consists of the line $y = -1$ for negative x, the point (0, 2), and the line $y = -5$ for positive x. It should be noted carefully that there is no formula expressing y in terms of x.

Experimental data, as well as such statistical data as vital statistics, populations, etc., in general cannot be expressed by means of mathematical formulas. It is often desirable, however, to have a graphical representation of such data for the use of scientists, businessmen, and

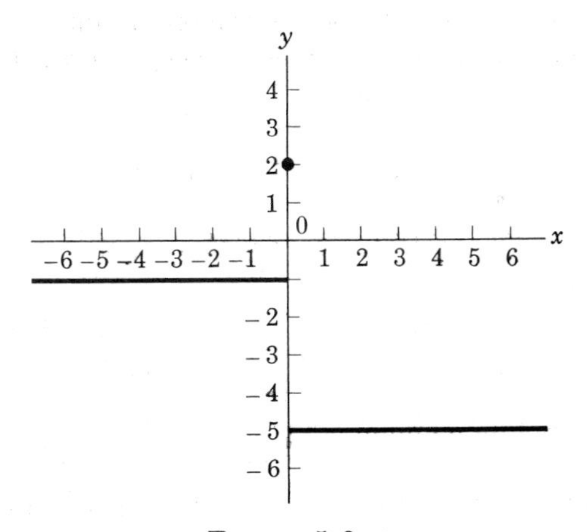

FIGURE 5–8

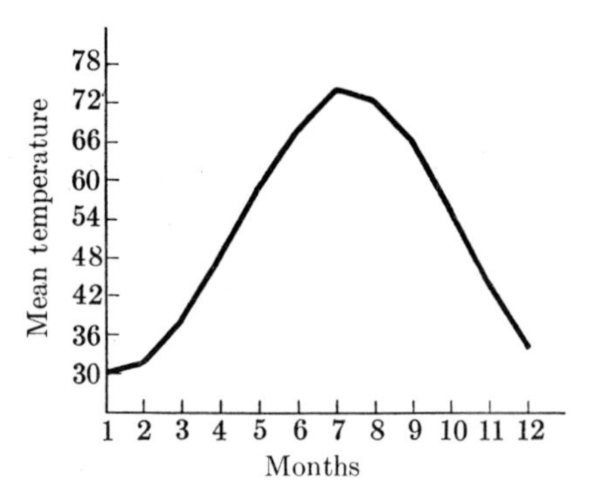

FIGURE 5–9

engineers. The graph in Fig. 5–9 shows the mean monthly temperature for New York City displayed as a function of time.

Month:	Jan.	Feb.	Mar.	Apr.	May	June	July	Aug.	Sept.	Oct.	Nov.	Dec.
Mean temp:	30°	31°	38°	48°	59°	68°	74°	72°	66°	56°	44°	34°

The construction of a graph representing empirical data differs in some ways from the construction of a graph of a function defined by a mathematical formula. We must decide how large the graph should be and then choose the units accordingly. We must also decide which is to be the independent variable (usually this is plotted on the horizontal axis). In situations where time is one variable, this is usually taken as the independent variable, so that the graph expresses the other variable as a function of the time. Moreover, the points obtained from plotting the given data represent all the actual points of the graph. Hence, in general, no curve connecting the points exists, unlike the case of functions defined by formula. However, since the graph is more meaningful if the points are joined, it is customary to connect them either by straight line segments as in Fig. 5–9, or by a smooth curve.

EXERCISE GROUP 5–5

1. The table gives the per capita public debt of the United States to the nearest dollar. Graph the debt as a function of the time.

Year:	1870	1880	1890	1900	1910	1920	1930	1940	1946
Debt:	$61	$42	$18	$17	$12	$228	$132	$326	$1908

2. The table gives the total private debt (individual and corporate) in billions of dollars in the United States. Graph the debt as a function of the time.

Year:	1919	1922	1925	1928	1931	1934	1937	1940	1943	1946
Debt:	$97.3	$109.7	$132.7	$156.8	$149.2	$126.5	$128.1	$129.8	$145.5	$150.0

3. The table gives the monthly average temperature for Milwaukee. Graph temperature as a function of the time.

Month:	Jan.	Feb.	Mar.	Apr.	May	June	July	Aug.	Sept.	Oct.	Nov.	Dec.
Temp:	21°	23°	33°	44°	54°	64°	71°	70°	63°	51°	37°	26°

4. The table gives the National Industrial Income for the United States in billions of dollars. Graph income as a function of the time.

Year:	1937	1938	1939	1940	1941	1942	1943	1944	1945	1946
Income:	$73.6	$67.4	$72.5	$81.3	$103.8	$136.5	$168.3	$182.3	$182.8	$178.2

5. The table gives the relative values of construction contracts for private housing in the United States, taking the average for 1923–1925 as 100. Graph the value as a function of the time.

Year:	1920	1925	1928	1929	1932	1935	1938	1941	1944	1946
Value:	30	124	126	87	13	21	45	89	16	143

6. The table gives the average price of 354 industrial stocks. Graph the price as a function of the time.

Year:	1926	1927	1928	1929	1930	1931
Price:	$90.3	$107	$139.4	$171.1	$127	$78.5
Year:	1932	1933	1934	1935	1936	1937
Price:	$41.8	$59.9	$73.4	$82.2	$115.2	$118.1

7. The table gives the production of meat in billions of pounds in the United States. Graph the production as a function of the time.

Year:	1934	1935	1936	1937	1938	1939	1940	1941	1942	1943	1944	1945
Prod:	17.3	14.4	16.8	15.7	16.5	17.5	19.0	19.5	21.7	24.1	24.7	22.9

8. The table gives passenger car production in the United States in millions of cars. Graph production as a function of time.

Year:	1915	1920	1922	1925	1929	1931	1932	1937	1938	1940	1941	1942
Prod:	0.9	1.9	2.3	3.7	4.6	1.97	1.14	3.92	2.0	3.72	3.78	0.22

9. The table gives the production of lumber in the United States in millions of board-feet. Graph production as a function of the time.

Year:	1869	1879	1889	1899	1909	1919	1929	1935	1941	1947	1949
Prod:	12,756	18,725	27,038	35,078	44,510	34,552	36,886	19,539	33,613	35,404	32,158

10. The table gives the production of electric energy in the United States in millions of kilowatt-hours. Graph production as a function of the time.

Year:	1925	1930	1935	1940	1942	1945	1947	1950
kw-hr:	61,451	91,112	95,287	141,837	185,979	222,486	253,739	328,998

11. The table gives the average hourly earnings in dollars (including overtime) in manufacturing industries in the United States. Graph earnings as a function of the time. (Draw separate graphs for durable goods and nondurable goods on same axes.)

Year:	1941	1942	1943	1944	1945	1946	1947	1948	1949	1950	1951	1952
Av hr earnings Durable goods	0.81	0.947	1.059	1.117	1.111	1.156	1.293	1.410	1.464	1.537	1.67	1.76
Av hr earnings Nondurable goods	0.64	0.723	0.803	0.861	0.904	0.912	1.171	1.278	1.325	1.378	1.48	1.54

5–8 Direct variation; inverse variation. Statements of functional dependence are frequently expressed, particularly in the natural sciences, in the language of variation, and in order to treat these statements quantitatively it is desirable to express them in mathematical notation. For example, in the study of physics one encounters Hooke's Law, which states that the force applied to stretch an elastic spring varies directly as the amount of elongation. In algebraic notation the statement becomes

$$F = k \cdot s,$$

where F is the force applied, s is the amount of elongation, and k is a constant. The constant k, called a *constant of proportionality*, is an essential part of any algebraic statement of variation. In a given situation k does not depend on the values of the variables. Thus, in the example, if a pair of corresponding values of F and s is known, the value of k can be found, and it remains the same for that spring whatever values of s (within the elastic limits of the spring) may be involved. Indeed the value of k in Hooke's Law is an attribute of the spring itself and is known as the *modulus of elasticity*.

EXAMPLE 1. In a spring to which Hooke's Law applies, a force of 18.6 lb stretches the spring by 1.27 in. Find k.

Solution. It is necessary merely to substitute the given values in the equation $F = ks$, obtaining

$$18.6 = k(1.27),$$

from which $k = 18.6/1.27 = 14.65$ lb/in.

A second kind of variation is involved in the statement "y varies inversely as x." Algebraically this becomes

$$y = \frac{k}{x},$$

for some constant of proportionality k.

EXAMPLE 2. If y varies inversely as the cube of x, and $y = 7$ when $x = 2$, express y as a function of x.

Solution. The inverse variation is now with respect to x^3, and we have

$$y = \frac{k}{x^3}.$$

Since $y = 7$ and $x = 2$ must satisfy this relation, we obtain

$$7 = \frac{k}{2^3} = \frac{k}{8},$$

and we find $k = 7 \cdot 8 = 56$. Substitution of this value of k in the general relation gives

$$y = \frac{56}{x^3},$$

which expresses y as a function of x.

We may now, in addition, find the value of y corresponding to any value of x. If Example 2 had the added requirement to find the value of y when $x = 1.2$, the method of Example 2 would be carried out completely, and $x = 1.2$ would be substituted in the function, so that

$$\text{for } x = 1.2, \qquad \text{we have } y = \frac{56}{(1.2)^3} = \frac{56}{1.728} = 32.41.$$

Other expressions in use are "is proportional to" for "varies directly," and "is inversely proportional to" for "varies inversely."

EXERCISE GROUP 5-6

1. If y varies directly as x, and $y = 2$ when $x = 5$, write y as a function of x and determine the value of y when $x = 7$.
2. If y varies directly as x^2, and $y = 4$ when $x = 3$, write y as a function of x and determine the value of y when $x = -2$.
3. If u varies inversely as v, and $u = 4$ when $v = 2$, write u as a function of v and determine the value of u when $v = 3$.
4. If w varies inversely as z^3, and $w = 3$ when $z = 2$, write w as a function of z and then determine the value of w when $z = 3$.
5. If v varies directly as u where $u = xy$, and $v = 10$ when $x = 2$ and $y = 4$, write v as a function of u and find the value of v when $x = 3$ and $y = 6$.
6. If v varies inversely as u where $u = y/x$, and $v = 5$ when $x = 10$ and $y = 3$, write v as a function of u and find the value of v when $x = 7$ and $y = -1$.
7. The surface area of a sphere varies as the square of the radius. The area is 16π square units when the radius is 2. Determine a formula expressing the surface area as a function of the radius.

8. The distance a falling body travels (neglecting air resistance) varies as the square of the time of fall. If the body falls 64 ft in 2 sec (starting from rest), how far did it fall the first second? How far will it fall in t seconds?

9. The surface area of a cube varies directly as the square of the length of an edge. The surface area is 24 square units when the length of an edge is 2 units. Determine a formula expressing the surface area as a function of the length of an edge.

10. The intensity of light on a plane surface varies inversely as the square of the distance of the surface from the source of light. What is the change in the intensity when the distance is cut in half?

11. The volume of a pyramid of fixed altitude varies directly as the area of the base. The volume is 35 cubic units when the rectangular base is 5 units wide and 9 units long. Determine a formula expressing the volume as a function of the area of the base.

12. The volume of a prism of fixed altitude varies as the area of the base. The volume is 80 cubic units when the base, which is a right triangle, has edges of 3, 4, and 5 units each. Determine a formula expressing the volume of the prism as a function of the area of the base.

13. According to Newton's Law of Gravitation the force of attraction between two objects varies inversely as the square of the distance between the centers of the objects. What is the change in the attracting force between two bodies when the distance between their centers is reduced by 50%?

14. Boyle's Law states that the pressure p of a gas at constant temperature varies inversely as the volume v. If $v = 500 \text{ in}^3$ when $p = 30 \text{ lb/in}^2$, express p as a function of v and determine the value of p when $v = 200 \text{ in}^3$.

5–9 Joint variation. The laws of nature are such that functional dependence often involves more than two variables. In such cases we speak of *joint variation*, which may involve direct variation on more than one variable, or inverse variation on more than one variable, or a combination of both direct and inverse variation.

In physics it is shown that the intensity of light falling on an object varies directly as the intensity of the source of illumination, and inversely as the square of the distance of the object from the source. In algebraic notation this becomes

$$I = k \cdot \frac{w}{d^2},$$

where I is used to designate the intensity of light on the object, w is the intensity of the source, d is the distance of the object from the source, and k is the constant of proportionality. The direct variation is indicated by the multiplication by w, and the inverse variation by the division by d^2.

EXAMPLE. The strength S of a rectangular beam varies directly as the width w and the square of the depth d. If a beam 2 in. wide and 4 in. deep will support 1200 lb, what weight will a beam 4 in. wide and 2 in. deep support?

Solution. The relation is $S = kwd^2$, and with $S = 1200$, $w = 2$, $d = 4$, we have $1200 = k \cdot 2 \cdot 4^2$, so that $k = \frac{75}{2}$, and the formula becomes

$$S = \tfrac{75}{2} wd^2.$$

Now we set $w = 4$, $d = 2$, and we find

$$S = \tfrac{75}{2} \cdot 4 \cdot 2^2 = 600 \text{ lb.}$$

We see that a 2×4 on edge as a "beam" will support twice as much as the same 2×4 lying flat as a "plank."

Exercise Group 5-7

1. If y varies jointly as x^2 and z, and $y = 3$ when $x = 2$ and $z = 6$, write y as a function of x and z, and determine the value of y when $x = -3$ and $z = 10$.

2. If s varies jointly as r^2 and t, and $s = 3$ when $r = 2$ and $t = 5$, write s as a function of r and t, and determine the value of s when $r = -5$ and $t = 3$.

3. If u varies directly as v^2 and inversely as w^3, and $u = 5$ when $v = 3$ and $w = 2$, write u as a function of v and w, and then determine the value of u when $v = -5$ and $w = 2$.

4. If y varies directly as x^3 and inversely as z^2, and $y = 7$ when $x = -5$ and $z = 3$, write y as a function of x and z, and determine the value of y when $x = 2$ and $z = -3$.

5. W varies jointly as u and v^2 and inversely as t^3, and $W = 27$ when $u = 3$, $v = 2$, and $t = 2$. Write W as a function of u, v, and t and then determine the value of W when $u = 5$, $v = 3$, and $t = 4$.

6. S varies directly as r^2 and inversely as the product v^3t, and $S = 36$ when $r = 3$, $v = 2$, and $t = 5$. Write S as a function of r, v, and t and then determine the value of S when $r = 5$, $v = 4$, and $t = 3$.

7. Y varies jointly as x and z^2 and inversely as u^3 and v, and $Y = 90$ when $x = 5$, $z = 3$, $u = 2$, and $v = -4$. Write Y as a function of x, z, u, and v, and then determine the value of Y when $x = 3$, $z = -7$, $u = 4$, and $v = 5$.

8. The lumber required to build a closet in the corner of a room varies directly as the sum of the width and length of the closet. Which would require the least lumber, a closet 4×4 ft or one 3.5×5 ft?

9. Labor costs vary jointly as the number of workers and the average number of hours of work per worker per week. If the labor costs are $105,307 per week when there are 1200 workers with an average work week of 36.4 hours per worker, what will the labor costs be (to the nearest dollar) with an average work week of 38 hours per worker and a working force of 1100 men?

10. The gravitational attraction between two objects varies as the product of their masses and inversely as the square of the distance between their centers of mass. What will be the change in the attraction between the two objects if their masses are cut in half and the distance between their centers is also cut in half?

11. Under certain conditions the thrust T of a propeller varies jointly as the fourth power of its diameter and the square of the number of revolutions per

minute that it is turning. What is the change in T when the diameter is decreased 50% and the revolutions are increased 25%?

12. The lift of an airplane wing varies as the area of the wing and the square of the velocity of the plane. Compute the change in the lift (a) if the wing area is reduced 50% and the velocity increased 50%, (b) if the wing area is increased 50% and the velocity reduced 50%.

13. The crushing load of a pillar varies as the fourth power of its diameter and inversely as the square of its length. If a load of 56 tons will crush a 6-in. pillar which is 30 ft high, what diameter must a 20-ft pillar (20 ft high) have if it is to support a load of 8 tons?

14. The safe load for a uniformly distributed load on a horizontal beam, supported at both ends, varies jointly as the breadth and the square of the depth and inversely as the distance between the supports. If a beam 8 ft long, 2 in. wide, and 6 in. deep can safely support 1800 lb, how much can a beam 16 ft long, 2 in. wide, and 8 in. deep safely support?

15. The time required for an elevator to lift a weight varies jointly as the weight and the distance through which the weight is lifted and inversely as the power of the motor. If 30 sec are required for a 4-hp motor to lift 600 lb through 50 ft, what power is necessary to lift 1000 lb 150 ft in 40 sec?

Review Exercises

In Exercises 1–4, the given number pairs define a function f with domain consisting of all real numbers for which the second expression is defined. In each case find $f(-3)$ and $f(5)$.

1. $(x, 2x^2)$
2. $\left(x, \dfrac{3x}{5 - 2x}\right)$
3. $(x, 5 + 2x - 3x^2)$
4. $(x, x - x^{-2})$
5. Given $f(x) = 15 - 2x - x^2$, find $f(-1)$, $f(0)$, $f(3)$, $f(-a)$.
6. Given $G(y) = (5 - y)/(y - 4)$, find $G(-2)$, $G(0)$, $G(-\frac{3}{2})$, $G(-x)$.
7. If $f(x) = (3x - 5)/2x$ and $G(x) = x^2/(2x + 3)$, compute $G[f(-1)]$.

Draw the graph of each of the functions in Exercises 8–11.

8. $\dfrac{x - 1}{x^2}$
9. $2 - 3x - x^2$
10. $3x - \dfrac{5}{x}$
11. $3x^2 - x^3$

In each of Exercises 12–15, find the directed distance from the first point to the second point.

12. $(7, -3)$, $(-5, -3)$
13. $(2, -7)$, $(2, 6)$
14. $(3, 5)$, $(3, -12)$
15. $(-13, 7)$, $(3, 7)$

In each of Exercises 16–19, determine the coordinates of the point midway between the two given points and also the distance between them.

16. $(-3, 5)$, $(8, -17)$
17. $(15, -9)$, $(-2, 17)$
18. (p, q), (r, s)
19. (a, d), (b, c)

20. The following table gives the population in thousands for the years indicated. Graph the population as a function of the time.

Year:	1880	1890	1900	1910	1920	1930	1940	1950
Pop:	503	1,100	1,699	2,185	2,702	3,376	3,397	3,621

21. The following table gives the petroleum production in the United States for the years indicated. Graph the production as a function of the time.

Year:	1925	1930	1935	1940	1945	1950	1955
Prod:	763,743	898,011	996,596	1,353,214	1,713,655	1,973,574	2,484,521

22. The cube of the diameter of a solid steel shaft varies directly as the hp (horsepower) transmitted and inversely as the number of revolutions per minute that it turns. If a $\frac{1}{2}$ in. shaft turning at 3000 rpm will transmit 50 hp, determine the cube of the diameter of the shaft needed to transmit 200 hp when turning at 2500 rpm.

23. The thickness of a pipe of d inches internal diameter required to withstand a pressure of p lb per in.^{2} varies jointly as the diameter and the pressure. If a given pipe $\frac{1}{8}$ in. thick and 6 in. in diameter will withstand 50 lb per in.^{2} pressure, how thick must a 1-in. pipe of the same material be to withstand 150 lb per in.^{2} pressure?

24. The mass in grams of a metal deposited through electrolytic conduction varies jointly as the time, the current passing through the solution, and the atomic weight of the element being used, and inversely as the valence of the element. A mass of 1.22 grams of nickel (atomic weight 56.68, valence 2) is deposited in one hour by a current of one ampere. How much zinc (atomic weight 65.37, valence 2) would be deposited in $\frac{1}{2}$ hour by a current of 1.5 amperes?

25. The kinetic energy of a body varies jointly as the mass of the body and the square of its velocity. If the kinetic energy is 2420 foot pounds when the mass is 10 lb and the velocity is 22 ft per sec, determine the kinetic energy of a 3000-lb automobile traveling 60 miles per hour.

26. A cylindrical tin can is to be constructed with a given fixed volume V, but with variable dimensions. Express the amount A of tin required as a function of the radius r of the base (neglect the thickness of the tin).

27. An open box (no top) is to be made from a sheet of tin 12×16 inches by cutting equal squares from each of the four corners and bending up the edges. Let x be the length of a side of the squares cut out and then express the volume V of the box as a function of x.

28. A right circular cone is inscribed in a sphere of radius 16 inches. Express the volume of the cone as a function of its altitude.

29. A trough of rectangular cross section is to be made from a long rectangular sheet of metal 20 inches wide, by bending up the edges. Express the cross-sectional area of the trough as a function of its depth.

30. Show that the diagonals of a rectangle bisect each other. (*Hint:* Determine the midpoint of each diagonal.)

CHAPTER 6

THE TRIGONOMETRIC FUNCTIONS

6–1 Introduction to the trigonometric functions. Historically, the origins of the study of trigonometry lie in the determination of distances, areas, and directions on the earth by the use of triangles, for purposes of what we know as surveying. For mathematics, however, the measurement aspect of the study has assumed minor importance, although it is still significant. *The mathematics of trigonometry involves the study of the trigonometric functions, the mode of variation of these functions, and the relations among them.* The applications of trigonometry from this point of view are many, both in science and in engineering.

In algebra several classes of function, that is, certain algebraic, exponential, and logarithmic functions, are studied from various points of view. The content of the subject of trigonometry may then be described, in a very real sense, merely as the extension of algebra to the class of trigonometric functions or, briefly, as the algebra of the trigonometric functions. It is then implicit in this statement that the definitions, properties, and theorems of algebra carry over without change. Furthermore, the concepts and results of plane geometry have their use in the development of certain properties of the functions, and also in the applications involving measurement.

6–2 General angles. Familiarity with the general angle and its measurement is prerequisite to the study of the trigonometric functions. Let us consider two *half-lines*, that is, two straight lines meeting at the point O, terminating at O, but extending indefinitely in the direction away from O. If A and B are two points, one on each of these lines, we shall designate the lines as OA and OB, as in Fig. 6–1, and shall define what is meant by angle as follows.

DEFINITION 6–1. *An angle that OB makes with OA shall mean an amount of rotation about O, in the plane of OA and OB, which is required to make OA coincide with OB.*

The designation of an angle thus requires an *initial line*, such as OA, a *terminal line*, such as OB, and an *amount of rotation*. (A discussion of the measurement of the amount of rotation in an angle appears in Section 6–3.) The intersection O of OA and OB is called the *vertex* of the angle.

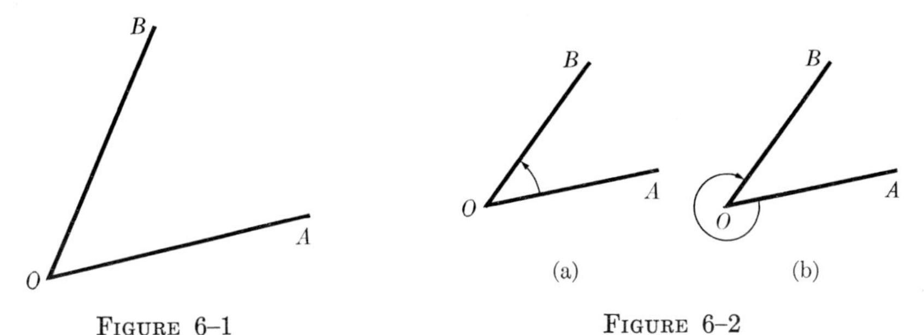

FIGURE 6-1 FIGURE 6-2

The student should note that the definition mentions *an* angle, rather than *the* angle. For one thing, a line may rotate in a plane about a point in either of two directions, designated as *clockwise* and *counterclockwise,* the clockwise direction being that of the motion of the hands of a clock, and the counterclockwise direction being opposite to that of the motion of the hands of a clock. The direction of rotation of an angle is not specified in the definition. Thus, Fig. 6-2(a) shows an angle that OB makes with OA, measured in a counterclockwise direction, while (b) shows an angle with the initial and terminal lines in the same position, measured in a clockwise direction.

The counterclockwise direction of rotation will be taken as the positive direction, and a clockwise rotation will be negative.

Furthermore, the definition of angle does not specify that the rotation is to cease the first time the terminal side is reached. It is thus clear that the angle that OB makes with OA is not uniquely determined. In fact, the totality of all angles that OB makes with OA in Fig. 6-2(a) is obtained by adding any number of complete rotations, positive or negative, to the angle shown.

6-3 Degree measure of an angle. The two units of angular measure to be considered for our purposes are the *degree* and the *radian.* The angle indicated in Fig. 6-3(a) is a complete positive rotation, that in (b) is a positive straight angle, or half of a complete positive rotation, and that in (c) is a positive right angle, or half of a positive straight angle. A *degree* (°) is *defined* as $\frac{1}{360}$ of a complete rotation, or, equiva-

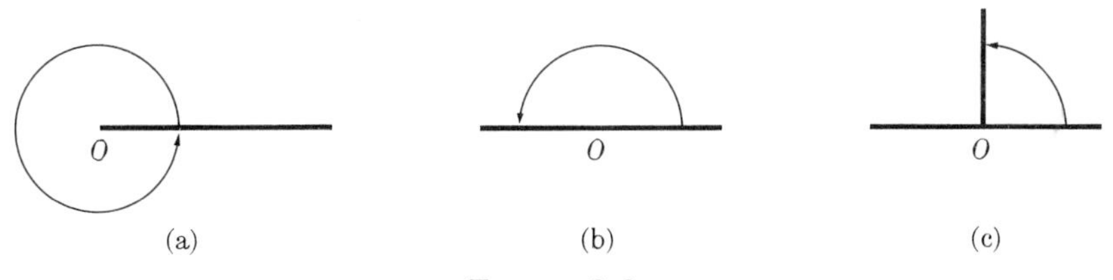

FIGURE 6-3

lently, as $\frac{1}{180}$ of a straight angle, or $\frac{1}{90}$ of a right angle, all positive; a *minute* (′) is defined as $\frac{1}{60}$ of a degree, and a *second* (″) is $\frac{1}{60}$ of a minute. The degree measures of the angles indicated in Fig. 6–3 are then given as 360°, 180°, and 90°, respectively.

EXAMPLES. $\frac{1}{4}(90°) = 22°\,30'$; $\frac{1}{16}(90°) = 5°\,37'\,30''$;

$$\tfrac{1}{8}° = \tfrac{1}{8}(60') = 7.5' = 7'\,30'';$$

$$11'' = \tfrac{11'}{60} = 0.183'; \qquad 43'' = \tfrac{43'}{60} = 0.717'.$$

6–4 Radian measure of an angle. The second unit of angular measure to be considered will now be introduced. Consider a circle of radius r, as shown in Fig. 6–4, and lay off on the circumference, in the positive direction, an arc AB of length r, starting at any point A. *The positive angle AOB at the center of the circle, subtended by this arc of length r, will be taken as a unit of angular measure, and will be designated as* 1 *radian* (abbreviated as *rad*).

The student should convince himself, in the course of the following discussion, that *this unit is independent of the length of the radius of the circle.*

It is clear that the radian is large in relation to the degree, something less than 60°; the precise relation between the two units will now be determined. Since for the length C of the circumference of a circle we have the formula $C = 2\pi r$, it follows that an arc of length r can be laid off in the positive direction exactly 2π times in order to cover the complete circumference. Hence a complete rotation requires 2π rad in radian measure, and 360° in degree measure, so that the desired relation between the two measures is

$$\boxed{2\pi \text{ rad} = 360°.}$$

To convert from one type of measure to the other we usually use the following relations, which are easily obtained from the preceding one:

$$\boxed{1 \text{ rad} = \frac{180°}{\pi} = 57.296° = 57°17'45'' \text{ (approx.)}}$$

and

$$\boxed{1° = \frac{\pi}{180} \text{ rad} = 0.017453 \text{ rad (approx.).}}$$

When no unit of measurement is indicated for an angle, it will be understood that radian measure is implied.

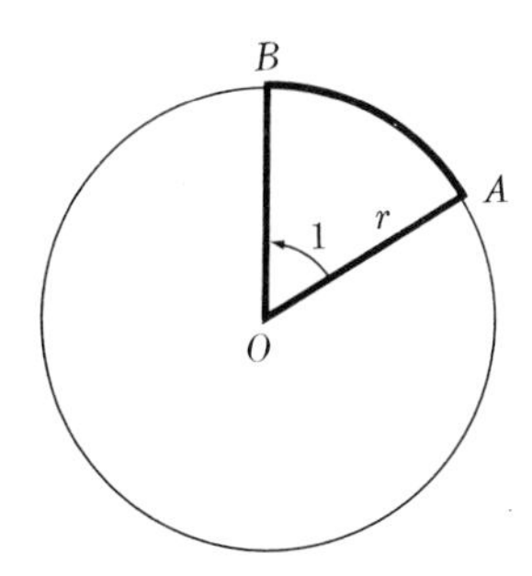

FIGURE 6–4

EXAMPLE 1. $180° = \pi \text{ rad}; \qquad 90° = \pi/2 \text{ rad};$

$$-315° = -315 \times \frac{\pi}{180} \text{ rad} = -\frac{7\pi}{4} \text{ rad};$$

$$116° = 116(0.017453) \text{ rad} = 2.025 \text{ rad (approx.)}.$$

EXAMPLE 2. $\frac{5\pi}{6} \text{ rad} = \frac{5\pi}{6} \cdot \frac{180°}{\pi} = 150°;$

$$-\frac{9\pi}{4} \text{ rad} = -\frac{9\pi}{4} \cdot \frac{180°}{\pi} = -405°;$$

$$1.67 \text{ rad} = 1.67 \times 57.296° = 95.684° = 95° \, 41' \, 2.4'' \text{ (approx.)}.$$

It must be understood, in any radian measure involving π, that π is the familiar number $\pi = 3.14159\ldots$. Thus, a straight angle of π rad is also, to two decimals, 3.14 rad.

EXERCISE GROUP 6–1

Express each of the angles in Exercises 1–20 in degrees.

1. $\pi/2$	2. $\pi/3$	3. $3\pi/4$	4. $2\pi/15$
5. $-7\pi/6$	6. $13\pi/6$	7. $\pi/15$	8. $\pi/36$
9. 3π	10. $-\pi/18$	11. $\pi/12$	12. $4\pi/9$
13. $-3\pi/2$	14. $3\pi/5$	15. $3\pi/8$	16. $-5\pi/3$
17. $7\pi/4$	18. $-8\pi/5$	19. $7\pi/3$	20. 0.7π

Express each of the angles in Exercises 21–32 in degrees, minutes, and seconds.

21. 1.3 rad	22. 2.2 rad	23. 0.75 rad	24. 1.08 rad
25. 0.01 rad	26. 0.16 rad	27. 7 rad	28. 1.54 rad
29. 2.13 rad	30. −3.07 rad	31. −7.13 rad	32. 23.1 rad

Express each of the angles in Exercises 33–44 in radians, in terms of π.

33. 210°	34. 160°	35. 315°	36. 390°
37. 405°	38. 105°	39. 300°	40. 75°
41. 720°	42. 900°	43. 108°	44. 48°

Express each of the angles in Exercises 45–56 as a decimal number of radians.

45. $43° 18'$	46. $52° 27' 10''$	47. $110°$
48. $197°$	49. $211° 48' 27''$	50. $68°$
51. $113° 23'$	52. $343° 17'$	53. $-213° 37'$
54. $-413° 16'$	55. $137° 43' 57''$	56. $814° 24' 35''$

6–5 Standard position of an angle. The reference angle. The axes (also called the coordinate axes) divide the plane into four parts, or *quadrants*, each of which may be characterized by the signs of the coordinates of a point in it. The quadrant in which x and y are both positive is designated as Q_1; then Q_2, Q_3, and Q_4 are the quadrants met successively in a counterclockwise rotation about the origin. We may tabulate this information as follows:

	Q_1	Q_2	Q_3	Q_4
x:	+	−	−	+
y:	+	+	−	−

Points on the coordinate axes are not in any quadrant; the axes actually separate the quadrants.

An angle θ is said to be in *standard position* if its vertex is at the origin of a rectangular coordinate system, and the initial line of θ lies along the positive x-axis. When an angle is in standard position, the terminal line will lie either in some quadrant, or on one of the axes. *If the terminal side of an angle in standard position lies in a certain quadrant, we say also that the angle lies in that quadrant.* Thus, the negative angle θ shown in Fig. 6–5 is in standard position, and is said to lie in Q_3.

EXAMPLE 1. Consider the angles $45° + n \cdot 90°$, where n may be any integer. If $n = 0$, the angle is $45°$ and is in Q_1; if $n = 1$, the angle is $135°$ and is in Q_2; if $n = 2$, the angle is in Q_3, and so on.

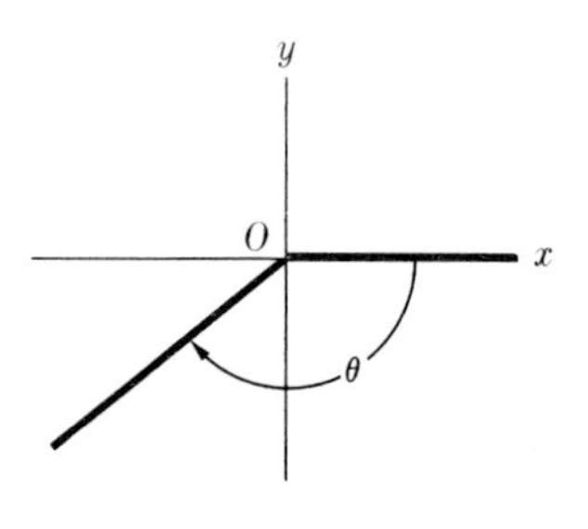

FIGURE 6–5

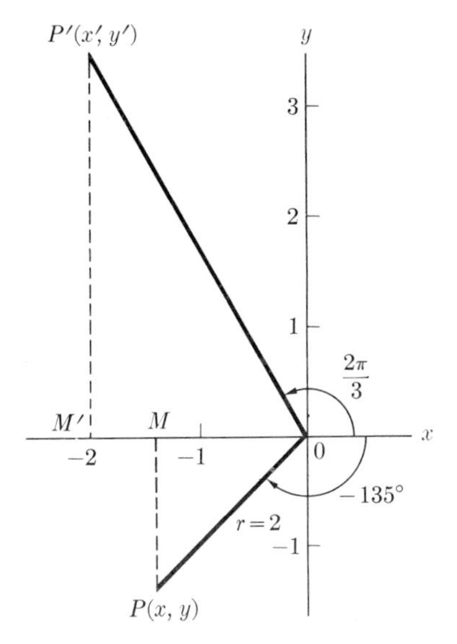

FIGURE 6–6

Angles which, when placed in standard position, have the same terminal side, are said to be *coterminal*. As an illustration, it is easy to see that 135°, −225°, and 495° are coterminal angles.

When an angle is placed in standard position, one of the angles between its terminal line and the x-axis will be either a positive acute angle, or a right angle, or zero. The angle thus described is known as the *reference angle* for θ. The reference angle, unless it is a right angle or zero, can always be said to lie in Q_1. For example, if the angle shown in Fig. 6–5 is −140°, the reference angle is made with the negative x-axis and is 40°. We may define the reference angle formally as follows:

DEFINITION 6–2. *The reference angle for an angle θ is the smallest nonnegative angle between the terminal line of θ and the x-axis, when θ is in standard position.*

In general, the reference angle for θ is some multiple of 180°, or of π, plus or minus θ. To find the reference angle one should draw θ in standard position, or think of it as so drawn. Thus, the reference angle for 313° is 47°, that for 847° is 53°, and the one for $8\pi/3$ is $\pi/3$.

EXAMPLE 2. Draw the angle −135° in standard position, and find the point on the terminal side for which $r = 2$.

Solution. The angle −135° is shown in Fig. 6–6. If $OP = 2$, we have

$$x^2 + y^2 = 4. \tag{1}$$

Since angle $MOP = 45°$, and x and y are both negative, we have $y = x$. Then (1) gives

$$2x^2 = 4, \qquad x = -\sqrt{2}.$$

Hence the point is $P(-\sqrt{2}, -\sqrt{2})$.

EXAMPLE 3. Draw the angle $2\pi/3$ in standard position, and find the point (x', y') on its terminal side for which $x' = -2$.

Solution. The angle $2\pi/3$ is also shown in Fig. 6–6 in standard position. The angle $P'OM'$ is $\pi/3$ or 60°. Hence, by a theorem of plane geometry the length of OP' is twice that of OM', and $OP' = 4$. Then, by the distance formula we have

$$x'^2 + y'^2 = 4^2, \qquad \text{and} \qquad y'^2 = 4^2 - (-2)^2 = 12;$$

since y' is positive in Q_2, we obtain $y' = \sqrt{12} = 2\sqrt{3}$. The desired point is then $(-2, 2\sqrt{3})$.

EXERCISE GROUP 6–2

In Exercises 1–8, draw the given angle in standard position, and find the point on the terminal side of the angle for which $r = 1$.

1. 30° 2. 120° 3. $-45°$ 4. $-150°$
5. $\pi/4$ 6. $4\pi/3$ 7. $-5\pi/6$ 8. $-11\pi/4$

In Exercises 9–16, determine the quadrant in which the angle lies, and also determine the reference angle.

9. 128° 10. $-73°$ 11. $-219°$ 12. 433°
13. 318° 30′ 14. $-143°$ 18′ 15. 91° 09′ 16. 182° 57′

In Exercises 17–26, determine whichever of the quantities x, y, r are not given, and plot the corresponding point P.

17. $x = 3$, $r = 5$, P in Q_4 18. $x = 5$, $y = -12$
19. $y = 7$, $r = 10$, P in Q_2 20. $r = 17$, $y = 8$
21. $r = \sqrt{14}$, $y = \sqrt{10}$ 22. $r = 9$, $x = 6\sqrt{2}$
23. $r = 2\sqrt{5}$, $x = 3y$ 24. $r = 3$, $y = 3x$
25. $r = 1 + y$, $x = -2$ 26. $r = x + 1$, $y = -3$

In Exercises 27–35 find the quadrant in which the angle lies if θ is a positive acute angle.

27. $\theta + 180°$ 28. $\theta - 540°$ 29. $\theta + 270°$
30. $270° - \theta$ 31. $450° + \theta$ 32. $-810° - \theta$
33. $\theta - \pi/2$ 34. $5\pi/2 - \theta$ 35. $7\pi/2 + \theta$

6–6 Definitions of the trigonometric functions. The necessary groundwork for defining the trigonometric functions has now been laid. We shall designate the *radius vector* of a point P in a coordinate system as the line OP drawn from the origin to the point; the *length* of OP, always

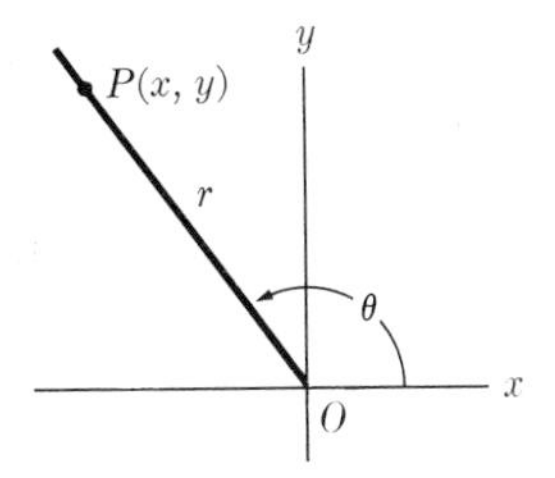

FIGURE 6–7

taken as positive or zero, will be called the *polar distance* of P. If x, y, r are the coordinates and polar distance of a point not on the coordinate axes, six ratios can be formed with these quantities; these ratios will be, *once the manner in which an angle determines these ratios is known*, the six trigonometric functions of the angle. The trigonometric functions to be defined are the *sine, cosine, tangent, cotangent, secant,* and *cosecant.*

DEFINITION 6–3. *If θ is any angle other than an integral multiple of $90°$, place θ in standard position. Let $P(x, y)$, with polar distance r, be a point (not the origin) on the terminal line of θ when so placed.* (See Fig. 6–7.) *The trigonometric functions of θ are then defined as follows (with the abbreviation of each name given):*

$$\sin\theta = \frac{y}{r} = \frac{\text{ordinate of } P}{\text{polar distance of } P},$$

$$\cos\theta = \frac{x}{r} = \frac{\text{abscissa of } P}{\text{polar distance of } P},$$

$$\tan\theta = \frac{y}{x} = \frac{\text{ordinate of } P}{\text{abscissa of } P},$$

$$\cot\theta = \frac{x}{y} = \frac{\text{abscissa of } P}{\text{ordinate of } P},$$

$$\sec\theta = \frac{r}{x} = \frac{\text{polar distance of } P}{\text{abscissa of } P},$$

$$\csc\theta = \frac{r}{y} = \frac{\text{polar distance of } P}{\text{ordinate of } P}.$$

Each trigonometric function may be expressed in the notation of Section 5–5. Thus, for the sine function we have $(\theta, \sin \theta)$, and we really have a distinct function when θ is in degrees and when θ is in radians. Much of what we shall do will apply to both functions. At other times we shall distinguish between them.

It is apparent, on careful study of this definition, that the values of the trigonometric functions of any angle can be found immediately, once the coordinates of a point on the terminal line of the angle in standard position are known.

EXAMPLE 1. Determine the values of the trigonometric functions of θ, if the point $(2, -5)$ lies on the terminal line of θ when θ is in standard position.

Solution. The polar distance of the given point can be found directly from the distance formula and is

$$r = \sqrt{2^2 + (-5)^2} = \sqrt{4 + 25} = \sqrt{29}.$$

The above definitions then give

$$\sin \theta = \frac{y}{r} = -\frac{5}{\sqrt{29}}, \qquad \cos \theta = \frac{x}{r} = \frac{2}{\sqrt{29}},$$

$$\tan \theta = \frac{y}{x} = -\frac{5}{2}, \qquad \cot \theta = \frac{x}{y} = -\frac{2}{5},$$

$$\sec \theta = \frac{r}{x} = \frac{\sqrt{29}}{2}, \qquad \csc \theta = \frac{r}{y} = -\frac{\sqrt{29}}{5}.$$

Note that these results do not depend on the kind of measure used for θ.

The trigonometric functions as defined above are functions of θ in the sense of Section 5–5; when a value, other than a multiple of 90° or of $\pi/2$, is assigned to θ, the values of the respective functions of θ are determined. The proof of this important fact requires merely the proof that the value of any of the above ratios depends only on the angle and is independent of the choice of the point P on the terminal side of θ, and this is a simple matter by use of similar triangles. For angles which are multiples of 90° or of $\pi/2$, and hence not included in the above definition, the definitions will appear in Section 6–8.

All properties of the trigonometric functions are based ultimately on these definitions. A number of these properties will be treated in what follows. Two simple, but important, properties are mentioned here. The first one involves coterminal angles, which were defined in Section 6–5. Since the values of the trigonometric functions of any angle depend only on x, y, r of a point on its terminal line, and the terminal line is the same for coterminal angles, we have at once the following result.

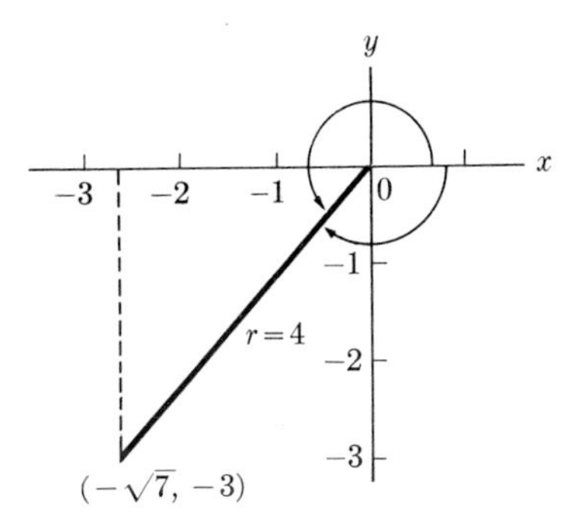

FIGURE 6–8

THEOREM 6–1. *The same-named trigonometric functions of coterminal angles are equal.*

Accordingly, statements such as the following can be made immediately:

$$\cos 395^\circ = \cos 35^\circ, \quad \tan 315^\circ = \tan(-45^\circ), \quad \csc(-753^\circ) = \csc 327^\circ,$$
$$\sin 4\pi/3 = \sin(-2\pi/3) = \sin(-8\pi/3).$$

The second property concerns the signs of the trigonometric functions in the various quadrants. For example, in the second quadrant x is negative and y and r are positive. Hence, the sine of any angle in Q_2 is the quotient of two positive numbers and must be positive, while the cosine is the quotient of numbers of opposite sign, and must be negative. In this manner the following chart for the signs of the trigonometric functions is obtained.

+	+
−	−

$\sin \theta$, $\csc \theta$

−	+
−	+

$\cos \theta$, $\sec \theta$

−	+
+	−

$\tan \theta$, $\cot \theta$

EXAMPLE 2. Find the remaining trigonometric functions of θ if $\sin \theta = -\frac{3}{4}$ with θ in Q_3.

Solution. Let $P(x, y)$ with polar distance r be a point on the terminal line of θ in standard position (Fig. 6–8). Then by the definition of $\sin \theta$, we must have

$$\frac{y}{r} = -\frac{3}{4}.$$

We may choose any positive value for r, and then choose y such that $y = -\frac{3}{4}r$. For example, $r = 1$, $y = -\frac{3}{4}$, or $r = 2$, $y = -\frac{3}{2}$ may be used. However, we seek convenient values, and choose for this purpose $r = 4$, so that $y = -3$. Then by the distance formula we obtain $x = -\sqrt{4^2 - (-3)^2} = -\sqrt{7}$

(since x must be negative in Q_3). The definitions of the other functions give immediately

$$\cos\theta = -\frac{\sqrt{7}}{4}, \qquad \tan\theta = \frac{-3}{-\sqrt{7}} = \frac{3}{\sqrt{7}}, \qquad \cot\theta = \frac{\sqrt{7}}{3},$$

$$\sec\theta = -\frac{4}{\sqrt{7}}, \qquad \csc\theta = -\frac{4}{3}.$$

In Fig. 6–8 two of the possible angles θ are shown. The values of the functions which have been obtained apply also to any angle coterminal with the angles shown.

If the restriction that θ lie in Q_3 be removed, θ may also be in Q_4, in which case $x = \sqrt{7}$, and the corresponding values of the remaining functions would be

$$\cos\theta = \frac{\sqrt{7}}{4}, \qquad \tan\theta = -\frac{3}{\sqrt{7}}, \qquad \cot\theta = -\frac{\sqrt{7}}{3},$$

$$\sec\theta = \frac{4}{\sqrt{7}}, \qquad \csc\theta = -\frac{4}{3}.$$

Exercise Group 6–3

In Exercises 1–12, find the values of the six trigonometric functions of the angle θ, which is in standard position, if:

1. $(-3, 4)$ is on the terminal line of θ.
2. $(40, -9)$ is on the terminal line of θ.
3. $(-2, -4)$ is on the terminal line of θ.
4. $(-5, -12)$ is on the terminal line of θ.
5. $(7, -24)$ is on the terminal line of θ.
6. $(-12, 9)$ is on the terminal line of θ.
7. for some point on the terminal line of θ, $r = 8$, $x = 2$.
8. for some point on the terminal line of θ, $r = 15$, $y = -5$.
9. for some point on the terminal line of θ, $x = 3$, $r = 2y$.
10. for every point on the terminal line of θ, $x = y$.
11. for every point on the terminal line of θ, $x = -y$.
12. for every point on the terminal line of θ, $3x = -4y$.

In Exercises 13–36, find the values of the remaining trigonometric functions of θ.

13. $\sin\theta = \frac{4}{5}$, $\cos\theta$ negative.
14. $\tan\theta = \frac{2}{3}$, $\cos\theta$ negative.
15. $\sec\theta = 3$, $\sin\theta$ positive.
16. $\cos\theta = \frac{5}{13}$, $\sin\theta$ positive.
17. $\cot\theta = -\frac{3}{4}$, $\sec\theta$ positive.
18. $\csc\theta = -2$, $\cot\theta$ positive.
19. $\csc\theta = -\frac{13}{12}$, $\tan\theta$ positive
20. $\sec\theta = -\frac{13}{12}$, $\csc\theta$ negative.
21. $\tan\theta = -\frac{7}{24}$
22. $\sin\theta = \frac{24}{25}$
23. $\sin\theta = \frac{3}{5}$
24. $\cot\theta = \frac{12}{5}$
25. $\sin\theta = \frac{\sqrt{3}}{2}$, θ in Q_2
26. $\cos\theta = -\frac{7}{25}$, θ in Q_3

27. $\cot\theta = -\frac{3}{4}$, θ in Q_4
28. $\sec\theta = \frac{13}{5}$, θ in Q_4
29. $\csc\theta = -\frac{25}{24}$, θ in Q_3
30. $\tan\theta = -\frac{\sqrt{3}}{3}$, θ in Q_2
31. $\cos\theta = \frac{1}{3}$
32. $\tan\theta = 7$
33. $\sec\theta = -6$
34. $\cos\theta = -\frac{2}{5}$
35. $\cot\theta = -5$
36. $\csc\theta = 11$

6–7 Trigonometric functions of special angles. The values of the trigonometric functions of any angle can be approximated as closely as desired; a table of values will be discussed later. However, for certain simple angles the *exact* values of the trigonometric functions can be found geometrically. Specifically, the angles 30°, 45°, and 60° are shown in Fig. 6–9 in standard position, with a convenient point chosen on the terminal line of each by use of results from plane geometry. Thus, in (a) and (c) the length of the side of the right triangle opposite the 30° angle must be one-half that of the hypotenuse; in (b) the two legs of the 45° right triangle must be equal. It is then clear that in Fig. 6–9 (a) we may choose $y = 1$, $r = 2$, and then compute the value of x as $\sqrt{3}$; in (c) we choose $x = 1$, $r = 2$, and compute $y = \sqrt{3}$; in (b) we choose $x = y = 1$ and compute $r = \sqrt{2}$. The definitions of Section 6–6 may now be applied directly, and the table of values appearing on the next page is obtained.

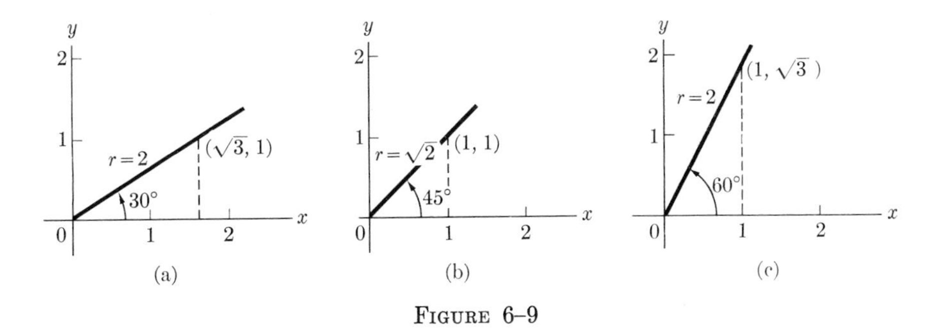

FIGURE 6–9

The same procedure can be used to find the trigonometric functions of any angle for which 30°, 45°, or 60° is the reference angle, upon taking into consideration the appropriate signs of x and y in the various quadrants. For, any such angle will lead to an auxiliary right triangle in which a 30°, 45°, or 60° angle appears.

EXAMPLE 1. Find the values of the six trigonometric functions of 210°.

Solution. With the angle drawn in standard position, as in Fig. 6–10, the point $(-\sqrt{3}, -1)$, with $r = 2$, is chosen on the terminal line. The functions of 210° are then

$$\sin 210° = \frac{y}{r} = -\frac{1}{2}, \qquad \cos 210° = \frac{x}{r} = -\frac{\sqrt{3}}{2},$$

$$\tan 210° = \frac{y}{x} = \frac{-1}{-\sqrt{3}} = \frac{\sqrt{3}}{3}, \qquad \cot 210° = \frac{-\sqrt{3}}{-1} = \sqrt{3},$$

$$\sec 210° = \frac{2}{-\sqrt{3}} = \frac{-2\sqrt{3}}{3}, \qquad \csc 210° = -2.$$

θ	$\sin\theta$	$\cos\theta$	$\tan\theta$	$\cot\theta$	$\sec\theta$	$\csc\theta$
30°	$\frac{1}{2}$	$\frac{\sqrt{3}}{2}$	$\frac{1}{\sqrt{3}} = \frac{\sqrt{3}}{3}$	$\sqrt{3}$	$\frac{2}{\sqrt{3}} = \frac{2\sqrt{3}}{3}$	2
45°	$\frac{1}{\sqrt{2}} = \frac{\sqrt{2}}{2}$	$\frac{1}{\sqrt{2}} = \frac{\sqrt{2}}{2}$	1	1	$\sqrt{2}$	$\sqrt{2}$
60°	$\frac{\sqrt{3}}{2}$	$\frac{1}{2}$	$\sqrt{3}$	$\frac{1}{\sqrt{3}} = \frac{\sqrt{3}}{3}$	2	$\frac{2}{\sqrt{3}} = \frac{2\sqrt{3}}{3}$

EXAMPLE 2. Show that $\sin^2(-\pi/6) + \cos^2(-\pi/6) = 1$.

Solution. In Fig. 6–11 the angle $-\pi/6$ is shown in standard position. We may choose the point P on the terminal line with $x = \sqrt{3}$, $y = -1$, $r = 2$. The notation $\sin^2\theta$ is understood to mean the square of $\sin\theta$, so that $\sin^2\theta = (\sin\theta)^2$. Since $\sin(-\pi/6) = -\frac{1}{2}$ and $\cos(-\pi/6) = \sqrt{3}/2$, we have

$$\sin^2\left(-\frac{\pi}{6}\right) + \cos^2\left(-\frac{\pi}{6}\right) = \left(-\frac{1}{2}\right)^2 + \left(\frac{\sqrt{3}}{2}\right)^2 = \frac{1}{4} + \frac{3}{4} = 1,$$

and the desired relation is proved.

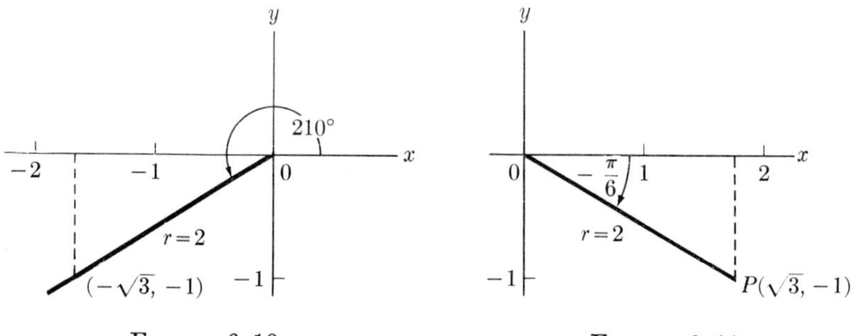

FIGURE 6–10 FIGURE 6–11

6–8 Trigonometric functions of quadrantal angles. The definitions in Section 6–6 were stated so as to avoid those angles which are multiples of 90°, since for such angles either $x = 0$ or $y = 0$, and certain of the functions are undefined. Angles which are multiples of 90° are called *quadrantal angles.* When these angles are in standard position, their terminal lines do not actually lie in any quadrant, but rather separate the quadrants. Accordingly, we say that the quadrantal angles lie in no quadrant.

For any quadrantal angle in standard position a point on the terminal line can always be chosen with $r = 1$. Then either x or y will be zero, and the other one will be ± 1. *We now define the trigonometric functions of the quadrantal angles in the same manner as for other angles, but with the necessary restriction that when a denominator is zero, the corresponding function is undefined for that angle.*

EXAMPLE. Find the values of those trigonometric functions of 180° which are defined.

Solution. The terminal line of 180° in standard position is the negative x-axis. We choose the point on this line for which $r = 1$, $x = -1$, $y = 0$. The definitions which involve y in the denominator do not apply, and we have

$$\sin 180^\circ = \frac{0}{1} = 0, \qquad \cos 180^\circ = \frac{-1}{1} = -1,$$

$$\tan 180^\circ = \frac{0}{-1} = 0, \qquad \cot 180^\circ \text{ is undefined},$$

$$\sec 180^\circ = \frac{1}{-1} = -1, \qquad \csc 180^\circ \text{ is undefined}.$$

In this manner we may obtain the following table, in which a dash indicates that the corresponding value is undefined:

θ		$\sin\theta$	$\cos\theta$	$\tan\theta$	$\cot\theta$	$\sec\theta$	$\csc\theta$
0°	0	0	1	0	—	1	—
90°	$\frac{\pi}{2}$	1	0	—	0	—	1
180°	π	0	−1	0	—	−1	—
270°	$\frac{3\pi}{2}$	−1	0	—	0	—	−1

The values of the trigonometric functions of the special angles, together with the quadrantal angles, are not only important in themselves, but also serve as landmarks in studying the variation of the functions. In fact, these values can be used by themselves to give rough graphs of the functions.

EXERCISE GROUP 6–4

Draw the angles in Exercises 1–20 in standard position, and determine the values of their trigonometric functions.

1. 30°	2. 45°	3. $2\pi/3$	4. $\pi/3$
5. 135°	6. -210°	7. 0	8. $\pi/2$
9. 270°	10. -180°	11. 2π	12. $-5\pi/2$
13. 300°	14. 315°	15. $11\pi/6$	16. 3π
17. 480°	18. -720°	19. $4\pi/3$	20. $5\pi/4$

Use the values of the trigonometric functions of the indicated angles to verify the statements in Exercises 21–36.

21. $\sin^2 120^\circ + \cos^2 120^\circ = 1$
22. $\cos 240^\circ = \cos^2 120^\circ - \sin^2 120^\circ$
23. $\sin 300^\circ = 2 \sin 150^\circ \cos 150^\circ$
24. $\cos 60^\circ = \sqrt{\frac{1}{2}(1 + \cos 120^\circ)}$
25. $\sin \pi/4 \cos \pi/2 + \cos \pi/4 \sin \pi/2 = \sin 3\pi/4$
26. $\sin \pi/6 \cos \pi/3 - \cos \pi/6 \sin \pi/3 = -\frac{1}{2}$
27. $2 \sin 3\pi/4 \cos 3\pi/4 = -1$
28. $\tan^2 225^\circ + 1 = \sec^2 225^\circ$
29. $\cos (180^\circ + 45^\circ) = -\cos 45^\circ$
30. $\sin 135^\circ = \sqrt{\dfrac{1 - \cos 270^\circ}{2}}$
31. $\tan 330^\circ \cot 330^\circ = 1$
32. $\cot^2 3\pi/2 + 1 = \csc^2 3\pi/2$
33. $\tan 2\pi/3 = \dfrac{\sin 4\pi/3}{1 + \cos 4\pi/3}$
34. $\sin (\pi - \pi/3) = \sin \pi/3$
35. $\tan (360^\circ - 30^\circ) = -\tan 30^\circ$
36. $\cos (90^\circ - 30^\circ) = \sin 30^\circ$

6–9 The use of a table of trigonometric functions. Except for certain functions of the quadrantal angles, the trigonometric functions, as we have seen, exist for all angles. In a preceding section it was also seen that, for certain special angles, these values can be found exactly, perhaps in terms of radicals. However, the method of finding the values of these functions for an arbitrary angle must be left for more advanced mathematics courses. Suffice it to say that these values have been computed and tabulated. In Table 2 of the Appendix appears a 4-place table of values of the trigonometric functions, for angles between 0° and 90°.

It should be understood that in this table the values of the functions, which are, in general, infinite decimals, are given correct to four figures, that is, are *rounded off* to four figures. This means that if the part of the number after the last figure amounts to less than $\frac{1}{2}$ unit in the fourth figure, that part is dropped; if it is more than $\frac{1}{2}$ unit in that place, one is added to the digit in that place; if it is exactly $\frac{1}{2}$ unit in that place, then one is added or not, whichever makes the resulting last digit even.

The arrangement of the table must be clearly understood. It is based on an important property of the trigonometric functions now to be presented. Let θ and θ' be *complementary angles*, that is, angles between 0° and 90° for which $\theta + \theta' = 90°$. In Fig. 6–12 two such angles are shown in standard position, with the points P and P' chosen so that $OP = OP'$. It is easy to show, by use of congruent triangles, that $x' = y$ and $y' = x$; hence, by definition, we have

$$\sin \theta = \frac{y}{r} = \frac{x'}{r} = \cos \theta',$$

and in a similar fashion it follows that

$$\cos \theta = \sin \theta', \qquad \tan \theta = \cot \theta',$$
$$\cot \theta = \tan \theta', \qquad \sec \theta = \csc \theta',$$
$$\csc \theta = \sec \theta'.$$

The six trigonometric functions fall into three *pairs of cofunctions*, the sine and cosine, the tangent and cotangent, and the secant and cosecant. The result that has been proved may be stated as follows.

THEOREM 6–2. *Any trigonometric function of a positive acute angle is equal to the cofunction of the complementary angle.*

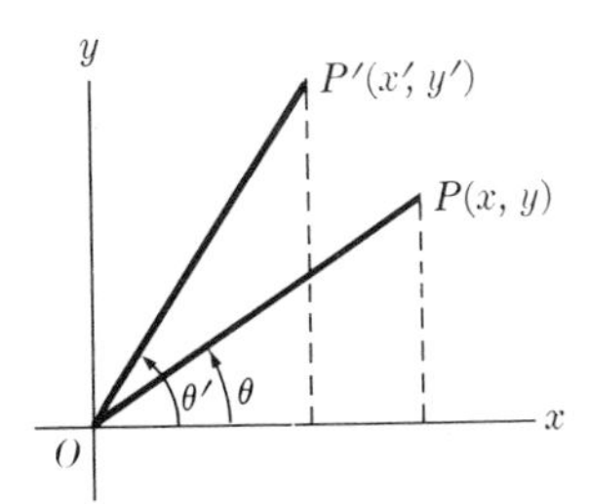

FIGURE 6–12

We may now examine the arrangement of the table. In the left-hand column the angles increase, as one reads downward, in steps of 10′, from 0° to 45°. The values of the functions appear in the columns to the right, with the names of the functions for these angles appearing at the head of each column. It is not necessary, however, to continue the table from 45° to 90°. By the above theorem we may use the values already tabulated if the columns are renamed. Thus, the angles which are between 45° and 90° appear in the extreme right-hand column, increasing as one reads upward, and the corresponding names of the functions appear at the bottom of each column. For example, from the table we find $\tan 29° 20' = 0.5619$. The same value, of course, appears as $\cot 60° 40'$. Similarly,

$$\sin 68° 10' = 0.9283 = \cos 21° 50'.$$

EXAMPLE 1. Find the angle θ between 0° and 90° if $\tan 2\theta = 0.4950$.

Solution. It is clear that the value found directly from the table will be that of 2θ. From the table we find $\tan 26° 20' = 0.4950$, so that

$$2\theta = 26° 20', \qquad \text{and} \qquad \theta = 13° 10'.$$

The use of the table can be extended to angles of any magnitude. We know that the reference angle is always between 0° and 90°. Furthermore, whenever x, y, r are known for a point on the terminal line of an angle, the point on the terminal line of the reference angle, when in standard position, with the same r, will have coordinates which are positive and differ from x and y, respectively, at most in sign. Hence, corresponding functions of an angle and its reference angle differ at most in sign. Accordingly, it is sufficient to find the same-named function of the reference angle, and then to assign the proper sign as determined by the quadrant in which the given angle lies.

EXAMPLE 2. Use Table 2 to find $\cos 239° 10'$.

Solution. The reference angle for 239° 10′ is 59° 10′, and from the table we find $\cos 59° 10' = 0.5125$. Since 239° 10′ is in Q_3, the value of the cosine is negative. Hence,

$$\cos 239° 10' = -\cos 59° 10' = -0.5125.$$

EXAMPLE 3. Use Table 2 to find $\cot(-434°)$.

Solution. The reference angle is 74°, and we find $\cot 74° = 0.2867$. Since the cotangent function is negative in Q_4, we have

$$\cot(-434°) = -\cot 74° = -0.2867.$$

EXERCISE GROUP 6–5

In Exercises 1–36, use Table 2 to find the value of the indicated trigonometric function.

1. $\tan 18° 50'$
2. $\cos 74° 20'$
3. $\sin 44° 50'$
4. $\cot 4° 40'$
5. $\sec 37° 20'$
6. $\csc 64° 10'$
7. $\cot 23°$
8. $\sin 48° 10'$
9. $\cos 87° 20'$

10. $\tan 47° 30'$
11. $\csc 36° 20'$
12. $\sec 83° 30'$
13. $\sin 83° 20'$
14. $\cos 14° 50'$
15. $\tan 72° 40'$
16. $\cot 58° 10'$
17. $\sec 123°$
18. $\csc 132°$
19. $\tan 117°$
20. $\cot 95°$
21. $\cos 216°$
22. $\sin (-231°)$
23. $\csc (-243°)$
24. $\sec 234°$
25. $\tan (-317°)$
26. $\cot (-293°)$
27. $\sin 329°$
28. $\cos 334°$
29. $\csc (-346°)$
30. $\sec (-216° 10')$
31. $\cot (-351°)$
32. $\tan (-126°)$
33. $\cos (-173° 10')$
34. $\sin 212° 20'$
35. $\csc 258°$
36. $\sec (-313° 10')$

In Exercises 37–72, use Table 2 to find the smallest positive angle θ in each case.

37. $\tan \theta = 2.989$
38. $\cot \theta = 0.5022$
39. $\sin \theta = 0.9730$
40. $\cos \theta = 0.1334$
41. $\sec \theta = 1.062$
42. $\csc \theta = 1.081$
43. $\cot \theta = 2.455$
44. $\sin \theta = 0.4120$
45. $\cos \theta = 0.4462$
46. $\tan \theta = 0.4279$
47. $\csc \theta = 5.016$
48. $\sec \theta = 6.277$
49. $\sin \theta = 0.1822$
50. $\cos \theta = 0.6884$
51. $\tan \theta = 0.1644$
52. $\cot \theta = 0.9545$
53. $\sec \theta = 171.9$
54. $\csc \theta = 1.402$
55. $\cos \theta = 0.9858$
56. $\tan \theta = 1.024$
57. $\cot \theta = 17.17$
58. $\sec \theta = 1.379$
59. $\csc \theta = 57.30$
60. $\sin \theta = 0.6988$
61. $\sin \theta = -0.9945$
62. $\cos \theta = -0.0640$
63. $\tan \theta = -10.39$
64. $\cot \theta = -0.2186$
65. $\sec \theta = -4.560$
66. $\csc \theta = -1.038$
67. $\cos \theta = -0.7470$
68. $\tan \theta = -0.8491$
69. $\cot \theta = -1.664$
70. $\sec \theta = -1.167$
71. $\csc \theta = -1.540$
72. $\sin \theta = -0.6041$

Express each of the following as a function of the angle complementary to the given angle.

73. $\sin 18° 32'$
74. $\cos 43° 17'$
75. $\tan 73° 29'$
76. $\cot 84° 36'$
77. $\sec 67° 58'$
78. $\csc 53° 42'$
79. $\cos 38° 47'$
80. $\tan 5° 53'$
81. $\cot 13° 48'$
82. $\sec 49° 28'$
83. $\csc 68° 22'$
84. $\sin 56° 26'$

Review Exercises

Express each of the angles in Exercises 1–4 in radians.

1. $225°$
2. $96°$
3. $336°$
4. $213° 17'$

Express each of the angles in Exercises 5–8 in degrees, minutes, and seconds.

5. $\frac{11\pi}{12}$
6. $-\frac{19\pi}{15}$
7. 2.06 rad
8. -1.36 rad

In Exercises 9–14, determine the values of the other five trigonometric functions in each case. In Exercises 12–14, a, b, and c are positive.

9. $\cos\theta = -\frac{2}{3}$ 10. $\tan\theta = 5$ 11. $\csc\theta = 3$

12. $\sin\theta = a$ 13. $\cot\theta = b$ 14. $\sec\theta = c$

In Exercises 15–26, write the values of the six trigonometric functions for the angles indicated.

15. $315°$ 16. $\frac{3\pi}{2}$ 17. $\frac{3\pi}{4}$ 18. $120°$

19. $210°$ 20. π 21. -5π 22. $-135°$

23. $510°$ 24. $\frac{11\pi}{4}$ 25. $420°$ 26. $-2025°$

CHAPTER 7

LINEAR EQUATIONS AND SYSTEMS OF LINEAR EQUATIONS

7–1 Introduction. The equals sign (=) has been used frequently in the preceding pages to indicate that two numbers were equal. We now wish to use the equals sign to express the equality of two quantities one or both of which may contain a letter such as x, whose value is initially unknown. A statement of equality, in which such an unknown appears, between two quantities is called an *equation* if the equality holds for at least one value of the letter involved. Any value of the letter for which the equality holds is called a *solution of the equation*, and the procedure by which solutions are found is called *solving the equation.*

EXAMPLE. The equation $3x - 5 = 2x + 4$ imposes the condition that the value of x must be 9, so that $x = 9$ is a solution of the equation.

Equations of the type illustrated in the above example, which hold for only a limited number of values of the letters which appear, are called *conditional equations,* as contrasted with equations which are true for all permissible values of the unknowns involved. Equations of the latter type are called *identities* and at times the symbol (≡) is used instead of the equals sign to emphasize that the equation is an identity. An example of an identity would be $3x + y \equiv 3(x + y) - 2y$; this equality holds for all values of x and y.

Since a conditional equation holds true for only a limited number of values of the unknown, it may be possible to find those values of the unknown for which the equation is true.

7–2 On solving equations. Methods of solving or working with equations are based on the *assumption that a solution exists,* that is, that there are one or more values of the unknown for which the given equation is satisfied. On this basis the permissible steps are:

1. *Equal quantities may be added to or subtracted from both sides of an equation.*
2. *Both sides of an equation may be multiplied by equal, nonzero quantities, or divided by equal, nonzero quantities.*

The implication is that any value which satisfies the original equation will also satisfy any equation obtained by applying the above steps. But care is required in applying Step 2; if the multipliers or divisors contain the unknown, it is possible that the new equation may contain more or fewer solutions than the original equation. The safeguards that should be applied in this case are:

Whenever both members of an equation are multiplied or divided by equal quantities involving the unknown, check in the original equation all tentative solutions obtained, in order to determine whether they actually are solutions. If both members are divided by a quantity containing the unknown, and this quantity vanishes for a value of the unknown, consider the possibility that this value may also be a solution of the original equation.

The *ultimate criterion or test* as to whether a quantity is a solution of an equation is: *Does that quantity satisfy the equation?*

EXAMPLES. The equation $2x = 4$ has the solution $x = 2$, but the equation $2x(x - 1) = 4(x - 1)$ obtained by multiplying both members of the original equation by $x - 1$ has an additional solution $x = 1$. If $x = 1$ is tested in the original equation, it fails the test.

The equation $x - 1 = 4$ has the solution $x = 5$, but squaring both members, which is an application of Step 2 above, gives $(x - 1)^2 = 16$, which has the additional solution $x = -3$. This value fails the test.

The equation $x^2 - x = 0$ has the two solutions $x = 0, x = 1$. But if both members are divided by x, the new equation $x - 1 = 0$ is satisfied only by $x = 1$. A root has been "lost" by the division.

If both members of the equation $x/(x - 1) - 1/(x^2 - x) = 1$ are multiplied by $x^2 - x$, the LCD, we obtain $x^2 - 1 = x^2 - x$, whose solution is $x = 1$. However, $x = 1$ is not a solution of the original equation, the fractions being undefined when $x = 1$ (the denominators vanish).

7–3 The linear function. Linear equations in one unknown. Among the functions we shall study, the simplest, apart from the function $f(x) = c$, where c is a constant, is the function $f(x) = mx + b$, where m and b are constants. It is called a *linear* function, and the graph of the function $y = mx + b$ is always a *straight line.* This line intersects the y-axis at the point $(0, b)$; b is called the *y-intercept* of the line. In the notation introduced in Chapter 5, we have $b = f(0)$. The constant m is called the *slope of the line.* It is a measure of *the rate at which the function changes as x changes.* Thus when the value of x increases by one unit, the value of the linear function changes by m units; if m is positive the function increases as x increases, while if m is negative the function decreases as x increases. If $m = 0$ the straight line is parallel to the x-axis.

The only straight line which cannot be represented by a function of the type $mx + b$ is one which is parallel to the y-axis. The equation of such a line is $x = c$ (constant). For example, the equation $x = -2$ represents a straight line parallel to the y-axis and two units to the left of it.

EXAMPLE 1. The income of a business is \$1000 a week and the expenses are \$900 a week. If the business was worth \$8000 at the start, obtain the function showing the value of the business at the end of t weeks, assuming that the profits are retained in the business.

Solution. Since income exceeds expenses by \$100 a week, *the rate of increase of the function* is $m = 100$; the value of the function at $t = 0$ is 8000, that is, $b = f(0) = 8000$, since the original value was 8000. If t represents the number of weeks, the desired function is $f(t) = 100t + 8000$.

The time at which the business is worth a specified amount is of particular interest. For example, the time at which the business is worth \$10,000 is seen to be $t = 20$ weeks, for, with $t = 20$, we have

$$100 \cdot 20 + 8000 = 10{,}000.$$

This value of t may also be thought of as the value of t for which the function

$$(100t + 8000) - 10{,}000, \qquad \text{or} \qquad 100t - 2000$$

vanishes.

More generally, if we set the function $mx + b$ equal to c, we get

$$mx + b = c, \quad \text{or} \quad mx + b - c = 0.$$

The value of x which satisfies the equation in either of the two forms is then $x = (c - b)/m$. From the second form of the equation it is seen that for this value of x the value of the function $mx + b - c$ is zero.

DEFINITION 7-1. *A number a is a zero of a function $f(x)$ if $f(a) = 0$.*

In the above example, $(c - b)/m$ is a zero of the function

$$mx + b - c.$$

It is clear that there is a close connection between *zeros* of functions and *solutions* or *roots* of equations. In fact, a zero of $f(x)$ is a solution of the equation $f(x) = 0$. The finding of the zeros of a function involves the solving of an equation.

EXAMPLE 2. Find the zeros of the function

$$\frac{2x + 7}{5} + \frac{3x - 5}{4} + \frac{33}{10}.$$

Solution. The zeros of the function are the roots of the equation

$$\frac{2x + 7}{5} + \frac{3x - 5}{4} + \frac{33}{10} = 0.$$

Multiplying each member of the equation by 20, which is the least common multiple of the denominators, we have

$$4(2x + 7) + 5(3x - 5) + 2 \cdot 33 = 0,$$

or

$$8x + 28 + 15x - 25 + 66 = 0, \quad \text{and} \quad 23x = -69.$$

Hence $x = -3$ is the zero of the given function.

EXAMPLE 3. Solve the equation $a^2x + 4c^2x - 10c = 5a - 4acx$ for x.

Solution.

$$\begin{aligned} a^2x + 4acx + 4c^2x &= 5a + 10c, \\ (a^2 + 4ac + 4c^2)x &= 5(a + 2c), \\ (a + 2c)^2x &= 5(a + 2c), \\ x = \frac{5(a + 2c)}{(a + 2c)^2} &= \frac{5}{a + 2c}. \end{aligned}$$

The solution just obtained is also the zero of the function

$$a^2x + 4c^2x - 10c - (5a - 4acx).$$

EXERCISE GROUP 7–1

In Exercises 1–4, graph the function, and for each give the value of $f(0)$ and the rate of change m.

1. $2x + 5$ 2. $3x - 2$ 3. $-3x + 7$ 4. $cx + d$

5. Given $f(x) = 3x + 5$, distinguish between $f(0)$ and the value of x for which $f(x) = 0$.

In Exercises 6–23, solve for x, y, or z, whichever appears.

6. $3x - 5 = x + 2$

7. $2x - 5 = 3 - x$

8. $2y - \frac{3}{2} = 5y + \frac{1}{3}$

9. $3(z - \frac{1}{5}) = 2(\frac{1}{3} - 2z)$

10. $\dfrac{2}{3} - x = -3 - \dfrac{x}{5}$

11. $\frac{2}{7} - \frac{1}{5}x = \frac{2}{5} - \frac{3}{7}x$

12. $0.26z - 0.42 = 0.13 + 0.15z$

13. $0.17 - 0.23x = 0.15 + 1.9x$

14. $\dfrac{3x - 5}{4} + \dfrac{4x - 7}{20} = \dfrac{12}{5} + \dfrac{x - 3}{4}$

15. $\dfrac{x - 7}{3} + \dfrac{2x - 5}{15} = 4 - \dfrac{2x}{5}$

16. $3x - \dfrac{3 - 2x}{7} = 2 + \dfrac{7 - x}{5}$

17. $4 + \dfrac{x - 5}{6} = \dfrac{2}{3} - \dfrac{3 - 2x}{2}$

18. $7y - a = 2by + 5$ 19. $ay - by = c$

20. $a^2x + 6acx - 21c = 7a - 9c^2x$

21. $ay + b^2 = a^2 + by$

22. $acx - bdx + d^2 = c^2 + adx - bcx$

23. $4(x - 1)^2 = (2x - 1)(2x + 1)$

7-4 Fractional equations. We shall understand by a *fractional equation* an equation containing fractions in which the unknown appears in one or more denominators. The usual method of solution is to remove the fractions by multiplying both members of the equation by the LCD of the fractions which appear. If the resulting equation is linear we are in a position to solve it. In view of the discussion of Section 7-2 there then remains the matter of checking in the original equation all values obtained in this manner.

EXAMPLE 1. Solve the equation

$$\frac{2x}{3+x} + \frac{3+x}{3} = 2 + \frac{x^2}{3(x-3)}.$$

Solution. The LCD of the fractions is $3(x - 3)(3 + x)$. Multiplying both members of the equation by the LCD we have

$$2x \cdot 3(x - 3) + (3 + x)^2(x - 3) = 2 \cdot 3(x - 3)(3 + x) + x^2(3 + x),$$

which expanded becomes

$$6x^2 - 18x + x^3 + 3x^2 - 9x - 27 = 6x^2 - 54 + x^3 + 3x^2.$$

This equation reduces to $-27x - 27 = -54$, which has the solution $x = 1$. Substituting $x = 1$ in the original equation, we have

$$\frac{2}{4} + \frac{4}{3} = 2 + \frac{1}{(-6)}, \quad \text{or,} \quad \tfrac{11}{6} = \tfrac{11}{6}.$$

Hence $x = 1$ is the only solution.

When an equation contains only one trigonometric function of a variable, the same procedure may be used to solve for that function as with an equation containing just the variable. If the resulting equation is linear in that function, the value of that function which satisfies the equation may be easily obtained.

EXAMPLE 2. Solve the following equation for $\tan x$:

$$\frac{\tan x}{1 + \tan x} + 2 = \frac{3 \tan x}{2 + \tan x}.$$

Solution. Multiplying both members of the equation by the LCD, which is $(1 + \tan x)(2 + \tan x)$, we have

$$\tan x(2 + \tan x) + 2(1 + \tan x)(2 + \tan x) = 3 \tan x(1 + \tan x).$$

Upon expanding and collecting terms, we obtain

$$3 \tan^2 x + 8 \tan x + 4 = 3 \tan^2 x + 3 \tan x.$$

Subtraction of $3 \tan^2 x + 3 \tan x + 4$ from both members gives $5 \tan x = -4$, from which we obtain

$$\tan x = -\tfrac{4}{5}.$$

Since neither denominator vanishes for this value, it is the solution.

Exercise Group 7–2

Solve each of the following equations for x or y, whichever appears.

1. $\dfrac{x+4}{3x} = \dfrac{3x-8}{4x}$

2. $\dfrac{3(x-1)}{x+7} = -\dfrac{3}{5}$

3. $\dfrac{1}{x} + \dfrac{3}{x+1} = \dfrac{2}{3(x^2+x)}$

4. $\dfrac{x-\frac{1}{2}}{x+\frac{1}{4}} = \dfrac{x+\frac{1}{2}}{x-\frac{1}{4}}$

5. $\dfrac{0.6-0.4x}{0.06x-0.07} + \dfrac{3-2x}{0.4-0.3x} = 0$

6. $\dfrac{1+2x}{x-4} = \dfrac{4x^2+5x}{2x^2-7x-4}$

7. $\dfrac{x-1}{x+2} + \dfrac{2x^2-7}{2x^2+7x+6} = \dfrac{4x-3}{2x+3}$

8. $\dfrac{1}{x+2} - \dfrac{1}{x-1} = \dfrac{2}{x^2-1}$

9. $\dfrac{2}{x-1} - \dfrac{1}{x} = \dfrac{1}{x^2-x}$

10. $\dfrac{12(1-x^2)}{3+2x-x^2} + \dfrac{7x}{3-x} = \dfrac{5x}{x+1}$

11. $\dfrac{3-x}{1-x} - \dfrac{5-x}{7-x} = 1 - \dfrac{x^2-2}{7-8x+x^2}$

12. $\dfrac{cz}{a^2-b^2} - z - \dfrac{c}{a+b} = b - a$

13. $\dfrac{4x}{2x-1} = 2 + \dfrac{5}{x}$

14. $\dfrac{y+6}{y-2} - \dfrac{11}{y^2-12y+20} = \dfrac{y+3}{y-10}$

15. $5 + \dfrac{2}{3 - \dfrac{1}{4 - x}} = \dfrac{45}{8}$

16. $\dfrac{b + x}{b} + \dfrac{2x}{b + x} + \dfrac{x^2}{b(b - x)} = 2$

17. $\dfrac{1 - \dfrac{1 + \dfrac{1 - x}{2}}{3}}{4} = 1$

18. $\dfrac{\dfrac{x}{x - 1} - 1}{\dfrac{x}{x - 1} + 1} = \dfrac{\dfrac{x}{x + 1} - 1}{\dfrac{x}{x + 1} + 1}$

In Exercises 19–28, solve for the trigonometric function which appears.

19. $\dfrac{7 - 3 \sin x}{2 - \sin x} = 4$

20. $\dfrac{\cos x}{\cos x + 1} + 2 = \dfrac{3 \cos x}{\cos x + 2}$

21. $\tan x - 1 = \dfrac{2 \tan x}{5} - \dfrac{7}{5}$

22. $\dfrac{\cot x}{\cot x - 1} - \dfrac{3}{\cot x + 1} = 1$

23. $\dfrac{1}{\sec x} - \dfrac{\sec x + 5}{2 \sec x + 8} + \dfrac{1}{2} = 0$

24. $\dfrac{\csc x}{1 + \csc x} + 6 = \dfrac{7 \csc x}{2 + \csc x}$

25. $\dfrac{2 \sin x + 1}{2 \sin x - 1} - \dfrac{2 \sin x - 1}{1 + 2 \sin x} + \dfrac{8}{1 - 4 \sin^2 x} = 0$

26. $\dfrac{\tan x - 1}{\tan x + 1} - \dfrac{1}{3} = \dfrac{2 \tan x + 3}{\tan x + 1} - \dfrac{5}{4}$

27. $\dfrac{5 \cot x}{\cot x - 3} - \dfrac{\cot x}{1 + \cot x} = 4$

28. $\dfrac{1 + \sec x}{2 \sec x - 3} = \dfrac{7 + \sec x}{5 + 2 \sec x}$

7–5 Applications of linear equations in one unknown. There are many problems in business, engineering, mathematics, science, etc., which require the solution of an equation. First of all the statement of the problem permits the writing of an equation in terms of some initially unknown quantity whose value must be found. The solution of the equation then provides the solution of the problem. We shall consider here problems which give rise to linear equations. The procedures will be illustrated by examples; some of the more common ones may be classified into the following types.

PERCENTAGE AND SIMPLE INTEREST. The change in a quantity is often conveniently expressed as a *percentage*. For example, a 10 percent, written as 10%, increase means an increase of $\frac{10}{100}$ or $\frac{1}{10}$ of the quantity. Thus an increase of 3% in a population of 600,000 means an increase of

$$0.03(600{,}000) = 18{,}000.$$

If P is the increased population, we may also write

$$P = 600{,}000 + 0.03(600{,}000)$$
$$= 600{,}000(1 + 0.03) = 600{,}000(1.03) = 618{,}000.$$

Similarly, *simple interest* is expressed as a percentage of the original amount, or *principal*. We may say, for example, that a sum of money is invested at 3% simple interest per year. Then the rate r is $r = 3\%$ or $r = 0.03$. If P dollars are invested for t years at simple interest at a rate r, the amount A, which is the principal plus interest, is given by

$$\boxed{A = P + Prt = P(1 + rt),} \tag{1a}$$

and the interest itself, i, is given by

$$\boxed{i = Prt.} \tag{1b}$$

EXAMPLE 1. If \$10,000 amounts to \$11,250 at the end of 5 yr, find the rate of interest.

Solution. By formula (1a), we have

$$11{,}250 = 10{,}000(1 + 5r).$$

Hence

$$1 + 5r = \frac{11{,}250}{10{,}000}, \quad \text{or} \quad 5r = 1.125 - 1 = 0.125$$

and

$$r = 0.025 = 2.5\%.$$

EXERCISE GROUP 7–3

1. (a) If a number x is increased by 25%, what is the new number?
   (b) What is the new number if x is decreased by 75%?
2. If a number x is increased by 25%, and the new number is increased by 30%, what is the final number?
3. If \$1620 is the interest on \$12,000 for a 3 yr period, what is the rate of simple interest?
4. Find the amount of money that must be invested now at 5% simple interest to have an amount of \$4000 in 18 mo.
5. Determine the rate at which \$1 must be invested at simple interest to amount to \$2 in 10 yr.
6. If \$120 is invested at a 6% annual rate for 6 mo, and the new amount is reinvested at the same rate for an additional 6 mo, find the amount of the investment at the end of the year.

7. If \$120 is invested at a 6% annual rate for 4 mo, and the new amount is reinvested at the same rate for 4 additional months, and the process repeated once more, find the amount at the end of the year.

8. Assuming that a house depreciates 2% of its original value each year, and that the original cost was \$21,000, find the value of the house at the end of 17 yr.

9. Find the amount of money that must be invested at 4% simple interest for a period of 7 yr to have \$5000 at the end of the seven years.

GEOMETRIC PROBLEMS. In the application to geometric problems any of the formulas and theorems of geometry may be used.

EXAMPLE 2. Find the radius of a circle if an increase of 2 in. in the radius increases the area by 28π in^2.

Solution. Let the length of the radius be r. Then the area of the circle is πr^2, and an increase of 2 in. in the radius gives an area of $\pi(r+2)^2$. Hence,

$$\pi(r+2)^2 - \pi r^2 = 28\pi, \quad \text{or} \quad (r+2)^2 - r^2 = 28.$$

Expanding and collecting terms we have

$$4r + 4 = 28, \quad 4r = 24, \quad \text{and} \quad r = 6 \text{ in.}$$

EXERCISE GROUP 7-3 *Continued*

10. The perimeter of a rectangle is 12, and the base is x. What is the length of the altitude?

11. A circle has radius r. What is the radius of a circle which has twice the circumference of the first circle?

12. The perimeter of an isosceles triangle is 18 and the base is x. What is the length of another side?

13. Find the length of the side of a square if a decrease of one inch in each side decreases the area by 14 in^2.

14. One side of a rectangle is 7 more than the other side. Find the side of a square whose area equals that of the rectangle, if the side of the square is 3 more than the shorter side of the rectangle.

15. If the diameter of a sphere is increased by 10%, what will be the % increase in the volume? (The volume of a sphere is $\frac{1}{6}\pi d^3$.)

16. A circle and sphere both have the same radius. The area of the circle is what percent of the surface area of the sphere? (The surface area of a sphere is $4\pi r^2$.)

UNIFORM MOTION. When an object travels at a constant speed r it is known from physics that if the distance it travels in time t is given by s, then

$$\boxed{s = rt, \quad \text{or} \quad r = \frac{s}{t}, \quad \text{or} \quad t = \frac{s}{r}.} \qquad (2)$$

EXAMPLE 3. A pilot notices that when the wind velocity is 20 mph (miles per hour) he can fly 6 miles with the wind in the same time that is needed to fly 4 miles against the wind. What is his air speed (rate in still air)?

Solution. Let the air speed be r. Then the ground speed (rate with respect to the ground) is $r + 20$ when flying with the wind and $r - 20$ when flying against the wind. Since the time is the same in each case, the third form of formula (2) gives

$$\frac{6}{r+20} = \frac{4}{r-20}.$$

To remove the fractions we multiply both members of the equation by the LCD $= (r + 20)(r - 20)$, and we obtain

$$6(r - 20) = 4(r + 20), \quad 6r - 120 = 4r + 80, \quad 2r = 200, \quad r = 100 \text{ mph}.$$

If the speed during a trip is not uniform, the *average speed* is the total distance traveled divided by the total elapsed time.

EXERCISE GROUP 7–3 *Continued*

17. A train travels at a uniform speed of 50 mph. (a) Express the total distance traveled as a function of the time t in hours. (b) How many hours are required for the train to cover 1225 mi?

18. A train traveled 60 mi the first hour and 50 mi each hour thereafter. (a) Express the total distance traveled as a function of the time t in hours. (b) How many hours are required for the train to cover 1225 mi?

19. A car travels 50 mph for 3 hr and then 40 mph for 5 hr. Find the average speed for the entire trip.

20. A train traveling 30 mph starts $\frac{3}{4}$ hr before a second train that travels 35 mph. How many hours will be required for the second train to overtake the first?

21. An airplane with a 20 mph head wind takes the same length of time to fly 840 mi that it does to travel 960 mi with a 20 mph tail wind. What is the air speed of the plane?

22. In a one-mile race the times of the first and second place runners are 4 min and 4 min, 1.1 sec, respectively. How far behind the winner is the second place runner at the finish?

23. A car traveling 40 mph has been gone 3 hr when a second car is sent after it. If the second car travels 60 mph, when will it overtake the first car, and at what point?

24. A car travels 120 mi in 3 hr. Find the speed that must be maintained on the return trip if the average speed for the round trip is 45 mph.

MIXTURES. In mixture problems the amount of a given substance present is frequently given as a percentage of the total. Whether this is the case or not, it is usually necessary to determine the amount of the substance present in a final mixture; this determination is based on the following evident statement:

The amount of a substance present in the final mixture is equal to the sum of the amounts of that substance present in the different parts.

EXAMPLE 4. What part of a 40% solution of alcohol in water must be replaced by pure alcohol to obtain a 60% solution of alcohol?

Solution. Let us assume one unit of the mixture at the start, and let x be the amount of the original (40%) mixture to be removed. Of the original unit amount 0.4 is alcohol, while the amount of alcohol removed is $0.4x$. Hence the alcohol in the remaining solution is $0.4 - 0.4x$. The entire amount x added is alcohol, so that the final mixture contains $(0.4 - 0.4x) + x$ alcohol. But this alcohol must equal 60% of one unit or 0.6. Then

$$(0.4 - 0.4x) + x = 0.6, \qquad 0.6x = 0.2, \qquad x = \tfrac{1}{3}.$$

Thus the amount removed is $\frac{1}{3}$ of the original unit amount, or $33\frac{1}{3}\%$.

EXERCISE GROUP 7-3 *Continued*

25. If 50 cc of a 20% acid solution and 100 cc of a 30% acid solution are combined, what % acid solution results?

26. If 40 cc of a 40% acid solution, 70 cc of a 50% acid solution, and 50 cc of pure acid are combined, what % acid solution results?

27. How many cubic centimeters of a 70% solution of sulphuric acid must be added to 100 cc of a 40% solution to obtain a 50% solution?

28. How many cubic centimeters of pure sulphuric acid must be added to 100 cc of a 40% solution to obtain a 60% solution?

29. How many cubic centimeters of a 40% solution of sulphuric acid must be added to 100 cc of a 20% solution to obtain a 30% solution of the acid?

30. How much of a 20 qt mixture of 30% alcohol and 70% water must be drained off and replaced by pure alcohol to obtain a mixture of 50% alcohol and 50% water?

31. In an alloy of copper and tin weighing 24 lb, 35% is copper. How many pounds of copper must be added so that the new alloy is 40% copper?

SUMMARY. In order to apply equations to the solution of problems stated in words, we "translate" the verbal statements into statements in mathematical symbols. This is accomplished by

1. Introducing a letter to represent a suitable unknown quantity.
2. Using the information given in the statement to obtain an equation involving that letter.
3. Solving the equation for the unknown.

EXERCISE GROUP 7–3 *Continued*

32. The numerator of a fraction is $\frac{1}{3}$ of the denominator. If the numerator is increased by 4 and the denominator by 2, the value of the resulting fraction is $\frac{1}{2}$. Find the fraction.

33. The denominator of a fraction is 2 more than the numerator. If the numerator is increased by 1 and the denominator by 2, the value of the fraction is unchanged. Find the fraction.

34. Find a number such that 8 less than 4 times the number equals 3 more than twice the number.

35. The difference of two positive numbers is 3; if 5 is added to each, the quotient of the smaller by the larger is 0.8. Find the numbers.

36. The earth and Venus revolve around the sun in approximately 365 and 225 days, respectively. Find, to the nearest day, the time it takes Venus to gain one revolution on the earth.

37. A man left $\frac{1}{3}$ of his property to his wife, $\frac{1}{4}$ to his daughter, and the remainder, which was $14,000, to his son. How much money did the man leave?

38. The monthly rates of a gas company are a fixed charge of $5.27 for the first 30 ft^3 of gas used and 9.5 cents per ft^3 for all gas used in excess of 30 ft^3. Express the cost C (in dollars) as a function of x, where x represents the number of cubic feet of gas used. (Assume that x is greater than 30.)

7–6 Systems of two linear equations in two unknowns. In Section 7–3 we were interested in finding the zero of a linear function or, equivalently, in finding the abscissa of the point where the graph of the linear function crosses the x-axis. If, instead of the x-axis, the graph of a second linear function is involved in this manner, the problem becomes that of finding the point of intersection of two straight lines when they are drawn on the same coordinate system. Algebraically, this means that we are to find pairs of numbers which at the same time satisfy two linear equations in two unknowns. A *solution* of a system of two equations is a pair of numbers that satisfies both equations; such a pair of numbers constitutes *one* solution.

Consider the equation $ax + by = c$ which, if $b \neq 0$, can be written in the form

$$y = -\frac{ax}{b} + \frac{c}{b}.$$

As was seen in Section 7–3 the graph of this equation is a straight line, with slope $m = -(a/b)$. If $b = 0$ and $a \neq 0$, then $ax + by = c$ reduces to

$$x = \frac{c}{a},$$

which also represents a straight line. If $a = b = 0$, then $ax + by = c$ reduces to $c = 0$, which is trivial. Hence the graph of $ax + by = c$ is always a straight line, and two such graphs will either (1) intersect in a

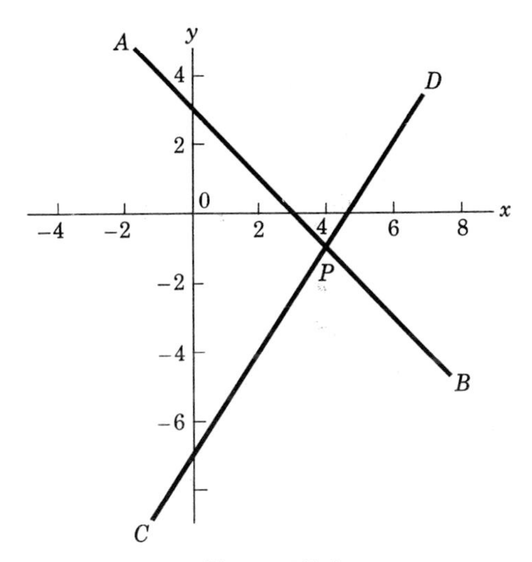

FIGURE 7–1

single point, or (2) be parallel, or (3) be coincident. In case (1) the coordinates (x, y) of the point of intersection satisfy the equations of the two graphs and constitute the solution of the problem. In case (2) no solution exists and the two equations are said to be *inconsistent.* In case (3) the pair of equations has infinitely many solutions, since the coordinates of every point on the graph are a solution, and the equations are said to be *dependent.*

EXAMPLE 1. Find the point of intersection of the graphs of the equations:

$$\begin{cases} x + y = 3, \\ 3x - 2y = 14. \end{cases}$$

Geometric solution. In Fig. 7–1, AB is the graph of the first equation, and CD is the graph of the second equation. The point of intersection P of the two graphs is the only point on both lines. The coordinates of P satisfy both equations and represent the desired solution of the problem. From the graph, P seems to be the point $(4, -1)$. These coordinates satisfy both equations, and hence are the exact coordinates of the point of intersection of the two lines.

Algebraic solution. Multiply both members of the first equation by 2, to make the term in y similar to that in the second equation, and add the resulting members to the corresponding members of the second equation. This eliminates y and gives

$$5x = 20, \qquad \text{or} \qquad x = 4.$$

Substitute this value in the first equation, and obtain

$$4 + y = 3, \quad \text{or} \quad y = -1.$$

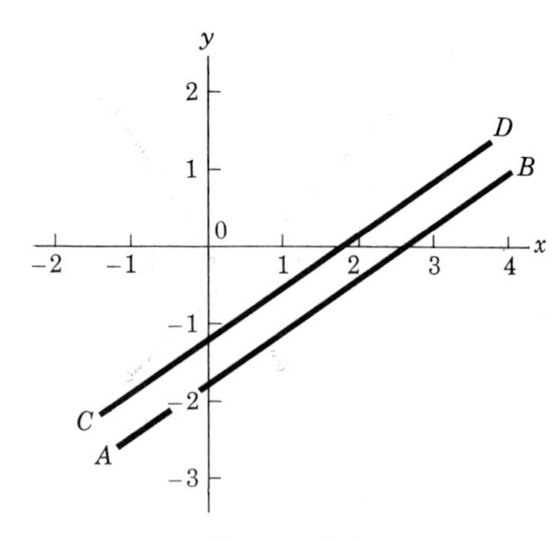

FIGURE 7–2

Thus the desired solution is

$$x = 4, \quad y = -1.$$

EXAMPLE 2. Determine whether there is a point of intersection of the graphs of $2x - 3y = 5$ and $6x - 9y = 10$.

Geometric discussion. In Fig. 7–2, the graph of the first equation is the line AB through the point $(1, -1)$ with slope $\frac{2}{3}$, and the graph of the second equation is the line CD through the point $(\frac{2}{3}, -\frac{2}{3})$, with slope $\frac{2}{3}$. Since the slope is the same in both cases, the lines are parallel. Hence there is no point of intersection and the equations are *inconsistent.*

Algebraic discussion. If the members of the first equation are multiplied by 3, and if the members of the resulting equation are subtracted from the corresponding members of the second equation, we obtain the clearly absurd relation

$$0 = -5.$$

The steps that were taken were based on the assumption that the given equations had a solution. The fact that an impossible conclusion results proves that the assumption was false. In other words, the two equations have no common solution, and are therefore inconsistent.

EXAMPLE 3. Find the point of intersection of the graphs of $3x - y = 5$ and $9x - 3y = 15$.

Solution. It is obvious that any pair of values (x, y) which satisfies the first equation also satisfies the second equation. Hence the same straight line is the graph of both equations. It follows that there is no unique solution, but rather that every point on the common line is a solution. The two equations are *dependent;* in fact, if both members of the first equation are multiplied by 3, the second equation is obtained.

To solve the pair of dependent equations algebraically it is sufficient to assign an arbitrary value to x (or y), and then to solve for y (or x) in either equation.

In the preceding examples the geometrical properties were described to illustrate the meaning of the algebraic solution. Frequently only algebraic solutions are required.

EXAMPLE 4. Solve for x and y: $\begin{cases} 3x + 5y = 9, \\ 7x - 10y = 8. \end{cases}$

Solution. Multiply each member of the first equation by 2 and add each member of the resulting equation to the corresponding member of the second equation, getting $13x = 26$, or $x = 2$. Then set $x = 2$ in the first equation, obtaining $6 + 5y = 9$ or $y = \frac{3}{5}$. The desired solution is $x = 2$, $y = \frac{3}{5}$.

EXERCISE GROUP 7–4

In Exercises 1–34, solve the system of equations for x and y.

1. $2x - 3y + 5 = 0,$
   $3x + 2y = 12.$

2. $3x + 5y + 1 = 0,$
   $2y - 4x = 10.$

3. $4x - 6y = 2,$
   $30x - 42y = 17.$

4. $5x + 7y = 1,$
   $2x - 3y = 12.$

5. $4x - 3y = 3,$
   $-7x + 4y = 1.$

6. $2x + 5y = 28,$
   $5x - 8y = 29.$

7. $10x + 3y = 174,$
   $3x + 10y = 125.$

8. $\frac{3}{2}x + 1 = -\frac{4}{3}y,$
   $8x + 3y = 7.$

9. $\frac{2}{3}x - \frac{3}{4}y = \frac{3}{2},$
   $10x + 21y = 1.$

10. $3x + 5y - 9 = 0,$
    $5y - \frac{7}{2}x + 4 = 0.$

11. $\frac{1}{3}x - \frac{1}{4}y = 2,$
    $\frac{1}{4}x - \frac{1}{2}y = 7.$

12. $\dfrac{x + y - 2}{x - y} + \dfrac{1}{3} = 0$
    $\dfrac{3x + y - 3}{x - y} = \dfrac{1}{11}$

13. $\dfrac{2x - 1}{2} - \dfrac{4y - 1}{3} = \dfrac{1}{2},$
    $\dfrac{3x + 1}{3} + \dfrac{1}{2} = \dfrac{4y + 1}{2}.$

14. $\dfrac{5}{x} + \dfrac{2}{y} = 1,$
    $\dfrac{13}{x} + \dfrac{8}{y} = 1.$

15. $\dfrac{2}{x} + \dfrac{3}{y} = 2,$
    $\dfrac{1}{x} - \dfrac{1}{y} + 9 = 0.$

16. $\dfrac{2}{5x} + \dfrac{5}{2y} = 7,$
    $\dfrac{5}{2x} + \dfrac{1}{y} = \dfrac{29}{2}.$

17. $7x + 3y = 0.5,$
$3x - 7y = 2.7.$

18. $2x + 3y + 0.9 = 0,$
$3x + 4y = -1.1.$

19. $-2x + y = 0.1,$
$3x + 5y = -4.7.$

20. $bx + ay = 2ab,$
$ax - by = a^2 - b^2.$

21. $bx + a^2 - ay = b^2 + by,$
$ax - by = a^2.$

22. $ax - by = a^2 + b^2,$
$bx - ay = 2ab.$

23. $x - ay = a + b,$
$ax - ay = a^2 + b.$

24. $2x - 3y + z = 0,$
$5x - 2y - 3z = 0.$

25. $3x - 7y - 10z + 4 = 0,$
$4x - 3y - 7z - 1 = 0.$

26. $2x + 3y + 4z = 0,$
$3x + 4y + 5z = 0.$

27. $10x + 7y - a = 0,$
$3bx - 2by - 2ab = \dfrac{2ab}{35}.$

28. $2ax - 3by = 2a^2 - 3bc,$
$ay - cx = 3bc - 2a^2.$

29. $0.3b^2x + 1.5c^2y = -2.91b^2c^2,$
$1.7c^2x - 1.3b^2y = 3.06c^4 + 2.99b^4.$

30. $2ax + by - cx = 3ab - bc,$
$(a - b)x - by + 2cy = 2ac - b^2.$

31. $\dfrac{5x + 4y - 3}{9x - y + 5} + \dfrac{3}{4} = 0,$
$\dfrac{2x - 3y + 3}{5x - 4y + 5} - \dfrac{2}{3} = 0.$

32. $\dfrac{3x + 2y - 5}{2x - 3y + 4} - \dfrac{2}{3} = 1,$
$\dfrac{x - 2y + 3}{-x + y - 5} - \dfrac{3}{4} = 1.$

33. $\dfrac{1}{x - 1} + \dfrac{2}{y + 2} = 3,$
$\dfrac{3}{2x - 2} + \dfrac{4}{y + 2} = 5.$

34. $\dfrac{2}{2x + 3} + \dfrac{1}{y - 1} = 10,$
$\dfrac{3}{2x + 3} + \dfrac{4}{y - 1} = 20.$

7-7 Algebraic solution of three linear equations in three unknowns. To solve a system of three linear equations in three unknowns, one of the unknowns is eliminated from a pair of the equations, and the same unknown is also eliminated from another pair of the equations. The resulting pair of two equations in two unknowns can then be solved.

EXAMPLE. Solve the system of equations

$$\begin{cases} 2x - y - 4z = 3, \\ -x + 3y + z = -10, \\ 3x + 2y - 2z = -2. \end{cases}$$

Solution. To eliminate y from the first two equations, we multiply the first by 3, the second by 1, and add, getting

$$5x - 11z = -1.$$

Similarly, to eliminate y from the first and third equations, we multiply the first by 2, the third by 1, and add:

$$7x - 10z = 4.$$

We now have the system of two equations in two unknowns:

$$\begin{cases} 5x - 11z = -1, \\ 7x - 10z = 4. \end{cases}$$

Multiplying the first of this pair by 7, the second by -5, and adding, we have

$$-27z = -27, \quad \text{hence} \quad z = 1.$$

Substituting $z = 1$ in either of the equations in x and z, we find $x = 2$, and substituting $z = 1$ and $x = 2$ in one of the original equations, we find $y = -3$. The solution is $x = 2$, $y = -3$, $z = 1$.

To solve a system of four equations in four unknowns, the system is first reduced to a system of three equations in three unknowns.

Exercise Group 7–5

In Exercises 1–18, solve the system of equations for x, y, and z (and w in Exercises 17 and 18).

1. $7x + y + 3z = 52,$
   $4x - 5y + 6z = 13,$
   $x + 15y - 9z = 52.$

2. $2x + 3y + 5z = 11,$
   $-3x + 2y - z = -10,$
   $x - 4y + 3z = 18.$

3. $2x + 3y + z = 3,$
   $6x - 6y - 2z = -1,$
   $6x - 3y - 3z = -1.$

4. $3x + 2y - z = -2,$
   $5x - y + 3z = 8,$
   $3x + 5y + 7z = 7.$

5. $3x + 4y - z = 2,$
   $-2x - 3y + 2z = 6,$
   $2x - 2y + 3z = 44.$

6. $2x + y - 2z = 4,$
   $8x + y + z = 1,$
   $3y - z = 3.$

7. $2x + 3y + 4z = -7,$
   $-3x + 4y + 5z = -3,$
   $x + 2y - 3z = 7.$

8. $3x + 4y + 6z = 3,$
   $5x - 6y - 9z = 5,$
   $12x + 18y - 24z = -5.$

9. $3x - 2y + 3z = -2,$
   $x + 2y + 3z = \frac{16}{3},$
   $2x + 3y - 5z = 5.$

10. $x + y + z = 4a,$
    $x - y + 2z = 4a + 2b,$
    $2x + y - z = a + b.$

11. $bx + ay - 3z = 2ab - 3c,$
$cx - by + az = 2ac - b^2,$
$ax + cy - bz = a^2.$

12. $bx - ay + cz = b^2,$
$cx + ay - bz = bc + ac - ab,$
$ax + ay - bz = ac.$

13. $ax + by + 2z = (a + b)^2,$
$ax + by - 2z = (a - b)^2,$
$bx - ay = 0.$

14. $x + 2y - 2z - 10u = 0,$
$6x + 5y + 2z - 4u = 0,$
$2x - y - 16z - 2u = 0.$

15. $3x + 2y + z - 10u = 0,$
$2x - 3y - z - 2u = 0,$
$5x - y + 2z - 28u = 0.$

16. $\frac{2}{x} + \frac{5}{y} - \frac{7}{z} = 9,$
$\frac{5}{x} - \frac{1}{y} + \frac{3}{z} = 16,$
$\frac{7}{x} + \frac{6}{y} + \frac{1}{z} = 34.$

17. $4x - y + z + 2w = 1,$
$3x + 2y - z + 2w = -12,$
$-2x + 3y + 2z - 3w = 10,$
$x + y + z + w = -2.$

18. $2x + y + z + 7w = 19,$
$-5x + y - 2z + w = 2,$
$3x - y - z - 5w = -3,$
$x - 3y - 3z - 7w = -1.$

7–8 Applications of systems of linear equations. The discussion of Section 7–5 applies equally well here. The only difference here is that many problems require, or are facilitated by, the introduction of more than one unknown, and then it becomes necessary to obtain more than one equation. In fact it is essential that there must be as many independent equations as there are unknowns if a unique solution is to be found. Some illustrative examples will help clarify the methods.

EXAMPLE 1. The area of a trapezoid (a quadrilateral with two parallel sides) is equal to one-half the product of the sum of the two parallel sides by the distance between them. We are to construct a trapezoid with an area of 54 in.^{2}, in which one of the parallel sides is 2 in. longer than the other and the distance between them is 6 in. Find the lengths of the parallel sides.

Solution. Let us use two unknown quantities, the lengths of the parallel sides. Let x be the length of the shorter one and y the length of the longer one. From the above statements we then have

$$y = x + 2, \qquad 6 \cdot \frac{x + y}{2} = 54.$$

These equations reduce to

$$y - x = 2, \qquad y + x = 18,$$

which are then readily solved to give $x = 8$ and $y = 10$ as the desired lengths.

EXAMPLE 2. What is the capital of a person whose income from investment is \$1302, when $\frac{1}{3}$ of it is invested at 4%, $\frac{1}{5}$ at 6%, and the remainder at 5%?

Solution. We need to know the amounts invested at each interest rate; thus,

let x = the amount invested at 4%,
" y = the amount invested at 6%,
" z = the amount invested at 5%.

The part invested at 5% must be $1 - \frac{8}{15} = \frac{7}{15}$ of the total. The total capital can then be expressed either as $3x$ or $5y$ or $\frac{15}{7}z$. We then have as two independent equations

$$3x = 5y, \qquad 5y = \tfrac{15}{7}z.$$

The third equation is derived from the fact that the sum of the incomes from the different parts is equal to the total income, and is

$$0.04x + 0.06y + 0.05z = 1302.$$

From the first two equations, $x = 5y/3$, $z = 7y/3$; substituting these in the third equation, we have

$$0.04\frac{5y}{3} + 0.06y + 0.05\frac{7y}{3} = 1302,$$

or, on multiplying both members by 3,

$$0.2y + 0.18y + 0.35y = 3906,$$

and

$$0.73y = 3906, \qquad y = \frac{3906}{0.73} = 5350.68 \quad \text{(dollars)}.$$

The total capital is then $5y = 5(5350.68) = \$26{,}753.40$.

Exercise Group 7–6

1. If the larger of two numbers is divided by the smaller, the quotient is 2 and the remainder is 1. If the larger is divided by 20 more than the smaller, the quotient is 1 and the remainder is 15. Find the numbers.

2. Find two numbers whose sum is 1154 and whose difference is 527.

3. Two points move at constant rates along the circumference of a circle whose length is 180 ft. When the points both move in the same direction around the circle they are together every 20 sec, and when they move in opposite directions they meet every 4 sec. What is the rate of each?

4. We have three alloys as follows: By weight

A is 60% lead, 25% zinc, and 15% copper;
B is 20% lead, 50% zinc, and 30% copper;
C is 20% lead, 30% zinc, and 50% copper.

To obtain 15 oz of an alloy which contains equal amounts (by weight) of lead, zinc, and copper, how many ounces of *A*, *B*, and *C* must be melted and mixed together?

5. Find two fractions, with numerators 2 and 3 respectively, whose sum is $\frac{17}{12}$, and such that when their denominators are interchanged, their sum is $\frac{3}{2}$.

6. If 3 is added to both the numerator and denominator of a fraction, its value is $\frac{1}{2}$. If 1 is subtracted from both the numerator and denominator, its value is $\frac{1}{6}$. Find the fraction.

7. A sum of money at simple interest amounted in 16 yr to \$16,000, and in 18 yr to \$17,000. What was the sum of money and the rate of interest?

8. The sums of \$1200 and \$1400 are invested at different rates and their annual interest is \$111. If the rates of interest were interchanged, the annual interest would be \$110. Find the rates of interest.

9. A takes 2 hr longer than B to walk d mi, but if A should double his speed, he would walk it in 1 hr less than B. Find the time B needs to walk the d mi.

10. If a rectangle were 100 ft longer and 25 ft narrower, its area would be 2500 ft^2 larger. If it were 100 ft shorter and 50 ft wider, its area would be 5000 ft^2 smaller. What are the dimensions of the rectangle?

11. The front wheel of a car makes 6 revolutions more than the rear wheel in going 120 yd. If the circumference of the front wheel is increased by 25%, and that of the rear wheel by 20%, the 6 becomes 4. Find the circumference of each wheel.

12. Find the linear function of x which has the values 8 and 10 when x has the values -2 and 3, respectively.

13. Find the function of the form $2x^2 + ax + b$ which has the values -5 and 61 when x has the values -1 and 5, respectively.

14. Find A and B if the equation $A(x - 1) + B(x - 2) = 3x - 2$ holds for all values of x. (*Hint:* The equation must be satisfied for any two values of x chosen at random.)

15. Find the function of the form $ax^2 + bx + c$ which takes on the values -14, -4, and -2 when $x = -2$, 0, and 2 respectively.

16. Find the function of the form $a + b/x + c/x^2$ which takes on the values -4, 0, and $\frac{5}{4}$ when $x = \frac{1}{2}$, 1, and 2 respectively.

17. A sum of \$10,000 is partly invested at 5%, partly at 4%, and partly at 3%, bringing a total yearly interest of \$390. The 5% investment brings \$10 more interest yearly than the 4% and 3% investments together. How much money is invested at 3%, 4%, and 5% respectively?

18. A, B, and C working together can do a piece of work in 1 day, A and C together in $1\frac{1}{2}$ days, and B and C together in 2 days. How many days would each of them require to do the work alone?

19. A tank can be filled by pipes A and B in 72 min, by pipes B and C in 120 min, and by pipes A and C in 90 min. How much time would be needed for each pipe to fill the tank?

20. The perimeter of a triangle is 39 in. The longest side is 7 in. less than the sum of the other two, and one of these two is twice as large as the difference of the remaining two. Find the length of each side.

21. Find the values of A, B, and C if the equation

$$A(x - 2)(x - 3) + B(x - 1)(x - 3) + C(x - 1)(x - 2) = x^2 + 3$$

holds for all values of x.

Review Exercises

In Exercises 1–10, solve for x.

1. $\dfrac{3x+7}{5} - \dfrac{2x-3}{3} = \dfrac{7}{15} - 3$

2. $1 - \dfrac{2x+3}{7} + \dfrac{3-2x}{5} = -\dfrac{1}{5}$

3. $2x - 1 - \dfrac{3x-1}{x+1} = 2(x-1)$

4. $3 - \dfrac{2x+3}{3x-2} + \dfrac{x-1}{2-3x} = 0$

5. $1 - \dfrac{2x^2+3x+5}{2x^2+x-1} + \dfrac{3}{1-2x} = 0$

6. $\dfrac{5}{2x} - \dfrac{3x-2}{2x-3} = -\dfrac{3}{2}$

7. $1 - \dfrac{2x^2+5x+7}{2x^2-x-3} = \dfrac{1}{2x-3}$

8. $\dfrac{3x+2}{x+1} + 2 = \dfrac{4x+5}{x+1}$

9. $\dfrac{3}{x+2} + \dfrac{8}{x^2+x-2} = \dfrac{2}{1-x}$

10. $\dfrac{5}{x+5} - \dfrac{2}{x-3} = \dfrac{6(x+1)}{15-2x-x^2}$

11. How many cubic centimeters of a 60% solution of sulphuric acid must be added to 200 cc of a 30% solution to obtain a 40% solution of the acid?

12. If the radius of a sphere is increased by 10%, what is the % change in the surface of the sphere? in the volume of the sphere?

13. If the interest for one year on an investment of \$3174 is \$142.83, what is the rate of interest on the investment?

14. An airplane with a 15 mph head wind takes 50% longer to fly 540 mi than it does to fly 440 mi with a 15 mph tail wind. What is the air speed of the plane?

In Exercises 15–28, solve each of the systems of equations.

15. $5x + 3y = -1,$
$7x + 5y = 1.$

16. $\dfrac{3}{2}x + \dfrac{5}{3}y = 2,$
$\dfrac{5}{4}x + \dfrac{7}{3}y = \dfrac{9}{2}.$

17. $\dfrac{3}{2}x + \dfrac{10}{3}y = 2,$
$3x + \dfrac{5}{2}y = -\dfrac{1}{2}.$

18. $4x - 3y = 0.1,$
$0.5x + 0.2y = 0.04.$

19. $bx - ay = 0,$
$ax + by = a^2 + b^2.$

20. $cx - dy = ac + bd,$
$ax + cy = a^2 - bc.$

21. $2x + 3y + z = -1,$
$3x - 4y - 2z = 5,$
$5x - 3y - 3z = 2.$

22. $5x + 4y + 3z = 1,$
$2x - 3y + 11z = 1,$
$x + 2y - z = 1.$

23. $ax + cy + bz = a^2 + 2bc,$
$bx + ay + cz = 2ab + c^2,$
$cx - by + az = 2ac - b^2.$

24. $x + y + z = a,$
$bx + by + az = \frac{3}{2}ab - \frac{b^2}{2},$
$x - y + z = a + b.$

25. $2x - 3y - 2z = 2,$
$3x + y + z = 4,$
$x + 2y + z = 0.$

26. $x + y + z = 1,$
$2x + 3y - z = 1,$
$3x + 2y + 3z = 1.$

27. $x + y + z = b,$
$x + y = 0,$
$2x + z = a + b.$

28. $bx - ay + z = c,$
$x + cy - bz = a,$
$cx + y - az = b.$

29. An airplane took 4 hr to fly 1800 mi, flying with a tail wind, and $4\frac{1}{2}$ hr for the return flight with a head wind. Find the wind velocity and the air speed of the airplane.

30. We wish to obtain a 50% solution of alcohol by mixing a 40% solution and a 65% solution of alcohol. What percentage of the final solution should be taken from each of the two given solutions?

CHAPTER 8

QUADRATIC EQUATIONS AND THE QUADRATIC FUNCTION

8–1 Solving a quadratic equation by factoring. A natural extension of the discussion of linear functions and equations in Chapter 7 is the consideration of functions of the type $ax^2 + bx + c$, where a, b, and c are constants with $a \neq 0$. These are *quadratic functions*, and when such a function is set equal to zero a *quadratic equation* results.

It often happens that the quadratic function $ax^2 + bx + c$ is factorable, in which case the corresponding quadratic equation can be solved by factoring. Consider the equation

$$-2x^2 + 3x + 5 = 0,$$

which can be written as

$$(-2x + 5)(x + 1) = 0.$$

For a product of quantities to be zero it is necessary for at least one of the quantities to be zero, so that to obtain all possible values of x satisfying the equation, each factor must be set equal to zero, whenever possible. Hence

$$-2x + 5 = 0 \text{ and } x = \tfrac{5}{2}, \qquad \text{or} \qquad x + 1 = 0 \text{ and } x = -1.$$

There are *two* solutions of the equation, $x = \frac{5}{2}$ and $x = -1$.

EXAMPLE. Solve the equation $3x^2 + 5x = 0$.

Solution. It was pointed out in Section 1–11 that division by zero is impossible. Thus we must not divide by x since x might be equal to zero. Instead of dividing by x we factor the left member of the equation to obtain

$$x(3x + 5) = 0.$$

Therefore $x = 0$; or $3x + 5 = 0$ and $x = -\frac{5}{3}$. The two solutions of the given equation are $x = 0$ and $x = -\frac{5}{3}$.

EXERCISE GROUP 8–1

In Exercises 1–42, solve the equation by factoring.

1. $x^2 - 5x + 6 = 0$
2. $x^2 + 3x = 10$
3. $x^2 - 2x - 63 = 0$
4. $x^2 - 13x + 30 = 0$
5. $x^2 - 4x - 21 = 0$
6. $x^2 - 14x + 45 = 0$

7. $x^2 - 9x = 52$
8. $x^2 + 4x = 77$
9. $x^2 - 54 = -3x$
10. $8x + 65 = x^2$
11. $x^2 + 4ax - 21a^2 = 0$
12. $x^2 + 4ax = 45a^2$
13. $x^2 + x = bx + b$
14. $ax + x = a + x^2$
15. $px^2 - p^2x - x = -p$
16. $3x^2 + 5x = 0$
17. $15x = 5x^2$
18. $9x^2 - 16 = 0$
19. $16x^2 = 25$
20. $33x^2 = 11x$
21. $a^2x^2 = b^2$
22. $4x^2 + 12x + 9 = 0$
23. $9x^2 + 30x + 25 = 0$
24. $16x^2 - 24x + 9 = 0$
25. $4x^2 + 25 = 20x$
26. $a^2x^2 + 2abx + b^2 = 0$
27. $p^2x^2 + 4pqx + 4q^2 = 0$
28. $2x^2 - 5x + 3 = 0$
29. $2x^2 + x - 3 = 0$
30. $3x^2 - 5x - 2 = 0$
31. $5x + 4 = 6x^2$
32. $2x^2 + 5x = 12$
33. $7x^2 - 5 = 2x$
34. $10x^2 = 21 - 29x$
35. $x + 2 = 15x^2$
36. $31x = 6x^2 + 35$
37. $2x^2 - 9x - 161 = 0$
38. $2x^2 + 13x = -15$
39. $10x^2 = 31x + 14$
40. $31x = 35x^2 + 6$
41. $\dfrac{7}{x+5} - \dfrac{8}{x-6} = \dfrac{3}{x-1}$
42. $2x^2 + (a + 2b)x + ab = 0$

8–2 Solving a quadratic equation by completing the square. In Chapter 2 we considered the two type forms

$$(x + a)^2 = x^2 + 2ax + a^2,$$
$$(x - a)^2 = x^2 - 2ax + a^2.$$

In either case the constant term, a^2, is the square of one-half of the coefficient of x, that is, the square of $\frac{1}{2}(2a)$ or of $\frac{1}{2}(-2a)$. This observation permits us to solve the following type of problem.

EXAMPLE 1. What number must be added to $x^2 + 3x$ to make the sum a perfect square?

Solution. The square of $\frac{1}{2}$ of 3 is $(\frac{3}{2})^2 = \frac{9}{4}$, which is the desired number. By adding this to $x^2 + 3x$ we have

$$x^2 + 3x + \tfrac{9}{4} = (x + \tfrac{3}{2})^2.$$

We shall now develop a method for solving the quadratic equation

$$ax^2 + bx + c = 0, \qquad (a \neq 0),$$

by the method of completing the square, regardless of whether the left member is factorable or not.

In this section we shall apply the method to specific examples, and shall leave the general development to the following section.

EXAMPLE 2. Solve the equation $3x^2 + 5x - 7 = 0$.

Solution. (a) Add 7 to both members, and then divide both members by 3, getting

$$x^2 + \tfrac{5}{3}x = \tfrac{7}{3}.$$

(b) We now add $(\frac{5}{6})^2 = \frac{25}{36}$ to the left member to obtain a perfect square there, and add the same number to the right member, obtaining

$$x^2 + \tfrac{5}{3}x + \tfrac{25}{36} = \tfrac{7}{3} + \tfrac{25}{36}.$$

This can be written as

$$(x + \tfrac{5}{6})^2 = \tfrac{109}{36}.$$

(c) We now extract the square root of both members, which gives

$$x + \frac{5}{6} = \pm\frac{\sqrt{109}}{6}, \qquad \text{or} \qquad x = \frac{-5 \pm \sqrt{109}}{6}.$$

The two solutions are

$$x = \frac{-5 + \sqrt{109}}{6} \qquad \text{and} \qquad x = \frac{-5 - \sqrt{109}}{6},$$

which can be verified by direct substitution.

The method used here for obtaining x is called *solving a quadratic equation by completing the square.* In the following example the method is applied to an equation which can also be solved by factoring.

EXAMPLE 3. Solve by completing the square: $-2x^2 + 3x + 5 = 0$.

Solution.

$$x^2 - \tfrac{3}{2}x - \tfrac{5}{2} = 0,$$
$$x^2 - \tfrac{3}{2}x + \tfrac{9}{16} = \tfrac{5}{2} + \tfrac{9}{16} = \tfrac{49}{16},$$
$$(x - \tfrac{3}{4})^2 = \tfrac{49}{16},\ x - \tfrac{3}{4} = \pm\tfrac{7}{4},$$

Therefore $x = \frac{3}{4} \pm \frac{7}{4}$, and the two solutions are

$$x = \tfrac{10}{4} = \tfrac{5}{2} \qquad \text{and} \qquad x = -\tfrac{4}{4} = -1.$$

EXERCISE GROUP 8-2

In Exercises 1–21, solve the equation by completing the square.

1. $3x^2 - x - 2 = 0$
2. $2x^2 - 3x = 5$
3. $x^2 - 2x - 5 = 0$
4. $5x^2 - 3x + 4 = 0$
5. $x^2 + ax - 6 = 0$
6. $3x^2 + bx + c = 0$
7. $7x^2 + 16 = 0$
8. $2x^2 + 13 = 3x$
9. $9x^2 + 5x = 0$

10. $3x^2 - 5x + 17 = 0$ 11. $2x^2 - 5x + 7 = 0$ 12. $3x^2 + 6x - 11 = 0$
13. $ax^2 - 2x + 7a = 0$ 14. $3x^2 - 12x + 5 = 0$ 15. $3x^2 - ux + 2 = 0$
16. $px^2 + qx + r = 0$ 17. $cx^2 + bx + a = 0$ 18. $7x^2 = 2x - 5$
19. $c = 2ax - x^2$ 20. $b = ax^2 - dx$ 21. $ax^2 = 5 - x^2 + 7x$

8–3 Solving a quadratic equation by formula. By applying the method of completing the square to the general quadratic equation

$$ax^2 + bx + c = 0, \qquad (a \neq 0), \tag{1}$$

we shall develop a formula which may be used to solve any quadratic equation.

Divide each member of Eq. (1) by a, obtaining

$$x^2 + \frac{b}{a}x + \frac{c}{a} = 0. \tag{2}$$

Now subtract c/a from both members of the equation, getting

$$x^2 + \frac{b}{a}x = -\frac{c}{a}. \tag{3}$$

The left member of this equation will become the square of a linear function if $(b/2a)^2$ is added, which is permissible if the same quantity is also added to the right member. This gives

$$x^2 + \frac{b}{a}x + \frac{b^2}{4a^2} = \frac{b^2}{4a^2} - \frac{c}{a}, \tag{4}$$

which may in turn be written as

$$\left(x + \frac{b}{2a}\right)^2 = \frac{b^2 - 4ac}{4a^2}. \tag{5}$$

If now the square root of each side is taken, we have

$$x + \frac{b}{2a} = \pm\sqrt{\frac{b^2 - 4ac}{4a^2}}, \tag{6}$$

or

$$\boxed{x = \frac{-b \pm \sqrt{b^2 - 4ac}}{2a}.} \tag{7}$$

Equation (7) is known as the *quadratic formula.* Using the formula to solve an equation consists of identifying the values of a, b, and c and then substituting these values in (7). After the substitution of the values it will frequently be necessary to simplify the result, as will be illustrated in the following examples.

EXAMPLE 1. Use the quadratic formula to solve the equation

$$3x^2 + 4x - 5 = 0.$$

Solution. A comparison of the given equation $3x^2 + 4x - 5 = 0$ with the equation $ax^2 + bx + c = 0$ shows that $a = 3$, $b = 4$, and $c = -5$. Hence, by Eq. (7) we have

$$x = \frac{-4 \pm \sqrt{16 - 4 \cdot 3(-5)}}{2 \cdot 3}$$

$$= \frac{-4 \pm \sqrt{16 + 60}}{6} = \frac{-4 \pm \sqrt{4 \cdot 19}}{6}$$

$$= \frac{-4 \pm 2\sqrt{19}}{6} = \frac{-2 \pm \sqrt{19}}{3}.$$

EXAMPLE 2. Use the quadratic formula to solve $2x^2 - 5x + 8 = 0$.

Solution. Proceeding as in Example 1 we see that $a = 2$, $b = -5$, and $c = 8$. We get

$$x = \frac{5 \pm \sqrt{25 - 4 \cdot 2 \cdot 8}}{2 \cdot 2} = \frac{5 \pm \sqrt{-39}}{4} = \frac{5 \pm i\sqrt{39}}{4}.$$

Whereas the method of completing the square can always be used to solve a quadratic equation, it almost never is used for this purpose in practice. Its importance here revolves around its use in the derivation of the quadratic formula. The suggested procedure for solving a given quadratic equation is as follows:

1. *Try to solve the equation by factoring.*
2. *If a factorization is not possible or is not readily apparent, use the quadratic formula.*

EXERCISE GROUP 8-3

In Exercises 1-30, solve the equation by using the quadratic formula.

1. $3x^2 + x - 2 = 0$
2. $2x^2 + 3x = 5$
3. $x^2 + 2x - 5 = 0$
4. $5x^2 + 3x + 4 = 0$
5. $x^2 - ax - 6 = 0$
6. $3x^2 - bx + c = 0$
7. $7x^2 = 2x - 5$
8. $170 = 22x - x^2$
9. $x^2 - 2 = 2ix$, $(i = \sqrt{-1})$
10. $x^2 + 6\sqrt{7}x + 55 = 0$

11. $21x^2 + 20 = 43x$
12. $20x^2 = x - 3$
13. $6(x^2 + 1) = 13x$
14. $x^2 - \sqrt{5}x - 1 = 0$
15. $x^2 + 2 = 2\sqrt{3}x$
16. $2x^2 - 7 = 3x$
17. $2x^2 = 5(x + 1)$
18. $3(x + 1) = 5x^2$
19. $2x - 1 = x - x^2$
20. $3x^2 + 1 = 2(x - 2)$
21. $3(x^2 + x) = -2x^2 - 7$
22. $x(2x - 5) + x - 3 = 0$
23. $px^2 - p^2x = x - p$
24. $5x + 3 = ax^2 + a$
25. $2x^2 + ax + 2bx + ab = 0$
26. $x(3x + b) = c(3x + b)$
27. $ax^2 - bx + c = x^2$
28. $bx^2 + cx = ax - d$
29. $x^2 + ax + bx = (a + b)^2$
30. $b^2x^2 - abx = a^2$

Solve the equations in Exercises 31–44 by any appropriate method.

31. $x^2 - 22x + 170 = 0$
32. $3x(3 - x) + \frac{1}{5} = 1 - 2x$
33. $x^2 + 102x + 2597 = 0$
34. $5x(x - 2) + \frac{1}{4} = 1 - 3x$
35. $13x^2 - 30 = 6(1 + x)^2 + 63$
36. $x^2 + (a + b)x = 2a^2 - 5ab + 2b^2$
37. $a^2x^2 - b^2x^2 - 4abx = a^2 - b^2$
38. $abx^2 - (a^2 + b^2)x + ab = 0$
39. $a^2x^2 - x^2 - 2a^2x + a^2 = 0$
40. $px^2 + p^2x + x = -p$
41. $\dfrac{x - 5}{x + 3} - \dfrac{80}{x^2 - 9} = \dfrac{1}{2} + \dfrac{x - 8}{3 - x}$
42. $\dfrac{a + x}{b + x} + \dfrac{b + x}{a + x} = \dfrac{5}{2}$
43. $a + x = \dfrac{1}{a} + \dfrac{1}{x}$
44. $\dfrac{x - 1}{x + 1} = \dfrac{x + 1}{x - 1} - 1$

8–4 The quadratic function. In the preceding sections of this chapter we have been concerned with finding those values of x which make the quadratic function $ax^2 + bx + c$ $(a \neq 0)$ zero. We shall now consider the function for all values of x, and shall use the very effective method of studying a function through its graph.

We shall draw the graph of the quadratic function, and from the graph and the analysis leading to the graph we shall learn many properties of the function. Let us write

$$y = ax^2 + bx + c.$$

In determining pairs of values (x, y) which satisfy this equation, we can be guided in our choice of values of x *by expressing the quadratic function in terms of the square of a linear function of* x, as follows. The first step is to transpose c to the left member and then factor out a from the right member:

$$y - c = a\left(x^2 + \frac{b}{a}x\right).$$

We then complete the square within the parentheses on the right by adding $b^2/4a^2$. This means that we are adding $a \cdot (b^2/4a^2) = b^2/4a$ to the right member, and we add the same quantity to the left member, so that we have

$$y - c + \frac{b^2}{4a} = a\left(x^2 + \frac{b}{a}x + \frac{b^2}{4a^2}\right) = a\left(x + \frac{b}{2a}\right)^2,$$

or

$$y - \frac{4ac - b^2}{4a} = a\left(x + \frac{b}{2a}\right)^2.$$

Since the square of any real number is either positive or zero, we see that the smallest value of $[x + (b/2a)]^2$ will occur when $x = -b/2a$, and is zero. If a is positive, the left member must be positive or zero and the smallest value that y can have is $(4ac - b^2)/4a$, which will occur when $x = -b/2a$, so that $[-b/2a, (4ac - b^2)/4a]$ is the lowest point on the graph. If a is negative, the point with these coordinates is the highest point on the graph. In either case the curve is called a *parabola* and the point $[-b/2a, (4ac - b^2)/4a]$ is called the *vertex* of the parabola. By taking values of x on each side of $-b/2a$ and computing the corresponding values of y, we obtain a set of points which, when plotted and joined by a smooth curve, give the graph of the function.

The abscissa of the vertex can also be found by using the formula $x = -b/2a$, and the ordinate can then be found by substituting this value of x in the function.

EXAMPLE 1. Graph the function $3x^2 + 5x - 7$.

Solution. Let $y = 3x^2 + 5x - 7$, and apply the method described above. Then

$$y + 7 + \tfrac{25}{12} = 3(x^2 + \tfrac{5}{3}x + \tfrac{25}{36})$$

or

$$y + \tfrac{109}{12} = 3(x + \tfrac{5}{6})^2.$$

The vertex of the graph is thus at $(-\frac{5}{6}, -\frac{109}{12})$. We now take values of x on each side of $x = -\frac{5}{6}$, compute the corresponding values of y, and obtain the table of values

x:	-4	-3	-2	-1	$-\frac{5}{6}$	0	1	2
y:	21	5	-5	-9	$-\frac{109}{12}$	-7	1	15

from which the graph can be constructed (Fig. 8-1).

EXAMPLE 2. Graph the function $-2x^2 + 3x + 6$.

Solution. Let $y = -2x^2 + 3x + 6$, and proceed as above. Then

$$y - 6 - \tfrac{9}{8} = -2(x^2 - \tfrac{3}{2}x + \tfrac{9}{16})$$

or

$$y - \tfrac{57}{8} = -2(x - \tfrac{3}{4})^2.$$

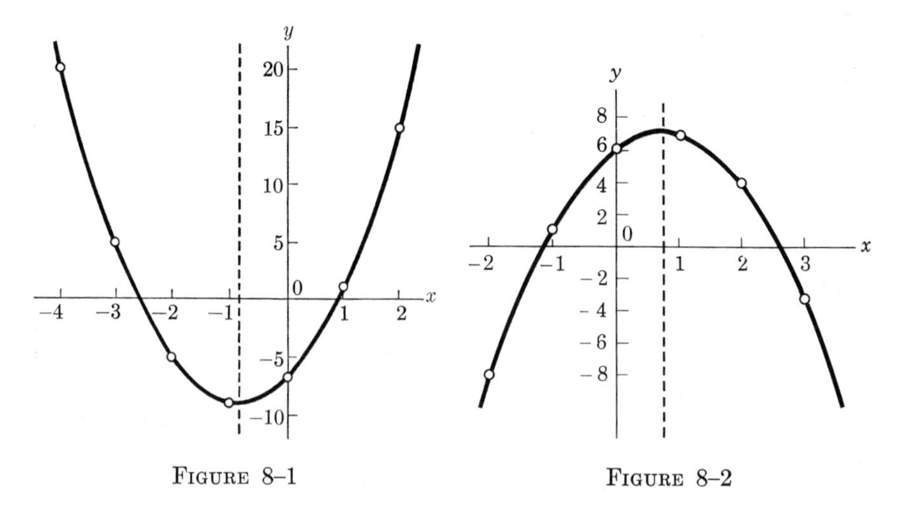

FIGURE 8–1

FIGURE 8–2

The vertex of the graph is at $(\frac{3}{4}, \frac{57}{8})$. Using values of x on each side of $x = \frac{3}{4}$, we obtain the table

x:	-2	-1	0	$\frac{3}{4}$	1	2	3
y:	-8	1	6	$\frac{57}{8}$	7	4	-3

and the resulting graph (Fig. 8–2).

The following summarizes the preceding analysis:

1. *The graph of the function* $ax^2 + bx + c$ *is a* U-*shaped or inverted* U-*shaped curve with its vertex at*

$$\left[-\frac{b}{2a}, \frac{4ac - b^2}{4a}\right].$$

This curve is called a parabola.

2. *The graph is symmetrical with respect to the line* $x = -b/2a$. *(If the graph is drawn on a sheet of paper and the paper is then folded along the line* $x = -b/2a$, *the two halves of the curve will coincide.)*

3. *If* a *is positive the curve opens upward and the vertex is the lowest point on the graph (minimum); if* a *is negative the curve opens downward and the vertex is the highest point on the graph (maximum).*

4. *The graph must either cross the* x-*axis in two distinct points, or be tangent to it, or not touch it at all.*

Exercise Group 8–4

1. Draw on the same axes the graphs of the functions $2x^2$, $2x^2 + 1$, $2x^2 - 3$.
2. Draw on the same axes the graphs of the functions $2x^2 + 3x + 1$, $2x^2 + 3x$, $2x^2 + 3x - 2$.

In each of Exercises 3–26, find the coordinates of the vertex, and draw the graph of the function.

3. $2x^2 - 3x - 4$
4. $x^2 - \frac{1}{2}x + 1$
5. $2x^2 - 8x + 2$
6. $-3x^2 + 6x - 1$
7. $-x^2 - x + 2$
8. $-3x^2 + 6x - 4$
9. $x^2 + 2x$
10. $3x^2 + 3x - 3$
11. $-2x^2 + 2x - 4$
12. $2x^2 - 0.75x + 1$
13. $x^2 + 6x + 5$
14. $3x^2 + 7$
15. $0.2x^2 - 2.2x$
16. $\frac{1}{3}x^2 + \frac{2}{3}x - 2$
17. $4x^2 + 8x - 3$
18. $-2x^2 + 3x - 4$
19. $3x^2 + 4x + 5$
20. $-3x^2 + 6x$
21. $x - x^2$
22. $-3x^2 + 1$
23. $-2x^2 - x$
24. $(x - 1)^2 + 3(x - 1) + 1$
25. $y^2 + 3y + 2$
26. $-2y^2 + 3y - 1$

(*Hint* for Exercises 25 and 26: Set the function equal to x.)

8–5 Applications of quadratic functions and equations. It was pointed out in Section 7–4 that many problems can be solved by reducing them to algebraic equations and then solving the resulting equations. In Section 7–4 our interest was confined to problems that can be reduced to linear equations; in this section we shall be interested in problems which reduce to quadratic equations, or involve quadratic functions. A few examples will illustrate the methods.

Example 1. Determine two numbers which differ by 2 and whose product is 288.

Solution. Let the smaller number be x; then the larger number must be $x + 2$. We then have

$$x(x + 2) = 288 \qquad \text{or} \qquad x^2 + 2x - 288 = 0.$$

On factoring the left member we obtain

$$(x + 18)(x - 16) = 0 \qquad \text{so that} \qquad x = 16 \text{ or } x = -18.$$

Thus, the two numbers are 16 and 18, or -18 and -16.

Example 2. A merchant finds that he can sell 1000 items per week if he prices the item at a profit of \$1 per item. He also finds that for each 5-cent increase in price the number of items sold decreases by 2%, while for each 5-cent decrease in price the sales volume increases by 2%. What should be the profit per item for the maximum profit?

Solution. If x is the number of 5-cent increases in price, the profit per item will be $1 + 0.05x$ and the number of items sold will be $1000\ (1 - 0.02x)$. The total profit is then given by the function

$$1000(1 - 0.02x)(1 + 0.05x) = 1000 + 30x - x^2.$$

From Section 8–4 we know that the maximum of this function is attained at $x = -(30/-2) = 15$. Thus the greatest profit is achieved by making a profit of $[1 + 0.05(15)] = 1.75$ per unit even though the number sold will be only 700.

Exercise Group 8–5

1. If an object is projected vertically upward from the ground with an initial velocity of v_0 ft/sec, its distance S above the ground at the end of t sec is given by the formula

$$S = v_0 t - \tfrac{1}{2}gt^2,$$

where g is the acceleration of the object due to gravity (=32 ft/sec/sec approx.). Draw the graph of S as a function of t if $v_0 = 56$. How high will the object rise above the ground? How long will it take to fall to the ground again? How high will it be at the end of 2 sec?

2. A man operates a rooming house with 26 rooms. He finds that he can keep all rooms rented at $20 a month each but will have one vacancy for each $1 per month added to this price. Express his gross income in terms of the number x of dollars charged in excess of $20. Graph the function and determine what rental will provide a maximum gross income.

3. Find the value of k so that the vertex of the graph of the function $2x^2 - kx + 2$ lies on the x-axis.

4. Find the maximum value of the product of two numbers if their sum is 4.

5. Find the minimum value of the product of two numbers if their difference is 4.

6. Find the dimensions of the largest rectangle that can be inscribed in an isosceles triangle with altitude 8 in. and base 4 in. if one side of the rectangle is along the base of the triangle.

7. It is necessary to form a rectangular field with one side lying along a stream. If 100 yd of wire fence are available to fence in the three exposed sides, find the maximum area that can be enclosed.

8. Find the value of k if the vertex of the graph of the function $2x^2 - kx + 1$ lies on the line $y = x$.

9. An object is sold for $11, which includes a profit of as many percent as the number of dollars of original cost. Find the original cost.

10. The dimensions of a picture are 11×14 in. The area of the frame is to be approximately one-third the area of the picture. Find the frame's width.

11. From Exercise 1 above, we have $S = v_0 t - 16t^2$. Solve for t in terms of S (when $v_0 = 56$), and from the result obtain the value of t for $S = 49$ and also the value of t when the object reaches the ground again.

12. If each side of a square were increased by $\frac{3}{2}$ ft, the area would be increased by $\frac{87}{4}$ sq yd. Find the side of the square.

13. If a uniform border is added to a rug which is 6 ft by 9 ft, the area is increased by 34 ft^2. Find the width of the border.

14. If the radius of a circle were increased by one yard, its area would be increased by 15π sq yd. Find the radius of the circle. (*Hint:* The area A of a circle of radius r is given by $A = \pi r^2$.)

15. To pave a room with square tiles of a certain size, 360 tiles are needed. If each tile were one inch longer and one inch wider, 250 tiles would be needed. Find the dimensions of the tiles.

16. The sum of a number and its reciprocal is 1. Find the number.

17. Find the area of a square whose diagonal is 10 in. longer than a side.

18. Find three consecutive odd integers the sum of whose squares is 251.

19. The length of a rectangle is 6 more than twice the width, and the diagonal is 39. Find the dimensions.

20. A pilot whose air speed was 250 mph found that it took him 24 min longer to fly 495 mi against the wind than to fly the same distance with the wind. Find the wind velocity.

21. An open gutter with rectangular cross section is to be made from a strip of metal 12 in. wide, by turning up the same amount of material on each edge. Determine the amount that should be turned up to make the area of the cross section a maximum.

8-6 Character of the roots of a quadratic equation. The roots of the general quadratic equation $ax^2 + bx + c = 0$ $(a \neq 0)$ are given in terms of the coefficients a, b, and c by the quadratic formula. Let the roots be designated by r_1 and r_2, where

$$r_1 = \frac{-b + \sqrt{b^2 - 4ac}}{2a}, \qquad r_2 = \frac{-b - \sqrt{b^2 - 4ac}}{2a}.$$

It is obvious from the above relations that if $b^2 - 4ac = 0$, then $r_1 = r_2 = -b/2a$. Conversely, if $r_1 = r_2$, then $r_1 - r_2 = 0$, from which it follows that

$$r_1 - r_2 = \frac{2\sqrt{b^2 - 4ac}}{2a} = 0, \qquad \text{so that} \qquad b^2 - 4ac = 0.$$

The quantity $b^2 - 4ac$ is called the *discriminant* of both the equation $ax^2 + bx + c = 0$, and of the function $ax^2 + bx + c$.

We introduce here symbols to represent the relations "greater than" and "less than." The following notation is commonly employed:

$a > b$ means that "a is greater than b,"

$a < b$ means that "a is less than b."

If the discriminant is not zero, then of course $r_1 \neq r_2$ (read: r_1 is not equal to r_2), but additional information can be obtained. For if a, b, c

are real, then whether r_1 and r_2 are real or imaginary depends on the sign of $b^2 - 4ac$. If $b^2 - 4ac > 0$, then r_1 and r_2 will be real; if $b^2 - 4ac < 0$, then r_1 and r_2 will be imaginary.

These results can be immediately related also to the corresponding function $ax^2 + bx + c$ with zeros r_1 and r_2, and to the graph of the function $ax^2 + bx + c$.

Summarizing, we have the following results, if a, b, c are real:

(1) *$r_1 = r_2$ if and only if $b^2 - 4ac = 0$, in which case the vertex of the graph of the function $ax^2 + bx + c$ is on the x-axis;*

(2) *r_1 and r_2 are* real *and $r_1 \neq r_2$ if $b^2 - 4ac > 0$, in which case the graph of the function $ax^2 + bx + c$ crosses the x-axis in two distinct points;*

(3) *r_1 and r_2 are* imaginary *and $r_1 \neq r_2$ if $b^2 - 4ac < 0$, in which case the graph of the function $ax^2 + bx + c$ does not cross or touch the x-axis;*

(4) *Let a, b, c be rational numbers. Then r_1 and r_2 are also rational and the function $ax^2 + bx + c$ can be factored if and only if $b^2 - 4ac$ is the square of a rational number.*

If a, b, c are not real, then also $r_1 = r_2$ if and only if $b^2 - 4ac = 0$.

EXAMPLE 1. Without solving the equation

$$2x^2 - 3x + 5 = 0,$$

determine the nature of its roots.

Solution. $a = 2$, $b = -3$, $c = 5$. The discriminant is

$$b^2 - 4ac = 9 - 4(2)(5) = -31 < 0.$$

Hence the roots are unequal and are imaginary.

EXAMPLE 2. Determine h so that the graph of the function $3x^2 - 4x - 2h$ does not cross or touch the x-axis.

Solution. Since the graph does not cross or touch the x-axis, the zeros of the function must be imaginary and by (3) above we must have $b^2 - 4ac < 0$. Hence,

$$b^2 - 4ac = 16 + 24h < 0,$$

and the values of h are: $h < -\frac{2}{3}$.

EXAMPLE 3. Can the expression $16x^2 - 76x + 21$ be factored?

Solution. The discriminant is

$$b^2 - 4ac = (76)^2 - 4 \cdot 16 \cdot 21 = 5776 - 1344 = 4432,$$

which is not a perfect square. Hence by (4) the expression cannot be factored into rational factors.

Exercise Group 8–6

In each of Exercises 1–18, compute the discriminant, and from its value determine the nature of the roots of the given equation.

1. $x^2 - 5x + 6 = 0$
2. $2x^2 - 3x - 5 = 0$
3. $3x^2 + 2x + 4 = 0$
4. $2x^2 + 4x + 2 = 0$
5. $3x^2 = 15$
6. $3x - 2 = 5x^2$
7. $2x^2 + 3x = 0$
8. $x^2 - 6x + 9 = 0$
9. $x^2 + x + 1 = 0$
10. $6x = 3x^2 + 2$
11. $10x + 1 = -25x^2$
12. $5x^2 = 2x - 1$
13. $2x^2 + 9x = 4$
14. $7x - 11 = 4x^2$
15. $16x^2 + 25 = 40x$
16. $\frac{4}{3}x^2 - x + \frac{1}{2} = 0$
17. $0.1x^2 + 2.3 = 1.7x$
18. $\sqrt{2}x^2 - 6x + \dfrac{9\sqrt{2}}{2} = 0$

In each of Exercises 19–24, use the value of the discriminant to determine the values of k for which the equation will have equal roots.

19. $3x^2 - 2kx + 1 = 0$
20. $2kx^2 - 5x + 2 = 0$
21. $5x^2 - 3x + k = 0$
22. $3x^2 - 4kx + 5k = 0$
23. $kx^2 - 3x^2 + 2kx - 5 = 0$
24. $kx^2 + x + k = 0$

8–7 Relations between the roots and coefficients of the quadratic equation. For convenience we shall rewrite the formulas for the roots of a quadratic equation. They are

$$r_1 = \frac{-b + \sqrt{b^2 - 4ac}}{2a}, \qquad r_2 = \frac{-b - \sqrt{b^2 - 4ac}}{2a}.$$

By adding these values, we find

$$r_1 + r_2 = -\frac{2b}{2a} = -\frac{b}{a}, \tag{8}$$

and by multiplying r_1 and r_2 and simplifying the result, we obtain

$$r_1 \cdot r_2 = \frac{b^2 - (b^2 - 4ac)}{4a^2} = \frac{4ac}{4a^2} = \frac{c}{a}. \tag{9}$$

If we designate the sum of the roots by S and the product by P, *the formulas are*

$$\boxed{S = -\frac{b}{a}, \qquad P = \frac{c}{a}.} \tag{10}$$

Formula (10) permits us to write any quadratic equation in the form

$$ax^2 + bx + c = a(x^2 - Sx + P) = 0,$$

and, since $a \neq 0$, we have another form for a quadratic equation:

$$\boxed{x^2 - Sx + P = 0.} \tag{11}$$

Substituting $r_1 + r_2$ for S and r_1r_2 for P in (11), we have

$$x^2 - (r_1 + r_2)x + r_1r_2 = 0;$$

on factoring the left member, we obtain

$$\boxed{(x - r_1)(x - r_2) = 0.} \tag{12}$$

Both (11) and (12) are very useful when it is desired to obtain a quadratic equation for which the roots are known.

EXAMPLE 1. Without finding the roots of the equation $3x^2 + 7x - 9 = 0$, determine the sum and product of these roots.

Solution. From Eqs. (8) and (9) above, we have, since $a = 3$, $b = 7$, $c = -9$,

$$r_1 + r_2 = -\frac{b}{a} = -\frac{7}{3}, \qquad r_1 \cdot r_2 = \frac{c}{a} = \frac{-9}{3} = -3.$$

EXAMPLE 2. Determine the value of the constant h so that the zeros of the function $3hx^2 + 5x + 7hx + 9$ are numerically equal but opposite in sign.

Solution. The stated condition becomes $r_1 = -r_2$; then $r_1 + r_2 = 0$, and since $a = 3h$ and $b = 5 + 7h$, we have

$$0 = -\frac{b}{a} = -\frac{5 + 7h}{3h}, \qquad \text{so that} \qquad h = -\frac{5}{7}.$$

EXAMPLE 3. Find a quadratic equation whose roots are $3 + 2\sqrt{3}$ and $3 - 2\sqrt{3}$.

Solution. From the given values of r_1 and r_2 we find that $S = 6$ and that $P = -3$. The desired equation is $x^2 - Sx + P = 0$, which takes the form $x^2 - 6x - 3 = 0$.

EXAMPLE 4. Find the value of the constant k if in the equation $2x^2 - kx^2 + 4x + 5k = 0$ one root is the reciprocal of the other.

Solution. From the given equation we see that $a = 2 - k$, $b = 4$, and $c = 5k$. If one root is the reciprocal of the other, then $r_1 = 1/r_2$, which reduces to $r_1 \cdot r_2 = 1$. Thus we have $P = 5k/(2 - k) = 1$ or $5k = 2 - k$. This reduces to $6k = 2$ or $k = \frac{1}{3}$.

EXAMPLE 5. Find the value of the constant k in the equation

$$2x^2 - kx + 3k = 0$$

if the difference of the roots is $\frac{5}{2}$.

Solution. If the roots are r_1 and r_2, we have

$$r_1 - r_2 = \frac{5}{2}, \qquad r_1 + r_2 = \frac{k}{2}.$$

Solving these equations simultaneously we find

$$r_1 = \frac{k+5}{4}, \qquad r_2 = \frac{k-5}{4}, \qquad \text{hence} \qquad r_1 r_2 = \frac{k^2 - 25}{16}.$$

But $r_1 r_2 = 3k/2$. Hence $(k^2 - 25)/16 = 3k/2$, which becomes

$$k^2 - 24k - 25 = 0;$$

this yields the two solutions $k = -1$ and $k = 25$.

EXERCISE GROUP 8-7

In Exercises 1–9, determine the sum and product of the roots of each equation.

1. $2x^2 - 3x + 7 = 0$
2. $-3x^2 + 2x - 5 = 0$
3. $7 - 5x = 3x^2$
4. $3x^2 = 7$
5. $a + bx = cx^2$
6. $dx + 5 = bx^2$
7. $cx + b = dx^2$
8. $ax^2 + bx = 0$
9. $x^2 - ix + 1 = 0$

In Exercises 10–21, find a quadratic equation whose roots are the given numbers.

10. $\frac{1}{4}, -\frac{2}{3}$
11. $2, -3$
12. $1 - \sqrt{3}, 1 + \sqrt{3}$
13. $-2, \frac{5}{2}$
14. $1 + i, 1 - i$
15. $\frac{1}{2}(-1 \pm i\sqrt{3})$
16. $a, 3a$
17. $-\frac{1}{4}, -\frac{2}{3}$
18. $-3 + 2i, -3 - 2i$
19. $2 + \sqrt{5}, 2 - \sqrt{5}$
20. $\frac{1}{3}(1 \pm 2i\sqrt{3})$
21. $\sqrt{a}/(\sqrt{a} \pm \sqrt{a - b})$

In each of Exercises 22–29, find the value of the constant h for which:

22. One root is zero: $2x^2 + hx + 3h + 4 = 0$.
23. One root is zero: $3hx^2 - 2x + 5h^2 = h$.
24. One root is the negative of the other: $3x^2 - hx + 7 = 0$.
25. One root is the negative of the other: $x^2 + 3hx + h^2 = x + 5$.
26. One root is 2: $hx^2 - 3x + 5h = x^2$.
27. One root is 3: $3hx^2 - 5x + 2h = 0$.
28. One root is the reciprocal of the other: $hx^2 - 5x + 2 = 0$.
29. One root is twice the other: $hx^2 + 36x + 18 = 0$.

8–8 Equations in quadratic form. The methods developed in Sections 8–1, 8–2, and 8–3 for determining the roots of a quadratic equation apply equally well to any equation which can be reduced to a quadratic equation by means of a substitution, that is, to *an equation which is quadratic in a function of* x.

EXAMPLE 1. Solve for x: $3x^4 - 4x^2 - 7 = 0$.

Solution. Let $v = x^2$, then $3v^2 - 4v - 7 = 0$, which is quadratic in v, so that the original equation is quadratic in x^2. By factoring, we have $(3v - 7)(v + 1) = 0$, and the values of v are $v = \frac{7}{3}, -1$. But $x = \pm\sqrt{v}$, therefore

$$x = \pm\sqrt{\frac{7}{3}} = \pm\frac{\sqrt{21}}{3},$$

and

$$x = \pm\sqrt{-1} = \pm i.$$

The four roots are

$$x = \pm\frac{\sqrt{21}}{3}, \quad \pm i.$$

EXAMPLE 2. Solve for x: $x^4 + 6x^3 + 2x^2 - 21x - 18 = 0$.

Solution. Completing the square on the first two terms leads to

$$(x^4 + 6x^3 + 9x^2) - 9x^2 + 2x^2 - 21x - 18 = 0,$$

or

$$(x^2 + 3x)^2 - 7(x^2 + 3x) - 18 = 0. \qquad (13)$$

Let $v = x^2 + 3x$; then

$$v^2 - 7v - 18 = 0,$$

or

$$(v - 9)(v + 2) = 0;$$

therefore

$$v - 9 = 0, \quad x^2 + 3x - 9 = 0 \quad \text{and} \quad x = \frac{-3 \pm 3\sqrt{5}}{2},$$

or

$$v + 2 = 0, \quad x^2 + 3x + 2 = 0 \quad \text{and} \quad x = -1, -2.$$

The four solutions are

$$x = -1, \quad -2, \quad \frac{-3 \pm 3\sqrt{5}}{2}.$$

Equation (13) is quadratic in $x^2 + 3x$.

Exercise Group 8-8

Determine all values of x satisfying each of the equations in Exercises 1–20.

1. $x^4 - 10x^2 + 9 = 0$
2. $x^4 - 5x^2 + 4 = 0$
3. $x^6 + 9x^3 + 8 = 0$
4. $x^6 - 19x^3 - 216 = 0$
5. $x^6 - 9x^3 + 8 = 0$
6. $x^4 - 13x^2 + 36 = 0$
7. $2x^4 - 13x^2 + 21 = 0$
8. $\dfrac{1}{x^2} - \dfrac{2}{x} = 8$
9. $\dfrac{1}{x^2} + \dfrac{3}{x} + 2 = 0$
10. $\dfrac{1}{x^4} - \dfrac{5}{x^2} - 36 = 0$
11. $(x^2 + 1)^2 + 4(x^2 + 1) - 45 = 0$
12. $(x^2 + 1)^2 + 6(x^2 + 1) + 8 = 0$
13. $(x^2 - x)^2 - 14(x^2 - x) + 24 = 0$
14. $(x^2 + x)^2 - 22(x^2 + x) + 40 = 0$
15. $3(x^2 + 3x)^2 - 2(x^2 + 3x) - 5 = 0$
16. $(x^2 - x - 20)(x^2 - x - 42) = 504$
17. $(x^2 + 2x - 1)(x^2 + 2x - 2) = 2$
18. $x^2 + 5x - 5 = \dfrac{6}{x^2 + 5x}$
19. $3\left(\dfrac{1}{x} + 1\right)^2 + 5\left(\dfrac{1}{x} + 1\right) = 2$
20. $\dfrac{x^2}{x + 1} + \dfrac{2(x + 1)}{x^2} = 3$

Solve each of the following equations for the trigonometric function which appears, and if x can be found without tables, find those values in the range $0 \leqq x < 2\pi$, i.e., for x between 0 and 2π, including 0.

21. $3 \sin^{1/2} x - 1 = 2 \sin^{1/4} x$
22. $2 \sin^4 x - \sin^2 x - 1 = 0$
23. $\sqrt{3} \tan x + 2 \tan^{1/2} x = \sqrt{3}$
24. $\cot^4 x - 2 \cot^2 x = 3$
25. $20 \sin^4 x - 23 \sin^2 x + 6 = 0$
26. $6 \cos^4 x + \cos^2 x = 2$

8-9 Irrational equations. Irrational equations are equations in which the unknown appears in one or more radicals. In general, the process of solving such an equation will involve the raising of quantities to certain powers. Since the even power of either a positive or negative quantity is positive, it follows that the process of raising to even powers may lead to an equation which has solutions which are not roots of the given equation. In other words, the method of solution may yield some values which are not roots, as well as those which are roots. The only certain way to determine which of the values found are roots is to *check in the original equation* all values obtained. Some examples will make this clear. Recall that if $x > 0$ there are two square roots of x, one of which is positive and the other negative. We agree that in this case the symbol $\sqrt{x}$ is to mean the *positive* square root of x.

EXAMPLE 1. Solve the equation $\sqrt{x+7} + x = 13$.

Solution. Subtract x from both members, which gives $\sqrt{x+7} = 13 - x$. Then square both members, obtaining

$$x + 7 = (13 - x)^2 = 169 - 26x + x^2,$$

$$x^2 - 27x + 162 = 0,$$

$$(x - 9)(x - 18) = 0 \qquad \text{and} \qquad x = 9, 18.$$

Checking the value $x = 9$ in the original equation, we find

$$\sqrt{9+7} + 9 = 13,$$

and $x = 9$ is seen to be a root. However, if we try to check $x = 18$, we find

$$\sqrt{18+7} + 18 \neq 13,$$

so that $x = 18$ is *not* a root of the original equation. Hence there is only one solution, $x = 9$, of the problem.

EXAMPLE 2. Solve $\sqrt{3x-5} + \sqrt{2x+3} + 1 = 0$.

Solution. As in the solution of Example 1 we isolate one of the radicals, obtaining

$$\sqrt{3x-5} = -1 - \sqrt{2x+3}.$$

Squaring both members gives

$$3x - 5 = 1 + 2\sqrt{2x+3} + 2x + 3,$$

which can be simplified to

$$2\sqrt{2x+3} = x - 9.$$

Squaring both members of this equation gives

$$4(2x + 3) = x^2 - 18x + 81,$$

and this can be reduced to

$$x^2 - 26x + 69 = 0,$$

whose roots are $x = 3, 23$.

Checking these results in the original equation gives

$$\sqrt{9-5} + \sqrt{6+3} + 1 \neq 0 \qquad \text{and} \qquad x = 3 \text{ is not a root;}$$

$$\sqrt{69-5} + \sqrt{46+3} + 1 \neq 0 \qquad \text{and} \qquad x = 23 \text{ is not a root.}$$

Thus we see that *the given equation has no solution.*

EXAMPLE 3. Solve $3\sqrt{2x+1} - 3\sqrt{x+4} = \sqrt{x-3}$.

Solution. Squaring both sides, we get

$$9(2x+1) - 18\sqrt{2x+1}\sqrt{x+4} + 9(x+4) = x - 3.$$

We now simplify this equation and rewrite it so that the radical term appears by itself on one side of the equation. Thus,

$$-18\sqrt{2x+1}\sqrt{x+4} = -26x - 48.$$

Dividing both sides by -2 gives

$$9\sqrt{2x+1}\sqrt{x+4} = 13x + 24,$$

and now squaring both sides, we get

$$81(2x^2 + 9x + 4) = 169x^2 + 624x + 576,$$

which reduces to

$$x^2 - 15x + 36 = 0,$$

so that $x = 3, 12$.

Substituting these values in the original equation, we find

$$3\sqrt{25} - 3\sqrt{16} = \sqrt{9} \quad \text{and} \quad x = 12 \text{ is a root;}$$

$$3\sqrt{7} - 3\sqrt{7} = 0 \quad \text{and} \quad x = 3 \text{ is a root.}$$

EXERCISE GROUP 8-9

In Exercises 1–30, determine all values of x which satisfy the equation.

1. $\sqrt{x+2} = 3$
2. $\sqrt{x+2} = a^2$
3. $\sqrt{x+3} = 2 + \sqrt{x}$
4. $\sqrt{x} + \sqrt{x+1} = 2$
5. $\sqrt{2x-5} = 2 + \sqrt{x-2}$
6. $\sqrt{3+x} + \sqrt{3x-2} = 1$
7. $\sqrt{10+x} = \sqrt{7x-6} - 2$
8. $\sqrt{6x-3} = 2 + \sqrt{3x-1}$
9. $\sqrt{2x-7} + \sqrt{2x+9} = 8$
10. $4x + 3 = \sqrt{7x^2 + 12x + 9}$
11. $x - \sqrt{5x+9} - 1 = 0$
12. $\sqrt{4x-1} = \sqrt{x+3} + \sqrt{x-2}$
13. $\sqrt{x-2} + \sqrt{3+2x} = 2$
14. $\sqrt{x+3} + \sqrt{x+8} = 5\sqrt{x}$
15. $\sqrt{2x+3} - \sqrt{4x-1} = \sqrt{6x-2}$
16. $\sqrt{4x+2} - \sqrt{2x} = \sqrt{2}$
17. $2\sqrt{x+4} = \sqrt{9-x} + \sqrt{x+1}$
18. $\sqrt{5+2x} - \sqrt{x-1} = \sqrt{x-6}$
19. $\sqrt{9-x^2} - \sqrt{4x^2+15} = \sqrt{3}$
20. $\sqrt{4x^2+15} - \sqrt{9-x^2} = \sqrt{3}$

21. $4\sqrt{x-2} - 2\sqrt{2x+3} = \sqrt{x+1}$

22. $\sqrt{2x-4} + \sqrt{3x+4} - \sqrt{10x-4} = 0$

23. $\sqrt{2x+17} + \sqrt{2x-4} = \frac{7}{2}\sqrt{x}$

24. $\sqrt{13 + 3\sqrt{x + 5 + 4\sqrt{x+1}}} - 5 = 0$

25. $\sqrt{2x-3} + 2\sqrt{3x-2} = 5$

26. $\sqrt{2x+7} - \sqrt{x+3} = \sqrt{2-x}$

27. $\dfrac{\sqrt{x+2}}{\sqrt{x-2}} - 10 = \dfrac{\sqrt{x-2}}{\sqrt{x+2}}$

28. $\dfrac{\sqrt{3x^2+4} + \sqrt{x^2+5}}{\sqrt{3x^2+4} - \sqrt{x^2+5}} = 7$

29. $\sqrt{x^2+3} + \dfrac{4}{\sqrt{x^2+3}} = 4$

30. $\dfrac{\sqrt{x}}{21-\sqrt{x}} + \dfrac{21-\sqrt{x}}{\sqrt{x}} = \dfrac{5}{2}$

31. The positive square root of a number is increased by 1 when the number is increased by 19. Find the number.

32. If a number is increased by 72, its positive square root is increased by 4. Find the number.

33. The square root of 3 less than twice a given number is 1 more than the square root of 2 more than the number. Find the number.

34. Find the dimensions of a rectangle if the diagonal is 2 more than the longer side, which in turn is 2 more than the shorter side.

In each of the following exercises, find the value of the trigonometric function which satisfies the given equation, and if x can be found without tables, find those values of x in the range $0 \leqq x < 2\pi$.

35. $\sqrt{3 + 2\sin x} - \sqrt{-1 + 4\sin x} = \sqrt{-2 + 6\sin x}$

36. $\sqrt{\cos x + 3} = 2 + \sqrt{\cos x}$

37. $\sqrt{2 + \tan x} + \sqrt{2(5\tan x + 8)} = \sqrt{10 + 3\tan x}$

38. $2 - \sqrt{\cot x} = \sqrt{1 + \cot x}$

Review Exercises

In Exercises 1–6, use the method of completing the square to solve for x.

1. $5x^2 - 13x = 3$
2. $5x^2 + 13 = 3x$
3. $2x^2 + 3x + 5 = 0$
4. $3x^2 - 5x - 7 = 0$
5. $3x^2 - 2x + 8 = 0$
6. $6x^2 + x + 35 = 0$

In Exercises 7–18, use the quadratic formula in solving for x.

7. $3ax^2 - 2bx + 3a = 0$
8. $rx^2 + qx + p = 0$
9. $2ax^2 - cx + a = 0$
10. $ax^2 + cx + b = x$
11. $bx^2 + cx + a = x$
12. $x^2 + ax + b = c$
13. $2x^2 + 3x + 5 = 0$
14. $3x^2 + 2x = 17$
15. $5x^2 = 13 - 3x$
16. $2x^2 + 7 = 5x$
17. $5x^2 - 3x + 7 = 0$
18. $17 = 5x - x^2$

In Exercises 19–30, solve for x by the most appropriate method.

19. $2x^2 + bx + 6 = cx^2 + 3x$
20. $x^2 + ax + b = cx - dx^2$
21. $bx + c = ax^2 + d$
22. $x^2 + cx + d = ax^2 + bx$
23. $2x + 13 = ax^2 + bx - c$
24. $(x - b)^2 = a(x - c)$
25. $6x^2 + x = 35$
26. $6x^2 = 31x - 35$
27. $3x^2 = 2(x + 4)$
28. $ax^2 + bc = (b + ac)x$
29. $bx(x - a) = c(a - x)$
30. $(ax + b)^2 = x^2$

In Exercises 31–36, determine the values of k for which the given equation will have equal roots.

31. $x^2 + kx - 3k = 0$
32. $x^2 + 2kx + 5 = k$
33. $kx^2 = 2x^2 - 5kx + 7$
34. $(x - 2k)^2 = k(x - 2)$
35. $3x^2 + 5x + k = kx^2$
36. $(x + 2k)^2 = k(x + 2)$

In Exercises 37–42, determine the character of the roots and also the sum and product of the roots (without finding the roots).

37. $3x^2 + 5x - 7 = 0$
38. $2x^2 + 3x = 5x - 7$
39. $(3x + 1)^2 = 3(x - 3)$
40. $(3 - x)^2 = 5(x + 1)$
41. $x(x - 2) = 3(x - 3)$
42. $(x - 1)(x - 2) = 2x(x - 3)$

In Exercises 43–52, find all values of x which satisfy the given equation.

43. $x^6 + 9x^3 + 8 = 0$
44. $x^4 + 12x^2 - 64 = 0$
45. $x^4 + 16x^2 = 225$
46. $(4x^2 - 5)^2 - 3(4x^2 - 5) = 4$
47. $3(x^2 + 1)^2 = 2(x^2 + 5)$
48. $\sqrt{2 - x} + \sqrt{x - 1} = \sqrt{2x - 3}$
49. $\sqrt{x - 5} + \sqrt{x + 7} = 2\sqrt{x - 1}$
50. $2\sqrt{2x + 1} - \sqrt{x + 3} = \sqrt{3x - 1}$
51. $\sqrt{9x + 3} = \sqrt{1 - 3x} + \sqrt{3 - 6x}$
52. $\sqrt{25x - 15} + \sqrt{x + 9} = 2\sqrt{3x + 7}$

CHAPTER 9

CIRCLE RELATIONS. RIGHT TRIANGLES

9–1 Relations in a circle. Radian measure of angles was introduced in Section 6–4. We consider here an application that is not specifically related to trigonometric functions. Let AB, of length s, be an arc on a circle of radius r (Fig. 9–1), and let θ be the angle subtended at the center of the circle by AB. Since the length of arc on a circle is proportional to the subtended angle, we have, for some constant k,

$$s = k\theta.$$

To find the value of the constant of proportionality k, we note that if θ is measured in radians, then $s = 2\pi r$ when $\theta = 2\pi$, since the complete circumference of a circle subtends an angle about the center O which is a complete rotation. Hence $k = r$ and, on substituting this value in the above equation, we have the desired *relation for the length of arc s on a circle in terms of the central angle θ*,

$$\boxed{s = r\theta, \qquad \theta \text{ in radians.}} \tag{1}$$

The area of the sector AOB, that is, of the part of the circle bounded by radii OA and OB, and arc AB, and with central angle θ, is also proportional to θ. Hence, for some constant K, we have

$$A = K\theta.$$

To determine the value of K, we use the fact that if θ is in radians, then $A = \pi r^2$ when $\theta = 2\pi$, since a complete rotation at O corresponds to a sector which is the entire circle. Hence $K = \frac{1}{2}r^2$, and *the formula for the area of AOB in terms of the central angle θ is*

$$\boxed{A = \tfrac{1}{2}r^2\theta, \qquad \theta \text{ in radians.}} \tag{2}$$

The appropriate formulas for converting back and forth from radian measure to degree measure appear in Section 6–4.

EXAMPLE 1. Find the length of arc on a circle of radius 16 in. corresponding to a central angle of 112°, and find also the area of the sector formed by the angle.

Solution. For both quantities the radian measure of the angle is required; thus, we obtain

$$112° = 112 \times \frac{\pi}{180}\text{ rad} = 1.955 \text{ rad.}$$

By (1) the length of arc s is then

$$s = r\theta = 16 \times 1.955 = 31.280 \text{ in.},$$

and by (2) the area A of the sector is

$$A = \tfrac{1}{2}r^2\theta = \tfrac{1}{2}(256)(1.955) = 250.240 \text{ in}^2.$$

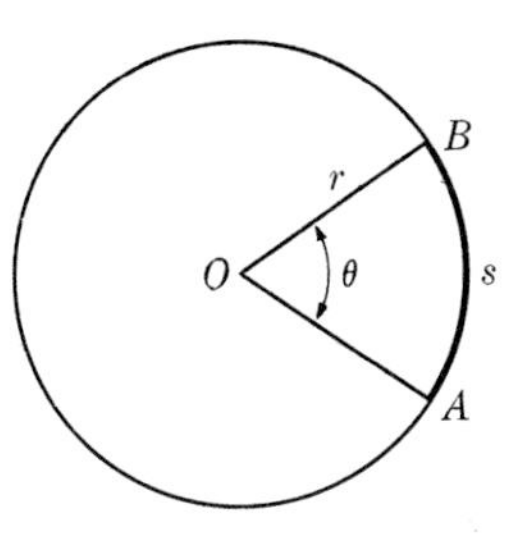

FIGURE 9-1

Suppose OA revolves about the center of the above circle in such a way that in equal intervals of time equal angles are traversed. *The angular speed of OA is then defined as the angle traversed per unit time.* Let OA revolve through an angle θ in the time t. If ω denotes the angular speed of OA, we have the formula

$$\boxed{\omega = \frac{\theta}{t}.} \tag{3}$$

As OA revolves at a *constant* angular speed about O, the point A moves along the circle with a constant linear speed, that is, in such a way that *the same length of arc is traversed in any unit time.* If v denotes the linear speed of A on the circle, then the corresponding formula is

$$\boxed{v = \frac{s}{t}.} \tag{4}$$

Dividing both members of Eq. (1) by t, we have

$$\frac{s}{t} = r\frac{\theta}{t};$$

by (3) and (4) this equation gives the important *relation between the angular speed ω of OA, and the linear speed v of A, as*

$$\boxed{v = r\omega, \qquad \omega \text{ in radians per unit time.}} \tag{5}$$

EXAMPLE 2. The outer radius of the wheels of an automobile is 28 in. If the vehicle is traveling 30 mph, at how many revolutions per second are the wheels turning about their centers?

Solution. As a wheel rotates through any angle θ, the distance s through which the vehicle moves is given by the length of arc on the circumference subtended by θ, so that $s = r\theta$. If both members of this equation are divided by t, it is then clear that the linear speed v of the vehicle and the angular speed ω of the wheels are related by Eq. (5). We have $v = 30$ mph $= 528$ in/sec; hence, by (5),

$$\omega = \frac{v}{r} = \frac{528}{28} \text{ rad/sec} = 18.9 \text{ rad/sec}.$$

Since a complete revolution corresponds to a central angle of 2π, we divide by 2π to convert ω to revolutions per second, and find

$$\frac{\omega}{2\pi} = \frac{18.9}{2\pi} \text{ rev/sec} = 3.01 \text{ rev/sec}.$$

Exercise Group 9–1

In each of Exercises 1–18, the central angle and radius of the circle involved have the values given. Find the length of the intercepted arc, and the area of the sector.

1. 2 rad, 3 ft
2. 0.5 rad, 2 ft
3. 2.3 rad, 5 in.
4. 1.6 rad, 7 in.
5. 150°, 7 ft
6. 270°, 125 ft
7. 18°, 150 cm
8. 108°, 30 cm
9. 225°, 176 cm
10. 315°, 165 cm
11. 8° 30′, 80 yd
12. 17° 50′, 35 yd
13. 317° 10′, 0.05 in.
14. 331° 20′, 0.07 in.
15. 50°, 213 ft
16. 40°, 312 ft
17. 73°, 0.004 ft
18. 190°, 0.003 ft

Find the measure of the central angle in both radians and degrees, and the area of the sector, if the values of the intercepted arc and radius are those given in each of Exercises 19–30. The first quantity in each case is the arc length.

19. 27 in., 9 in.
20. 13 ft, 3.5 ft
21. 213 cm, 105 cm
22. 49 cm, 12.3 cm
23. 3.05 ft, 8.13 ft
24. 2.34 in., 15.6 in.
25. 217 in., 4.3 ft
26. 4.3 ft, 217 in.
27. 125 cm, 5 m
28. 35.2 in., 3.2 ft
29. 2.8 ft, 53.2 in.
30. 215 cm, 3 m

31. The tires of an automobile are 30 in. in diameter and the automobile is traveling at a speed of 60 mph (88 ft/sec). Find the angular speed of the wheels in rad/sec.

32. A rotary lawn mower has a blade 16 in. in diameter and the motor runs at a speed of 3400 rpm. What is the linear speed in ft/sec of the tip of the blade?

33. The propeller of a small airplane is 74 in. from tip to tip and it makes 2400 rpm at cruising speed. Find the linear speed in ft/sec of the tip of the blade.

34. In driving around a circular curve on a highway, the driver notes that the length of the curve is 0.2 mi and that the car turns through an angle of 20°. What is the radius of the curve in feet?

35. A curve on a highway, in the form of an arc of a circle, is 660 ft long. If the radius of the circle is 2521 ft, find the angle in degrees through which a car turns in going around the curve.

36. What is the angular speed, in rad/sec, of the hour hand of a clock?

37. Let us assume that the moon travels around the earth at a uniform linear speed in a circular orbit. If the orbit is 239,000 mi in radius and if it takes the moon $27\frac{1}{3}$ days to make one complete revolution, what is the linear speed in mi/sec of the moon in its orbit?

38. The moon subtends an angle of approximately 31′ to an observer on the earth. Find the approximate diameter of the moon if it is assumed to be 239,000 mi distant from the observer. (*Hint:* Consider the diameter of the moon as a circular arc.)

39. An electric motor which runs at 3000 rpm has a 4 in. (4 in. in diameter) pulley which drives a belt. Find the linear speed (in ft/sec) of the belt. If the belt drives another pulley which is 10 in. in diameter, find the angular speed in rad/sec of this second pulley.

9–2 Interpolation in the trigonometric table. In the applications of trigonometry the values of the trigonometric functions are often required for angles given more accurately than to the nearest 10′. Table 2 may be used to find the values of the functions for angles which are given to any number of minutes. *The method to be used is that of linear interpolation.* By the process of *direct interpolation* the table may be used to find the values of the functions of such angles, and by *inverse interpolation* the table may be used to find an angle to the nearest minute when the value of a trigonometric function of the angle is known.

The principle of linear interpolation, as applied here, is that a sufficiently small arc of the graph of a trigonometric function may be replaced by a straight line.

We may interpret this principle to mean that the difference between angles sufficiently close in value is proportional to the difference between the corresponding values of any trigonometric function.

In applying interpolation to a table of trigonometric functions, it is important to keep in mind that as the angle increases from 0° to 90°, the sine, tangent, and secant also increase, while the cosine, cotangent, and cosecant decrease.

Example 1. Find tan 53° 18′.

Solution. The given angle lies between 53° 10′ and 53° 20′. Hence, by the above principle, we have

$$\frac{\tan 53^\circ 18' - \tan 53^\circ 10'}{\tan 53^\circ 20' - \tan 53^\circ 10'} = \frac{53^\circ 18' - 53^\circ 10'}{53^\circ 20' - 53^\circ 10'},$$

which becomes

$$\frac{\tan 53^\circ 18' - 1.335}{1.343 - 1.335} = \frac{8}{10}.$$

This equation can be solved for tan 53° 18′ as

$$\begin{aligned}\tan 53^\circ\,18' &= 1.335 + 0.8 \times (1.343 - 1.335)\\ &= 1.335 + 0.8 \times 0.008\\ &= 1.335 + 0.006\\ &= 1.341.\end{aligned}$$

Note that this value is rounded off to four figures. The entire process can be abbreviated in the following schematic manner:

$$10\left[\begin{array}{l} 8\left[\begin{array}{ll}53^\circ\,10' & 1335\\ 53^\circ\,18' & x\end{array}\right]h \\ \quad\; 53^\circ\,20' \quad 1343 \end{array}\right]8 \qquad \begin{aligned}\frac{h}{8} &= \frac{8}{10}, \quad h = 0.8 \times 8,\\ h &= 6 \text{ (to nearest integer)},\end{aligned}$$

where the differences in the values of the function are understood to be in the last decimal places. Hence,

$$x = \tan 53^\circ\,18' = 1.335 + 0.006 = 1.341.$$

EXAMPLE 2. Find cos 18° 27′.

Solution. Schematically, we have

$$10\left[\begin{array}{l} 7\left[\begin{array}{ll}18^\circ\,20' & 9492\\ 18^\circ\,27' & x\end{array}\right]h \\ \quad\; 18^\circ\,30' \quad 9483 \end{array}\right]9 \qquad \begin{aligned}\frac{h}{9} &= \frac{7}{10}, \quad h = \frac{63}{10},\\ h &= 6 \text{ (to nearest integer)}.\end{aligned}$$

Hence, since the cosine is a decreasing function in the first quadrant,

$$x = 0.9492 - 0.0006 = 0.9486.$$

A similar procedure, and corresponding schematic arrangement, can be used for inverse interpolation.

EXAMPLE 3. Find θ if $\sin\theta = 0.7423$.

Solution. From the table we see that $\sin\theta$ is between sin 47° 50′ and sin 48°. The schematic arrangement becomes

$$19\left[\begin{array}{l} 11\left[\begin{array}{ll}7412 & 47^\circ\,50'\\ 7423 & \theta\end{array}\right]h \\ \quad\;\; 7431 \quad 48^\circ \end{array}\right]10, \qquad \begin{aligned}\frac{h}{10} &= \frac{11}{19}, \quad h = \frac{110}{19},\\ h &= 6 \text{ (to nearest integer)}.\end{aligned}$$

Hence, we obtain

$$\theta = 47^\circ\,50' + 6' = 47^\circ\,56'.$$

EXAMPLE 4. Find θ if $\cot\theta = 2.172$.

Solution. Schematically, we have

$$16\left[5\left[\begin{matrix}2177 & 24^\circ\,40' \\ 2172 & \theta\end{matrix}\right]h \atop \begin{matrix}2161 & 24^\circ\,50'\end{matrix}\right]10, \qquad \frac{h}{10} = \frac{5}{16}, \quad h = \frac{50}{16},$$

$$h = 3 \text{ (to nearest integer).}$$

Hence,

$$\theta = 24^\circ\,40' + 3' = 24^\circ\,43'.$$

Exercise Group 9-2

Use Table 2 to find the values of the trigonometric functions in Exercises 1-24.

1. $\sin 31^\circ\,14'$
2. $\cos 42^\circ\,37'$
3. $\tan 63^\circ\,46'$
4. $\cot 74^\circ\,13'$
5. $\cos 84^\circ\,15'$
6. $\sin 59^\circ\,28'$
7. $\cot 17^\circ\,59'$
8. $\tan 22^\circ\,11'$
9. $\sin 7^\circ\,52'$
10. $\cos 53^\circ\,23'$
11. $\cot 46^\circ\,45'$
12. $\tan 15^\circ\,55'$
13. $\sin 213^\circ\,17'$
14. $\cos 312^\circ\,42'$
15. $\tan 173^\circ\,13'$
16. $\sec 47^\circ\,18'$
17. $\csc 132^\circ\,12'$
18. $\sec 217^\circ\,15'$
19. $\csc 313^\circ\,13'$
20. $\cot 284^\circ\,17'$
21. $\csc 42^\circ\,18'$
22. $\sec 147^\circ\,14'$
23. $\csc 413^\circ\,16'$
24. $\sec 343^\circ\,12'$

Use Table 2 to find the smallest value of the angle θ, such that $0^\circ < \theta < 180^\circ$, to the nearest minute in Exercises 25-48.

25. $\cos\theta = 0.7703$
26. $\sin\theta = 0.0099$
27. $\cot\theta = 4.536$
28. $\tan\theta = 0.6275$
29. $\sin\theta = 0.5116$
30. $\cos\theta = -0.1059$
31. $\tan\theta = -9.372$
32. $\cot\theta = 0.2365$
33. $\cot\theta = -0.8713$
34. $\sin\theta = 0.9162$
35. $\cos\theta = -0.5385$
36. $\tan\theta = -1.147$
37. $\sin\theta = 0.3537$
38. $\cos\theta = 0.6300$
39. $\tan\theta = 9.800$
40. $\sec\theta = 1.132$
41. $\csc\theta = 1.968$
42. $\cot\theta = -1.121$
43. $\sec\theta = -5.294$
44. $\csc\theta = 8.039$
45. $\sec\theta = -16.98$
46. $\csc\theta = 5.296$
47. $\csc\theta = 10.53$
48. $\sec\theta = 2.658$

9-3 Solution of right triangles. It has been mentioned, in Section 6-1, that the origins of the study of trigonometry lie in the determination of distances on the earth by the use of triangles. This process involves the solution of triangles. In the present chapter the methods which apply to the solution of right triangles are considered, while oblique triangles will be treated in Chapter 15.

A right triangle contains, in addition to the right angle, two acute angles, and the three sides, which are the *hypotenuse* and the two *arms* or *legs*. Let the sides and angles of the triangle be called the *parts of the triangle*. By theorems of plane geometry it is known that a right triangle is determined when, in addition to the right angle, any two parts, of which at least one is a side, are known. *To solve a right triangle shall mean to find all unknown parts.*

It will facilitate the solution of a right triangle to have formulas for the trigonometric functions of the acute angles in terms of the sides. We shall use a *standard lettering* ABC for a right triangle, with C as the vertex of the right angle, and with the side opposite any vertex designated by the similar lower-case letter.

Let right triangle ABC be placed in a coordinate system so that angle A is in standard position and side CB is perpendicular to the x-axis (Fig. 9–2). Then B is a point on the terminal side of angle A, and b, a, c are the coordinates and polar distance, respectively, of B. By the definitions of the trigonometric functions given in Section 6–6, we have

$$\sin A = \frac{a}{c} = \frac{\text{opposite side}}{\text{hypotenuse}},$$

$$\cos A = \frac{b}{c} = \frac{\text{adjacent side}}{\text{hypotenuse}},$$

$$\tan A = \frac{a}{b} = \frac{\text{opposite side}}{\text{adjacent side}},$$

$$\cot A = \frac{b}{a} = \frac{\text{adjacent side}}{\text{opposite side}},$$

$$\sec A = \frac{c}{b} = \frac{\text{hypotenuse}}{\text{adjacent side}},$$

$$\csc A = \frac{c}{a} = \frac{\text{hypotenuse}}{\text{opposite side}}.$$

In these equations the designations "opposite side" and "adjacent side" always refer to the angle involved. Once obtained, the formulas are, of course, independent of any coordinate system, and in particular, the verbal expressions apply to either acute angle of the triangle. Thus, if $\sec B$ is desired, the term "adjacent side" must be taken in relation to angle B, and we find that $\sec B = c/a$.

If an unknown angle of a right triangle is to be found, use is made of a trigonometric function of that angle which involves two known sides; to find an unknown side, a trigonometric function of a known angle is used which

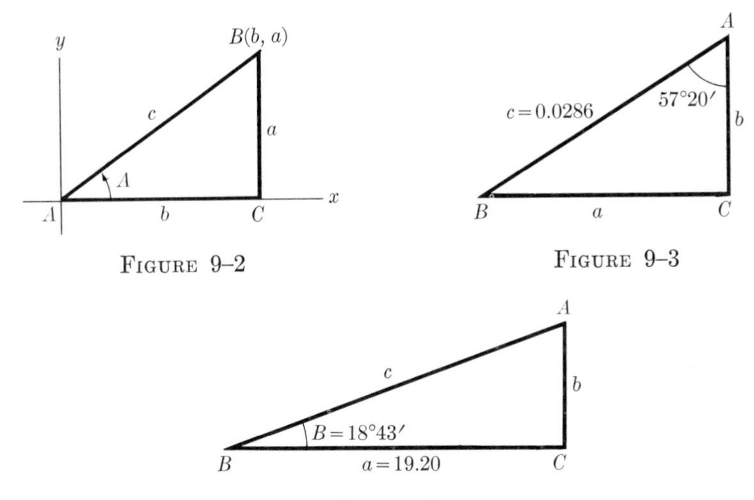

FIGURE 9-2

FIGURE 9-3

FIGURE 9-4

contains a known side and the unknown side. As a general rule it is desirable, where possible, to make use of given parts of a triangle in preference to parts which have been computed.

EXAMPLE 1. Solve the right triangle with $A = 57° 20'$, $c = 0.0286$.

Solution. To find side a we use the relation $\sin A = a/c$, which involves the known side c, and side a. This relation can be solved for a to give

$$a = c \sin A = 0.0286 \sin 57° 20'$$
$$= 0.0286 \times 0.8418 = 0.0241.$$

To find side b, we have similarly, using a relation which involves the given side c, and side b,

$$b = c \cos A = 0.0286 \cos 57° 20'$$
$$= 0.0286 \times 0.5398 = 0.0154.$$

Finally, we have $B = 90° - 57° 20' = 32° 40'$. (See Fig. 9-3.)

EXAMPLE 2. Solve the right triangle with $B = 18° 43'$, $a = 19.20$.

Solution. To find side c we solve the equation $\cos B = a/c$ for c; thus,

$$c = \frac{a}{\cos B} = \frac{19.20}{\cos 18° 43'} = \frac{19.20}{0.9471} = 20.27.$$

Side b is then found from the equation $\tan B = b/a$, as follows:

$$b = a \tan B = 19.20 \tan 18° 43' = 19.20 \times 0.3388 = 6.505.$$

Again, $A = 90° - 18° 43' = 71° 17'$. (See Fig. 9-4.)

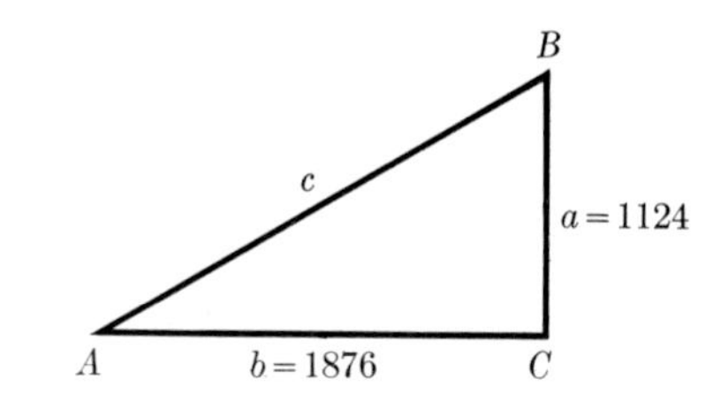

FIGURE 9–5

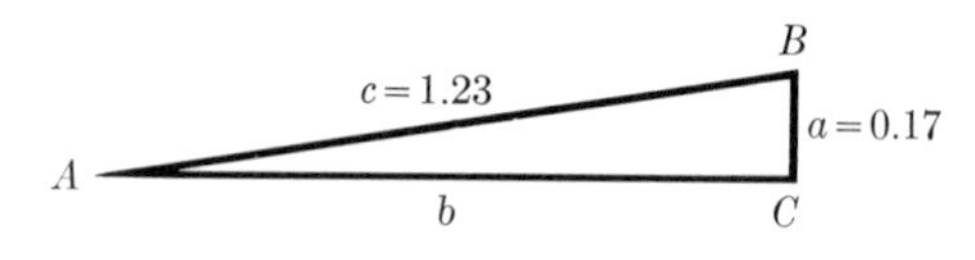

FIGURE 9–6

EXAMPLE 3. Solve the right triangle with $a = 1124$, $b = 1876$.

Solution. We may find angle A as follows, using a function of A which involves a and b (see Fig. 9–5):

$$\tan A = \frac{a}{b} = \frac{1124}{1876} = 0.5991; \qquad A = 30^\circ\, 56'.$$

Then the equation $\sin A = a/c$ may be solved for c, and we have

$$c = \frac{a}{\sin A} = \frac{1124}{\sin 30^\circ\, 56'} = \frac{1124}{0.5140} = 2187.$$

The remaining angle is $B = 90^\circ - 30^\circ\, 56' = 59^\circ\, 04'$.

EXAMPLE 4. Solve the right triangle with $a = 0.17$, $c = 1.23$.

Solution. We may find angle A as follows (see Fig. 9–6):

$$\sin A = \frac{a}{c} = \frac{0.17}{1.23} = 0.1382; \qquad A = 7^\circ\, 57'.$$

Then the equation $\cos A = b/c$ may be solved for b, and we have

$$b = c \cos A = 1.23 \times 0.9904 = 1.22.$$

Angle B is found to be $82^\circ\, 03'$.

EXERCISE GROUP 9–3

Solve the right triangles in Exercises 1–30. (It is assumed that $C = 90^\circ$.)

1. $c = 83.15$, $A = 73^\circ\, 12'$
2. $b = 32.10$, $A = 37^\circ\, 21'$
3. $a = 38.20$, $B = 69^\circ\, 38'$
4. $c = 76.03$, $B = 53^\circ\, 17'$

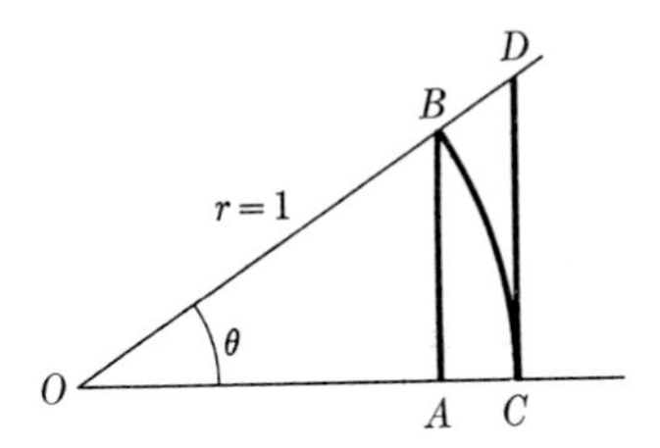

FIGURE 9–7

5. $b = 2.130$, $B = 32° 26'$
6. $a = 0.0316$, $A = 23° 48'$
7. $b = 390.2$, $A = 42° 23'$
8. $a = 276.1$, $B = 47° 54'$
9. $c = 89.36$, $B = 58° 15'$
10. $c = 312.2$, $A = 17° 59'$
11. $a = 1.325$, $b = 2.334$
12. $a = 0.1328$, $c = 2.017$
13. $b = 0.0162$, $c = 0.1838$
14. $c = 3127$, $b = 1732$
15. $c = 893.0$, $a = 431.5$
16. $b = 0.01307$, $a = 0.0017$
17. $a = 31.75$, $A = 21° 34'$
18. $a = 73.52$, $B = 84° 06'$
19. $b = 426.9$, $a = 249.6$
20. $b = 74.95$, $B = 43° 39'$
21. $a = 24.96$, $B = 31° 43'$
22. $a = 3.296$, $c = 4.532$
23. $b = 0.2964$, $B = 58° 17'$
24. $b = 2.917$, $c = 3.763$
25. $a = 0.1245$, $b = 0.2967$
26. $b = 3.761$, $a = 7.324$
27. $c = 8.934$, $A = 63° 05'$
28. $c = 49.61$, $B = 42° 12'$
29. $c = 0.4368$, $a = 0.2109$
30. $c = 4.784$, $b = 2.311$

31. Compare the lengths AB, CD, and the arc length CB for $\theta = 5°, 3°, 1°$ in Fig. 9–7.

32. A sector of angle θ is cut from a circle of radius a, and the remaining portion is used to form the curved surface of a right circular cone. Express the altitude of the cone as a function of θ.

33. Let A, B, C be the vertices of an oblique triangle, and let $BC = a$, $AC = b$, and $AB = c$. Draw altitude BD to side AC. Justify the following equations, if angle A is acute:

$$a^2 = |BD|^2 + |CD|^2 = c^2 - |AD|^2 + |CD|^2 = c^2 - |AD|^2 + (b - |AD|)^2.$$

Expand the right member and obtain the result

$$a^2 = b^2 + c^2 - 2bc \cos A.$$

Show that the derivation holds in essentially the same form if A is obtuse.

9–4 Approximate numbers. Almost all of the numbers which arise in applications of trigonometry as results of observation or measurement are approximate, or rather, approximations to exact numbers. Measurements of physical quantities are governed by the accuracy of the measuring devices used. If a length L is measured as 4.34 in., the implication is that the exact length in inches is closer to 4.34 than to any other two-decimal number and, in fact,

$$4.335 \leqq L \leqq 4.345.$$

Approximations are also used for numbers with many decimal places, or for numbers which cannot be represented by a finite decimal. The number π, which is an infinite decimal, is given to four decimal places as 3.1416; this means that 3.1416 is the number with four decimal places closest to the exact value of π, so that

$$3.14155 \leqq \pi \leqq 3.14165.$$

In the discussion of the accuracy of approximate numbers, the idea of *significant figures* plays an important part. In a number in decimal form any digit other than zero is always a significant figure. Zeros may or may not be significant. Zeros between nonzero digits are significant, while initial zeros are never significant. Whether final zeros in a number are significant or not depends on what is intended. For example, if 2030 is an approximate number, the first three digits are certainly significant. If the final zero is not meant to be significant, the exact number is merely known to be in the range

$$2025 \leqq x \leqq 2035.$$

However, if the final zero is meant to be significant, the exact number lies in the smaller range

$$2029.5 \leqq x \leqq 2030.5.$$

We shall agree that *final zeros which appear after the decimal point are significant.* It is then possible to express any number N in the form

$$N = m \cdot 10^c,$$

where $1 \leqq m < 10$, all digits of m are significant, and c is some integer. A number in this form is said to be in *scientific notation.* Thus, if 2030 has three significant figures it is written as 2.03×10^3, while with four significant figures the number is written as 2.030×10^3.

A number is said to be *correct to n significant figures* if the error in the $(n + 1)$st figure is at most 5; a number is *correct to n decimal places* if the error is at most 5 in the $(n + 1)$st decimal place.

Rounding off a number was explained in Section 6–9 in relation to the trigonometric table. A similar procedure applies in rounding off a number in any place, before or after the decimal point. In the former case, enough zeros are added to give the correct number of places before the decimal point. In any case, the rounded-off number has its last significant figure in the place in question.

EXAMPLES. 4.146 rounded off in the second decimal place is 4.15.

4.146 rounded off in the first decimal place is 4.1.

4146 rounded off in the tens place is 4150, with the zero not significant, or in scientific notation, 4.15×10^3.

20.75 rounded off in the first decimal place is 20.8, in accordance with our agreement to make the last figure even.

In general, the accuracy of a number is governed by the number of significant figures, and not by the size of the number. The numbers 4.146 and 4146 are thus equally accurate, if they are correct in the figures given.

9–5 Operations with approximate numbers. The results of arithmetic operations with approximate numbers are themselves of course subject to error, and it becomes necessary to know how such errors are propagated.

If the exact numbers $x = 20.4$ and $y = 8.709$ are added, the sum is 29.109. However, if x and y are merely known to be correct in the figures given, we have

$$20.35 \leqq x \leqq 20.45$$

$$8.7085 \leqq y \leqq 8.7095.$$

It can be shown that

$$29.0585 \leqq x + y \leqq 29.1595$$

where $29.0585 = 20.35 + 8.7085$, and $29.1595 = 20.45 + 8.7095$. It follows that the sum, which lies between 29.0585 and 29.1595, can certainly not be given to more than one decimal. Even correct to one decimal, the sum may be either 29.1 or 29.2. There is then nothing gained by carrying to more than two decimals any of the numbers to be added. If we round off 8.709 in the second decimal place as 8.71, and add 20.4, we get 29.11. This is then rounded off in the first decimal place, and the result is 29.1, of which the last figure may still be in error.

The product of the exact numbers 14.326 and 8.93 is 127.93118. However, if the numbers are merely known to be correct in the figures given, the product of the corresponding exact numbers must lie between

$$14.3255 \times 8.925 = 127.8550875$$

and

$$14.3265 \times 8.935 = 128.0072775.$$

Thus there is no justification in giving the product more accurately than to three significant figures, as 128, which is also the product to three significant figures of 14.33 and 8.93.

Similar considerations will show that in the division of two approximate numbers, the quotient cannot be given more accurately than the less accurate number.

We shall not give proofs here, but the preceding discussion should indicate the reasonableness of the following rule.

RULE. *Before adding (or subtracting) approximate numbers, round off each number in the place to the right of the last significant figure of the numbers which is farthest to the left with respect to the decimal point; the sum is then rounded off in the place of the last significant figure.*

Before multiplying or dividing numbers, round off the more accurate numbers to one more significant figure than in the least accurate number; the result is then rounded off to the number of significant figures of the least accurate number.

EXAMPLE. Use the above rule to compute the sum of 23.79, 0.3246, 23450, and 34.278 to the accuracy permissible.

Solution. Write the numbers to be added in a column as displayed:

```
   23.79
    0.3246
23450.
   34.278
```

The last significant figures of these numbers are 9, 6, 5, and 8. We note that of these last significant numbers the 5 is the "farthest to the left with respect to the decimal point." This last significant figure 5 is in the ten's place and so in accordance with the rule we round off each number in the unit's place (which is the place to the right of the ten's place). After rounding off in the unit's place we obtained the numbers illustrated. Then according to the rule we round the sum off in the ten's place obtaining 23510 as the desired sum.

```
   24.
    0.
23450.
   34.
------
23508.
```

It should be understood that the last figure of any result obtained by applying the stated rule may still be in error. Furthermore, in the application of this rule, the position of the decimal point is relevant only in addition or subtraction.

A convenient working rule concerning significant figures in the solution of a triangle will now be given.

RULE. *Accuracy to two significant figures in the sides of a triangle corresponds to accuracy in the angles to the nearest degree; accuracy to three significant figures corresponds to accuracy in the angles to the nearest* 10 *minutes; accuracy to four significant figures corresponds to accuracy in the angles to the nearest minute.*

Exercise Group 9–4

Round off the numbers in Exercises 1–12 to (1) four significant figures; (2) to three significant figures.

1. 23.4567 2. 0.03421507 3. 0.003452356 4. 2.173421
5. 2178563 6. 7132.475 7. 0.96154 8. 0.089755
9. 2.32509 10. 304780.1 11. 0.012345 12. 0.013245

Express the maximum possible error in the approximate quantities given in Exercises 13–21.

13. 31.2 cm 14. 0.023 in. 15. 4350 ft (last 0 significant)
16. 6.3127 mi 17. 71.826 ft^3 18. 20300 $in.^2$ (last 0 not significant)
19. 0.0013 yd 20. 21789 cm^2 21. 354100 $in.^3$ (last 0 significant)

Perform the indicated operations in Exercises 22–31, and round off the results to the correct number of significant figures.

22. $0.39678 - 2.34 + 8.2$ 23. $3.2756 + 2.436 - 3.26$
24. $8.96 + 1.317 - 5.23479$ 25. $76.93 - 23.5 + 3.1697$
26. $(54.960)(35.2)$ 27. $(317.5)(3.12)$ 28. $(0.235)(2.3)$
29. $43.1 \div 0.00034$ 30. $0.00041 \div 2.167$ 31. $(3.123)^2$

In Exercises 32–43, find the value of θ ($0 < \theta < 90°$) as accurately as is justified by the given data.

32. $\sin\theta = 0.353$ 33. $\cos\theta = 0.63$ 34. $\tan\theta = 2.4$
35. $\cot\theta = 0.57$ 36. $\sec\theta = 72.3$ 37. $\csc\theta = 5.296$
38. $\tan\theta = \dfrac{2.314}{3.16}$ 39. $\sin\theta = \dfrac{3.14}{21.13}$ 40. $\cos\theta = \dfrac{41.3}{59.61}$
41. $\sec\theta = \dfrac{9.33}{3.1}$ 42. $\csc\theta = \dfrac{86.75}{52}$ 43. $\cot\theta = \dfrac{9.834}{8.9}$

Solve the right triangles in Exercises 44–53, and round off the results to the correct number of significant figures.

44. $a = 24.96$, $B = 31°$ 45. $a = 3.296$, $c = 4.5$
46. $b = 0.2964$, $B = 58°$ 47. $b = 2.9$, $c = 3.763$
48. $a = 0.0036$, $b = 0.2967$ 49. $b = 3.761$, $a = 7.32$
50. $c = 8.934$, $A = 63° 05'$ 51. $c = 49.61$, $B = 42°$
52. $c = 0.436$, $a = 0.21$ 53. $c = 4.784$, $b = 2.3$

9–6 Applications of right triangles. In the applications of trigonometry important situations arise in which the determination of an angle or of a distance can be made to depend on the solution of one or more right triangles, or perhaps a partial solution in the sense that not all of the unknown parts are called for. In each problem a figure should be drawn, and analyzed for a method of solution.

One type of application involves problems stated in terms of *angle of elevation*, or *angle of depression*. If a point B is above the level of a point

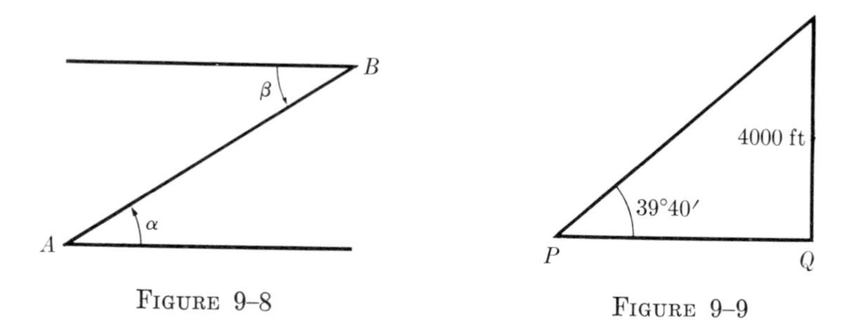

FIGURE 9–8

FIGURE 9–9

A, the *angle of elevation* of B from A is the angle that the line AB makes with a horizontal line through A in the same vertical plane as AB, that is, angle α in Fig. 9–8. On the other hand, angle β, the angle that AB makes with a horizontal line through B in the same vertical plane as AB, is called the *angle of depression* of A from B. It is clear from the figure that $\alpha = \beta$. However, it should be understood that the angle of elevation and angle of depression are different concepts. The term angle of elevation applies when the observed object is above the observer, while the term angle of depression applies when the observed object is below the observer.

EXAMPLE 1. The angle of elevation of an airplane from a point P on the ground is 39° 40′. Find the distance from P to the point on the ground directly beneath the plane, if the altitude of the plane is 4000 ft.

Solution. The situation is depicted in Fig. 9–9, with QP as the desired distance. We have at once, from right triangle PQR,

$$QP = 4000 \cot 39^\circ 40' = 4000 \times 1.206 = 4824 \text{ ft.}$$

A second type of application concerns the use of directions on the earth. Two modes of designating directions are in common use. One of these uses the angle by which the direction deviates from north or south to the east or west. Thus, in Fig. 9–10 the direction of B from A in this system is written as N 40° E, while the direction of A from B is S 40° W. The second method simply uses the angle from the north direction to the given direction, *measured clockwise.* In this system the direction of B from A in Fig. 9–10 is given as 40°, and the direction of A from B is 220°. In either system the north direction which is used as the reference line is drawn through the point from which the direction is determined.

EXAMPLE 2. A ship bears S 38° 20′ W from a point A on shore, at a distance of 1550 ft. How far south of A is the ship?

Solution. Figure 9–11 shows the relevant information, with point B representing the position of the ship. The desired distance is represented by AC.

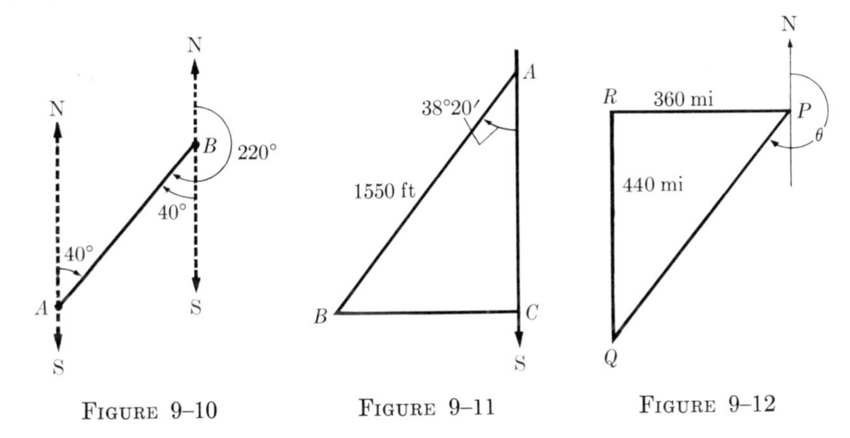

FIGURE 9–10 FIGURE 9–11 FIGURE 9–12

Then, from right triangle ABC, we have

$$\begin{aligned} AC &= 1550 \cos 38° \, 20' = 1550 \times 0.7844 \\ &= 1216 \text{ ft.} \end{aligned}$$

However, if the given angle is correct only to the nearest $10'$, the distance is given as 1220 ft.

EXAMPLE 3. Two planes start at the same point at the same time, one flying due east at 180 mph, the second flying due south at 220 mph. What is the bearing of the second ship from the first at the end of two hours?

Solution. At the end of two hours plane P is 360 mi east of the starting point R, and plane Q is 440 mi south of R (Fig. 9–12). From right triangle PQR we have

$$\tan \measuredangle RPQ = \tfrac{440}{360} = 1.222.$$

Hence, since the given data present no greater accuracy in the angle than the nearest $10'$, we obtain

$$\measuredangle RPQ = 50° \, 40'.$$

The bearing of Q from P, indicated by θ in the figure, is then

$$\theta = 270° - 50° \, 40' = 219° \, 20'.$$

EXERCISE GROUP 9–5

1. From a point 135 ft from, and in the same horizontal plane with, the base of a flagpole, the angle of elevation of the top is 32°. Find the height of the flagpole.

2. From an observation balloon which is 200 ft high, the angle of depression of an object is 8° 20′. How far is the object from a point directly under the balloon and in the same horizontal plane with the object?

3. A pilot, wishing to check his speed, flies on a level course at an altitude of 1000 ft. He observes that an object on the ground straight ahead has an angle of depression of 10° and that 15 sec later the same object has an angle of depression of 21°. How fast is he traveling?

4. An airplane is observed flying directly toward us and at a given instant we observe the angle of elevation of the plane to be 8° 40′. Fifteen seconds later the plane is directly overhead and we estimate its speed to be 300 mph. Approximately how high is it flying (in feet)?

5. Two ships start from the same place at the same time and one sails for 3 hr on a course of 63° at 12 knots (nautical miles per hour), while the other sails for 3 hr on the course 333° at 15 knots. Determine the distance between the ships and the direction from the first to the second at the end of the 3 hr.

6. A ship sails for 5 hr on a course 133° at 15 knots and then sails for 7 hr on a course of 223° at 14 knots. At the end of the 12 hr, how far is the ship from its starting place and in what direction?

7. An aircraft carrier is sailing on a course of 318° with a speed of 30 knots. A plane takes off and flies on a course of 48° at a speed of 300 knots. What is the distance and direction from the plane to the carrier at the end of 5 hr?

8. An airplane pilot observes that two buoys in the water under him have angles of depression of 19° and 23°, respectively. If the buoys are known to be 2 mi apart and if a point directly under the plane is on the line joining the two buoys and between them, how high is the plane?

9. From the top of a lighthouse, 150 ft above sea level, the angle of depression of a buoy is 13° 24′, and the angle of depression of a point on shore, which lies directly between the buoy and the lighthouse, is 63° 17′. How far is the buoy from this point on shore?

10. An observer on the fourth floor of a building determines that the angle of depression of the foot of a building across the street is 39° and that the angle of elevation of the top of the same building is 49°. If the street is 70 ft wide, find the height of the observed building.

11. The driver of a car observes that a forest ranger's lookout tower is in a direction which makes an angle of 15° with the highway. After driving 10 mi he notes that the direction to the lookout tower makes an angle of 25° with the highway. Assuming that the road is straight, how far is the lookout tower from the highway?

12. A motorist on a level highway observes that the angle of elevation of the top of a mountain is 5° and after driving 4 mi directly toward the mountain he observes that the angle of elevation of the top of the mountain is 9°. How high above the road is the top of the mountain?

13. An observer is 200 ft from a building that has a flagpole on top of it. He observes that the angle of elevation of the top of the building is 24° 10′ and that the angle of elevation of the top of the flagpole is 28° 50′. What is the approximate height of the flagpole?

14. While flying over a small lake, a pilot observes that he is at an altitude of 500 ft, and that the angle of depression of a point on one side of the lake is 5° 30′ and that of a point on the opposite side of the lake is 7°. Assuming that the point directly under the plane is on the line joining the two points on the shore of the lake, how far is it across the lake?

15. The smaller angle between two intersecting lines is $43° 24'$ and a circle whose radius is 3187 ft is tangent to both lines. Find the distance from the point of tangency to the point of intersection of the two lines when the circle is in the smaller angle, and also when it is in the larger angle.

16. Each side of a regular hexagon (six equal sides and six equal angles) is 24 in. long. Find the radius of the inscribed circle.

17. Two pulleys have diameters of 12 in. and 8 in., respectively, and their centers are 4 ft apart. If the two pulleys are to be belted together (the belt uncrossed), what must be the length of the belt?

18. If the belt in Exercise 17 is crossed, how long must it be?

19. Assuming that the earth is a sphere with a radius of 3960 mi, find the radius of the parallel of latitude which passes through Milwaukee. (The latitude of Milwaukee is $43° 03'$.) What is the length of arc of $1°$ of this parallel of latitude?

9–7 Vectors. A further group of applications concerns problems involving such physical concepts as can be treated as examples of the general concept of vector. The idea of a vector, and the manner in which vectors are combined, will be introduced by a consideration of velocity.

Suppose a plane is flying in a given direction with a given speed. If the direction is maintained while the speed is altered, the velocity is different. Likewise, if the speed is maintained while the direction is altered, the velocity is again different. In other words, the velocity of the plane is composed of both the speed and the direction; if either one is altered, the velocity is different.

It is then reasonable to represent a velocity by a directed line segment, drawn in the direction of the velocity, and with its length denoting the magnitude (speed) of the velocity. A directed line segment as thus described is called a *vector*. It is now apparent that a velocity may be represented by such a vector; we also say, more briefly, that *a velocity is a vector*. In the same sense, other physical concepts, such as force, acceleration, angular velocity, and directed distance, each of which involves a magnitude and a direction, are vectors.

Now suppose our plane is flying due east. If a wind is blowing due north, the resulting motion of the plane will be in some direction between east and north, the actual direction and speed, and therefore the velocity, being in some manner a combination of the velocities of the plane and the wind. We shall accept the statement that experimentation shows that the combined effect of any two velocity vectors, or force vectors, or other similar vectors, is given by the *vector sum*, or *resultant*, which will now be defined.

DEFINITION 9–1. *If two vectors OA and OB have the same initial point O, the vector sum, or resultant, of OA and OB is defined as the diagonal OC of the parallelogram constructed with OA and OB as sides* (Fig. 9–13).

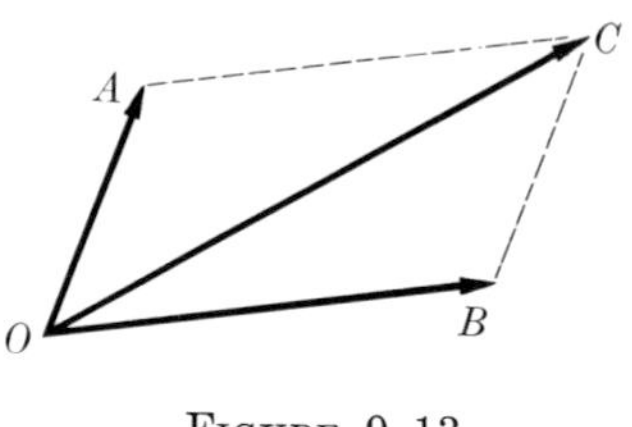

FIGURE 9–13

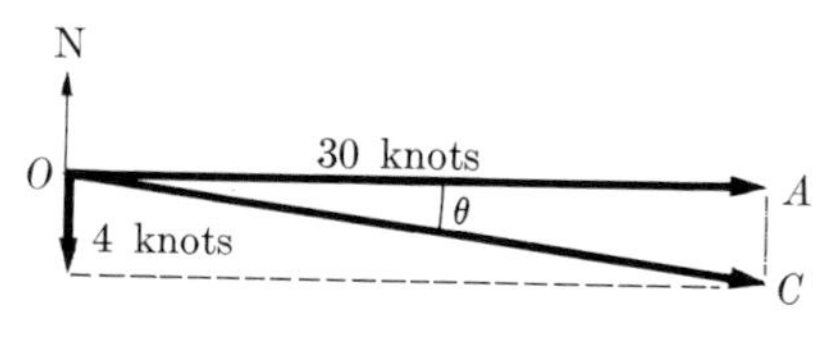

FIGURE 9–14

Often, a problem at hand requires the breaking down of a vector, rather than the addition of two vectors. Whenever a vector is expressed as a resultant of two vectors, these two vectors are called *components* of the vector sum. The breaking down of a vector in this way is called a *resolution* of the vector into components. For example, we may say that the vector OC in Fig. 9–13 has been resolved into the two components OA and OB.

EXAMPLE 1. A ship is headed due east at 30 knots (nautical miles per hour), while the current carries the ship due south at 4 knots. Find the resultant velocity of the ship.

Solution. The velocities combine as vectors, with the resultant vector OC in Fig. 9–14 representing in both magnitude and direction the actual velocity of the ship. From triangle OAC we have

$$\tan\theta = \tfrac{4}{30} = 0.1333, \qquad \theta = 8°.$$

Hence the direction of OC, or the *course* of the ship, is

$$90° + 8° = 98°.$$

To find the net speed, or the length of OC, we may, with the simple numbers involved, use the Pythagorean theorem, and obtain:

$$\text{speed} = \sqrt{4^2 + 30^2} = \sqrt{916} = 30 \text{ knots}.$$

A number of problems involve the following terminology, as used in air navigation. The *airspeed* is the speed the plane would have in still air, or the speed of the plane relative to the air; the *heading* is the direction of the plane relative to the air. Thus, if there is no wind, the magnitude and direction of the velocity are given by the airspeed and heading. However, when a wind is blowing, the magnitude and direction of the resultant velocity are called the *groundspeed* and the *course*, respectively.

EXAMPLE 2. A 20 mph south wind (that is, from the south) is blowing. At what speed should a plane head due west to be on course 279° 10′? What will be the ground speed?

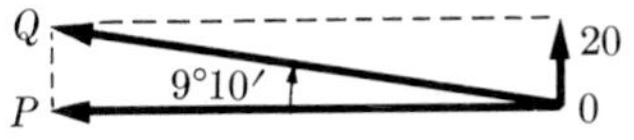

FIGURE 9–15

Solution. In the vector diagram in Fig. 9–15, the airspeed is given by the length OP, the groundspeed by the length OQ. From the triangle OPQ, we find

$$\begin{aligned} \text{airspeed} &= 20 \cot 9^\circ\, 10' = 20(6.197) = 124 \text{ mph}, \\ \text{groundspeed} &= 20 \csc 9^\circ\, 10' = 20(6.277) = 126 \text{ mph}. \end{aligned}$$

The resolution of a vector into components is illustrated in considering the weight of an object resting on an inclined plane. It was stated earlier that a force is a vector. The weight, which is a force acting vertically downward, can be resolved into two components, one acting perpendicular to the inclined plane, the other acting parallel to the plane.

EXAMPLE 3. What force, acting parallel to an inclined plane which makes an angle of 30° with the horizontal, is required to hold a weight of 80 lb stationary on the plane (assuming no friction)?

Solution. In Fig. 9–16, the vector PR, representing the weight, is the sum of the vectors PS and PQ, representing the components of the weight parallel to the plane and perpendicular to the plane, respectively. The required force F is equal to PS in length, but opposite in direction. Clearly, angle PRS is also 30°. Hence

$$F = 80 \sin 30^\circ = 80 \times \tfrac{1}{2} = 40 \text{ lb}.$$

The principle of resolving a vector into components can be employed to find the resultant of any number of coplanar vectors acting at the same point. We choose two directions (usually perpendicular) and resolve each vector into its components in these directions. The sum of the components in either direction will be the component of the resultant vector in that direction. In particular, if the sum of a set of vectors is zero, the sum of the components in any direction must vanish.

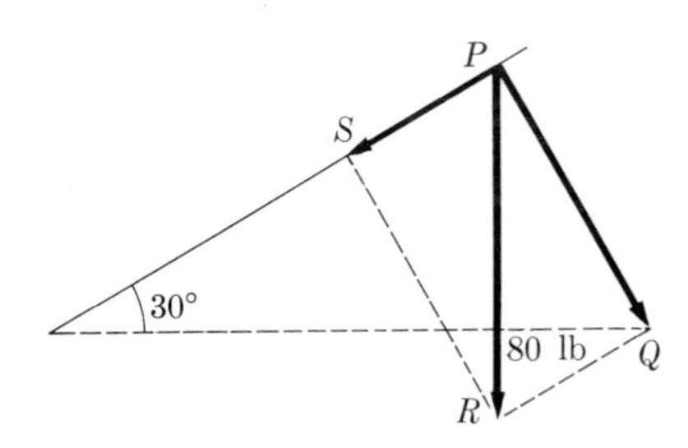

FIGURE 9–16

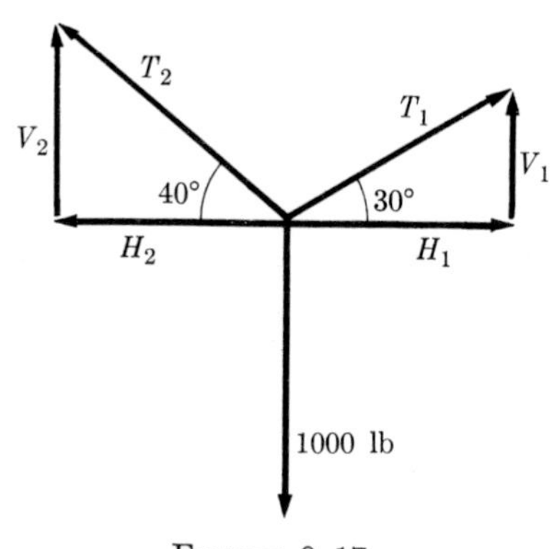

FIGURE 9–17

EXAMPLE 4. A weight of 1000 lb is supported by two cables which make angles of 30° and 40°, respectively, with the horizontal. Find the tension in each cable.

Solution. There are three forces acting on the weight: the pull of gravity, which is 1000 lb directed downward, and the two tensions, each acting along the respective cable. Since this system of forces is in equilibrium, their sum is zero. Hence, the sum of the horizontal components must vanish, and the sum of the vertical components must vanish. Stated differently, the sum of the horizontal components to the right must equal the sum of those to the left, and the sum of the upward vertical components must equal the sum of the downward ones. The tensions T_1 and T_2 can be resolved into horizontal components H_1 and H_2, respectively, and vertical components V_1 and V_2. Then, by the above principle,

$$H_1 = H_2 \quad \text{and} \quad V_1 + V_2 = 1000.$$

On expressing the components in terms of T_1 and T_2, we have, from Fig. 9–17,

$$\begin{aligned} H_1 &= T_1 \cos 30°, & H_2 &= T_2 \cos 40°, \\ V_1 &= T_1 \sin 30°, & V_2 &= T_2 \sin 40°, \end{aligned}$$

and the above equations become

$$0.8660T_1 = 0.7660T_2, \qquad 0.5000T_1 + 0.6428T_2 = 1000.$$

Solving these equations, we find from the first one that $T_1 = 0.8845T_2$. Substituting this value in the second equation, we obtain

$$1.0850T_2 = 1000,$$

which yields $T_2 = 922$ lb (to the nearest pound). Then $T_1 = 0.8845 \times 922 = 815$, and the desired tensions are

$$T_1 = 815 \text{ lb}, \qquad T_2 = 922 \text{ lb}.$$

Exercise Group 9-6

Find the horizontal and vertical components of each vector in Exercises 1-10.

1. Magnitude is 175 and direction makes an angle of 43° 17′ with the horizontal.
2. Magnitude is 213 and direction makes an angle of 17° 39′ with the vertical.
3. Magnitude is 312 and direction makes an angle of 54° 46′ with the horizontal.
4. Magnitude is 42.37 and direction makes an angle of 5° 13′ with the vertical.
5. Magnitude is 127 and the vertical component is twice the horizontal component.
6. Magnitude is 731 and the horizontal component is five times the vertical component.
7. Magnitude is 213 and is double the magnitude of the vertical component.
8. Magnitude is 51.69 and direction makes an angle of 217° 14′ with the vertical.
9. Magnitude is M and direction makes an angle θ with the horizontal.
10. Magnitude is K and direction makes an angle θ with the vertical.

Find the resultant of the forces shown in Fig. 9-18 under the stated conditions, in each of Exercises 11-16.

11. $F_1 = 0, \theta_2 = 0°, F_2 = 300, F_3 = 100$
12. $F_1 = 0, F_2 = 100, F_3 = 200, \theta_2 = 60°$
13. $\theta_1 = 0°, \theta_2 = 45°, F_1 = F_2 = F_3 = 100$
14. $F_1 = F_2 = F_3 = 100, \theta_1 = \theta_2 = 30°$
15. $\theta_1 = 30°, \theta_2 = 60°, F_1 = 100, F_2 = 200, F_3 = 300$
16. $\theta_1 = 180°, \theta_2 = 30°, F_1 = 100, F_2 = 200, F_3 = 300$

17. An airplane has an airspeed of 240 mph on a heading of 212° 10′. The wind is blowing at 30 mph from the direction 122° 10′. Find the groundspeed and course of the plane.

18. An airplane maintains an airspeed of 350 mph on a heading of 153° 12′. There is a 25 mph wind from the direction 243° 12′. Find the course flown by the plane and also its groundspeed.

19. A pilot must fly from A to B in 2 hr. The distance is 500 mi in the direction 52° 20′. If the wind is blowing 20 mph from the direction 142° 20′, what heading and airspeed must the pilot maintain?

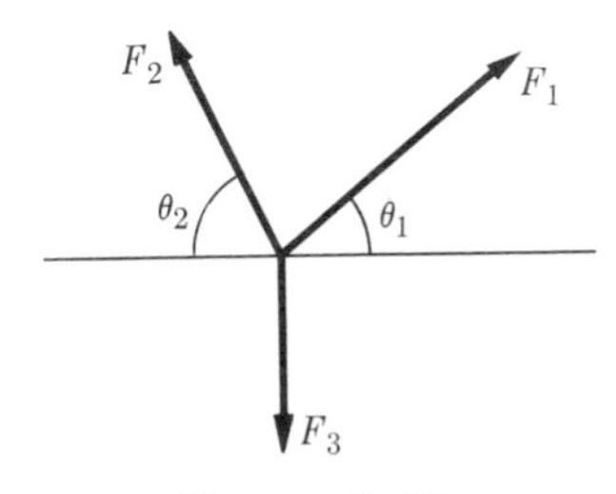

Figure 9-18

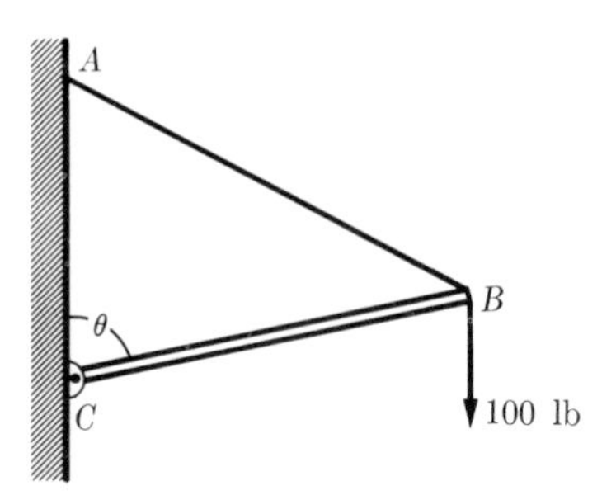

FIGURE 9–19

20. A pilot wishes to fly 319 mi in the direction 274° 30′. The wind is blowing from the south at 22 mph and the pilot decides to fly on a heading of 270°. What airspeed must he maintain and how long will it take him to reach his destination?

21. An automobile weighing 3000 lb is standing on a smooth driveway which is inclined 5° with the horizontal. Find the force (parallel to the driveway) necessary to keep the car from rolling down the driveway.

In Fig. 9–19 a beam BC of negligible weight is fastened to a wall AC with a hinge at C and is supported at B by a cable AB. A weight of 100 lb is supported at B. Find the tension T in the cable AB and the compression C in the beam BC under the following conditions:

22. $AC = BC = 4$ ft, $\theta = 90°$
23. $AC = BC = AB$
24. $AC = BC = 4$ ft, $\theta = 120°$
25. $AC = BC = 4$ ft, $\theta = 45°$
26. $AC = 4$ ft, $BC = 8$ ft, $\theta = 90°$
27. $AC = 4$ ft, $BC = 2$ ft, $\theta = 90°$

28. A 1000-lb weight is to be supported by two cables, one of them with a tension of 700 lb and making an angle of 60° with the horizontal. Find the tension in the other cable, and the angle it should make with the horizontal.

29. A sphere of 1000 lb weight is supported by two smooth inclined planes, as shown in Fig. 9–20. Find the force which each plane exerts on the sphere.

30. A weight W is supported by two cables, as shown in Fig. 9–21. Find the tension in each cable.

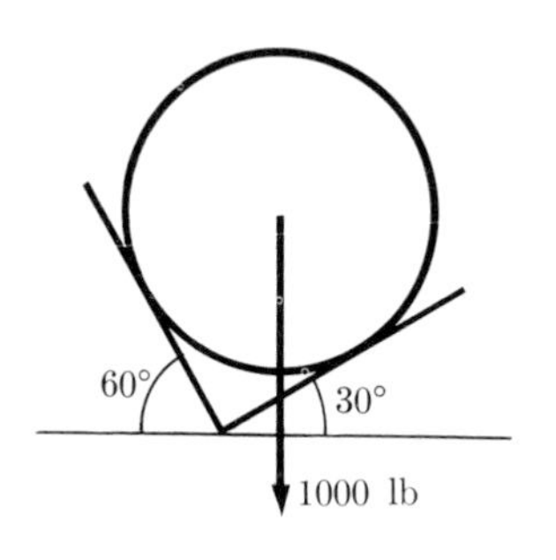

FIGURE 9–20

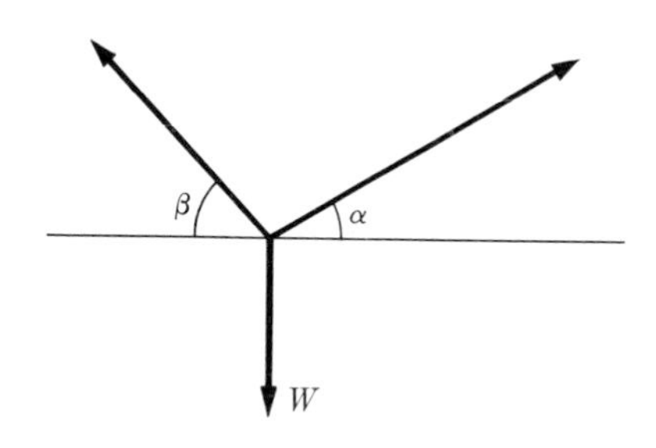

FIGURE 9–21

Review Exercises

Solve the right triangles in Exercises 1–4, and round off the results to the correct number of significant figures.

1. $a = 31.94$, $B = 23°$
2. $c = 1.3$, $A = 36°\ 03'$
3. $b = 2.3$, $c = 3.246$
4. $a = 3.942$, $b = 1.23$

5. At what airspeed should an airplane fly on a heading of 270° to maintain a course of 260° 32′, if a 15 mph north wind (from the north) is blowing?

6. A river has a current of 3.5 mph. A man in a motor boat, with a speed in still water of 8 mph, heads directly across the river. Find his speed and the direction in which he will travel.

7. A force of 275 lb is acting at an angle of 47° with the horizontal. Find its horizontal and vertical components.

8. A ship is sailing due north at a speed of 15 mph. A man walks across the deck from west to east, at the rate of 5 ft/sec. Find the direction and magnitude of the man's actual velocity.

9. Find the height of a vertical pole which casts a shadow 73 ft long on the level ground when the altitude (angle of elevation) of the sun is 53° 12′.

10. A metal nut $\frac{1}{2}$ in. thick is in the shape of a regular hexagon, the distance between parallel sides being $1\frac{1}{2}$ in. There is a circular hole $\frac{1}{2}$ in. in diameter through the center. Find the volume of the metal in the nut.

CHAPTER 10

GRAPHS OF THE TRIGONOMETRIC FUNCTIONS

10–1 The graphs of $y = \sin x$ and $y = \cos x$. In Chapter 6 it was seen that each trigonometric function is defined for all angles, with the exception of certain quadrantal angles. Our interest now turns to the behavior of the trigonometric functions "in the large," so to speak. We desire an over-all view of each function, apart from its values for individual angles. The graphs of the functions serve ideally for this purpose.

It is familiar from Chapter 5 that the graph of any equation in x and y consists of the aggregate of all points (x, y) whose coordinates satisfy the equation. The graphs of the trigonometric functions will be obtained by setting y equal to each function and graphing the resulting equation.

Let us consider, as an example, the function

$$y = \sin x. \tag{1}$$

The graph of this function consists of the aggregate of all points (x, y) whose coordinates satisfy (1). Here x and y are numbers, and the meaning of this function is that when x is given a value, the corresponding value of y is obtained by finding the sine of x radians. Thus, if $x = \pi/3$, $y = \sin \pi/3 = 0.87$; if $x = \frac{3}{4}$, $y = \sin \frac{3}{4} = 0.68$. The fact that x represents the radian measure of an angle is no more significant for the graph than the fact that in the equation $A = x^2$ for the area of a square, the length of the side x may be in feet. The same scale is used on both axes, and the point on the x-axis representing π is placed, as nearly as possible, at $\pi = 3.1416$. For convenience, this point may often be placed at $x = 3$. Similar considerations apply to the other trigonometric functions.

In what follows we shall assume the truth of the statement that the graphs of the trigonometric functions are smooth curves, that is, that the curves have no corners or vertices. A table of values, for special and quadrantal angles, follows:

x	0	$\frac{\pi}{6}$	$\frac{\pi}{4}$	$\frac{\pi}{3}$	$\frac{\pi}{2}$	$\frac{2\pi}{3}$	$\frac{3\pi}{4}$	$\frac{5\pi}{6}$	π	$\frac{7\pi}{6}$	$\frac{5\pi}{4}$	$\frac{4\pi}{3}$	$\frac{3\pi}{2}$	$\frac{5\pi}{3}$	$\frac{7\pi}{4}$	$\frac{11\pi}{6}$
$y = \sin x$	0	.50	.71	.87	1	.87	.71	.50	0	−.50	−.71	−.87	−1	−.87	−.71	−.50
$y = \cos x$	1	.87	.71	.50	0	−.50	−.71	−.87	−1	−.87	−.71	−.50	0	.50	.71	.87
$y = \tan x$	0	.58	1	1.73	—	−1.73	−1	−.58	0							

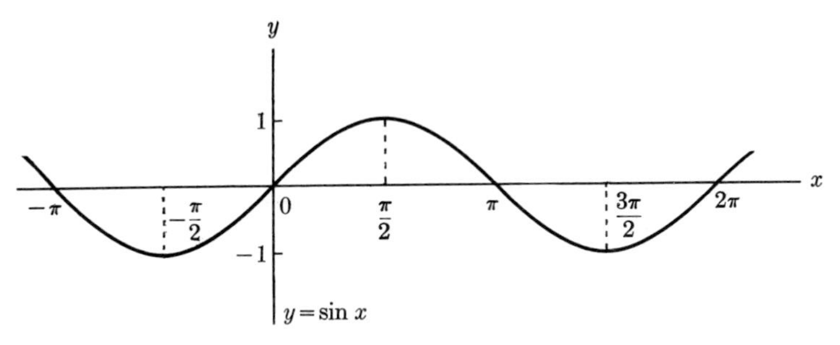

FIGURE 10–1

If the points (x, y), with $y = \sin x$ from the above table, are plotted and joined by a smooth curve, the portion of the graph of $y = \sin x$ between $x = 0$ and $x = 2\pi$ is obtained (Fig. 10–1).

We know that any angle between 2π and 4π will have, when placed in standard position, the same terminal line as some angle between 0 and 2π. Hence, as we know from Chapter 6, the sine of such an angle will be the same as the sine of this smaller coterminal angle. In fact, as x varies from 2π to 4π, the values of $\sin x$ will duplicate the values it has for x between 0 and 2π, and the graph of $\sin x$ between $x = 2\pi$ and $x = 4\pi$ will be a repetition of the graph between $x = 0$ and $x = 2\pi$. The same will be true of the graph of $\sin x$ between $x = 4\pi$ and $x = 6\pi$, $x = -2\pi$ and $x = 0$, $x = -4\pi$ and $x = -2\pi$, and so on. The complete graph of $\sin x$ may then be obtained by repeating indefinitely to the right and to the left that part of the graph which lies between $x = 0$ and $x = 2\pi$. The graph is shown in Fig. 10–1.

The repetitive nature of the function $\sin x$ as described above holds for any portion of the graph of length 2π, not alone the part between $x = 0$ and $x = 2\pi$, and is expressed in the statement that $\sin x$ is *periodic* with a *period* of 2π. The general property of periodicity of a function is defined as follows.

DEFINITION 10–1. *A function $f(\theta)$ is said to be periodic, with period α, if α is the smallest positive number for which*

$$f(\theta + \alpha) = f(\theta), \qquad \text{for all } \theta \text{ for which } f(\theta) \text{ is defined.}$$

The periodicity of $\sin x$ is expressed in the equation

$$\sin (x + 2\pi) = \sin x, \qquad \text{for all values of } x.$$

The graph of $y = \cos x$. To graph the so called cosine curve we plot the points (x, y) from the above table with $y = \cos x$, join them by a

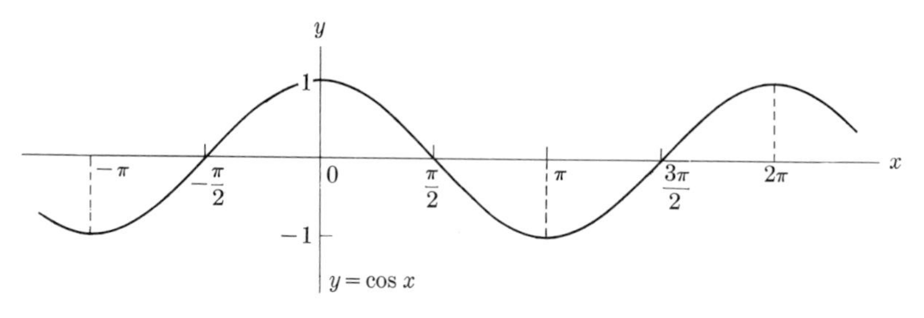

FIGURE 10–2

smooth curve, and obtain the portion of the graph in Fig. 10–2 between $x = 0$ and $x = 2\pi$. Similar considerations apply to the function $\cos x$ as to $\sin x$; we have also

$$\cos(x + 2\pi) = \cos x, \qquad \text{for all values of } x,$$

and $\cos x$ is periodic with period 2π. By repeating indefinitely to the right and to the left the portion of the graph of $\cos x$ which lies between $x = 0$ and $x = 2\pi$, we obtain the complete graph, as shown in Fig. 10–2.

In addition to the periodicity of the trigonometric functions, an important feature of the sine and cosine curves is the regularity of the oscillation between the maximum and minimum values of the functions (Figs. 10–1 and 10–2).

DEFINITION 10–2. *The amplitude of a regularly oscillating function is one-half of the maximum minus the minimum values of the function.*

According to this definition, the amplitudes of $\sin x$ and $\cos x$ are both 1.

EXERCISE GROUP 10–1

In Exercises 1–9, construct the graph of each function by plotting the points obtained by assigning values to x on the interval $-\pi/2 \leqq x \leqq 2\pi$ corresponding to the special and quadrantal angles, and in each instance give the amplitude and the period.

1. $y = \sin x$
2. $y = \cos x$
3. $y = \cos(-x)$
4. $y = \sin(-x)$
5. $y = \frac{1}{2}\cos x$
6. $y = \frac{1}{3}\sin x$
7. $y = \frac{5}{2}\cos x$
8. $y = -2\sin x$
9. $y = -\frac{3}{5}\cos x$

By assigning suitable values to x, obtain a table of values for each of the following functions, and then construct the graph.

10. $y = \cos 3x$
11. $y = \sin 3x$
12. $y = \sin 2x$
13. $y = \cos 2x$
14. $y = \sin \frac{1}{2}x$
15. $y = \cos \frac{1}{3}x$

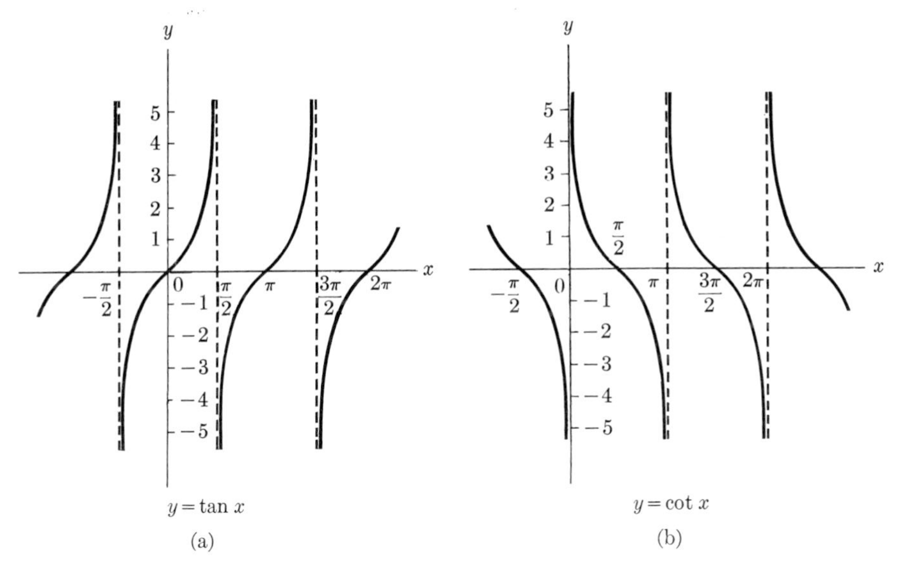

FIGURE 10–3

10–2 The graphs of the other trigonometric functions. Examination of the values of $\tan x$ from $x = 0$ to $x = \pi/2$ (see Table 2 in the Appendix, for example) shows that as x increases so does the $\tan x$. In fact $\tan x$ increases indefinitely as x gets close to $\pi/2$, in such a manner that $\tan x$ *can be made as large as we like by taking x close enough to, and less than,* $\pi/2$. For $x = \pi/2$ there is of course no value of the tangent. This behavior of $\tan x$ for x in the first quadrant and near $\pi/2$ is expressed in the statement

$$\tan\left(\frac{\pi}{2}\right)^{-} = \infty,$$

and appears in the graph of $\tan x$ in Fig. 10–3(a) in the way the graph rises as x gets closer to the line $x = \pi/2$ on the left.

As soon as x passes $\pi/2$, the tangent is negative, and very small algebraically (i.e., a large negative number) for x close to but greater than $\pi/2$. We describe this behavior of $\tan x$ for x in Q_2 and near $\pi/2$ by the statement

$$\tan\left(\frac{\pi}{2}\right)^{+} = -\infty,$$

and note the graph of $\tan x$ in Fig. 10–3(a) for $x > \pi/2$.

The function $\tan x$ has a period of π, so that the complete graph may be obtained by repeating that portion of the graph between $x = 0$ and $x = \pi$, and in this manner we obtain the graph in Fig. 10–3(a).

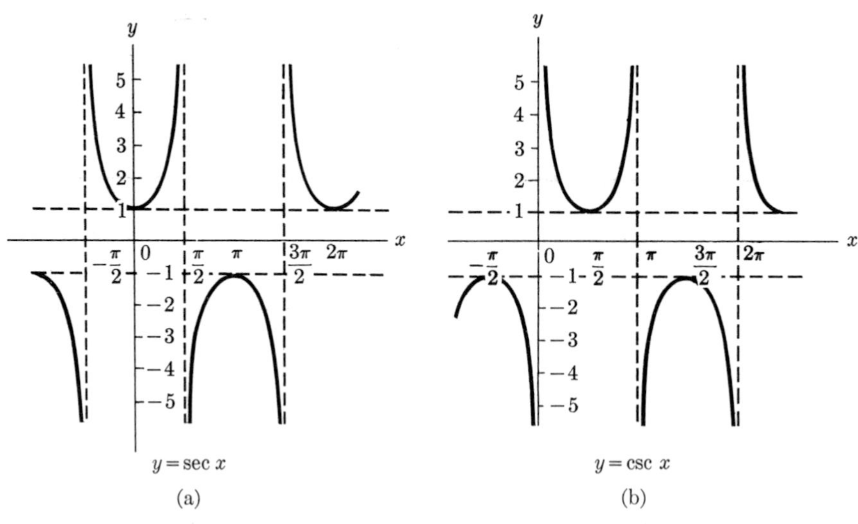

FIGURE 10–4

The graphs of the remaining functions may also be obtained similarly, and appear in Fig. 10–3(b) and Fig. 10–4(a) and (b). We may use the graphs of the trigonometric functions to determine various properties of the functions. In particular we note that only $y = \sin x$ and $y = \cos x$ of the six basic trigonometric functions have amplitudes.

EXERCISE GROUP 10–2

In Exercises 1–9, construct the graph of each function by plotting the points obtained by assigning values to x on the interval $-\pi/2 \leqq x \leqq 2\pi$ corresponding to the special and (where possible) quadrantal angles.

1. $y = \tan x$
2. $y = \cot x$
3. $y = \sec x$
4. $y = \csc x$
5. $y = \tan(-x)$
6. $y = \frac{1}{4}\tan x$
7. $y = \frac{7}{3}\tan x$
8. $y = -\tan x$
9. $y = -\cot x$

By assigning suitable values to x, obtain a table of values for each of the following functions, and then construct the graph.

10. $y = \tan 2x$
11. $y = \tan \frac{1}{2}x$
12. $y = \cot 2x$
13. $y = \cot 3x$
14. $y = \sec 2x$
15. $y = \csc 2x$

10–3 Rapid sketching. The graphs of the functions $y = a\sin(bx + c)$ and $y = a\cos(bx + c)$. We shall consider here a method of rapid sketching of certain graphs related to the basic trigonometric functions. The purpose of the rapid sketching of the graphs of functions is to show the essential features of these graphs, by relating the functions to certain basic functions, and by making use of the known graphs of the latter. More

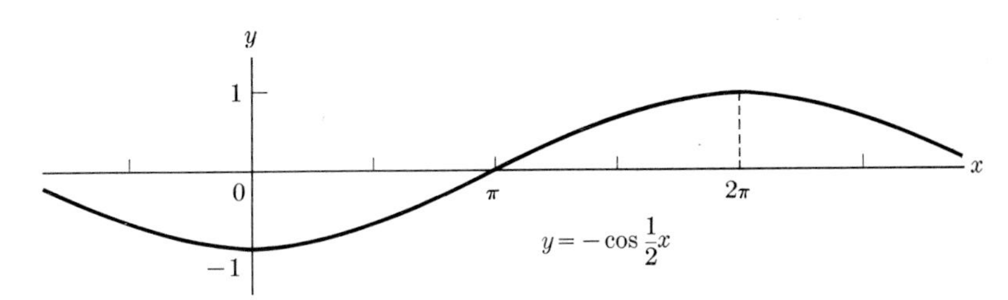

FIGURE 10–5

carefully drawn graphs can then be made, when necessary, by use of special values, or by use of a more extensive table of values.

In particular, the graphs of the functions

$$y = a \sin (bx + c) \qquad \text{and} \qquad y = a \cos (bx + c) \tag{2}$$

can be analyzed in terms of the changes in the sine and cosine curves caused by the values of a, b, and c. The graph of any such function can be drawn if the maximum and minimum points, and the points where the curve crosses the x-axis are known.

Since the sine and cosine functions vary between -1 and 1, the functions in (2) will vary between $-a$ and a, regardless of the values of b and c. Thus the *amplitude* of the graphs of the functions in (2) is a if $a > 0$ (and $-a$ if $a < 0$). Furthermore, since $a \sin x$ and $a \cos x$ go through a complete cycle as x increases by 2π, the functions in (2) will go through a complete cycle as $bx + c$ increases by 2π, which occurs as x increases by $2\pi/b$ if $b > 0$ (and $-2\pi/b$ if $b < 0$). Hence the functions in (2) have the period $2\pi/b$ if $b > 0$ and $-2\pi/b$ if $b < 0$. With the knowledge of the amplitude and period, the functions in (2) may be graphed if only one maximum point, for example, is known.

EXAMPLE 1. Draw the graph of $y = -\cos x/2$.

Solution. Because of the minus sign, the maximum and minimum points will be the reverse of what they are for $\cos x/2$. The effect of the value $x/2$ instead of x will be that y goes through its cycle of values twice as slowly as for $\cos x$. Hence the curve makes a complete cycle as x goes from 0 to 4π; it has a minimum at $x = 0$, a maximum at $x = 2\pi$, and crosses the x-axis at $x = \pi$ and $x = 3\pi$. A portion of the graph of $y = -\cos x/2$ is shown in Fig. 10–5.

EXAMPLE 2. Draw the graph of $y = 3 \sin (2x + \pi/2)$.

Solution. Let us write the function as

$$y = 3 \sin \left[2\left(x + \frac{\pi}{4}\right)\right].$$

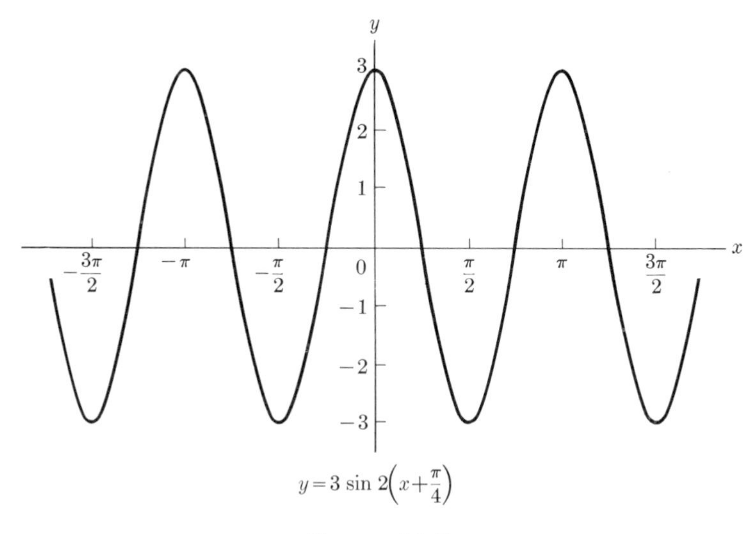

FIGURE 10–6

A maximum value $y = 3$ occurs where $2x + \pi/2 = \pi/2$, or $x = 0$; a minimum value $y = -3$ occurs where $2x + \pi/2 = 3\pi/2$, or $x = \pi/2$. Moreover, $y = 0$ when

$$2x + \frac{\pi}{2} = 0, \qquad \text{or} \qquad x = -\frac{\pi}{4}; \qquad 2x + \frac{\pi}{2} = \pi, \qquad \text{or} \qquad x = \frac{\pi}{4}.$$

Knowing the periodic nature of the sine function, we can then draw the graph of $y = 3 \sin (2x + \pi/2)$ as in Fig. 10–6.

It is noteworthy that only a maximum point and the next minimum point (or the reverse) are needed to graph either function in (2), since the graph of the function crosses the x-axis at a value of x which is halfway between the corresponding abscissas.

EXAMPLE 3. Find the smallest non-negative abscissa for which the function

$$y = 2 \sin \left(\frac{\pi}{2} - 3x\right)$$

has consecutive maximum and minimum points.

Solution. A maximum occurs if $\pi/2 - 3x = \pi/2$, or $x = 0$. The period is $2\pi/3$. Hence a minimum occurs at $x = \pi/3$.

EXERCISE GROUP 10–3

For each of the following, find a consecutive pair of maximum and minimum points. Sketch the graph of each through at least a period and a half.

1. $y = 2 \cos x$ 2. $y = \sin \frac{1}{2}x$ 3. $y = -2 \sin x$

4. $y = -\frac{1}{2}\cos 2x$
5. $y = -3\cos\frac{1}{2}x$
6. $y = -2\sin\frac{1}{3}x$
7. $y = 2\cos(-x)$
8. $y = 3\sin(-x)$
9. $y = -3\cos(-x)$
10. $y = -2\sin(-x)$
11. $y = \sin\left(x - \frac{\pi}{2}\right)$
12. $y = \cos\left(x + \frac{\pi}{3}\right)$
13. $y = \sin\left(\frac{\pi}{3} - x\right)$
14. $y = \cos\left(\frac{\pi}{4} - x\right)$
15. $y = \cos(3x - \pi)$
16. $y = \sin(2x + \pi)$
17. $y = \cos(\pi - 3x)$
18. $y = \sin\left(\frac{\pi}{2} - 2x\right)$

10–4 Graphing by addition of ordinates. A further method, useful in the rapid sketching of certain functions, is known as *addition of ordinates.* The method applies to a function $y = f(x)$ where $f(x)$ can be written as a sum of two functions,

$$y = f(x) = f_1(x) + f_2(x), \tag{3}$$

and where the graphs of $f_1(x)$ and $f_2(x)$ are either known or can be quickly obtained. Then if we set

$$y_1 = f_1(x), \qquad y_2 = f_2(x),$$

we have, of course,

$$y = y_1 + y_2. \tag{4}$$

By virtue of (4), points on the graph of (3) can be obtained by adding, for any value of x, the ordinates y_1 and y_2, and joining the points thus obtained by a smooth curve. For the best use of the method, the addition of ordinates should be done graphically, either with a pair of dividers, or with any straight edge on which the lengths of the ordinates can be marked. As many values of x may be used as are necessary; these should usually include values for which either y_1 or y_2 vanishes, values for which either y_1 or y_2 has a maximum or minimum, and values for which $y_1 = y_2$.

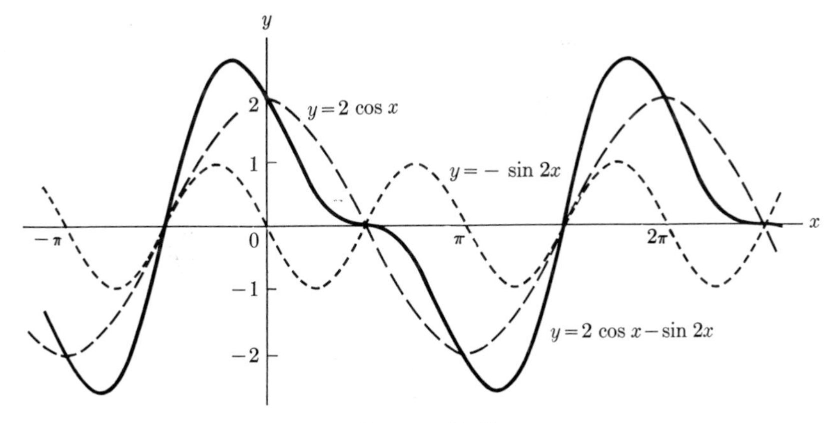

FIGURE 10–7

EXAMPLE. Draw the graph of $y = 2 \cos x - \sin 2x$.

Solution. Let us set $y = y_1 + y_2$, where

$$y_1 = 2 \cos x, \qquad y_2 = -\sin 2x.$$

The minus sign is incorporated in y_2 because it is simpler to add ordinates than to subtract. We then draw the graphs of the functions y_1 and y_2 in the same coordinate system, as in Fig. 10–7. The addition of ordinates as described above yields the heavily drawn curve. Some of the values of x used in the construction of the curve are also indicated.

EXERCISE GROUP 10–4

Sketch the graph of each of the functions in Exercises 1–20 for x in at least the interval $-\pi \leqq x \leqq 2\pi$.

1. $y = x + \sin x$
2. $y = 2x + \cos x$
3. $y = \dfrac{x^2}{10} + \sin x$
4. $y = \dfrac{x^3}{25} + \cos 2x$
5. $y = -x + \sin 2x$
6. $y = -\dfrac{x^2}{8} + \cos x$
7. $y = \sin x + \cos x$
8. $y = \sin x + \sin 2x$
9. $y = \cos x - \sin 2x$
10. $y = \sin x - \cos 2x$
11. $y = \sin x + \cos 2x$
12. $y = 2 \sin 2x + \cos \frac{1}{2}x$
13. $y = 2 \cos \frac{1}{2}x - \sin 2x$
14. $y = \sin \frac{1}{2}x - \cos 2x$
15. $y = \sin \frac{1}{2}x - \cos \frac{1}{3}x$
16. $y = 2 \sin \frac{1}{3}x - 3 \cos \frac{1}{2}x$
17. $y = \frac{1}{2} \sin 2x + \frac{1}{3} \cos 3x$
18. $y = -\frac{1}{2} \sin 3x + \frac{1}{3} \cos 2x$
19. $y = \sin \left(x - \dfrac{\pi}{3}\right) + \cos x$
20. $y = \sin x + \cos \left(x + \dfrac{\pi}{3}\right)$

REVIEW EXERCISES

Sketch the graph of each of the following functions through at least one period. In each case, determine the period and also, where applicable, the amplitude.

1. $y = 2 \tan x$
2. $y = 3 \cos 2x$
3. $y = \frac{1}{2} \sin 3x$
4. $y = 3 \sec x$
5. $y = 2 \cot 3x$
6. $y = \frac{1}{3} \cos \frac{1}{2}x$
7. $y = 3 \sin 2x$
8. $y = 2 \sin \frac{1}{3}x$
9. $y = 3 \tan 2x$
10. $y = 2 \csc 3x$
11. $y = \cot \frac{1}{3}x$
12. $y = \sin \frac{2}{3}x$
13. $y = 2 \cos (x + \pi)$
14. $y = 2 \sin \left(x - \dfrac{\pi}{2}\right)$
15. $y = \frac{1}{2} \sin (2x - \pi)$
16. $y = \frac{1}{2} \cos \left(3x + \dfrac{\pi}{2}\right)$
17. $y = -3 \sin \left(\dfrac{\pi}{3} - 2x\right)$
18. $y = -\cos (\pi - 3x)$
19. $y = \sin x + 2 \cos x$
20. $y = \sin x - \cos 2x$
21. $y = \sin \frac{1}{2}x + \cos \frac{1}{3}x$
22. $y = 2 \sin 2x + \cos \frac{1}{2}x$

CHAPTER 11

INVERSE TRIGONOMETRIC, EXPONENTIAL, AND LOGARITHMIC FUNCTIONS

11–1 Inverse functions and their graphs. All functions which are studied in mathematics can be classified either as *algebraic functions* or *transcendental functions.* The class of algebraic functions includes the *polynomials* (also called rational integral functions), the *rational fractions* [functions of the form $f(x)/g(x)$, where $f(x)$ and $g(x)$ are polynomials with $g(x) \neq 0$], and certain *irrational functions* of which the simplest are obtained by extracting roots of rational functions. There are also a great many other, less simple, algebraic functions.

The class of *transcendental functions* consists of all functions which are not algebraic. In this class are the *trigonometric functions,* which were defined in Section 6–6. Other important categories of transcendental functions are the *inverse trigonometric functions,* the *exponential functions,* and the *logarithmic functions,* the subject of the present chapter.

Consider the function defined by $f(x) = x^2$, which we may set equal to y, to obtain the equation $y = x^2$. This equation may now be solved for x to give $x = \pm\sqrt{y}$. Let us choose the plus sign and write $g(y) = \sqrt{y}$. If we replace y by x in the latter function, we find $g(x) = \sqrt{x}$, which is called an *inverse function* of $f(x) = x^2$.

In general, if an equation

$$y = f(x) \tag{1}$$

can be solved for x as a function of y, and this solution is written as

$$x = g(y), \tag{2}$$

the function $g(x)$ is called an *inverse function* of $f(x)$. The function $g(x)$ will have $f(x)$ as an inverse, with a domain which is part of the domain of (1). As illustrated above by the function $f(x) = x^2$, more than one inverse function may exist. We may then select a particular inverse function and fix our attention on that one.

It should be emphasized that what determines a function is the mode of operation on the variable, and not the variable itself. Thus x^2 and y^2 really indicate the same function, although the variables differ. Similarly, $\sin x$ and $\sin y$ represent the same function, and in general, so do $f(x)$ and $f(y)$.

The pairs of values (x, y) which satisfy (2) will also satisfy (1) so that the graph of (2) will coincide with all or part of the graph of (1).

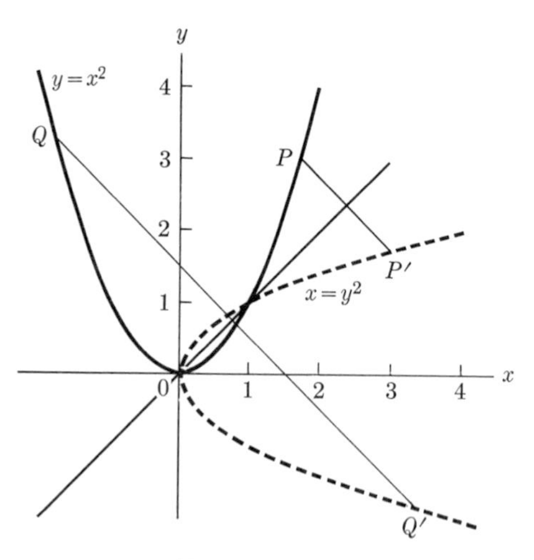

FIGURE 11–1

We now wish to interchange the roles of x and y, and to consider the graph of the function

$$y = g(x). \tag{3}$$

This graph is then part of the graph of

$$x = f(y) \tag{4}$$

where $g(x)$ is an inverse of $f(x)$. Thus, if f is a given function, we may assign values to y, compute the corresponding values of x from (4) and join the points (x, y) by a smooth curve. However, we may make a more direct use of the graph of (1). Since (1) and (4) differ only in that x and y are interchanged, we may *draw the curve which is situated with respect to the x-axis just as the graph of* (1) *is situated with respect to the y-axis.* In either case we then choose a part of the graph to correspond to our choice of the inverse function.

For example, if the graph of $y = x^2$ is shown in Fig. 11–1 as the solidly drawn curve, the graph of $x = y^2$ or $y = \pm\sqrt{x}$ will be the dotted curve. A point such as P on $y = x^2$ corresponds to the point P' on $x = y^2$. The graph of the function $y = \sqrt{x}$ is then the part of the dotted curve for which $y \geqq 0$.

11–2 Introduction to the inverse trigonometric functions. For each of the trigonometric functions an inverse function may be defined. We write the general solution of the equation $y = \sin x$ as $x = \arcsin y$, with a similar notation applied to the other trigonometric functions. In general, in the discussion of the inverse trigonometric functions we should like to have x as the independent variable, and accordingly shall consider the equation

$$y = \arcsin x, \tag{5}$$

which is read just as it is written. Here x is a number such that $-1 \leqq x \leqq 1$, and y is also a number (actually, a number of radians). Because of the periodicity of the sine function, there are innumerably many values of $\arcsin x$ for any value of x. For example, if $x = \frac{1}{2}$, then $y = \arcsin \frac{1}{2}$ represents any number (of radians) such that $\sin y = \frac{1}{2}$. Thus, y may have any of the values $\pi/6 + 2n\pi$ or $5\pi/6 + 2n\pi$ ($n = 0, \pm 1, \pm 2, \ldots$). We say that $\arcsin x$ is *multiple-valued*, and more particularly, that it is *infinitely many-valued*.

It is essential to realize that all knowledge concerning the equation $y = \arcsin x$ is derived from our knowledge of $\sin x$ and the complete equivalence of the equations $y = \arcsin x$ and $x = \sin y$. In this connection it is helpful to interpret $\arcsin x$ as "an angle whose sine is x." This equivalence, and similar ones for the other trigonometric functions, are shown in the following arrangement:

$$\begin{array}{|c|}\hline y = \text{arcsin}\, x \leftrightarrow x = \sin y; \\ \hline \end{array}$$

$$\begin{array}{|c|}\hline y = \text{arccos}\, x \leftrightarrow x = \cos y; \\ \hline \end{array}$$

$$\begin{array}{|c|}\hline y = \text{arctan}\, x \leftrightarrow x = \tan y; \\ \hline \end{array}$$

$$\begin{array}{|c|}\hline y = \text{arccot}\, x \leftrightarrow x = \cot y; \\ \hline \end{array} \tag{6}$$

$$\begin{array}{|c|}\hline y = \text{arcsec}\, x \leftrightarrow x = \sec y; \\ \hline \end{array}$$

$$\begin{array}{|c|}\hline y = \text{arccsc}\, x \leftrightarrow x = \csc y. \\ \hline \end{array}$$

In each case the two equations are equivalent.

We may now easily draw the graphs of equations such as (5). For example, to graph $y = \arccos x$ we need merely graph $y = \cos x$, and then interchange the roles of x and y. The graphs of the equations in (6), which appear in Fig. 11–2, may all be obtained in this fashion.

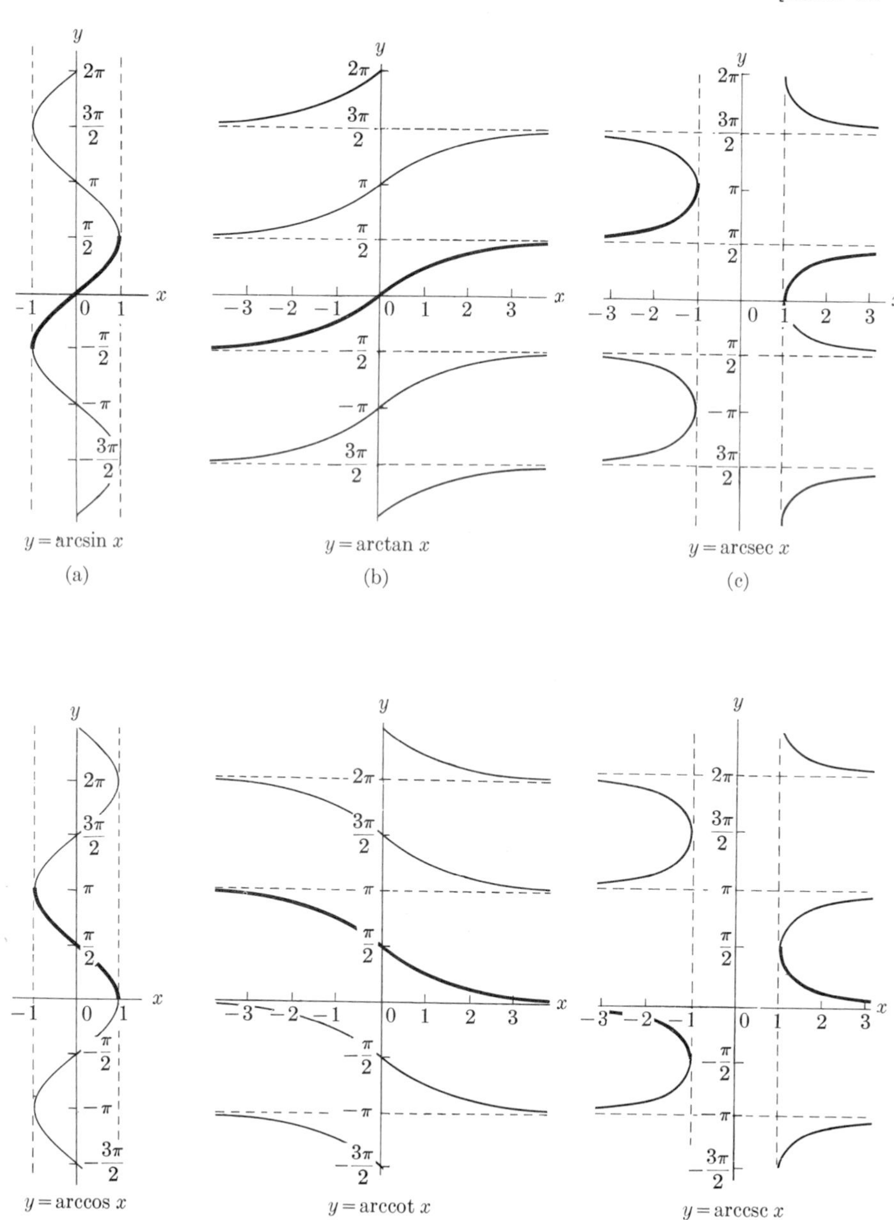
y = arcsin x
(a)
y = arctan x
(b)
y = arcsec x
(c)
y = arccos x
(d)
y = arccot x
(e)
y = arccsc x
(f)

FIGURE 11–2

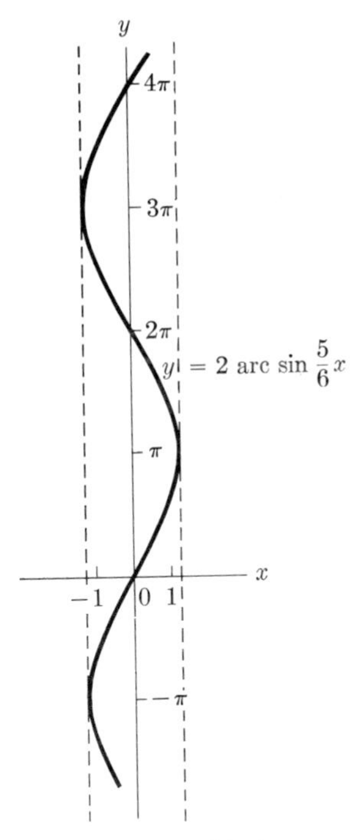

FIGURE 11-3

As an aid in sketching related functions, it will be helpful, when the terms period and amplitude apply to a trigonometric function, to apply the terms *inverse period* and *inverse amplitude* to the inverse function. For example, the equation $y = 2 \arcsin \frac{5}{6}x$ is equivalent to $x = \frac{6}{5} \sin y/2$, which has a period of 4π and amplitude of $\frac{6}{5}$. The same values then represent the inverse period and inverse amplitude of $y = 2 \arcsin \frac{5}{6}x$. The inverse period indicates regularity of behavior of the graph with respect to y, and inverse amplitude indicates the extent of the graph with respect to x.

EXAMPLE 1. Draw the graph of the equation $y = 2 \arcsin \frac{5}{6}x$.

Solution. As we have seen, the given equation has the inverse period 4π and the inverse amplitude $\frac{6}{5}$, since, for the equation $x = \frac{6}{5} \sin y/2$, the graph has a period of 4π and an amplitude of $\frac{6}{5}$. The graph appears in Fig. 11-3. Be sure to note the basic appearance of the sine curve, with the oscillation taking place along the y-axis.

We give another example, which illustrates the application of our notation to the solution of certain equations.

EXAMPLE 2. Express x in terms of y if

$$y = 2 \tan (3x + 1).$$

Solution. We require the solution of the equation for x. Solving first for $\tan (3x + 1)$, we obtain $\tan (3x + 1) = \frac{1}{2}y$, and by the definition of arctan, we find

$$3x + 1 = \arctan \tfrac{1}{2}y, \qquad \text{and} \qquad x = \tfrac{1}{3}(-1 + \arctan \tfrac{1}{2}y).$$

EXERCISE GROUP 11-1

Express the values of the quantities in Exercises 1-15 in general form.

1. $\arcsin \frac{\sqrt{2}}{2}$
2. $\arctan \sqrt{3}$
3. $\operatorname{arcsec} \frac{2\sqrt{3}}{3}$
4. $\arccos \frac{1}{2}$
5. $\operatorname{arccot} 1$
6. $\operatorname{arccsc} 2$
7. $\arcsin (-\frac{1}{2})$
8. $\arccos \left(-\frac{\sqrt{3}}{2}\right)$
9. $\arctan (-1)$
10. $\operatorname{arccot} \sqrt{3}$
11. $\arcsin \left(-\frac{\sqrt{3}}{2}\right)$
12. $\arccos (-1)$
13. $\arcsin 0$
14. $\arctan 0$
15. $\arccos 0$

In Exercises 16-27, solve for x in terms of y.

16. $y = 2 \tan x$
17. $3y = \sin 2x$
18. $y = 4 \cos \frac{x}{2}$
19. $2y = \sec \left(x - \frac{\pi}{4}\right)$
20. $y - 2 = \cos 3x$
21. $y = \sin (2x + 1)$
22. $y = 2 \arcsin x$
23. $y = \arctan \frac{x}{2}$
24. $2y = \operatorname{arccot} 3x$
25. $y - \frac{\pi}{2} = \arcsin x$
26. $2y - 1 = \arcsin \frac{x}{3}$
27. $y + \pi = \arctan (x - 1)$

Construct the graph of each of the equations in Exercises 28-36 for $-\pi \leqq y \leqq 2\pi$.

28. $y = \arcsin x$
29. $y = \arccos x$
30. $y = \arctan x$
31. $y = 2 \arcsin x$
32. $y = \frac{1}{2} \arccos x$
33. $y = \arcsin \frac{x}{2}$
34. $y = \arccos 2x$
35. $y = 2 \arcsin 3x$
36. $3y = \arctan 2x$

Sketch the graph of each of the equations in the following exercises. In each case, give the inverse period and (where applicable) the inverse amplitude.

37. $y = 2 \arctan x$
38. $y = \arctan 2x$
39. $y = 2 \arccos \frac{x}{2}$

40. $2y = \arccos 3x$ 41. $y = 3 \arcsin \frac{x}{2}$ 42. $y = 2 \arcsin \frac{x}{3}$

43. $y = \frac{\pi}{2} + \arcsin x$ 44. $y = \frac{1}{3} \arcsin 2x$ 45. $y = \arcsin (x + 1)$

46. $y - \pi = 2 \arccos 3x$ 47. $y - \frac{\pi}{3} = 3 \arcsin (2x - 1)$

11–3 The inverse trigonometric functions. The fact that y is multiple-valued in an equation such as $y = \arcsin x$ can often be a hindrance. Hence we single out for each of these equations a range of values of y in which y can have only one value, and define the corresponding set of pairs of values (x, y) as the *inverse trigonometric function*. The corresponding portions of the curves in Fig. 11–2 are then called the *principal parts* of these curves. There is lack of uniformity among authors concerning the choice of these values. The reason for our choice is that thereby the sum of the values of an inverse function and the inverse cofunction is now $\pi/2$, which is consistent with, and even more general than, the result of Section 6–9 that any trigonometric function of a positive acute angle is equal to the cofunction of the complementary angle. The principal part of each curve is shown more heavily in Fig. 11–2.

We shall denote the actual inverse trigonometric functions as thus defined by capitalizing the initial letter of the name. The ranges for the inverse trigonometric functions follow:

$$-\pi/2 \leqq \operatorname{Arcsin} x \leqq \pi/2, \qquad -\pi/2 \leqq \operatorname{Arccsc} x \leqq \pi/2,$$

$$-\pi/2 < \operatorname{Arctan} x < \pi/2, \qquad 0 < \operatorname{Arccot} x < \pi,$$

$$0 \leqq \operatorname{Arcsec} x \leqq \pi, \qquad 0 \leqq \operatorname{Arccos} x \leqq \pi.$$

EXAMPLE 1. $\operatorname{Arcsin} \frac{1}{2} = \pi/6$, $\operatorname{Arccos} \frac{1}{2} = \pi/3$,
$\operatorname{Arcsin} (-\frac{1}{2}) = -\pi/6$, $\operatorname{Arccos} (-\frac{1}{2}) = 2\pi/3$,
$\operatorname{Arctan} 1.437 = 55° 10'$, $\operatorname{Arctan} (-0.2095) = -11° 50'$.

EXAMPLE 2. Find $\operatorname{Arctan} (\tan 120°)$.

Solution. The desired angle is the one in the range (in degrees) $-90° < \theta < 90°$ for which the tangent is the same as $\tan 120°$, and is therefore $-60°$.

An important feature of inverse functions in general is that each function of a pair of inverse functions reverses the effect of the other. This idea is at first somewhat elusive, and the following two examples should be carefully studied.

EXAMPLE 3. Find sin arcsin x.

Solution. Let us set

$$\arcsin x = \theta. \tag{7}$$

Then the problem is to find $\sin \theta$. But by definition, (7) is equivalent to the statement

$$\sin \theta = x,$$

and the answer is

$$\sin \arcsin x = x.$$

EXAMPLE 4. Find Arcsin (sin x) if $-\pi/2 \leqq x \leqq \pi/2$.

Solution. Let $\sin x = y$. Then by definition, and since x is in the range of values for the Arcsin function, we have $x = \text{Arcsin } y$, which becomes

$$x = \text{Arcsin}\,(\sin x);$$

this is the desired solution.

EXERCISE GROUP 11–2

Express each of the quantities in Exercises 1–18 in degrees and minutes.

1. Arcsin $\dfrac{\sqrt{2}}{2}$
2. Arccos $\frac{1}{2}$
3. Arctan $\sqrt{3}$
4. Arccot 1
5. Arcsec $\dfrac{2\sqrt{3}}{3}$
6. Arccsc 2
7. Arcsin 0.8371
8. Arctan 2.318
9. Arccos 0.7373
10. Arccot 12.25
11. Arcsin (—0.6670)
12. Arccos (—0.3420)
13. Arctan (—3.271)
14. Arccot (—0.3153)
15. Arcsin (—0.3145)
16. Arccos (—0.3173)
17. Arcsin $(-\frac{1}{2})$
18. Arccos $\left(-\dfrac{\sqrt{3}}{2}\right)$

Express each of the quantities in Exercises 19–36 in radians.

19. Arcsin $\frac{1}{2}$
20. Arccos $(-\frac{1}{2})$
21. Arctan (—1)
22. Arccot $\sqrt{3}$
23. Arcsin $\left(-\dfrac{\sqrt{3}}{2}\right)$
24. Arccos (—1)
25. Arcsin 0
26. Arctan 0
27. Arccot 0
28. Arcsin (—1)
29. Arccos 0
30. Arctan $(-\sqrt{3})$
31. Arcsec (—2)
32. Arccsc $\left(-\dfrac{2\sqrt{3}}{3}\right)$
33. Arcsec (—1)
34. Arccsc (—1)
35. Arcsin (—0.1736)
36. Arccos (—0.9511)

Find the value of each expression in Exercises 37–51.

37. $\sin \operatorname{Arctan} \frac{3}{4}$
38. $\tan \operatorname{Arcsin} (-\frac{1}{2})$
39. $\cos \operatorname{Arcsin} \left(-\frac{\sqrt{3}}{2}\right)$
40. $\cot \operatorname{Arctan} 2$
41. $\sin \operatorname{Arccos} (-1)$
42. $\sec \operatorname{Arccos} \frac{1}{5}$
43. $\sin \operatorname{Arctan} (-\frac{5}{12})$
44. $\cos \operatorname{Arccot} \frac{3}{2}$
45. $\tan \operatorname{Arccos} \frac{2}{3}$
46. $\cot \operatorname{Arcsin} (-\frac{2}{5})$
47. $\sin \operatorname{Arccos} (-\frac{2}{3})$
48. $\cos (2 \operatorname{Arcsin} \frac{1}{2})$
49. $\sin \left(2 \operatorname{Arccos} \frac{\sqrt{3}}{2}\right)$
50. $\tan [2 \operatorname{Arcsin} (-1)]$
51. $\cot [2 \operatorname{Arctan} (-1)]$

11–4 Introduction to logarithms. The definitions of exponents given in Sections 4–1 and 4–2, together with the five laws of exponents from Section 4–1, will now be used to develop a process (defined in the next section) which may be used as a short cut for many arithmetical computations. The way in which exponents can serve in this manner will first be illustrated by some examples.

First let us note that from Table 1 we can obtain (accurate to three decimal places)

$$\sqrt{10} = 3.162 \qquad \text{and} \qquad \sqrt[3]{10} = 2.154.$$

Since $\sqrt{10} = 10^{1/2}$ and $\sqrt[3]{10} = 10^{1/3}$, we see that at least some numbers can be expressed as powers of 10. Once some numbers have been so expressed, additional numbers may be expressed as powers of 10 by use of the laws of exponents; some of these follow:

$$\begin{aligned} 1 &= 10^0, & 10 &= 10^1, & 100 &= 10^2 \\ 2.154 &= 10^{1/3}, & 21.54 &= 10 \cdot 10^{1/3} = 10^{4/3}, & 215.4 &= 10 \cdot 10^{4/3} = 10^{7/3}; \\ 3.162 &= 10^{1/2}, & 31.62 &= 10 \cdot 10^{1/2} = 10^{3/2}, & 316.2 &= 10 \cdot 10^{3/2} = 10^{5/2}. \end{aligned}$$

It is clear how other numbers may be similarly expressed as powers of 10.

An indication of the way in which the above representations may be used in certain computations appears in the following example.

EXAMPLE 1. Find the value of the product (3.162)(215.4).

Solution. Expressing the given values as powers of 10 we have

$$\begin{aligned} (3.162)(215.4) &= (10^{1/2})(10^{7/3}) = 10^{1/2+7/3} = 10^{17/6} \text{ (Law 1 of exponents)} \\ &= 10^{2.8333}. \end{aligned}$$

Up to this point the product of 3.162 and 215.4 has been expressed as a power of 10. To complete the solution and obtain a numerical answer we need to be able to find the value of $10^{2.8333}$. It is beyond the scope of this book to compute the value of $10^{2.8333}$ but, as we shall see later, the value of $10^{2.8333}$ can be found from Table 3 to be 681.3.

Thus we see that the multiplication of two numbers can be accomplished by expressing each number as a power of 10, then expressing the product as a power of 10 by adding the exponents; the resulting power of 10 can then be converted into the desired numerical answer by the use of Table 3, after the use of this table is learned.

In a similar manner we can divide two numbers, and find the powers and roots of numbers, as illustrated in the following examples.

EXAMPLE 2. Find the value of the quotient $31.62 \div 21.54$.

Solution. Proceeding as in Example 1 we have

$$\begin{aligned} 31.62 \div 21.54 &= 10^{3/2} \div 10^{4/3} = 10^{3/2-4/3} \\ &= 10^{1/6} = 10^{0.1667}. \end{aligned}$$

Later, we shall be able to find from Table 3 that $10^{0.1667} = 1.468$.

EXAMPLE 3. Find the value of $(2.154)^5$.

Solution. As in the preceding examples we express the given number as a power of 10, getting

$$(2.154)^5 = (10^{1/3})^5 = 10^{5/3} = 10^{1.667} = 46.45 \qquad \text{(from Table 3)}.$$

EXAMPLE 4. Find the value of $\sqrt[7]{3.162}$.

Solution. Since $3.162 = 10^{1/2}$ we have

$$\sqrt[7]{3.162} = (10^{1/2})^{1/7} = 10^{1/14} = 10^{0.0714}.$$

Turning again to Table 3 we find that $10^{0.0714} = 1.179$, which is then the value of $\sqrt[7]{3.162}$.

Thus we see that once numbers are expressed as powers of 10 the operations of multiplication, division, raising to powers, and the taking of roots are reduced to simple operations of addition, subtraction, multiplication, and division, respectively, performed on suitable exponents.

EXERCISE GROUP 11–3

Given $2 = 10^{0.3010}$, $3 = 10^{0.4771}$, $7 = 10^{0.8451}$, and $11 = 10^{1.0414}$, find the power of 10 which represents each of the following numbers.

1. $2 \cdot 3$	2. $2 \cdot 7$	3. $2 \cdot 3 \cdot 7$	4. $2 \cdot 7 \cdot 11$
5. $2 \div 3$	6. $3 \div 2$	7. $11 \div 7$	8. $7 \div 11$
9. $2^5 \cdot 3^2$	10. $3^4 \cdot 7^2$	11. $2^3 \cdot 7 \cdot 11^2$	12. $11^3 \cdot 7^2$
13. $3^3 \div 5^2$	14. $11^5 \div 7^3$	15. $2^5 \cdot 5^3 \cdot 7^{-4}$	16. $7^3 \cdot 11^2 \cdot 5^{-6}$
17. 63	18. 66	19. 432	20. 147

21. $11 \div 27$	22. $49 \div 33$	23. $99 \div 64$	24. 1980
25. 1782	26. $180 \div 121$	27. $891 \div 49$	28. $294 \div 77$
29. $\sqrt{2^3 \cdot 3^2}$	30. $\sqrt{77}$	31. $\sqrt[3]{294}$	32. $\sqrt[3]{1089}$
33. $\sqrt[5]{792}$	34. $\sqrt[7]{7^3 \cdot 6^5}$	35. $\sqrt[6]{1568}$	36. $\sqrt[4]{3234}$

11–5 Exponential and logarithmic functions. In the preceding section we encountered the problem of determining the value of a given power of 10. This problem is the determination of the value of y for a given value of x in the expression

$$y = 10^x. \tag{8}$$

However, this is a special case of the more general relation

$$y = b^x, \tag{9}$$

where b is any positive real number different from 1. We prefer to study this more general relation, which is called an *exponential function,* since values of b other than 10 will prove both interesting and useful. Note that this function involves a power, but differs fundamentally from the power function $y = x^b$ in that in the exponential function *the exponent is variable.*

Exponential functions occur frequently in applications of mathematics, some of which will be considered in Section 11–13.

In Section 11–4 we also encountered the problem of expressing a given number as a power of 10. This is the problem of solving Equation (8) for x as a function of y, which is, of course, a special case of the more general problem of solving (9) for x as a function of y. Such an expression of x as a function of y is known as the *inverse* of the exponential function and is called a *logarithmic function.* The study of this function is based on the meaning of *logarithm,* which will now be given.

DEFINITION 11–1. *A number u is said to be the* logarithm *of a positive real number v to the base b (where b is real, positive, and different from* 1) *if u is the exponent of the power to which b must be raised to obtain v.*

In symbols, *the logarithm function* is written as

$$\boxed{u = \log_b v}$$

and is read: "u equals the logarithm of v to the base b."

The number 1 cannot serve as a base of logarithms, since any power of 1 is equal to 1. The *logarithms of positive numbers only* will be considered here (logarithms of negative and imaginary numbers are defined in advanced courses).

It is important for the student to realize that *a logarithm is an exponent*, and that the following statements are valid.

The equations $u = \log_b v$ *and* $v = b^u$ *are equivalent by definition. Each of the functions* $u = \log_b v$ *and* $v = b^u$ *is the inverse of the other.*

EXAMPLES.

$\log_2 8 = 3$, since $8 = 2^3$; $\log_{10} 0.01 = -2$, since $0.01 = 10^{-2}$;

$\log_{1/3} 9 = -2$, since $9 = (\frac{1}{3})^{-2}$; $\log_{\sqrt{5}} 25 = 4$, since $25 = (\sqrt{5})^4$.

EXERCISE GROUP 11–4

Write each of the equations in Exercises 1–12 in logarithmic form.

1. $2^4 = 16$
2. $3^4 = 81$
3. $5^{-2} = \frac{1}{25}$
4. $(36)^{1/2} = 6$
5. $(27)^{1/3} = 3$
6. $(0.2)^{-3} = 125$
7. $\sqrt{81} = 9$
8. $8^{2/3} = 4$
9. $(17)^0 = 1$
10. $125^{4/3} = 625$
11. $(\frac{1}{3})^{-2} = 9$
12. $(64)^{5/6} = 32$

Write each of the equations in Exercises 13–24 in exponential form.

13. $\log_3 243 = 5$
14. $\log_{25} 5 = \frac{1}{2}$
15. $\log_7 343 = 3$
16. $\log_8 512 = 3$
17. $\log_{1.5} 3.375 = 3$
18. $\log_9 27 = 1.5$
19. $\log_{32} 128 = \frac{7}{5}$
20. $\log_{0.5} 16 = -4$
21. $\log_9 3 = 0.5$
22. $\log_{0.2} 625 = -4$
23. $\log_{16} 0.5 = -0.25$
24. $\log_a 1 = 0$

In each of Exercises 25–54, determine the value of b, x, or y, whichever is present.

25. $\log_2 16 = y$
26. $\log_3 9 = y$
27. $\log_3 9^{-1} = y$
28. $\log_{10} 100 = y$
29. $\log_{10} 0.001 = y$
30. $\log_{16} \frac{1}{8} = y$
31. $\log_{2\sqrt{3}} 144 = y$
32. $\log_8 128 = y$
33. $\log_{\sqrt{b}} \sqrt[4]{b^3} = y$
34. $\log_{10} x = 3$
35. $\log_{10} x = -2$
36. $\log_{10} x = 0.25$
37. $\log_2 x = -5$
38. $\log_5 x = -4$
39. $\log_7 x = \frac{2}{3}$
40. $\log_{16} x = \frac{7}{4}$
41. $\log_8 x = -\frac{8}{3}$
42. $\log_{512} x = -\frac{7}{9}$
43. $\log_b 3 = 0.5$
44. $\log_b 16 = -\frac{4}{3}$
45. $\log_b a = 1$
46. $\log_b a = -2$
47. $\log_b 0.008 = -3$
48. $\log_b 16^{-1} = \frac{4}{3}$
49. $\log_b \sqrt[4]{2} = \frac{1}{3}$
50. $\log_b 6 = -\frac{1}{2}$
51. $\log_b \sqrt{3} = 1$
52. $\log_b \sqrt[4]{b^3} = y$
53. $\log_b a^c = c$
54. $\log_k x^2 = c$

11–6 Graphs of the exponential and logarithmic functions. Many properties of the exponential and logarithmic functions are most easily recognized from a graph. The graphs of the functions

$$y = b^x \qquad \text{and} \qquad y = \log_b x$$

will be obtained for certain values of b; these graphs will then illustrate the general situation. For a given value of b the graphs of the two functions are known to be reflections, or mirror images, of each other in the line $y = x$. It is also helpful to note that for each function there is a distinct graph for each suitable value of b, but all such graphs fall into certain types.

EXAMPLE 1. Construct the graph of $y = 3^x$.

Solution. Assume values of x and compute the corresponding values of y, obtaining the following table of values:

x:	-3	-2	-1	0	1	2	3
y:	$\frac{1}{27}$	$\frac{1}{9}$	$\frac{1}{3}$	1	3	9	27

The points corresponding to these pairs of values are plotted on the coordinate system of Fig. 11–4 and these points are joined by a smooth curve, which is the desired graph of the function. Note that the values of y are all positive.

EXAMPLE 2. Construct the graph of $y = \log_2 x$.

Solution. The relation $y = \log_2 x$ is equivalent to $x = 2^y$. Hence we assume values of y and compute the corresponding values of x, getting the table

x:	$\frac{1}{8}$	$\frac{1}{4}$	$\frac{1}{2}$	1	2	4	8
y:	-3	-2	-1	0	1	2	3

The points corresponding to these values are plotted on the coordinate system in Fig. 11–5. The smooth curve joining these points is the desired graph of $y = \log_2 x$. It should be noted that the graph lies entirely to the right of the y-axis.

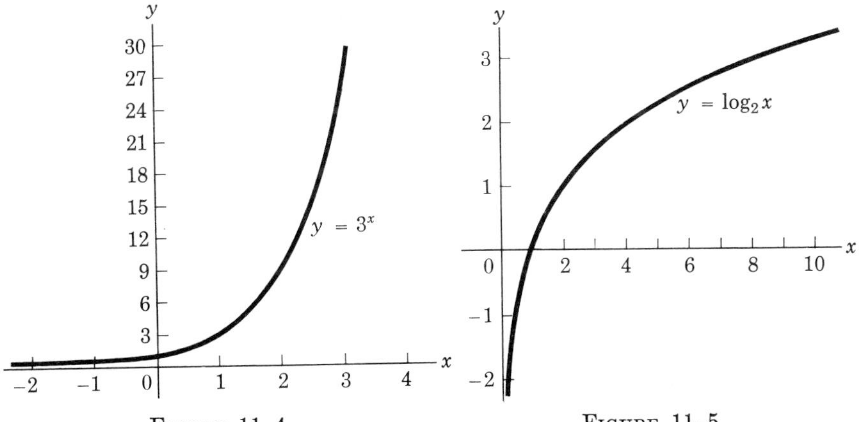

FIGURE 11–4

FIGURE 11–5

The graph of $y = \log_b x$ for any $b > 1$ will be similar to that in Fig. 11–5. Some of the properties of this function which can be noted from the graph are:

I. $\log_b x$ is not defined for negative values of x or zero.

II. $\log_b 1 = 0$.

III. If $x > 1$, then $\log_b x > 0$ ($>$ is symbol for "greater than").

IV. If $0 < x < 1$, then $\log_b x < 0$ ($<$ is symbol for "less than").

Exercise Group 11–5

In each of the following six exercises, graph the function for values of x from -3 to 3 and find at least some points for fractional values of x between -1 and 1.

1. 2^x 2. 3^x 3. 5^x 4. 10^x 5. 4^{-x} 6. 7^{-x}

In each of the following exercises, draw the graph of the given function. (*Hint:* The same values (x, y) satisfy the inverse relations $y = \log_b x$ and $x = b^y$.)

7. $\log_2 x$ 8. $\log_3 x$ 9. $\log_{10} x$ 10. $\log_{10} \dfrac{1}{x}$ 11. $\log_{10} (2x)$

12. $\log_{10} x^2$ 13. $10^{\log_{10} x}$ 14. $\log_{10} 10^x$ 15. $\log_{10} (-x)$ 16. $\frac{1}{2} \log_{10} x$

11–7 Properties of logarithms. In this section we shall consider three additional general properties of logarithms, properties which are particularly useful for purposes of computation. The properties to be proved are a direct consequence of the laws of exponents and the fact that logarithms are actually exponents. More specifically, they may be considered as laws of exponents expressed in terms of logarithms. We shall first give the appropriate laws of exponents.

LAWS OF EXPONENTS

A. $b^p b^q = b^{p+q}$.

B. If $b \neq 0$, $\dfrac{b^p}{b^q} = b^{p-q}$.

C. $(b^p)^q = b^{pq}$.

We proceed to the properties of logarithms.

I. $\boxed{\log_b uv = \log_b u + \log_b v.}$

Proof. Let $\log_b u = x$ and $\log_b v = y$. Then, by the definition of logarithms, $u = b^x$ and $v = b^y$. Hence

$$uv = b^x b^y = b^{x+y} \qquad \text{(Property A of exponents)},$$

and by applying the definition of logarithms to the last equation, we have

$$\log_b uv = x + y = \log_b u + \log_b v.$$

EXAMPLE 1. $\log_{10} 6 = \log_{10} (2 \times 3) = \log_{10} 2 + \log_{10} 3.$

II. $\boxed{\log_b u/v = \log_b u - \log_b v.}$

Proof. Proceed as in I above to obtain $u = b^x$ and $v = b^y$. Then $u/v = b^x/b^y = b^{x-y}$ (Property B of exponents). It follows that

$$\log_b u/v = x - y = \log_b u - \log_b v.$$

EXAMPLE 2. $\log_{10} \frac{3}{7} = \log_{10} 3 - \log_{10} 7.$

III. $\boxed{\log_b u^r = r \log_b u.}$

Proof. Let $\log_b u = x$; then, as above, $u = b^x$ and

$$u^r = (b^x)^r = b^{rx} \qquad \text{(Property C of exponents)}.$$

Hence

$$\log_b u^r = rx = r \log_b u.$$

EXAMPLE 3. $\log_{10} \sqrt[3]{7} = \log_{10} 7^{1/3} = \frac{1}{3} \log_{10} 7.$

It will prove very helpful to the student to state the above properties of logarithms in words, and to learn the verbal statements.

EXAMPLE 4. Express y in terms of x if

$$\log_b y = 2x + \log_b x.$$

Solution. Transposing $\log_b x$, we have

$$\log_b y - \log_b x = 2x,$$

and by Property II,

$$\log_b \frac{y}{x} = 2x.$$

Using the definition of logarithm, we obtain

$$\frac{y}{x} = b^{2x},$$

and the result is

$$y = x \cdot b^{2x}.$$

EXAMPLE 5. Establish the following equation, and determine all values of x for which it is valid:

$$\log_b x + \log_b (x - 1) = \log_b (x^2 - x).$$

Solution. The equation

$$x(x - 1) = x^2 - x$$

is clearly valid for all x. Hence, by Property I, the relation which is to be established is valid for all values of x for which the logarithms exist. We must then find the values of x for which x, $x - 1$, and $x^2 - x$ are all positive. If $x > 0$ and $x - 1 > 0$, then certainly $x^2 - x > 0$. Hence we require the values for which at the same time $x > 0$ and $x - 1 > 0$; thus, the values being sought are all values for which $x > 1$.

11-8 Common logarithms. Characteristic. Mantissa. For purposes of computation by means of logarithms the base 10 is usually used, and it is customary to omit the designation of the base. Hence, when no base is indicated, it will be understood that the base is 10.

We are familiar with the fact that any positive real number N can be expressed in *scientific notation*, that is, as the product of an integral (including zero) power of 10, and a positive real number m between 1 and 10. Thus,

$$N = m \cdot 10^c, \qquad 1 \leqq m < 10, \qquad c \text{ is an integer.} \tag{10}$$

For example, we have

$$31789.2 = 3.17892 \times 10^4, \qquad 0.00003219 = 3.219 \times 10^{-5},$$

where it is clear that the exponent of 10 is determined by the position of the decimal point in the original number. Application of Property I of Section 11-7 to the above relations gives

$$\begin{aligned} \log 31789.2 &= \log 10^4 + \log 3.17892 \\ &= 4 + \log 3.17892; \\ \log 0.00003219 &= \log 10^{-5} + \log 3.219 \\ &= -5 + \log 3.219. \end{aligned}$$

Moreover, if the position of the decimal point is changed in one of these numbers, the effect is to change the integer in the second expression for the logarithm. For each position the decimal point is moved to the left, the integer is decreased by 1, and for each position the decimal point is moved to the right, the integer is increased by 1.

Similarly, Eq. (10) gives, in general,

$$\log N = c + \log m, \qquad 1 \leqq m < 10. \tag{11}$$

Thus we see from (11) that if common logarithms are used, the logarithm of every positive real number N is the sum of an integer (positive, negative, or zero) and the logarithm of a number between 1 and 10. The integral part c is called the *characteristic* of $\log N$, and $\log m$ is the *mantissa* of $\log N$. Note that the base 10 is not being written; we shall continue this practice and omit the designation of the base except when a base other than 10 is used.

The characteristic of $\log N$ is obviously determined by the location of the decimal point in the number N, and is given by the following rule:

The first nonzero digit in N from the left is called the first *significant figure of N; the characteristic c of* $\log N$ *is the number of places from the first significant figure to the units place, being positive if the first significant figure is to the left of the units place, zero if it is at the units place, and negative if it is to the right of the units place.*

EXAMPLE 1. The characteristic

of $\log 2156$ is 3, since 3 significant figures are to the left of the units place,
of $\log 5.236$ is 0, since the first significant figure is in the units place,
of $\log 0.00052$ is -4, since the first significant figure is 4 places to the right of the units place.

To determine the mantissa of $\log N$, we must determine a number x such that

$$10^x = m, \qquad \text{where} \qquad 1 \leqq m < 10. \tag{12}$$

Since $1 = 10^0$ and $10 = 10^1$, it follows that the values of x satisfying (12) must satisfy the inequality

$$0 \leqq x < 1.$$

The mantissa x is thus seen to be the *positive* decimal part of the logarithm, or zero.

11-9 A table of logarithms. Some logarithms can be determined without a table. Thus,

$$\log 3.162 = 0.5000, \qquad \text{since } 10^{1/2} = \sqrt{10} = 3.162,$$

$$\log 2.154 = 0.3333, \qquad \text{since } 10^{1/3} = \sqrt[3]{10} = 2.154.$$

In general, however, mantissas are determined by methods which cannot be properly understood until the student has studied calculus. Hence we must accept values which have been computed and compiled in *tables of logarithms*. The first such table of common logarithms, that is, logarithms to the base 10, was published in 1624, having been computed by an Englishman, Henry Briggs (1561–1630).

Logarithm tables give only the logarithms of numbers between 1 and 10, or, more generally, the mantissas of the logarithms of positive numbers. We shall use a four-place table of logarithms; this will enable us to find the mantissas of the logarithms of four-digit numbers N. It should be understood that in a four-place table the mantissas, which are in fact infinite decimals, are given correct to four decimal places, that is, are *rounded off* to four decimal places.

The table of logarithms appears as Table 3 of the Appendix. We shall consider the *direct* use of the table, in which the logarithm of a number is found, and the *inverse* use, in which a number is to be found from the table when its logarithm is known. The table is arranged so that the first two significant figures of N appear in the column headed N, while the third significant digit of N appears in the row at the top of the table. The use of the table can now best be explained by some examples. We illustrate first the direct use of the table.

EXAMPLE 1. Determine log 213.

Solution. The characteristic is 2. To determine the mantissa, we look in the table in the column headed N and find 21. Directly to the right of this in the column headed 3, we find 3284. This number with a decimal point placed in front is the desired mantissa. Hence,

$$\log 213 = 2.3284.$$

When a logarithm is negative, we very often do not wish to lose the positive character of the decimal part; therefore we do not combine the characteristic and mantissa, although it is certainly correct to do so. If we add and subtract 10 we get what is known as the *standard form* of the logarithm. The following example will illustrate this.

EXAMPLE 2. Determine log 0.00317.

Solution. The characteristic is -3 and the mantissa is 0.5011. Therefore, we have

$$\begin{aligned}\log 0.00317 &= -3 + 0.5011 = (10 - 3 + 0.5011) - 10 \\ &= 7.5011 - 10. \quad (\textit{This is in standard form.})\end{aligned}$$

EXAMPLE 3. Determine the value of $\log \sqrt[3]{\frac{33}{14}}$.

Solution. From the table:

$$\begin{aligned} \log 33 &= 1.5185 \\ \log 14 &= 1.1461 \quad (-) \end{aligned}$$

By Property II, $\log \frac{33}{14} = 0.3724$

By Property III, $\log \sqrt[3]{\frac{33}{14}} = \frac{1}{3}(0.3724) = 0.1241.$

We now illustrate the *inverse* use of the table.

EXAMPLE 4. Determine x when $\log x = 3.1818$.

Solution. We look in the *body* of the table for the mantissa 0.1818 and find it in row 15 and column 2, so that the digits of x are 152. Since the characteristic is 3, the decimal point must be placed so that the first significant figure is three places to the left of the units place. Hence $x = 1520$.

EXAMPLE 5. Determine x when $\log x = 6.5490 - 10$.

Solution. Locate the mantissa 0.5490 in the table and note that the corresponding number is 354. The characteristic is $6 - 10$ or -4, and the decimal point must be placed so that the first significant figure is 4 places to the right of the units place. Hence $x = 0.000354$.

EXERCISE GROUP 11-6

In each of Exercises 1–24, make use of the properties of logarithms and Table 3 to find the value of the given logarithm.

1. $\log 2(7)$
2. $\log 7(11)$
3. $\log 2(3)7$
4. $\log 0.134(2.87)$
5. $\log 328(2.16)$
6. $\log 1.36(21.8)$
7. $\log 462(213)$
8. $\log 31.2(10^3)$
9. $\log \frac{11}{7}$
10. $\log \frac{29}{17}$
11. $\log \frac{19}{13}$
12. $\log \frac{253}{672}$
13. $\log \dfrac{2.31}{13.2}$
14. $\log \dfrac{32.1}{432}$
15. $\log \dfrac{0.215}{0.0314}$
16. $\log \dfrac{0.00427}{0.742}$
17. $\log (17)^2$
18. $\log (13)^3$
19. $\log \sqrt{19}$
20. $\log \sqrt[3]{123}$
21. $\log (17)^2\sqrt{13}$
22. $\log \sqrt[3]{\frac{13}{7}}$
23. $\log \sqrt{\dfrac{17}{(11)^2}}$
24. $\log \sqrt[3]{\dfrac{123(236)}{(23)^2}}$

In each of Exercises 25–33, use Table 3 to determine the value of x.

25. $\log x = 3.9325$
26. $\log x = 7.8519 - 10$
27. $\log x = 0.5855$
28. $\log x = 6.9854$
29. $\log x = 9.9647 - 10$
30. $\log x = 8.7396 - 10$
31. $\log x = 2.5988$
32. $\log x = 5.6149$
33. $\log x = 6.7839 - 10$

In each of Exercises 34–42, use the properties of logarithms and Table 3 to compute the value of x.

34. $x = (42)^2(11)$ 35. $x = \sqrt[3]{(39)^2}$ 36. $x = (94.7)^{5/7}$

37. $x = \sqrt{(297)^3/33}$ 38. $x = \sqrt[3]{(36.1)^2(0.94)}$ 39. $x = \dfrac{(1.39)^3}{\sqrt{1.75}}$

40. $x = \dfrac{15(23)18}{27}$ 41. $x = \dfrac{(235)(0.835)^2}{189}$ 42. $x = \dfrac{6.27\sqrt[3]{21.2}}{\sqrt{7.66}}$

In Exercises 43–48, use the properties of logarithms to verify each equation.

43. $\log (x^2 - x) = \log x + \log (x - 1)$
44. $\log (x^2 - 1) = \log (x + 1) + \log (x - 1)$
45. $\log x = \log (x^2 + 3x) - \log (x + 3)$
46. $\log (x - 1) = \log (x^2 + 2x - 3) - \log (x + 3)$
47. $\frac{1}{2} \log (x + 1) = \log \sqrt{\dfrac{x+1}{x-1}} + \frac{1}{2} \log (x - 1)$
48. $2 \log (x - 2) = \log \dfrac{(x - 2)^2}{(x + 3)^3} + 3 \log (x + 3)$

Rewrite each of the following equations so as to express y as a function of x; in each case reduce to simplest form.

49. $\log y = 3 \log x + \log 5$ 50. $\log y = k \log x + \log c$
51. $\log y = 2x + \log 7$ 52. $\log y = mx + \log c$
53. $\log y = kx + \log 10$ 54. $\log y = 3x - \log 10$
55. $2 \log y = 3 \log x + 4 \log 5$ 56. $a \log y = b \log x + c \log k$

11–10 Interpolation in the table of logarithms. Table 3 gives all mantissas to four decimal places, while only three significant figures appear for the number N. The logarithms of numbers with four significant figures can be found from the table by the principle of linear interpolation.

The principle of linear interpolation, as applied here, is that a sufficiently small arc of the graph of the logarithmic function may be replaced by a straight line.

We may interpret this principle to mean that the difference between two sufficiently close values of x is proportional to the difference between the corresponding values of the logarithmic function $\log x$. We illustrate first *direct interpolation.*

EXAMPLE 1. Determine log 3176.

Solution. The characteristic of the logarithm is 3, so that we may determine log 3.176 and then add 3. The value of log 3.176 must lie between log 3.17 and log 3.18, and by the principle of linear interpolation, the difference in the logarithms is proportional to the difference in the numbers, for small differences; hence we have

$$\frac{\log 3.176 - \log 3.17}{\log 3.18 - \log 3.17} = \frac{3.176 - 3.17}{3.18 - 3.17}.$$

From Table 3 we find that

$$\log 3.17 = 0.5011,$$

$$\log 3.18 = 0.5024.$$

Substituting these values, we obtain the equation

$$\frac{\log 3.176 - 0.5011}{0.5024 - 0.5011} = \frac{0.006}{0.01},$$

which may be solved for log 3.176 as

$$\begin{aligned}\log 3.176 &= 0.5011 + \frac{0.006}{0.01}(0.0013)\\ &= 0.5011 + 0.6 \times 0.0013\\ &= 0.5011 + 0.0008 = 0.5019.\end{aligned}$$

Hence the mantissa of log 3176 is 0.5019, and with a characteristic of 3, the value is

$$\log 3176 = 3.5019.$$

If log 0.3176 were desired, the mantissa would be determined in the same way, but with a characteristic of —1 the value would be

$$\log 0.3176 = 0.5019 - 1 = 9.5019 - 10.$$

Thus *the method for obtaining the mantissa of the logarithm of a four-digit number* can be described as follows:

1. *Disregard the decimal point and drop the fourth digit.*
2. *Subtract the mantissa corresponding to the remaining three-digit number from that corresponding to the next larger three-digit number.*
3. *Multiply the difference thus obtained by the fourth digit originally dropped, divide the product by* 10, *add the result to the smaller mantissa used in Step* 2, *and round off in the fourth decimal place.*

If the logarithm of a number with more than four digits is to be obtained from a four-place table, the number should first be rounded off in the fourth figure.

In the following example a self-explanatory schematic arrangement is used.

EXAMPLE 2. Determine log 51.83.

Solution. With the fourth digit dropped, the remaining three-digit number is 518, and the next larger one is 519. Schematically, we have

$$10\left[\begin{array}{ll} 3\left[\begin{array}{ll} 5180 & 7143 \\ 5183 & x \end{array}\right] h \\ \quad 5190 \quad 7152 \end{array}\right] 9, \qquad \frac{h}{9} = \frac{3}{10},$$

$$h = 3 \text{ (in last decimal place).}$$

Thus $x = 7146$, and $\log 51.83 = 1.7146$.

There is also the *inverse* problem of determining a four-digit number whose logarithm is given, or the problem of *inverse interpolation.*

EXAMPLE 3. Determine x when $\log x = 2.5615$.

Solution. We may find the number m such that $\log m = 0.5615$, and then place the decimal point as dictated by the characteristic. From the table we find that

$$\log 3.64 = 0.5611, \qquad \log 3.65 = 0.5623;$$

then $\log m$ must lie between these values. The equation of proportionality is

$$\frac{m - 3.64}{3.65 - 3.64} = \frac{0.5615 - 0.5611}{0.5623 - 0.5611},$$

which can be solved for m as

$$\begin{aligned} m &= 3.64 + 0.01 \times \frac{0.0004}{0.0012} \\ &= 3.64 + 0.01 \times 0.3 \\ &= 3.64 + 0.003 = 3.643. \end{aligned}$$

Since the characteristic of $\log x$ is 2, we obtain

$$x = 364.3.$$

In general, to determine the number corresponding to a mantissa not listed in the table, note the next smaller entry in the table and the next larger. Then subtract the next smaller mantissa from the given one and divide the result by the difference between the next larger and the next smaller, obtaining the quotient correct to one decimal. The digit thus obtained is the fourth digit of N. The first three digits correspond to the next smaller mantissa. The decimal point is then placed as dictated by the characteristic.

EXAMPLE 4. Determine x when $\log x = 3.6112$.

Solution. The mantissa of the logarithm is 0.6112. The next smaller mantissa in the table is 0.6107 and the next larger one is 0.6117. Schematically, we have

$$10\left[a\left[\begin{matrix}4080 & 6107\\ x & 6112\end{matrix}\right]5\atop \begin{matrix}4090 & 6117\end{matrix}\right]10, \qquad \frac{a}{10} = \frac{5}{10}.$$

Hence $a = 5$ in the fourth figure and $x = 4085$.

Exercise Group 11–7

In Exercises 1–12, use Table 3 to find the given logarithm.

1. $\log 314.2$
2. $\log 6.347$
3. $\log 83.75$
4. $\log 3569$
5. $\log 0.2468$
6. $\log 0.07426$
7. $\log 58340$
8. $\log 931300$
9. $\log 0.0001824$
10. $\log 0.004191$
11. $\log 0.06495$
12. $\log 3.843 \cdot 10^{-5}$

In Exercises 13–24, use Table 3 to find the value of x.

13. $\log x = 2.7415$
14. $\log x = 3.9536$
15. $\log x = 1.8754$
16. $\log x = 4.1861$
17. $\log x = 8.1972 - 10$
18. $\log x = 7.3083 - 10$
19. $\log x = 2.4237 - 5$
20. $\log x = 3.5511 - 6$
21. $\log x = 1.6239 - 6$
22. $\log x = 5.6419 - 10$
23. $\log x = 6.9779 - 13$
24. $\log x = 3.0247 - 8$

In Exercises 25–35, express each of the negative logarithms in standard form and then use Table 3 to find the value of x.

25. $\log x = -0.3029$
26. $\log x = \frac{1}{5}(9.0589 - 10)$
27. $\log x = 0.3(8.2341 - 10)$
28. $\log x = -2.8874$
29. $\log x = \frac{1}{3}(8.0432 - 10)$
30. $\log x = -1.4(2.3040)$
31. $\log x = 1.4832 - 2.7047$
32. $\log x = 3.4073 - 4.5$
33. $\log x = 1.3(2.4004 - 4.2)$
34. $\log x = (3.1 - 4.4) \div 2.5$
35. $\log x = 0.7(3.1627 - 5.2073)$

11–11 Computation with logarithms. The method involved in the use of logarithms for the purpose of computing certain numbers is to employ the properties of logarithms to obtain the logarithm of the number, and then to find the number from the table when its logarithm is known. A neat and orderly arrangement of the work will be found to be very helpful, particularly in the less simple computations. The student should pay very close attention to the following examples, and should cultivate the habit of arranging his work in a similar manner.

EXAMPLE 1. Compute the value of $Q = \dfrac{(315.7)^2\sqrt{23.46}}{\sqrt[3]{0.03128}}$.

Solution. From the properties derived in Section 11–7 we obtain

$$\log Q = 2\log 315.7 + \tfrac{1}{2}\log 23.46 - \tfrac{1}{3}\log 0.03128.$$

The following form for the computation is self-explanatory.

$$\begin{array}{rcl}
\log 315.7 &=& 2.4993\\
\log 23.46 &=& 1.3703\\
\log 0.03128 &=& 8.4952 - 10
\end{array}
\qquad
\begin{array}{rcll}
2\log 315.7 &=& 4.9986 & \\
\tfrac{1}{2}\log 23.46 &=& 0.6852 & (+)\\
\hline
\log N \text{ (numerator)} &=& 15.6838 - 10 & \\
\tfrac{1}{3}\log 0.03128 &=& 9.4984 - 10 & (-)\\
\hline
\log Q \text{ (quotient)} &=& 6.1854 & \\
Q &=& 1532000. &
\end{array}$$

Notice that $\log N$ was changed from 5.6838 to 15.6838 − 10; the reason is that 9.4984 − 10 was to be subtracted from it and we wanted the positive part of $\log N$ to be larger than the positive part of the number to be subtracted.

EXAMPLE 2. Compute the value of $\dfrac{3.142 \cdot 2031 \cdot \sqrt{3082}}{0.0231 \cdot \sqrt[3]{63.75}}$.

Solution. If we denote the number by Q, the logarithmic equation is

$$\log Q = \log 3.142 + \log 2031 + \tfrac{1}{2}\log 3082 - [\log 0.0231 + \tfrac{1}{3}\log 63.75].$$

The computation follows:

$$\begin{array}{rrcl}
 & \log 63.75 &=& 1.8044\\
(+) & \tfrac{1}{3}\log 63.75 &=& 0.6015\\
 & \log 0.0231 &=& 8.3636 - 10\\
\hline
 & \log D &=& 8.9651 - 10
\end{array}
\qquad
\begin{array}{rrcl}
 & \log 3082 &=& 3.4889\\
(+) & \tfrac{1}{2}\log 3082 &=& 1.7444\\
 & \log 3.142 &=& 0.4972\\
 & \log 2031 &=& 3.3077\\
\hline
 & \log N &=& 15.5493 - 10\\
(-) & \log D &=& 8.9651 - 10\\
\hline
 & \log Q &=& 6.5842\\
 & Q &=& 3839000.
\end{array}$$

EXERCISE GROUP 11–8

In each of the following exercises, compute the value of the given expression by thc use of Table 3.

1. (65.2)(5.398)
2. (31.27)(0.2896)
3. (0.07835)(4.392)
4. (12.34)(986.6)
5. 0.7895 ÷ 3.846
6. 1.732 ÷ 0.07325
7. $(4.317 \cdot 10^{-5})(8.196 \cdot 10^4)$
8. $68.42 \div (1492 \cdot 10^{-4})$

9. $(4.321)(0.4093)(62.74)$

10. $(0.5011)(1.402)(0.002431)$

11. $\dfrac{(39.62)(0.4397)}{438.5}$

12. $\dfrac{(213.5)(4.173)}{0.02453}$

13. $\dfrac{(4.386)(0.03974)}{0.5382}$

14. $\dfrac{(0.03174)(561.2)}{31780}$

15. $\sqrt{(4.283)(0.7893)}$

16. $\sqrt{(197.5)(0.2318)}$

17. $\sqrt[3]{9.376 \div 89.35}$

18. $\sqrt{463.2 \div 163.1}$

19. $\sqrt{\dfrac{0.02156}{312.7}}$

20. $\dfrac{21.75\sqrt{31.25}}{\sqrt[3]{107.6}}$

21. $\dfrac{\sqrt{3.176}\,\sqrt[3]{218.4}}{\sqrt[4]{325.7}}$

22. $\dfrac{\sqrt{3.981}\,\sqrt[3]{93.87}}{\sqrt[4]{9.435}}$

23. $\dfrac{(31.26)(2104)\sqrt{3210}}{0.2135\sqrt[3]{31.62}}$

24. $\dfrac{\sqrt{928.7}\,\sqrt[3]{4.365}}{8.219(0.6852)^{1/4}}$

25. $\left[\dfrac{54.2\sqrt{8.197}}{0.1324}\right]^{1/3}$

26. $\left[\dfrac{0.6345(83.74)}{0.7942(894.5)}\right]^{3/2}$

27. $\left[\dfrac{0.03124(3.176)}{\sqrt{132.4}}\right]^{3/4}$

28. $\sqrt[5]{\dfrac{-3.289(24.76)^3}{(0.08345)^2}}$

29. $\dfrac{(0.02314)^3(3.1416 \cdot 10^{-7})}{\sqrt{0.127}\,\sqrt[3]{0.1235}}$

30. $\dfrac{(1.025)^{-21}(3{,}176{,}000)}{(0.025)^{-13}}$

31. $\dfrac{(1.03)^{-15}}{2{,}037{,}000}$

32. $\dfrac{(1.03)^4(1.07)^3(1.04)^8}{(1.05)^3(1.08)^2(1.01)^{12}}$

11-12 Logarithms of the trigonometric functions. The numerical work in applications of trigonometry can often be facilitated by the use of logarithms. For example, it may be necessary in the solution of a triangle to compute the value of $a = 143 \sin 29° 20'$. From Table 2 we find $\sin 29° 20' = 0.4899$. Then for $\log a$ we have

$$\log a = \log 143 + \log 0.4899 = 2.1553 + (9.6901 - 10) = 1.8454,$$

for which Table 3 gives

$$a = 70.0.$$

Two references to tables were required to find $\log \sin 29° 20'$. Table 4, on the other hand, gives directly the common logarithms of the trigonometric functions, so that only one reference to a table is required. In those logarithms which are negative, the characteristic appears after the mantissa. We may always write such logarithms in standard form. Thus we find

$$\log \sin 29° 20' = 9.6901 - 10$$

by one reference to a table. Otherwise, the table operates just as for the natural functions, including the use of *linear interpolation.* We shall illustrate both *direct* and *inverse interpolation* in this table.

EXAMPLE 1. Find log cos 78° 43′ from Table 4.

Solution. The desired value is between log cos 78° 40′ and log 78° 50′. Schematically, we have

$$10\left[3\left[\begin{matrix}78^\circ\,40' & 2934\\ 78^\circ\,43' & x\end{matrix}\right]h \atop \begin{matrix}78^\circ\,50' & 2870\end{matrix}\right]64, \qquad \frac{h}{64} = \frac{3}{10}, \quad h = 19,$$

in which only the mantissas of the logarithms are indicated. Since log cos θ decreases as θ increases, $h = 19$ must be subtracted, in the last two decimal places, from log cos 78° 40′, and we find

$$\log\cos 78^\circ\,43' = (9.2934 - 10) - 0.0019 = 9.2915 - 10.$$

EXAMPLE 2. Use Table 4 to find θ if $\log\sin\theta = 9.7802 - 10$.

Solution. The angle must lie between 37° 00′ and 37° 10′. The interpolation is indicated in the scheme:

$$16\left[7\left[\begin{matrix}7795 & 37^\circ\,00'\\ 7802 & \theta\end{matrix}\right]h \atop \begin{matrix}7811 & 37^\circ\,10'\end{matrix}\right]10, \qquad \frac{h}{10} = \frac{7}{16}, \quad h = 4.$$

Hence,

$$\theta = 37^\circ\,00' + 04' = 37^\circ\,04'.$$

EXERCISE GROUP 11–9

Use Table 4 to find the value of the function in each of Exercises 1–12.

1. log sin 23° 15′
2. log cos 47° 13′
3. log tan 75° 12′
4. log cot 39° 17′
5. log sec 37° 24′
6. log csc 107° 41′
7. log sec 79° 35′
8. log csc 111° 57′
9. log cot 214° 37′
10. log sin 96° 18′
11. log cos 314° 16′
12. log tan 256° 29′

Use Table 4 to find the smallest positive value of θ in each of Exercises 13–24.

13. $\log\cos\theta = 9.5652 - 10$
14. $\log\tan\theta = 9.6763 - 10$
15. $\log\cot\theta = 9.7205 - 10$
16. $\log\sin\theta = 9.9587 - 10$
17. $\log\sec\theta = 0.0982$
18. $\log\csc\theta = 0.5571$
19. $\log\sin\theta = 8.5631 - 10$
20. $\log\cos\theta = 9.8959 - 10$
21. $\log\tan\theta = 8.6253 - 10$
22. $\log\cot\theta = 0.0261$
23. $\log\sec\theta = 0.2038$
24. $\log\csc\theta = 1.1477$

Use logarithms to solve the right triangles having the parts given in Exercises 25–33. (In all cases angle $C = 90^\circ$)

25. $A = 36° 18'$, $a = 173.6$
26. $B = 63° 13'$, $c = 0.3256$
27. $a = 0.3129$, $b = 1.346$
28. $a = 496300$, $c = 963500$
29. $A = 76° 36'$, $b = 24.33$
30. $b = 0.02147$, $c = 0.1842$
31. $B = 54° 05'$, $a = 3.148$
32. $a = 496.7$, $b = 96.45$
33. $B = 13° 27'$, $b = 2.347$

34. What airspeed should a pilot maintain on a heading of 270° to fly a course of 287° 30′, if a wind is blowing from the south at 40 mph?

35. A pilot notices that to fly a course of 98° 25′ he must maintain an airspeed of 247.6 mph on a heading of 90°. The wind is blowing from the north with what velocity?

36. A truck weighing 8926 lb moves up a ramp which is inclined 8° 32′ from the horizontal. What is the pressure of the truck against the ramp (perpendicular to the ramp)?

37. A weight of 2187 lb is suspended by two cables. One cable makes an angle of 36° 12′ with the horizontal and the other makes an angle of 27° 09′ with the horizontal. What is the tension in each cable?

38. A surveyor desired to find the distance from a point B to a point A on the opposite side of a river. He determines a point C which is 143.7 ft from B and such that the line BC is perpendicular to the line AB. He then measures angle BCA and finds it to be 31° 13′. What is the distance AB?

39. The navigator of a ship which is sailing due north notices a lighthouse in the direction N 62° 12′ W and after sailing one mile the bearing of the lighthouse is N 67° 17′ W. If the ship continues to sail a straight course, what will be the shortest distance between the ship and the lighthouse?

40. A force of 298.3 lb is directed at an angle of 43° 12′ with the horizontal. Compute the vertical and horizontal components of the force.

41. The cable on a vertical telegraph pole exerts a horizontal pull of 496.8 lb at a point 22.83 ft above the ground. A guy wire 27.8 ft long is attached to the pole at the same height above the ground and anchored to the ground at a point in the same horizontal plane with the foot of the pole. What is the tension in the guy wire required to counteract exactly the horizontal pull of the cable?

11-13 Exponential equations. Compound interest. Formulas giving the *amount* of a sum of money invested at *compound interest* involve exponential functions. A few examples will illustrate this type of application.

Example 1. If \$100 is invested at 3% interest compounded annually, how much will it amount to at the end of 18 yr?

Solution. The \$100 will amount to $100(1 + 0.03)$ at the end of the first year. Since interest is compounded annually, the principal during the second year is \$103, and hence the amount at the end of the second year will be $103 + 0.03(103)$ or $103(1 + 0.03)$, which can be written as $100(1.03)^2$. A continuation of this reasoning shows that at the end of 18 yr the amount A_{18} will be given by

$$A_{18} = 100(1.03)^{18} = \$170 \text{ (computed by logarithms).}$$

EXAMPLE 2. If \$100 is invested at 3% interest compounded quarterly, how much will it amount to in 18 yr?

Solution. Interest is now to be computed every 3 mos and added to the principal. However, the rate of 3% is the annual rate, so that the interest earned in 3 mos is $0.03/4 = 0.0075$. Hence, at the end of the first 3 mos, which is one interest period, the amount will be 100(1.0075). Then, as in Example 1, at the end of six mos, or two interest periods, the amount will be $100(1.0075)^2$, and at the end of 18 yr, or 72 interest periods, the amount A_{72} will be given by

$$A_{72} = 100(1.0075)^{72} = \$171.26 \text{ (by 7-place logarithms)}.$$

In general, we see that \$$P$ at interest rate r compounded j times a year will amount in t years to A_{jt}, where A_{jt} is given by

$$\boxed{A_{jt} = P\left(1 + \frac{r}{j}\right)^{jt}.} \tag{13}$$

This is an exponential function when jt is a variable.

EXAMPLE 3. How long will it take a sum of money (say \$1) to become doubled if invested at 4% interest compounded quarterly?

Solution. In Eq. (13) we set $P = 1$, $r = 0.04$, $j = 4$, $A_{4t} = 2$, and we have

$$2 = 1(1 + 0.01)^{4t}.$$

Then we apply logarithms to obtain

$$\begin{aligned} \log 2 &= \log 1 + \log (1.01)^{4t} \\ &= 0 + 4t \log 1.01. \end{aligned}$$

Solving this equation for $4t$ we have

$$4t = \log 2 \div \log 1.01,$$

so that we obtain for t the value

$$t = \frac{\log 2}{4 \log 1.01} = \frac{0.3010}{4(0.0043)} = \frac{0.3010}{0.0172} = 17.5 \text{ yr}.$$

Note that in this example the solution involves the division of one logarithm by another.

EXAMPLE 4. Determine the value of x such that $10^x = 3.142$.

Solution. By the definition of logarithms,

$$x = \log 3.142 = 0.4972.$$

EXAMPLE 5. Solve for x in the equation

$$3251 = 2184(1.02)^x.$$

Solution. Applying logarithms to both members of the given equation, we have

$$\log 3251 = \log 2184 + x \log 1.02.$$

Solving this last equation for x we obtain

$$x \log 1.02 = \log 3251 - \log 2184,$$

from which it follows that

$$x = \frac{\log 3251 - \log 2184}{\log 1.02} = \frac{3.5120 - 3.3393}{0.0086} = \frac{0.1727}{0.0086} = 20.08.$$

EXERCISE GROUP 11-10

In each of Exercises 1-18, determine the value of x to four significant figures.

1. $x = (1.03)^{17}$
2. $x = (1.015)^{32}$
3. $x = (1.04)^{-18}$
4. $x = (1.025)^{-12}$
5. $x = 23.41(1.03)^{15}$
6. $x = 1876(1.03)^{-12}$
7. $x = 3175(1.015)^{50}$
8. $2^x = 5$
9. $5^x = 7$
10. $7^x = 2$
11. $13^{2x} = 9(5^x)$
12. $11^{3x} = 7(2^x)$
13. $2186 = x(1.02)^{12}$
14. $1826 = 1000(1.02)^x$
15. $\dfrac{(1.03)^x - 1}{0.03} = 26.87$
16. $\dfrac{1 - (1.05)^{-x}}{0.05} = 15.37$
17. $2814 = 1407(1.015)^{2x}$
18. $2 = 1(1 + x)^{15}$

19. If \$100 is invested at 3% compounded annually, how much will it amount to at the end of 18 yr?

20. If \$1975 is invested at 4% compounded quarterly, how much will it amount to in 18 yr?

21. What sum of money invested now at 4% interest compounded quarterly, will amount to \$5000 at the end of 18 yr?

22. How long will it take a sum of money (say \$1) to become doubled if invested at 4% compounded semiannually?

23. At what interest (compounded annually) must a sum of money (say \$1) be invested if it is to become doubled in 15 yr?

24. At what interest compounded quarterly must a sum of money be invested if it is to become trebled in 25 yr?

11-14 Natural logarithms. Change of base. It has been mentioned that the base 10 is usually used for computational purposes. In advanced mathematics, however, when purposes other than computation are concerned, a different base is used, which results in simpler formulas. This base, denoted by the letter e, is an irrational number, whose precise definition cannot be given here, but it is sufficient for our purposes to give it to a number of decimals as

$$e = 2.718281828\ldots$$

Logarithms to the base e are called *natural* or *Naperian* logarithms. Tables of natural logarithms exist, but it is desirable to be able to evaluate such logarithms by use of a table of common logarithms. To do this we shall develop a general formula for converting from one base to any other base.

Let us consider the logarithm

$$y = \log_a x. \tag{14}$$

The equivalent exponential relation is

$$x = a^y.$$

Taking logarithms of both members to the base b, we have

$$\log_b x = y \log_b a,$$

which can be solved for y as

$$y = \frac{\log_b x}{\log_b a}.$$

Substituting the value of y from (14), we have

$$\boxed{\log_a x = \frac{\log_b x}{\log_b a}.} \tag{15}$$

This is the formula used for converting from a logarithm with the base b to a logarithm with the base a.

In particular, the formula becomes, for changing from common to natural logarithms,

$$\boxed{\log_e x = \frac{\log_{10} x}{\log_{10} e} = 2.303 \log_{10} x,} \tag{16}$$

and for converting from natural to common logarithms the formula is

$$\boxed{\log_{10} x = \frac{\log_e x}{\log_e 10} = 0.4343 \log_e x.} \tag{17}$$

EXAMPLE 1. Compute the value of $\log_{12} 17$.

Solution. By formula (15), with $a = 12$ and $b = 10$, we have

$$\log_{12} 17 = \frac{\log_{10} 17}{\log_{10} 12} = \frac{1.2304}{1.0792} = 1.1401.$$

EXAMPLE 2. Compute the value of $\log_e 7$.

Solution. Formula (16) yields, with $x = 7$,

$$\log_e 7 = 2.303 \log_{10} 7 = 2.303 \times 0.8451 = 1.946.$$

EXERCISE GROUP 11-11

In Exercises 1-15, use Table 3 to determine the value of the given logarithm.

1. $\log_2 31.76$
2. $\log_2 3.176$
3. $\log_e 43.91$
4. $\log_5 8132$
5. $\log_7 0.0034$
6. $\log_e 0.9371$
7. $\log_3 0.3146$
8. $\log_3 314.6$
9. $\log_e 3e^{75}$
10. $\log_5 (23.45)^7$
11. $\log_2 (0.3956)^{-3}$
12. $\log_{11} (31.72)^{3/2}$
13. $\log_e 213e^3$
14. $\log_e \frac{3782}{19}$
15. $\log_e \sqrt[5]{438.2}$
16. Prove that $\log_a b = 1/\log_b a$.

REVIEW EXERCISES

In Exercises 1-6, determine the value of x, y, or b, whichever is present.

1. $\log_3 81 = y$
2. $\log_b 16 = 2$
3. $\log_5 x = -1$
4. $\log_{1/3} 27 = y$
5. $\log_b \frac{1}{64} = -6$
6. $\log_{\sqrt{3}} x = 6$

In Exercises 7-12, sketch the graph of the given function.

7. 3^x
8. $2(5^x)$
9. $3(2^{-x})$
10. $\log_2 x$
11. $\log_3 (-x)$
12. $\log_2 (2x)$

In Exercises 13-15, use the properties of logarithms to verify each statement.

13. $\log (3x^2 + 6x) = \log 3 + \log x + \log (x + 2)$, if x is positive.
14. $\log \dfrac{49x^3}{13} = 2 \log 7 + 3 \log x - \log 13$, if x is positive.
15. $\log \dfrac{x^2}{(x - 1)^3} = 2 \log x - 3 \log (x - 1)$, if $x - 1$ is positive.

In Exercises 16-19, rewrite each of the given equations so as to express y as a function of x.

16. $\log y = 2 \log x + \log 3$
17. $\log y = 3x + \log 2$
18. $3 \log y - 2 \log x = 5 \log 4$
19. $2 \log y = 5x + 3 \log 10$

In Exercises 20–25, compute the value of the given expression by use of Table 3.

20. $\dfrac{(3.127)(428.3)}{\sqrt{0.002156}}$

21. $\dfrac{(314 \cdot 10^7)^{2/5}}{(31.78)^2\sqrt{917.6}}$

22. $\dfrac{\sqrt{31920}\sqrt{0.9346}}{\sqrt[4]{5172}}$

23. $\left[\dfrac{(0.03798)^2(8349)^3}{4351 \cdot 10^3}\right]^{1/7}$

24. $\dfrac{\sqrt{83.42}\sqrt[3]{0.3927}}{\sqrt[4]{1.234}\sqrt[5]{0.3416}}$

25. $\left[\dfrac{(3.127 \cdot 10^{-6})^2(72.31 \cdot 10^4)^3}{(317.4 \cdot 10^3)^4}\right]^{2/3}$

In Exercises 26–31, use Table 3 to determine the value of the given logarithm.

26. $\log_2 31.42$ 27. $\log_3 2.346$ 28. $\log_5 314.2$

29. $\log_e 1.285$ 30. $\log_e 12.85$ 31. $\log_e 245e^2$

In Exercises 32–37, determine the value of x, to three significant figures where possible.

32. $5^x = 17$ 33. $(0.23)^x = 0.41$ 34. $17^x = 7(3^x)$

35. $x = (0.9)^{0.4}$ 36. $(1.03)^x = 2$ 37. $(1 + x)^{18} = 2$

In Exercises 38–43, solve for x in terms of y.

38. $y = 3 \sin 2x$ 39. $y = 2 \cos 2x$ 40. $y = \arctan 3x$

41. $y = \arcsin 2x$ 42. $y = 3 \arccos \frac{1}{2}x$ 43. $y = a \tan bx$

Express each of the quantities in Exercises 44–49 in radians.

44. $\text{Arcsin}\,(-\frac{1}{2})$ 45. $\text{Arctan}\,\dfrac{1}{\sqrt{3}}$ 46. $\text{Arcsec}\,(-2)$

47. $\text{Arcsin}\,0.5225$ 48. $\text{Arctan}\,(-0.65)$ 49. $\text{Arcsec}\,1.392$

Find the value of each expression in Exercises 50–55.

50. $\sin \text{Arctan}\,\frac{4}{3}$ 51. $\tan \text{Arcsin}\,(-\frac{5}{13})$ 52. $\sec \text{Arctan}\,\frac{5}{12}$

53. $\sin \text{Arcsec}\,(-\frac{5}{4})$ 54. $\tan \text{Arcsec}\,(-3)$ 55. $\sec \text{Arcsin}\,(-0.5)$

CHAPTER 12

PROPERTIES OF THE TRIGONOMETRIC FUNCTIONS

12–1 The fundamental identities. In Section 6–6 it was seen that the values of the remaining trigonometric functions of an angle can be found if the value of one function of the angle is known. This would seem to indicate the existence of various relations among these functions, relations which are independent of the angle involved.

DEFINITION 12–1. *A statement of equality which is valid for all values of the variable for which the functions involved are defined is called an identity.*

Identities are familiar from algebra. A factorization, such as

$$x^3 + 1 = (x + 1)(x^2 - x + 1),$$

involves a statement of identity, the equation being valid for all values of x. Another algebraic identity is the equation

$$\frac{1}{x - 1} - \frac{1}{x + 1} = \frac{2}{x^2 - 1},$$

which holds for all values of x except $x = \pm 1$, for which at least one term is undefined. On the other hand, an equation such as

$$x^2 - 4 = 0,$$

which holds only for isolated values of x (here, $x = \pm 2$), is called a *conditional equation.*

Identities do exist among the trigonometric functions, and their study comprises a major part of so-called analytical trigonometry. The fundamental identities fall into three types: the *reciprocal identities*, the *ratio identities*, and the *squares* or *Pythagorean identities*. The *reciprocal identities* are perhaps the simplest, and follow directly from the definitions of the trigonometric functions. They are as follows, with each written in three equivalent forms:

$$\boxed{\sin\theta = \frac{1}{\csc\theta}, \quad \sin\theta\csc\theta = 1, \quad \csc\theta = \frac{1}{\sin\theta};} \tag{1}$$

$$\cos\theta = \frac{1}{\sec\theta}, \quad \cos\theta\sec\theta = 1, \quad \sec\theta = \frac{1}{\cos\theta}; \tag{2}$$

$$\tan\theta = \frac{1}{\cot\theta}, \quad \tan\theta\cot\theta = 1, \quad \cot\theta = \frac{1}{\tan\theta}. \tag{3}$$

For example, from the definitions of Section 6–6, we have, if θ is in standard position, and x, y, and r, with $r \neq 0$, are the coordinates and polar distance of a point on its terminal side,

$$\sin\theta = y/r, \qquad \csc\theta = r/y, \qquad (y \neq 0),$$

from which it follows at once that

$$\sin\theta\csc\theta = 1.$$

The other two forms of (1) follow immediately. Equations (2) and (3) are proved similarly.

The *ratio identities* also follow at once from the definition of the trigonometric functions (Section 6–6), and are

$$\tan\theta = \frac{\sin\theta}{\cos\theta}, \tag{4}$$

$$\cot\theta = \frac{\cos\theta}{\sin\theta}. \tag{5}$$

Finally, to prove the *squares* or *Pythagorean identities*, let any angle θ be placed in standard position, and let x, y, r, with $r \neq 0$, be the coordinates and polar distance of a point on its terminal side. By Section 5–4, we have the relation

$$x^2 + y^2 = r^2. \tag{6}$$

Division of both members by r^2 gives

$$\left(\frac{x}{r}\right)^2 + \left(\frac{y}{r}\right)^2 = 1,$$

and since $\cos\theta = x/r$, and $\sin\theta = y/r$, the squares identity

$$\sin^2\theta + \cos^2\theta = 1 \tag{7}$$

is obtained. Similarly, division of both members of (6) by x^2, with $x \neq 0$, yields the identity

$$\boxed{\sec^2 \theta = 1 + \tan^2 \theta.} \tag{8}$$

The third and final squares identity, derived in like manner, is

$$\boxed{\csc^2 \theta = 1 + \cot^2 \theta.} \tag{9}$$

12–2 On proving identities. In addition to the fundamental identities there are many other identities, some fairly complicated, involving the trigonometric functions. The need for them arises in various connections, in the study of calculus in particular. Facility in proving these identities depends to a large extent on great familiarity with the fundamental relations. No fixed procedure can be prescribed. In fact, a given identity can usually be proved in various ways. It is important, in the course of such a proof, to be able to look ahead, and foresee what a given step will yield. For example, by formula (8) we may replace $\sec^2 \theta$ by $1 + \tan^2 \theta$. By the same formula we may replace $\tan^2 \theta$ by $\sec^2 \theta - 1$, or $\sec^2 \theta - \tan^2 \theta$ by 1. However, it is not so easy to recognize that the number 1 may need to be replaced by $\sec^2 \theta - \tan^2 \theta$ or, by (7), by $\sin^2 \theta + \cos^2 \theta$.

EXAMPLE 1. Can $\sqrt{1 + 2 \sin \theta \cos \theta}$ be rationalized?

Solution. We may replace 1 by $\sin^2 \theta + \cos^2 \theta$. Then

$$\begin{aligned}\sqrt{1 + 2 \sin \theta \cos \theta} &= \sqrt{\sin^2 \theta + 2 \sin \theta \cos \theta + \cos^2 \theta} \\ &= \sqrt{(\sin \theta + \cos \theta)^2} = \pm(\sin \theta + \cos \theta).\end{aligned}$$

The generality of the identities has another aspect. The identities are stated in terms of θ, but any angle, such as 2θ, $\theta/2$, or even $\pi - \theta$, could appear, provided the same one is used throughout. Thus, the identities

$$\cos \frac{\theta}{2} \tan \frac{\theta}{2} = \sin \frac{\theta}{2} \qquad \text{and} \qquad \sin^2 3\theta = 1 - \cos^2 3\theta$$

follow at once from formulas (4) and (7) respectively, and the appearance of the angle $\theta/2$ or 3θ in these identities is not significant.

The proof of an identity can be achieved by transforming either member by the use of known identities, together with permissible operations, until the other member is obtained. By the same token, both members may be transformed independently until the same function results from the sequence of transformations. It is also possible to establish an identity by use of permissible operations on equations until a known identity is reached, but these steps must be reversible. For, as also with equations, each step involves the statement that *if the current relation is valid, then the resulting one is also valid.* In this manner, the final relation is merely shown to be possible, and must then be established either by direct substitution, or by a reversal of the steps.

We shall restrict the method of proof in what follows to working with one member of an identity until the other member is obtained. In the absence of a fixed method of procedure, the following suggestions should prove helpful.

1. *Choose the more complicated member as the one to be transformed.*
2. *If the member being transformed contains a sum of fractions, it may help to combine these fractions into a single fraction.*
3. *If the numerator of a fraction contains more than one term, it may help to express the fraction as a sum of fractions.*
4. *If the numerator or denominator of a fraction (or the entire member) can be factored, the factorization may suggest the next step.*
5. *In the absence of other steps to take, express each function in terms of sines and cosines.*
6. *At all times, in order to discover what step to take, keep in mind the other member of the identity, a comparison of which with the one being transformed may suggest what to do.*

EXAMPLE 2. Prove the identity

$$\frac{\csc^2 \theta/2 - \cot^2 \theta/2}{\sec^2 \theta/2} = \cos^2 \frac{\theta}{2}.$$

Solution. We choose the left member as the one to be transformed. By means of (9) we may replace $\csc^2 \theta/2 - \cot^2 \theta/2$ by 1. Then the left member can be written as

$$\frac{1}{\sec^2 \theta/2} = \cos^2 \frac{\theta}{2} \quad \text{[by (2)]}$$

and the identity is established.

EXAMPLE 3. Prove the identity $\cot 2\theta \cos 2\theta = \csc 2\theta - \sin 2\theta$.

Solution. With the use of (1) and (7) the right member may be written as

$$\frac{1}{\sin 2\theta} - \sin 2\theta = \frac{1 - \sin^2 2\theta}{\sin 2\theta} = \frac{\cos^2 2\theta}{\sin 2\theta} = \frac{\cos 2\theta}{\sin 2\theta} \cdot \cos 2\theta,$$

and by (5) this becomes $\cot 2\theta \cos 2\theta$.

EXAMPLE 4. Prove the identity

$$\frac{\sec \theta + 1}{\tan \theta} = \frac{\tan \theta}{\sec \theta - 1}.$$

Solution. There is no apparent reason for preferring to transform either member. We arbitrarily choose to transform the left member. To obtain $\sec\theta - 1$ in the denominator (since it appears there in the right member), we multiply numerator and denominator of the fraction by that quantity, and have

$$\frac{\sec\theta + 1}{\tan\theta}\cdot\frac{\sec\theta - 1}{\sec\theta - 1} = \frac{\sec^2\theta - 1}{\tan\theta\,(\sec\theta - 1)} = \frac{\tan^2\theta}{\tan\theta\,(\sec\theta - 1)} \quad \text{[by (8)]}$$

$$= \frac{\tan\theta}{\sec\theta - 1}$$

and the proof is complete.

The use of trigonometric identities is often involved in solving a (conditional) trigonometric equation.

EXAMPLE 5. Solve the equation $\tan^2 x + \sec^2 x = 7$ for x in terms of inverse trigonometric functions.

Solution. By Eq. (8) the left member of the equation becomes

$$\tan^2 x + \sec^2 x = \tan^2 x + (1 + \tan^2 x) = 2\tan^2 x + 1.$$

It follows that

$$2\tan^2 x + 1 = 7, \qquad \tan^2 x = 3, \qquad \text{and} \qquad \tan x = \pm\sqrt{3}.$$

In the notation of Section 11–2 the values of x can now be given as

$$x = \arctan(\pm\sqrt{3}).$$

EXAMPLE 6. Solve the equation $\cos^2\theta - \sin^2\theta = \cos\theta$ for θ.

Solution. By Eq. (7) the left member becomes

$$\cos^2\theta - \sin^2\theta = \cos^2\theta - (1 - \cos^2\theta) = 2\cos^2\theta - 1$$

and the equation reduces to

$$2\cos^2\theta - \cos\theta - 1 = 0.$$

This is an equation of quadratic form, quadratic in $\cos\theta$, and can be solved by factoring. Thus, we obtain

$$(2\cos\theta + 1)(\cos\theta - 1) = 0.$$

We may equate each factor to zero, and obtain as the values of $\cos\theta$,

$$\cos\theta = -\tfrac{1}{2}, \qquad \cos\theta = 1.$$

The solutions are then

$$\theta = \arccos\left(-\tfrac{1}{2}\right) = 120° + n \cdot 360°, \quad \text{or} \quad 240° + n \cdot 360°$$

and

$$\theta = \arccos 1 = n \cdot 360°, \quad \text{for any integer } n.$$

Exercise Group 12–1

In Exercises 1–10, reduce the first expression to the second, by use of the fundamental identities.

1. $\sin^2\theta(1 + \tan^2\theta)$, $\tan^2\theta$
2. $\tan^2\theta(1 - \sin^2\theta)$, $\sin^2\theta$
3. $\csc^2\theta(1 - \cos^2\theta)$, 1
4. $\sec^2\theta(\csc^2\theta - 1)$, $\csc^2\theta$
5. $\cos^2\theta(\sec^2\theta - 1)$, $\sin^2\theta$
6. $\cot^2\theta(1 - \cos^2\theta)$, $\cos^2\theta$
7. $\sec^2\theta + \csc^2\theta$, $\sec^2\theta\csc^2\theta$
8. $\dfrac{\sec\theta}{\sin\theta} - \dfrac{\sin\theta}{\cos\theta}$, $\cot\theta$
9. $\sin\theta(\csc\theta - \sin\theta)$, $\cos^2\theta$
10. $\sin\theta(\csc\theta + \sin\theta\sec^2\theta)$, $\sec^2\theta$

Prove that the equations in Exercises 11–47 are identities.

11. $\sin\theta\tan\theta + \cos\theta = \sec\theta$
12. $\dfrac{\sin\theta\cot\theta + \cos\theta}{\cot\theta} = 2\sin\theta$
13. $\csc^2\theta + \cot^2\theta + 1 = \dfrac{2}{\sin^2\theta}$
14. $\cos\theta\cot\theta + \sin\theta = \csc\theta$
15. $(1 - \sin\theta)(\sec\theta + \tan\theta) = \cos\theta$
16. $(\csc\theta - \cot\theta)(\sec\theta + 1) = \tan\theta$
17. $\dfrac{\cos^2\theta}{1 + \sin\theta} = 1 - \sin\theta$
18. $\dfrac{\sin\theta + \cos\theta}{\sin\theta - \cos\theta} = \dfrac{\tan\theta + 1}{\tan\theta - 1}$
19. $\dfrac{\sin\theta}{\sin\theta - \cos\theta} = \dfrac{1}{1 - \cot\theta}$
20. $\sec^2\theta + \csc^2\theta = \sec^2\theta\csc^2\theta$
21. $\dfrac{\sin^2\theta}{\sin^2\theta + \cos\theta} = \dfrac{\tan\theta}{\tan\theta + \csc\theta}$
22. $\dfrac{\sec\theta + 1}{\sec\theta - 1} = \dfrac{1 + \cos\theta}{1 - \cos\theta}$
23. $\dfrac{\csc\theta - 1}{\csc\theta + 1} = \dfrac{1 - \sin\theta}{1 + \sin\theta}$
24. $\dfrac{\sin\theta}{1 + \cos\theta} = \dfrac{1 - \cos\theta}{\sin\theta}$
25. $\tan\theta + \cot\theta = \sec\theta\csc\theta$
26. $\dfrac{\sin\theta}{\sin\theta + \cos\theta} = \dfrac{\tan\theta}{1 + \tan\theta}$
27. $\dfrac{\sin\theta}{\sin\theta + \cos\theta} = \dfrac{\tan\theta}{1 + \tan\theta}$
28. $\dfrac{\sin\theta}{1 - \cos\theta} = \dfrac{\tan\theta}{\sec\theta - 1}$
29. $\dfrac{\sin\theta + \tan\theta}{\cot\theta + \csc\theta} = \sin^2\theta\sec\theta$
30. $\dfrac{\sin^2\theta + 2}{\sin^2\theta - 2} = \dfrac{1 - 3\sec^2\theta}{1 + \sec^2\theta}$
31. $\csc^4\theta - \cot^4\theta = \csc^2\theta + \cot^2\theta$

32. $\dfrac{\sin\theta}{\sec\theta + 1} + \dfrac{\sin\theta}{\sec\theta - 1} = 2\cot\theta$

33. $\dfrac{\cot\theta}{\sec\theta - \tan\theta} - \dfrac{\cos\theta}{\sec\theta + \tan\theta} = \csc\theta + \sin\theta$

34. $\cos^4\theta - \sin^4\theta = 1 - 2\sin^2\theta$

35. $\cot^4\theta + \csc^2\theta = \csc^4\theta - \cot^2\theta$

36. $\cos^4\theta - \sin^4\theta = 2\cos^2\theta - 1$

37. $\csc^4\theta - 2\csc^2\theta\cot^2\theta = 1 - \cot^4\theta$

38. $\dfrac{\sin\theta}{1 + \cos\theta} + \dfrac{1 + \cos\theta}{\sin\theta} = 2\csc\theta$

39. $\dfrac{\sec^4\theta - 1}{\tan^2\theta} = 2 + \tan^2\theta$

40. $\dfrac{\cos^4\theta - \sin^4\theta}{1 - \tan^4\theta} = \cos^4\theta$

41. $\sec\theta + \tan\theta = \dfrac{\cos\theta}{1 - \sin\theta}$

42. $\csc^2\theta\tan^2\theta - \sin^2\theta\sec^2\theta = 1$

43. $\sec^2\theta\cot^2\theta - \cos^2\theta\csc^2\theta = 1$

44. $\csc\theta + \cot\theta = \dfrac{\sin\theta}{1 - \cos\theta}$

45. $\dfrac{\cos\theta}{\sec\theta} - \dfrac{\sin\theta}{\cot\theta} = \dfrac{\cos\theta\cot\theta - \tan\theta}{\csc\theta}$

46. $1 - \sin\theta = \dfrac{\cos\theta}{\sec\theta + \tan\theta}$

47. $\tan\theta + \cot\theta = \tan\theta\csc^2\theta$

In Exercises 48–54, express the value of each of the quantities, without radicals, under the given substitutions ($0 \leqq \theta < \pi/2$).

48. $\sqrt{1 + x^2}$ if $x = \tan\theta$

49. $\sqrt{1 + 4x^2}$ if $2x = \tan\theta$

50. $\sqrt{2 - 3x^2}$ if $\sqrt{3}x = \sqrt{2}\sin\theta$

51. $\sqrt{2x - x^2}$ if $x = 1 + \sin\theta$

52. $\sqrt{2x + x^2}$ if $x = \sec\theta - 1$

53. $(a^{2/3} - x^{2/3})^{3/2}$ if $x = a\cos^3\theta$

54. $\sqrt{x^2 - 4x}$ if $x = 2 + 2\csc\theta$

In each of Exercises 55–64, solve for x by use of the fundamental identities.

55. $\sin x = \cos x$

56. $\sin x = \tan x$

57. $\cos x = \cot x$

58. $1 - \sin^2 x = \cos x$

59. $\sec^2 x - 1 = \tan x$

60. $2\sin x\cos x = \sin x$

61. $\cos x = \dfrac{1 + \cos^2 x}{2}$

62. $\cos x = \dfrac{1 - \cos x}{2}$

63. $\cos^2 x - \sin^2 x = \sin x$

64. $\cos^2 x + \sin^2 x = \cos x$

12–3 The addition formulas. There are additional groups of identities which involve more than one angle, or multiples of an angle. The following are the *addition formulas*, which are identities involving two angles:

$$\boxed{\sin(A + B) = \sin A\cos B + \cos A\sin B,} \qquad (10)$$

$$\boxed{\cos(A+B) = \cos A \cos B - \sin A \sin B,} \tag{11}$$

$$\boxed{\tan(A+B) = \frac{\tan A + \tan B}{1 - \tan A \tan B}.} \tag{12}$$

The corresponding formulas for functions of $A - B$ are

$$\boxed{\sin(A-B) = \sin A \cos B - \cos A \sin B.} \tag{13}$$

$$\boxed{\cos(A-B) = \cos A \cos B + \sin A \sin B,} \tag{14}$$

$$\boxed{\tan(A-B) = \frac{\tan A - \tan B}{1 + \tan A \tan B}.} \tag{15}$$

These identities will be established in the following section, without any restriction on the magnitudes of the angles. Here we wish to emphasize their application.

EXAMPLE 1. Find the values of $\sin(A+B)$, $\sin(A-B)$, $\cos(A+B)$, $\cos(A-B)$, $\tan(A+B)$, and $\tan(A-B)$ if

$$\cos A = -\tfrac{4}{5}, \quad A \text{ in } Q_3, \qquad \text{and} \qquad \tan B = -\tfrac{5}{12}, \quad B \text{ in } Q_2.$$

Solution. Figure 12–1 shows an angle A in Q_3, and an angle B in Q_2. It follows that

$$\sin A = -\tfrac{3}{5}, \qquad \tan A = \tfrac{3}{4},$$
$$\sin B = \tfrac{5}{13}, \qquad \cos B = -\tfrac{12}{13}.$$

With the values for $\sin A$, $\cos A$, $\tan A$, and $\sin B$, $\cos B$, $\tan B$, we can

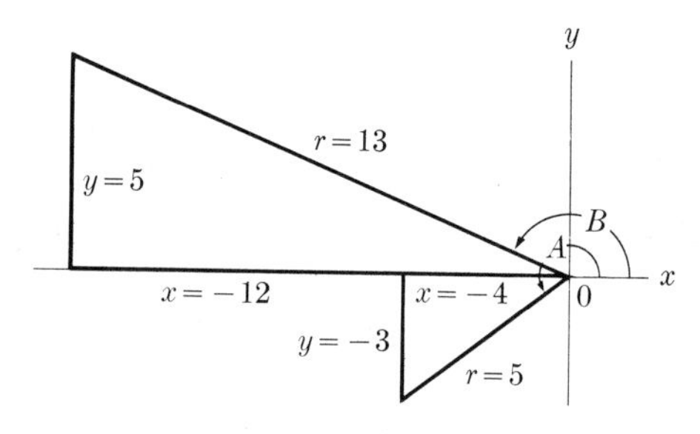

FIGURE 12–1

substitute in formulas (10), (11), (12), (13), (14), and (15) to obtain

$$\sin (A + B) = \left(-\frac{3}{5}\right)\left(-\frac{12}{13}\right) + \left(-\frac{4}{5}\right)\left(\frac{5}{13}\right) = \frac{36 - 20}{65} = \frac{16}{65};$$

$$\sin (A - B) = \left(-\frac{3}{5}\right)\left(-\frac{12}{13}\right) - \left(-\frac{4}{5}\right)\left(\frac{5}{13}\right) = \frac{36 + 20}{65} = \frac{56}{65};$$

$$\cos (A + B) = \left(-\frac{4}{5}\right)\left(-\frac{12}{13}\right) - \left(-\frac{3}{5}\right)\left(\frac{5}{13}\right) = \frac{48 + 15}{65} = \frac{63}{65};$$

$$\cos (A - B) = \left(-\frac{4}{5}\right)\left(-\frac{12}{13}\right) + \left(-\frac{3}{5}\right)\left(\frac{5}{13}\right) = \frac{48 - 15}{65} = \frac{33}{65};$$

$$\tan (A + B) = \frac{\frac{3}{4} + \left(-\frac{5}{12}\right)}{1 - \left(\frac{3}{4}\right)\left(-\frac{5}{12}\right)} = \frac{\frac{9 - 5}{12}}{\frac{48 + 15}{48}} = \frac{1}{3} \cdot \frac{48}{63} = \frac{16}{63};$$

$$\tan (A - B) = \frac{\frac{3}{4} - \left(-\frac{5}{12}\right)}{1 + \left(\frac{3}{4}\right)\left(-\frac{5}{12}\right)} = \frac{\frac{9 + 5}{12}}{\frac{48 - 15}{48}} = \frac{7}{6} \cdot \frac{16}{11} = \frac{56}{33}.$$

Of course $\tan (A + B)$ and $\tan (A - B)$ can be found more easily by the ratio identities after $\sin (A + B)$, $\cos (A + B)$, $\sin (A - B)$, and $\cos (A - B)$ are known, but the example illustrates the use of the addition formulas if the other functions are not known.

EXAMPLE 2. Use the appropriate addition formula to obtain the exact value of $\cos (3\pi/2 - \pi/3)$.

Solution. With the use of formula (14) it follows that

$$\begin{aligned} \cos \left(\frac{3\pi}{2} - \frac{\pi}{3}\right) &= \cos \frac{3\pi}{2} \cos \frac{\pi}{3} + \sin \frac{3\pi}{2} \sin \frac{\pi}{3} \\ &= 0 \cdot \frac{1}{2} + (-1) \cdot \frac{\sqrt{3}}{2} = -\frac{\sqrt{3}}{2}. \end{aligned}$$

EXAMPLE 3. Use the appropriate addition formula to prove the identity

$$\sin 3\theta \cos \theta - \cos 3\theta \sin \theta = \sin 2\theta.$$

Solution. If in formula (13) we set $A = 3\theta$ and $B = \theta$ we have

$$\sin (3\theta - \theta) = \sin 3\theta \cos \theta - \cos 3\theta \sin \theta,$$

which gives the desired identity, since $3\theta - \theta = 2\theta$.

EXAMPLE 4. Prove the identity

$$\frac{\tan (C - D) + \tan D}{1 - \tan (C - D) \tan D} = \tan C.$$

Solution. In formula (12) let $A = C - D$ and $B = D$. Then we have

$$\tan [(C - D) + D] = \tan C = \frac{\tan (C - D) + \tan D}{1 - \tan (C - D) \tan D}.$$

12–4 Proof of the addition formulas for general angles. In proving the addition formulas we shall first give a general proof of the addition formula (14) for $\cos (A - B)$. The other addition formulas will then be derived from this one. If we set $B = \theta$, $A = \theta + \phi$, the formula for $\cos (A - B)$ becomes

$$\cos \phi = \cos (\theta + \phi) \cos \theta + \sin (\theta + \phi) \sin \theta, \tag{16}$$

which is the form in which we shall prove the formula.

It is clear that if ϕ is a multiple of 2π, the above relation becomes, by the periodicity of the sine and cosine functions, $1 = \cos^2 \theta + \sin^2 \theta$, which we know to be valid. If ϕ is not a multiple of 2π, we may add to ϕ a suitable positive, negative, or zero multiple k of 2π so that $\alpha = \phi + 2k\pi$ is an angle between 0 and 2π. The angle θ is now drawn in standard position in a coordinate system, and α is drawn with its vertex at 0, and initial side on the terminal side of θ. We also draw a circle of radius 1 with center at 0. The point P in Fig. 12–2(a) on the terminal side of θ then has coordinates $(\cos \theta, \sin \theta)$, and the point Q on the terminal side of $\theta + \alpha$ has coordinates $[\cos (\theta + \alpha), \sin (\theta + \alpha)]$. Now rotate triangle OPQ through the angle $-\theta$, to assume the position $OP'Q'$ in Fig. 12–2(b), with $(1, 0)$ as the coordinates of P' and $(\cos \alpha, \sin \alpha)$ as the coordinates of Q'. Now the lengths of PQ and $P'Q'$ are equal and so are their squares. Applying the distance formula of Section 5–4 in each case, we have

$$(\cos \alpha - 1)^2 + \sin^2 \alpha = [\cos (\theta + \alpha) - \cos \theta]^2 + [\sin (\theta + \alpha) - \sin \theta]^2$$

or

$$\begin{aligned} \cos^2 \alpha - 2 \cos \alpha + 1 + \sin^2 \alpha \\ &= \cos^2 (\theta + \alpha) - 2 \cos (\theta + \alpha) \cos \theta + \cos^2 \theta \\ &\quad + \sin^2 (\theta + \alpha) - 2 \sin (\theta + \alpha) \sin \theta + \sin^2 \theta. \end{aligned}$$

If we apply the squares identity (7) to α on the left, and $\theta + \alpha$ and θ on the right, we obtain

$$\cos \alpha = \cos (\theta + \alpha) \cos \theta + \sin (\theta + \alpha) \sin \theta. \tag{17}$$

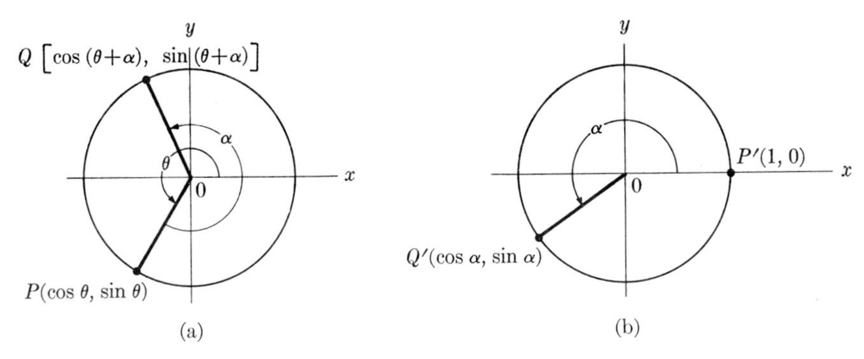

FIGURE 12–2

Now, $\cos(\theta + \alpha) = \cos(\theta + \phi + 2k\pi) = \cos(\theta + \phi)$, by the periodicity of the cosine function, and similarly $\sin(\theta + \alpha) = \sin(\theta + \phi)$ and $\cos\alpha = \cos\phi$. Substitution of them in (17) gives (16), and the proof of (14) is complete.

To prove (13) we first obtain some incidental relations from (14). Let $B = \pi/2$ in (14). Since $\cos\pi/2 = 0$ and $\sin\pi/2 = 1$, we obtain

$$\cos\left(A - \frac{\pi}{2}\right) = \sin A, \quad \text{for any angle } A. \tag{18}$$

In (18) let $A = B - \pi/2$; we get $\cos(B - \pi) = \sin(B - \pi/2)$. But by (14) again, $\cos(B - \pi) = -\cos B$. Hence, it follows that

$$\sin\left(B - \frac{\pi}{2}\right) = -\cos B, \quad \text{for any angle } B. \tag{19}$$

To derive (13) we replace A by $A - \pi/2$ in (14) which then becomes

$$\cos\left(A - \frac{\pi}{2} - B\right) = \cos\left(A - \frac{\pi}{2}\right)\cos B + \sin\left(A - \frac{\pi}{2}\right)\sin B. \tag{20}$$

But $\cos(A - B - \pi/2) = \sin(A - B)$, $\cos(A - \pi/2) = \sin A$, $\sin(A - \pi/2) = -\cos A$, by (18) and (19), and (20) becomes

$$\sin(A - B) = \sin A\cos B - \cos A\sin B,$$

which is (13).

We derive (15) by dividing the members of (13) by the corresponding members of (14) as follows, if $A - B$ is not an odd multiple of $\pi/2$:

$$\begin{aligned}\tan(A - B) &= \frac{\sin(A - B)}{\cos(A - B)} = \frac{\sin A\cos B - \cos A\sin B}{\cos A\cos B + \sin A\sin B}\\ &= \frac{(\sin A\cos B)/(\cos A\cos B) - (\cos A\sin B)/(\cos A\cos B)}{1 + (\sin A\sin B)/(\cos A\cos B)}\\ &= \frac{\tan A - \tan B}{1 + \tan A\tan B}.\end{aligned}$$

Letting $A = 0$ in (13), (14), and (15), we obtain

$$\sin(-B) = -\sin B, \quad \cos(-B) = \cos B, \quad \tan(-B) = -\tan B. \quad (21)$$

We can now obtain (10), (11), and (12), by replacing B by $-B$ in (13), (14), and (15) and using (21). For example, we have

$$\begin{aligned}\sin(A + B) = \sin[A - (-B)] &= \sin A \cos(-B) - \cos A \sin(-B)\\ &= \sin A \cos B + \cos A \sin B\end{aligned}$$

and (10) is established. Formulas (11) and (12) follow similarly.

Exercise Group 12–2

Find the values of $\sin(A + B)$, $\sin(A - B)$, $\cos(A + B)$, $\cos(A - B)$, $\tan(A + B)$, and $\tan(A - B)$ under the conditions stated in each of Exercises 1–6.

1. $\sin A = \frac{3}{5}$, A in Q_1; $\cos B = -\frac{5}{13}$, B in Q_2
2. $\tan A = \frac{3}{4}$, A in Q_3; $\sin B = -\frac{12}{13}$, B in Q_4
3. $\cos A = \frac{7}{25}$, A in Q_4; $\cos B = -\frac{4}{5}$, B in Q_2
4. $\sin A = \frac{5}{13}$, A in Q_2; $\tan B = \frac{7}{24}$, B in Q_3
5. $\cot A = \frac{12}{5}$, A in Q_3; $\cos B = -\frac{4}{5}$, B in Q_3
6. $\tan A = -\frac{5}{12}$, A in Q_2; $\cot B = -\frac{24}{7}$, B in Q_4

Apply the addition formulas in Exercises 7–18 to obtain the exact value in each case.

7. $\sin(60° - 45°)$
8. $\cos\left(\pi - \frac{\pi}{3}\right)$
9. $\cos\left(\frac{\pi}{2} - \frac{\pi}{3}\right)$
10. $\sin(270° + 30°)$
11. $\tan(45° + 60°)$
12. $\tan\left(\frac{\pi}{3} - \frac{\pi}{4}\right)$
13. $\sin(270° - 90°)$
14. $\cos\left(\pi - \frac{\pi}{6}\right)$
15. $\tan\left(\pi + \frac{\pi}{3}\right)$
16. $\tan(360° - 45°)$
17. $\sin\left(\frac{3\pi}{2} + \frac{\pi}{4}\right)$
18. $\cos(450° + 60°)$

Use the addition formulas to prove the identities in Exercises 19–39.

19. $\sin(90° + \theta) = \cos\theta$
20. $\cos(180° + \theta) = -\cos\theta$
21. $\tan(270° - \theta) = \cot\theta$
22. $\sin(2\pi - \theta) = -\sin\theta$
23. $\cos\left(\frac{\pi}{2} - \theta\right) = \sin\theta$
24. $\tan(180° - \theta) = -\tan\theta$
25. $\sin\left(\frac{\pi}{4} + \theta\right) = \frac{\sin\theta + \cos\theta}{\sqrt{2}}$
26. $\cos(60° + \theta) = \frac{\cos\theta - \sqrt{3}\sin\theta}{2}$
27. $\cos(60° - \theta) = \frac{\cos\theta + \sqrt{3}\sin\theta}{2}$

28. $\sin\left(\frac{\pi}{3} - \theta\right) = \frac{\sqrt{3}\cos\theta - \sin\theta}{2}$ 29. $\tan(120° + \theta) = \frac{\tan\theta - \sqrt{3}}{1 + \sqrt{3}\tan\theta}$

30. $\tan(315° - \theta) = \frac{1 + \tan\theta}{\tan\theta - 1}$

31. $\sin 2\theta \cos 3\theta + \cos 2\theta \sin 3\theta = \sin 5\theta$

32. $\cos\theta \cos 2\theta - \sin\theta \sin 2\theta = \cos 3\theta$

33. $\sin 3\theta \cos 2\theta - \cos 3\theta \sin 2\theta = \sin\theta$

34. $\cos 2\theta \cos\theta + \sin 2\theta \sin\theta = \cos\theta$

35. $\sin(A + B)\cos B - \cos(A + B)\sin B = \sin A$ (*Hint:* Let $A + B = \theta$.)

36. $\cos(A - B)\cos B - \sin(A - B)\sin B = \cos A$

37. $\frac{\tan(A + B) - \tan B}{1 + \tan(A + B)\tan B} = \tan A$

38. $\sec\theta = \csc\theta \sin 2\theta - \sec\theta \cos 2\theta$

39. $\csc\theta(\sin 3\theta \cos 2\theta - \cos 3\theta \sin 2\theta) = 1$

40. Find $\tan(A - B)$ if $\tan A = (x + ky)/(kx - y)$ and $\tan B = y/x$.

41. Find $\tan(x + y)$ if $\tan x = a/(1 + a)$ and $\tan y = 1/(1 + 2a)$.

12–5 The double-angle formulas. By setting $B = A$ in the addition formulas (10), (11), and (12) of Section 12–3, the *double-angle formulas* are obtained:

$$\boxed{\sin 2A = 2\sin A \cos A,} \tag{22}$$

$$\boxed{\cos 2A = \cos^2 A - \sin^2 A,} \tag{23a}$$

$$\boxed{\cos 2A = 1 - 2\sin^2 A,} \quad \text{[by (7)]} \tag{23b}$$

$$\boxed{\cos 2A = 2\cos^2 A - 1,} \tag{23c}$$

$$\boxed{\tan 2A = \frac{2\tan A}{1 - \tan^2 A}.} \tag{24}$$

For example, to prove (23a) we have

$$\cos 2A = \cos(A + A) = \cos A \cos A - \sin A \sin A = \cos^2 A - \sin^2 A.$$

These formulas possess a generality with regard to the angle which is perhaps not readily apparent. For example, if $A = \theta/2$, formula (22) gives

$$\sin\theta = 2\sin\frac{\theta}{2}\cos\frac{\theta}{2},$$

and with $A = 2\theta$, formula (23a) becomes

$$\cos 4\theta = \cos^2 2\theta - \sin^2 2\theta.$$

12–6 The half-angle formulas. Let formula (23b) be solved for $\sin A$, and let A be replaced by $A/2$. There results, at once, the formula,

$$\boxed{\sin\frac{A}{2} = \pm\sqrt{\frac{1-\cos A}{2}};} \tag{25}$$

a similar procedure with (23a) gives

$$\boxed{\cos\frac{A}{2} = \pm\sqrt{\frac{1+\cos A}{2}};} \tag{26}$$

and division of the members of (25) by the corresponding members of (26) yields

$$\boxed{\tan\frac{A}{2} = \pm\sqrt{\frac{1-\cos A}{1+\cos A}}.} \tag{27}$$

The three formulas thus derived are known as the *half-angle formulas.* In a sense they reverse the processes of the double-angle formulas, and they possess the same kind of generality with regard to the angle.

An alternative form of (27), involving no radical, may be obtained as follows, the reasons for the steps to be supplied by the student:

$$\tan A/2 = \frac{\sin A/2}{\cos A/2} = \frac{2\sin A/2\cos A/2}{2\cos^2 A/2},$$

so that we obtain the formula

$$\boxed{\tan\frac{A}{2} = \frac{\sin A}{1+\cos A} = \frac{1-\cos A}{\sin A}.} \tag{28}$$

The advantage of (28) over (27) is the lack of ambiguity of sign.

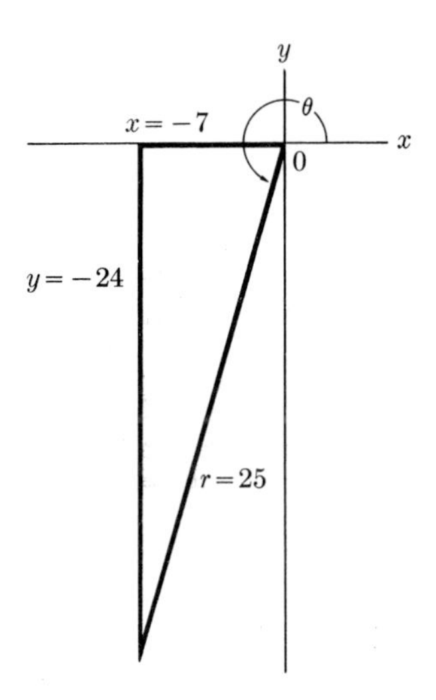

FIGURE 12–3

EXAMPLE 1. Find the exact values of $\sin \theta/2$, $\cos 2\theta$, and $\tan 3\theta$, if $\sin \theta = -\frac{24}{25}$, with θ in Q_3.

Solution. Figure 12–3 shows an angle θ drawn in standard position. It follows that

$$\cos \theta = -\tfrac{7}{25}, \qquad \tan \theta = \tfrac{24}{7}.$$

Then from formula (25) we have

$$\sin \frac{\theta}{2} = \pm\sqrt{\frac{1 - (-\frac{7}{25})}{2}} = \pm\sqrt{\tfrac{16}{25}} = \pm\tfrac{4}{5}.$$

Either sign may apply, since, with θ in Q_3, $\theta/2$ may be in Q_2 or in Q_4. (If θ is in Q_3, then $\theta = \alpha + 2n\pi$ where $\pi < \alpha < 3\pi/2$, n an integer. Hence $\theta/2 = \alpha/2 + n\pi$, where $\pi/2 < \alpha/2 < 3\pi/4$.)

Using formula (23c), we have

$$\cos 2\theta = 2(-\tfrac{7}{25})^2 - 1 = \tfrac{98}{625} - 1 = -\tfrac{527}{625}.$$

Finally, with $A = 2\theta$ and $B = \theta$ formula (12) gives

$$\tan (2\theta + \theta) = \tan 3\theta = \frac{\tan 2\theta + \tan \theta}{1 - \tan 2\theta \tan \theta}.$$

Thus, in order to find $\tan 3\theta$, we require the value of $\tan 2\theta$. Formula (24), together with the above value for $\tan \theta$, gives

$$\tan 2\theta = \frac{2(\frac{24}{7})}{1 - (\frac{24}{7})^2} = \frac{48}{7} \cdot \frac{49}{-527} = -\frac{336}{527}.$$

Hence, the above expression for $\tan 3\theta$ gives

$$\tan 3\theta = \frac{-\frac{336}{527} + \frac{24}{7}}{1 + \frac{336}{527} \cdot \frac{24}{7}} = \frac{10296}{(7)(527)} \cdot \frac{(7)(527)}{11753} = \frac{10296}{11753}.$$

EXAMPLE 2. Prove the identity

$$\cos \theta - \sin \frac{\theta}{2} = \left(1 - 2 \sin \frac{\theta}{2}\right)\left(1 + \sin \frac{\theta}{2}\right).$$

Solution. We choose to work with the right member. Upon multiplying out, we obtain

$$\begin{aligned}\left(1 - 2 \sin \frac{\theta}{2}\right)\left(1 + \sin \frac{\theta}{2}\right) &= 1 - \sin \frac{\theta}{2} - 2 \sin^2 \frac{\theta}{2} \\ &= \left(1 - 2 \sin^2 \frac{\theta}{2}\right) - \sin \frac{\theta}{2} \\ &= \cos \theta - \sin \frac{\theta}{2} \quad [\text{by (23b) with } A = \theta/2].\end{aligned}$$

EXAMPLE 3. Prove the identity

$$\sec \frac{\theta}{2} + \csc \frac{\theta}{2} = \frac{2\left(\sin \frac{\theta}{2} + \cos \frac{\theta}{2}\right)}{\sin \theta}.$$

Solution. Since all angles are $\theta/2$, except in the denominator of the right member, the step that suggests itself is to use formula (22) with $A = \theta/2$ to obtain

$$\sin \theta = 2 \sin \frac{\theta}{2} \cos \frac{\theta}{2}.$$

Then the right member can be written as

$$\begin{aligned}\frac{2\left(\sin \frac{\theta}{2} + \cos \frac{\theta}{2}\right)}{2 \sin \frac{\theta}{2} \cos \frac{\theta}{2}} &= \frac{1}{\cos \frac{\theta}{2}} + \frac{1}{\sin \frac{\theta}{2}} \\ &= \sec \frac{\theta}{2} + \csc \frac{\theta}{2},\end{aligned}$$

and the proof is complete.

EXAMPLE 4. Evaluate the expression $\sin (2 \operatorname{Arctan} \frac{1}{2})$.

Solution. Let $\theta = \operatorname{Arctan} \frac{1}{2}$. We then wish to find the value of $\sin 2\theta$, which may be done by use of formula (22). For this purpose we need $\sin \theta$ and $\cos \theta$.

But $\tan\theta = \frac{1}{2}$, with θ in Q_1 since θ is the value of the inverse tangent of a positive number. Hence

$$\sin\theta = \frac{1}{\sqrt{5}}, \qquad \cos\theta = \frac{2}{\sqrt{5}},$$

and we obtain

$$\sin 2\theta = 2\sin\theta\cos\theta = 2\left(\frac{1}{\sqrt{5}}\right)\left(\frac{2}{\sqrt{5}}\right) = \frac{4}{5}.$$

Exercise Group 12-3

Simplify each of the expressions in Exercises 1–12, by using a half-angle or double-angle formula with the appropriate angle.

1. $\sqrt{\dfrac{1-\cos 30^\circ}{2}}$
2. $\dfrac{\sin 30^\circ}{1+\cos 30^\circ}$
3. $\sin\theta\cos\theta$
4. $2\cos^2\dfrac{A}{2} - 1$
5. $1 - 2\sin^2 2A$
6. $\dfrac{2\tan 4\theta}{1-\tan^2 4\theta}$
7. $4\sin^2\theta\cos^2\theta$
8. $\cos^2 3\theta - \sin^2 3\theta$
9. $\dfrac{1-\cos 2\theta}{2}$
10. $\dfrac{1+\cos 3\theta}{2}$
11. $\dfrac{\sin 4\theta}{1+\cos 4\theta}$
12. $\dfrac{1-\cos 3\theta}{\sin 3\theta}$

In Exercises 13–22, compute the exact value of $\sin 2A$, $\cos 2A$, and $\tan 2A$ for

13. $\cos A = \frac{3}{5}$, if $0^\circ < A < 90^\circ$
14. $\sin A = -\frac{5}{13}$, if $180^\circ < A < 270^\circ$
15. $\tan A = \frac{4}{3}$, if $180^\circ < A < 270^\circ$
16. $\sec A = \frac{13}{12}$, if $3\pi/2 < A < 2\pi$
17. $\cot A = -\frac{5}{12}$, if $\pi/2 < A < \pi$
18. $\csc A = \frac{5}{4}$, if $\pi/2 < A < \pi$
19. $\sin A = \frac{2}{3}$, if $0 < A < \pi/2$
20. $\tan A = \frac{3}{2}$, if $\pi < A < 3\pi/2$
21. $\sec A = -\frac{6}{5}$, if $\pi < A < 3\pi/2$
22. $\cos A = \frac{3}{4}$, if $3\pi/2 < A < 2\pi$

In Exercises 23–32, compute the exact values of $\sin A/2$, $\cos A/2$, and $\tan A/2$ for

23. $\cos A = \frac{1}{2}$, if $3\pi/2 < A < 2\pi$
24. $\sin A = 1$, if $0^\circ < A < 360^\circ$
25. $\tan A = 0$, if $\pi/2 < A < 3\pi/2$
26. $\csc A = -1$, if $0 < A < 2\pi$
27. $\sin A = -\frac{3}{5}$, if $180^\circ < A < 270^\circ$
28. $\cos A = -\frac{5}{13}$, if $90^\circ < A < 180^\circ$
29. $\sec A = -\frac{17}{8}$, if $180^\circ < A < 270^\circ$
30. $\cot A = -\frac{4}{3}$, if $\pi/2 < A < \pi$
31. $\csc A = \frac{13}{12}$, if $\pi/2 < A < \pi$
32. $\sec A = -2$, if $180^\circ < A < 270^\circ$

Evaluate the expressions in Exercises 33–41.

33. $\cos(2 \text{ Arctan } \frac{1}{2})$
34. $\tan(2 \text{ Arctan } \frac{1}{2})$
35. $\sin(2 \text{ Arccos } \frac{3}{5})$
36. $\tan(\frac{1}{2} \text{ Arcsin } \frac{3}{5})$
37. $\cos(2 \text{ Arctan } x)$
38. $\sin(2 \text{ Arcsin } x)$
39. $\tan(\frac{1}{2} \text{ Arcsin } x)$
40. $\tan(\frac{1}{2} \text{ Arctan } x)$
41. $\cos(2 \text{ Arccot } x)$

Prove that the equations in Exercises 42–58 are identities.

42. $(\sin A + \cos A)^2 = 1 + \sin 2A$

43. $\cos^4 A - \sin^4 A = \cos 2A$

44. $2\cos^2 A = 1 + \cos 2A$

45. $\dfrac{\cos A + \sin A}{\cos A - \sin A} = \tan 2A + \sec 2A$

46. $2\cos^2 \dfrac{A}{2} - \cos A = 1$

47. $2 \csc 2A \cot A = 1 + \cot^2 A$

48. $2 \sin A + \sin 2A = \dfrac{2 \sin^3 A}{1 - \cos A}$

49. $\tan 3A \cos A - \sin A = \sin 2A \sec 3A$

50. $2 \cot 2A = \cot A - \tan A$

51. $\tan 2A - \tan A = \tan A \sec 2A$

52. $\tan \dfrac{A}{2} + \cot \dfrac{A}{2} = 2 \csc A$

53. $\dfrac{\sin A - \cos 2A}{\cos^2 A} = \dfrac{2 \sin A - 1}{1 - \sin A}$

54. $\sin \dfrac{A}{2} = \dfrac{1 - \cos A}{2 \sin A/2}$

55. $\cot \dfrac{A}{2} - \tan \dfrac{A}{2} = 2 \cot A$

56. $\sin 4A (\cos^2 2A - \sin^2 2A) = \dfrac{\sin 8A}{2}$

57. $\dfrac{2}{1 + \cos 2A} = \sec^2 A$

58. $\dfrac{\sin 3A}{\sin A} - \dfrac{\cos 3A}{\cos A} = 2$

59. Find the values of $\sin \theta$ and $\cos \theta$ in terms of t if $\tan \theta/2 = t$.

60. If

$$x = \cos 2\theta \quad \text{and} \quad y = \cos \theta,$$

eliminate θ and thus find the relation that exists between x and y.

12–7 The product and factor formulas. Let us write the expressions for $\sin(A + B)$ and $\sin(A - B)$. We have

$$\sin(A + B) = \sin A \cos B + \cos A \sin B,$$
$$\sin(A - B) = \sin A \cos B - \cos A \sin B.$$

Adding corresponding members of these two equations, we obtain

$$\sin(A + B) + \sin(A - B) = 2 \sin A \cos B$$

from which we obtain, on solving for $\sin A \cos B$, which appears in the right member,

$$\sin A \cos B = \tfrac{1}{2}[\sin(A + B) + \sin(A - B)]. \tag{29}$$

Similarly, addition of Eqs. (11) and (14) yields the formula

$$\cos A \cos B = \tfrac{1}{2}[\cos(A + B) + \cos(A - B)], \tag{30}$$

and subtraction of Eq. (11) from Eq. (14) gives

$$\sin A \sin B = \tfrac{1}{2}[\cos(A - B) - \cos(A + B)]. \tag{31}$$

Formulas (29), (30), and (31) are known as the *product formulas.*

Let us set $A + B = x$, and $A - B = y$. We may solve these equations to give $A = \frac{1}{2}(x + y)$, $B = \frac{1}{2}(x - y)$, and substitution of these in (29) gives

$$\sin x + \sin y = 2 \sin \tfrac{1}{2}(x + y) \cos \tfrac{1}{2}(x - y). \tag{32}$$

Replacing y by $-y$ in this formula gives, since $\sin(-y) = -\sin y$,

$$\sin x - \sin y = 2 \sin \tfrac{1}{2}(x - y) \cos \tfrac{1}{2}(x + y). \tag{33}$$

From (30) and (31) we obtain, by the above substitution,

$$\cos x + \cos y = 2 \cos \tfrac{1}{2}(x + y) \cos \tfrac{1}{2}(x - y), \tag{34}$$

$$\cos x - \cos y = -2 \sin \tfrac{1}{2}(x + y) \sin \tfrac{1}{2}(x - y). \tag{35}$$

Formulas (32), (33), (34), and (35) are called the *factor formulas.*

Note that *the product formulas express certain products of sines and cosines as sums, while the factor formulas express certain sums of sines and cosines as products.*

EXAMPLE 1. Find the value of $\sin 75° \sin 15°$.

Solution. By formula (31) we have

$$\begin{aligned}\sin 75° \sin 15° &= \tfrac{1}{2}[\cos (75° - 15°) - \cos (75° + 15°)]\\ &= \tfrac{1}{2}(\cos 60° - \cos 90°)\\ &= \tfrac{1}{2} \times \tfrac{1}{2} = \tfrac{1}{4}.\end{aligned}$$

EXAMPLE 2. Prove the identity

$$2 \cos \theta \sin 3\theta = \sin 4\theta + \sin 2\theta.$$

Solution. Formula (32) with $x = 4\theta$ and $y = 2\theta$ gives for the right member of the desired identity,

$$\begin{aligned}\sin 4\theta + \sin 2\theta &= 2 \sin \tfrac{1}{2}(4\theta + 2\theta) \cos \tfrac{1}{2}(4\theta - 2\theta)\\ &= 2 \sin 3\theta \cos \theta,\end{aligned}$$

and the identity is proved.

Alternate solution. Formula (29) with $A = 3\theta$ and $B = \theta$ gives for the left member of the desired identity,

$$\sin 3\theta \cos \theta = \tfrac{1}{2}[\sin (3\theta + \theta) + \sin (3\theta - \theta)],$$

which becomes

$$2 \sin 3\theta \cos \theta = \sin 4\theta + \sin 2\theta.$$

EXAMPLE 3. Prove the identity

$$\cos 3\theta = \cos \theta - 2 \sin 2\theta \sin \theta.$$

Solution. Formula (31) with $A = 2\theta$ and $B = \theta$ gives

$$\sin 2\theta \sin \theta = \tfrac{1}{2}[\cos (2\theta - \theta) - \cos (2\theta + \theta)].$$

Hence, the right member of the identity which is to be proved becomes

$$\cos \theta - 2[\tfrac{1}{2}(\cos \theta - \cos 3\theta)] = \cos \theta - \cos \theta + \cos 3\theta = \cos 3\theta,$$

which establishes the identity.

EXERCISE GROUP 12–4

Express the quantities in Exercises 1–10 as products.

1. $\sin 50° + \sin 10°$
2. $\cos 40° + \cos 22°$
3. $\sin 132° - \sin 50°$
4. $\sin 200° + \sin 100°$
5. $\cos 20° - \cos 15°$
6. $\sin 85° - \sin 25°$
7. $\sin 6\theta - \sin 2\theta$
8. $\cos \theta + \cos 2\theta$
9. $\cos 10\theta - \cos 4\theta$
10. $\sin 3\theta/2 + \sin \theta/2$

Express the quantities in Exercises 11–22 as sums or differences.

11. $\sin 20° \cos 40°$ 12. $\sin 20° \sin 40°$ 13. $\cos 100° \cos 36°$
14. $\cos 50° \sin 28°$ 15. $\sin 2\theta \cos \theta$ 16. $\sin 2\theta \sin 6\theta$
17. $\cos \theta \cos 3\theta$ 18. $\cos 4\theta \sin \theta$ 19. $\sin 7A \cos 8A$
20. $\sin 13B \sin 15B$ 21. $\cos 17C \cos 19C$ 22. $\cos 9\theta \sin 23\theta$

Prove that the following statements are identities.

23. $\dfrac{\cos A - \cos B}{\cos A + \cos B} = -\tan \dfrac{A - B}{2} \tan \dfrac{A + B}{2}$

24. $\dfrac{\cos 3A - \cos 4A}{\sin 4A + \sin 3A} = \tan \dfrac{A}{2}$

25. $\sin (A + B) \sin (A - B) = \sin^2 A - \sin^2 B$

26. $\cos (A + B) \cos (A - B) = \cos^2 A - \sin^2 B$

27. $\sin 5x - \sin \left(\dfrac{\pi}{2} - x\right) = 2 \cos \left(2x + \dfrac{\pi}{4}\right) \sin \left(3x - \dfrac{\pi}{4}\right)$

28. $\cos 3x + \cos \left(\dfrac{\pi}{2} - x\right) = 2 \cos \left(x + \dfrac{\pi}{4}\right) \cos \left(2x - \dfrac{\pi}{4}\right)$

29. $\dfrac{\sin (2A - B) + \sin B}{\cos (2A - B) + \cos B} = \tan A$

30. $\dfrac{\sin 2A + \sin 2B}{\cos 2A + \cos 2B} = \tan (A + B)$

31. $\cos (3A - 2B) + \cos (3A + 2B) = 2 \cos 3A \cos 2B$

32. $\sin A(\sin A + \sin 3A) = \cos A(\cos A - \cos 3A)$

33. $\sin A - \cos 2A - \sin 3A = -\cos 2A(2 \sin A + 1)$

34. $\sin 5A = 2 \cos 4A \sin A + \sin 3A$

35. $\sin 3A = 2 \sin 2A \cos A - \sin A$

36. $\dfrac{\sin 5A + \sin 3A}{\sin 2A \cos 2A} = 4 \cos A$

37. $\dfrac{\sin 6A - \sin 4A}{2 \sin A} = \cos 5A$

38. $\dfrac{\cos 3A + \cos A}{2 \cos^3 A - 2 \cos A} = 2 - \csc^2 A$

39. $\sin 4A = 2 \sin A \cos 3A + \sin 2A$

12–8 Trigonometric equations. In certain connections (in the study of calculus, in particular) the need arises for solving equations containing trigonometric functions of some variable. The solutions of a trigonometric equation consist of the value or values of the variable which reduce the equation to a (numerical) identity. In other words, the solution consists of those values of the variable which satisfy the equation. Thus, the solution of the equation

$$\sin x = -\tfrac{1}{2}$$

consists of the angles

$$x = 210° + n \cdot 360° \qquad \text{and} \qquad x = 330° + n \cdot 360°,$$

where n is any integer.

An equation may involve functions other than trigonometric. For example, the equation

$$2x + \tan x = 0$$

contains the linear function $2x$. In such an equation *the value of x in radians* that satisfies the equation is desired. Approximate methods of solution must be used, since no exact method exists. One such method would be to graph the equations $y_1 = -2x$ and $y_2 = \tan x$, and to find the intersections of the graphs obtained. The abscissas of these points are then the desired solutions, since, for any such value of x we have $y_1 = y_2$, and the above equation is satisfied. However, *we shall be concerned here with equations which contain only trigonometric functions and constants.*

Due to the great variety of trigonometric equations, it is hardly of advantage to define specific types and to develop methods of solution for these types. However, the following suggestions will prove helpful in a great many cases. In addition, effective use must be made of the identities among the trigonometric functions.

1. *If an equation can be expressed in terms of one trigonometric function of the same angle, an algebraic equation in that function results, and the methods for solving algebraic equations can be applied.*

2. *If an equation can be expressed in such a form that a product of trigonometric expressions is zero, then each factor should be set equal to zero, where possible. The solutions of the resulting equations will comprise the solution of the original equation.*

EXAMPLE 1. Solve the equation $2\cos^2\theta + 3\sin\theta = 0$.

Solution. On replacing $\cos^2\theta$ by $1 - \sin^2\theta$, the equation reduces to

$$2\sin^2\theta - 3\sin\theta - 2 = 0.$$

This is a quadratic equation in $\sin\theta$, in which the left member can be factored, so that we obtain

$$(2\sin\theta + 1)(\sin\theta - 2) = 0.$$

The second factor cannot be set equal to zero, since $\sin\theta$ cannot be greater than 1. By setting the first factor equal to zero, we find

$$\sin\theta = -\tfrac{1}{2},$$

and the solution is

$$\theta = 210° + n \cdot 360°, \qquad \text{or} \qquad \theta = 330° + n \cdot 360°, \quad n \text{ any integer.}$$

Example 2. Solve the equation $\tan 2\theta + \cot 2\theta = 2$, for angles θ such that $0 \leqq \theta < 2\pi$.

Solution. Since $\cot 2\theta = 1/\tan 2\theta$, the equation becomes

$$\tan 2\theta + \frac{1}{\tan 2\theta} = 2.$$

Multiplication of both members by $\tan 2\theta$ gives

$$\tan^2 2\theta + 1 = 2 \tan 2\theta, \qquad \text{or} \qquad \tan^2 2\theta - 2\tan 2\theta + 1 = 0.$$

The latter equation is quadratic in $\tan 2\theta$, and factorization yields

$$(\tan 2\theta - 1)^2 = 0, \qquad \text{so that} \qquad \tan 2\theta = 1.$$

Hence $2\theta = \pi/4 + n\pi$, from which we find $\theta = \pi/8 + n\pi/2$. The angles in the desired range occur for $n = 0, 1, 2$, and 3, and are

$$\theta = \pi/8, \quad 5\pi/8, \quad 9\pi/8, \quad 13\pi/8.$$

All of these values are solutions, since $\tan 2\theta$ and $\cot 2\theta$ are defined for them.

Another way of finding the values of θ in the desired range is to notice that the values of 2θ must be sought in the range $0 \leqq 2\theta < 4\pi$. Hence, we find

$$2\theta = \pi/4, \quad 5\pi/4, \quad 9\pi/4, \quad 13\pi/4,$$

from which the above values of θ are again found.

Example 3. Solve the equation $\sin\theta = \sin(\theta/2)$ for θ in the range $0 \leqq \theta < 2\pi$.

Solution. We may express the equation in terms of $\theta/2$ alone by the identity $\sin\theta = 2\sin(\theta/2)\cos(\theta/2)$. Thus, we obtain

$$2\sin\frac{\theta}{2}\cos\frac{\theta}{2} = \sin\frac{\theta}{2},$$

$$2\sin\frac{\theta}{2}\cos\frac{\theta}{2} - \sin\frac{\theta}{2} = 0,$$

$$\sin\frac{\theta}{2}\left(2\cos\frac{\theta}{2} - 1\right) = 0.$$

Setting each factor equal to zero, we have, on realizing that $\theta/2$ must lie between 0 and π,

$$\sin\frac{\theta}{2} = 0, \qquad \frac{\theta}{2} = 0, \qquad \theta = 0;$$

or

$$2\cos\frac{\theta}{2} - 1 = 0, \qquad \cos\frac{\theta}{2} = \frac{1}{2}, \qquad \frac{\theta}{2} = \frac{\pi}{3}, \qquad \theta = \frac{2\pi}{3}.$$

The solutions are then $\theta = 0$ and $\theta = 2\pi/3$.

A somewhat special type of trigonometric equation is of the form

$$A \sin \theta + B \cos \theta = C.$$

A method of solution is given in the following example.

EXAMPLE 4. Solve the equation $2 \sin \theta + 3 \cos \theta = 3$, for θ in the range $0 \leqq \theta < 360°$.

Solution. We may replace $\cos \theta$ by $\pm\sqrt{1 - \sin^2 \theta}$. Then the equation becomes

$$2 \sin \theta \pm 3\sqrt{1 - \sin^2 \theta} = 3.$$

If the term $2 \sin \theta$ is transposed, and if then both members are squared, we have

$$9(1 - \sin^2 \theta) = (3 - 2 \sin \theta)^2.$$

Expanding and simplifying, we obtain

$$13 \sin^2 \theta - 12 \sin \theta = 0,$$

which can be solved by factoring to give $\sin \theta = 0$ or $\frac{12}{13}$. We then obtain, in the desired range, $\theta = 0°, 67° 13', 112° 57', 180°$. These values must now be tested in the original equation, since, due to the step involving squaring, some of them may not be solutions. Substituting,

for $\theta = 0$ we have $2(0) + 3(1) = 3,$

for $\theta = 67° 13'$ we have $2\left(\frac{12}{13}\right) + 3\left(\frac{5}{13}\right) = \frac{24 + 15}{13} = 3,$

for $\theta = 112° 57'$ we have $2\left(\frac{12}{13}\right) + 3\left(-\frac{5}{13}\right) = \frac{24 - 15}{13} \neq 3,$

for $\theta = 180°$ we have $2(0) + 3(-1) \neq 3.$

Hence the only solutions are $\theta = 0$ and $\theta = 67° 13'$.

EXERCISE GROUP 12–5

Solve each of the following equations for all values of θ such that $0 \leqq \theta < 2\pi$.

1. $2 \sin \theta - 1 = 0$
2. $\cot \theta + 1 = 0$
3. $4 \cos^2 \theta - 3 = 0$
4. $3 \tan^2 \theta - 1 = 0$
5. $\sin 2\theta + \sin \theta = 0$
6. $\cos 2\theta - \cos \theta = 0$
7. $\sin^2 \theta - \cos^2 \theta + 1 = 0$
8. $\sin \theta - \sin \frac{\theta}{2} = 0$
9. $\cos \theta + \cos \frac{\theta}{2} = 0$
10. $2 \cos^2 \theta - \sin \theta - 1 = 0$
11. $2 \sin^2 \theta - 3 \cos \theta - 3 = 0$
12. $\cot \theta + 2 \sin \theta = \csc \theta$

13. $2\cos^2\theta - 2\cos 2\theta = 1$
14. $\cos 2\theta + 2\cos^2\frac{\theta}{2} = 6$
15. $\sin 2\theta \cos\theta + \cos 2\theta \sin\theta = 1$
16. $\cos 3\theta \cos\theta + \sin 3\theta \sin\theta = 0$
17. $\cot\theta - \tan\frac{\theta}{2} = 0$
18. $\tan 2\theta = \cot\theta$
19. $2\sin 2\theta - 2\cos\theta + 2\sin\theta = 1$
20. $2\cos^2 2\theta - 2\sin^2 2\theta = 1$
21. $\cot\frac{\theta}{2} + \sin 2\theta = \csc\theta$
22. $\tan\frac{\theta}{2} = \cos\theta - 1$
23. $\cos^2\frac{\theta}{2} - \sin^2\frac{\theta}{2} = \cos 2\theta$
24. $\sin^2\frac{\theta}{2} = \cos^2\theta$
25. $2\sin^2\frac{\theta}{2} = 1 - \sin\theta$
26. $2\cos^2 2\theta + \cos 2\theta - 1 = 0$
27. $\sin 6\theta - \sin 3\theta = 0$
28. $\cos^2 5\theta - \sin^2 5\theta = 1$
29. $2\sin^3 3\theta - \sin 3\theta = 1 - 2\sin^2 3\theta$
30. $\tan 4\theta + \cot 4\theta = 2$
31. $\dfrac{1-\cos\theta}{\sin\theta} = \sin\theta$
32. $\dfrac{\sin\theta}{1+\cos\theta} = 1 - \cos\theta$
33. $\dfrac{2\tan\theta}{1-\tan^2\theta} = \cos\theta$
34. $4\tan^2\theta = 3\sec^2\theta$
35. $\sin^2\frac{\theta}{2} - \cos\theta + 1 = 0$
36. $1 - 2\cos^2\theta = 2(1 - 2\sin^2\theta)$
37. $\cot\theta + 2\sin\theta = \csc\theta$
38. $2\cos^2 2\theta - 3\cos 2\theta + 1 = 0$
39. $2\sin^2\theta - \sin\theta = 1$

12–9 Reduction formulas. A number of formulas that were previously mentioned fall into a general category. For example, in Section 10–1 we had the formula $\sin(2\pi + x) = \sin x$. In Section 12–4 the formula $\sin(x - \pi/2) = -\cos x$ was obtained. Indeed, there is a wide variety of such formulas, each involving an angle of the form $n\pi/2 \pm x$ (n is an integer, positive, negative, or zero), and expressing a trigonometric function of such an angle as a function of x alone. The purpose of this section is to present a procedure for obtaining such formulas.

Let x, y, r, with $r \neq 0$, be the coordinates and polar distance of some point on the terminal side of an angle θ in standard position. The reference angle (Section 6–5) for θ is in Q_1, and it is clear that $|x|$, $|y|$, r are the corresponding quantities of some point on the terminal side of this angle in Q_1. It follows from the definition of the trigonometric functions that

Any function of θ is numerically equal to the same-named function of its reference angle. (36)

That is, the same-named functions of any angle and its reference angle differ at most in sign. For example, we have $\sec\theta = r/x$, which may be positive or negative, but the secant of the reference angle is $r/|x|$, which is always positive.

When (36) is applied, there remains only the determination of the proper sign. Since any function of the reference angle is positive, the required sign is simply the one determined by the sign of the given function for the quadrant in which the given angle lies.

EXAMPLE 1. By (36) we have $\cos 247° = \pm\cos 67°$. But $\cos 67° > 0$, and, since 247° is in Q_3, $\cos 247° < 0$. Hence the minus sign applies, and

$$\cos 247° = -\cos 67°.$$

EXAMPLE 2. $\tan(-592°) = -\tan 52°$, the minus sign applying since $-592°$ is in Q_2.

EXAMPLE 3. $\cos(-83°) = \cos 83°$, since $-83°$ is in Q_4, and in Q_4 the cosine function is positive.

Related to (36) is a variety of so-called *reduction formulas* involving functions of angles of the type $n\pi/2 \pm x$, where n is an integer, positive, negative, or zero. For example, we have seen that $\sin(\pi - x) = \sin x$ if x is between 0 and $\pi/2$. *This relation also holds for all values of* x, as the following application of the addition formula (13) shows:

$$\sin(\pi - x) = \sin\pi\cos x - \cos\pi\sin x = \sin x,$$

since $\sin\pi = 0$ and $\cos\pi = -1$. Similarly we have

$$\cos(\pi - x) = \cos\pi\cos x + \sin\pi\sin x = -\cos x.$$

With these results, and the ratio and reciprocal identities, we find

$$\tan(\pi - x) = \frac{\sin(\pi - x)}{\cos(\pi - x)} = \frac{\sin x}{-\cos x} = -\tan x,$$

$$\sec(\pi - x) = \frac{1}{\cos(\pi - x)} = \frac{1}{-\cos x} = -\sec x,$$

$$\cot(\pi - x) = -\cot x, \qquad \csc(\pi - x) = \csc x.$$

EXAMPLE 4. Express the trigonometric functions of $x - 3\pi/2$ in terms of the functions of x.

Solution. By the addition formulas,

$$\sin\left(x - \frac{3\pi}{2}\right) = \sin x\cos\frac{3\pi}{2} - \cos x\sin\frac{3\pi}{2} = \cos x,$$

$$\cos\left(x - \frac{3\pi}{2}\right) = \cos x\cos\frac{3\pi}{2} + \sin x\sin\frac{3\pi}{2} = -\sin x.$$

Then by the ratio and reciprocal identities

$$\tan\left(x - \frac{3\pi}{2}\right) = \frac{\sin\,(x - 3\pi/2)}{\cos\,(x - 3\pi/2)} = \frac{\cos x}{-\sin x} = -\cot x,$$

$$\sec\left(x - \frac{3\pi}{2}\right) = \frac{1}{\cos\,(x - 3\pi/2)} = \frac{1}{-\sin x} = -\csc x,$$

$$\cot\left(x - \frac{3\pi}{2}\right) = -\tan x,$$

$$\csc\left(x - \frac{3\pi}{2}\right) = \sec x.$$

By the method of these examples any reduction formula may be obtained. We notice that if n is even, any function of $n\pi/2 \pm x$ is expressed in terms of the same-named function of x, whereas if n is odd any function of $n\pi/2 \pm x$ is expressed in terms of the corresponding cofunction. Furthermore, the resulting formula holds for all values of x for which the functions are defined. We shall state a general result which encompasses all of these formulas.*

First let us use the symbol $f(x)$ [read: "function of x" or simply, "f of x"] to designate any of the six trigonometric functions, and co$f(x)$ to designate the corresponding cofunction.

EXAMPLE 5. If $f(x)$ designates $\sin x$ then co$f(x)$ will designate $\cos x$. If $f(x) = \cot x$ then co$f(x) = \tan x$.

With this notation we may state the general result.

THEOREM 12–1. *If $f(x)$ is any trigonometric function, then*

$$f\left(\pm x + n\,\frac{\pi}{2}\right) = \begin{cases} \pm\, f(x), & \text{if } n \text{ is even,} \\ \pm\, \mathrm{co}f(x), & \text{if } n \text{ is odd,} \end{cases} \tag{37}$$

where, for a given integer n, the appropriate sign in the right members applies for all values of x for which the functions are defined.

In applying this theorem to determine any reduction formula, it is necessary to note the multiple of $\pi/2$ which appears, and then to ascertain the appropriate sign. The following examples will make this clear.

EXAMPLE 6. Express $\tan\,[x - (3\pi/2)]$ as a trigonometric function of x.

---

* A proof appears in *College Algebra and Plane Trigonometry* by A. Spitzbart and Ross H. Bardell, pp. 207–209. Reading, Mass.: Addison-Wesley Publishing Co., Inc. (1955).

Solution. By the theorem we have at once, since an odd multiple of $\pi/2$ appears,

$$\tan\left(x - \frac{3\pi}{2}\right) = \pm\cot x,$$

where the applicable sign holds for all values of x except multiples of π. Since the sign that is determined by any value of x will then apply for all values of x, we may choose a value of x in Q_1 to make that determination. Accordingly, if $0 < x < \pi/2$, we have $\cot x > 0$; but then $x - 3\pi/2$ is in Q_2, and the tangent of an angle in Q_2 is negative. Hence the minus sign applies, and

$$\tan\left(x - \frac{3\pi}{2}\right) = -\cot x.$$

Thus, the sign in any of these *reduction formulas* can be determined by considering x in the range $0 < x < \pi/2$, that is, as a positive, acute angle, and, having been obtained in this manner, the sign applies generally.

EXAMPLE 7. Express $\cos(\pi - x)$ as a trigonometric function of x.

Solution. By the above theorem, the multiple of $\pi/2$ being even, we have

$$\cos(\pi - x) = \pm\cos x.$$

If $0 < x < \pi/2$, then $\pi - x$ is in Q_2, $\cos(\pi - x) < 0$, and $\cos x > 0$. Hence the minus sign applies, and

$$\cos(\pi - x) = -\cos x.$$

The reduction formulas as obtained are of course not restricted to any range. Thus, if $x = 7\pi/4$ the result of Example 7 becomes

$$\cos\frac{-3\pi}{4} = -\cos\frac{7\pi}{4},$$

which can also be verified directly.

EXAMPLE 8. The theorem of this section applies equally well when $n = 0$, and yields the following identities:

$$\boxed{\sin(-x) = -\sin x,} \qquad \boxed{\cos(-x) = \cos x,}$$

$$\boxed{\tan(-x) = -\tan x,} \qquad \boxed{\cot(-x) = -\cot x,}$$

$$\boxed{\sec(-x) = \sec x,} \qquad \boxed{\csc(-x) = -\csc x.}$$

EXAMPLE 9. Express $\cos 219^\circ 32'$ as the cosine of a positive acute angle.

Solution. The reference angle is $219^\circ 32' - 180^\circ = 39^\circ 32'$. By (37) we obtain $\cos 219^\circ 32' = \pm\cos 39^\circ 32'$. But $\cos 39^\circ 32' > 0$, and we know $\cos 219^\circ 32' < 0$ since $219^\circ 32'$ is in Q_3; hence $\cos 219^\circ 32' = -\cos 39^\circ 32'$.

EXAMPLE 10. Express $\cos 219^\circ 32'$ as the cofunction of a positive acute angle.

Solution. Since $219^\circ 32' = 3 \times 90^\circ - 50^\circ 28'$, we have by (37), $\cos 219^\circ 32' = \pm\sin 50^\circ 28'$. To determine the proper sign we note that $\cos 219^\circ 32' < 0$ and $\sin 50^\circ 28' > 0$. Hence the minus sign applies, and

$$\cos 219^\circ 32' = -\sin 50^\circ 28'.$$

Any formulas obtained by applying this theorem will agree with the formula obtained by the use of the addition, ratio, and reciprocal relations.

EXERCISE GROUP 12–6

Express the given quantity in each of Exercises 1–21 in terms of (a) the same function of the reference angle, (b) a function of an angle between 0° and 45°, and (c) the cofunction of a positive acute angle.

1. $\sin 123^\circ$
2. $\cos 132^\circ$
3. $\tan 117^\circ$
4. $\cot 243^\circ$
5. $\csc 317^\circ$
6. $\sec 95^\circ$
7. $\cos 329^\circ$
8. $\sin 293^\circ$
9. $\cot 943^\circ$
10. $\tan 218^\circ$
11. $\sec 312^\circ$
12. $\csc (-196^\circ)$
13. $\sin (-215^\circ 36')$
14. $\cos (-136^\circ 17')$
15. $\tan (-319^\circ 29')$
16. $\cot (-137^\circ 18')$
17. $\sec (-119^\circ 13')$
18. $\sin 212^\circ 46'$
19. $\cos 176^\circ 38'$
20. $\tan 98^\circ 57'$
21. $\cot 104^\circ 23'$

Verify each of the statements in Exercises 22–39.

22. $\sin (90^\circ - \theta) = \cos\theta$
23. $\cos (90^\circ - \theta) = \sin\theta$
24. $\tan (90^\circ - \theta) = \cot\theta$
25. $\cot (90^\circ - \theta) = \tan\theta$
26. $\sec (90^\circ - \theta) = \csc\theta$
27. $\csc (90^\circ - \theta) = \sec\theta$
28. $\sin\left(\theta + \frac{3\pi}{2}\right) = -\cos\theta$
29. $\sin (\theta + \pi) = -\sin\theta$
30. $\cos\left(\theta + \frac{5\pi}{2}\right) = -\sin\theta$
31. $\cos (\theta + 3\pi) = -\cos\theta$
32. $\sin\left(\theta - \frac{\pi}{2}\right) = -\cos\theta$
33. $\cos\left(\theta - \frac{3\pi}{2}\right) = -\sin\theta$
34. $\sin (\theta - 3\pi) = -\sin\theta$
35. $\cos (\theta - 5\pi) = -\cos\theta$
36. $\sin\left(\theta + \frac{n\pi}{2}\right) = (-1)^{(n-1)/2}\cos\theta$ (n an odd integer)
37. $\sin\left(\theta + \frac{n\pi}{2}\right) = (-1)^{n/2}\sin\theta$ (n an even integer)

38. $\cos\left(\theta + \frac{n\pi}{2}\right) = (-1)^{(n+1)/2} \sin\theta$ (n an odd integer)

39. $\cos\left(\theta + \frac{n\pi}{2}\right) = (-1)^{n/2} \cos\theta$ (n an even integer)

Express each of the following as a trigonometric function of θ and then verify each relation for (1) $\theta = 119°$, and (2) $\theta = -317°$.

40. $\sin(180° - \theta)$
41. $\tan(270° - \theta)$
42. $\sec(90° - \theta)$
43. $\tan(630° + \theta)$
44. $\csc(90° + \theta)$
45. $\cos(540° + \theta)$
46. $\tan(-180° - \theta)$
47. $\cot(-270° + \theta)$
48. $\cos(-270° - \theta)$

If $A + B + C = 180°$, prove the following statements.

49. $\sin A = \sin(B + C)$
50. $\cos A = -\cos(B + C)$
51. $\tan A = -\tan(B + C)$
52. $\cot A = -\cot(B + C)$
53. $\sec A = -\sec(B + C)$
54. $\csc A = \csc(B + C)$

Review Exercises

Prove each of the identities in Exercises 1–34.

1. $\sin^4\theta + \cos^2\theta = \cos^4\theta + \sin^2\theta$

2. $\frac{\sec\theta}{\csc\theta - \sec\theta} = \frac{\sin\theta}{\cos\theta - \sin\theta}$

3. $1 + \sin 2\theta = (\sin\theta + \cos\theta)^2$

4. $\frac{\sec\theta + 1}{\sec\theta - 1} = \frac{\tan\theta + \sin\theta}{\tan\theta - \sin\theta}$

5. $\tan\theta = \frac{1 - \cos 2\theta}{\sin 2\theta}$

6. $\tan\theta = \frac{\sin 2\theta}{1 + \cos 2\theta}$

7. $\sin 2\theta = \frac{2\tan\theta}{1 + \tan^2\theta}$

8. $\csc\theta = \frac{\sec^2\frac{\theta}{2}}{2\tan\frac{\theta}{2}}$

9. $1 + 2\cos\frac{\theta}{2} = \frac{\cos\frac{\theta}{2} - \cos\theta}{1 - \cos\frac{\theta}{2}}$

10. $\tan 2\theta = \frac{2}{\cot\theta - \tan\theta}$

11. $2\tan 2\theta - \sec^2\theta\tan 2\theta = 2\tan\theta$

12. $\frac{4\cos 2\theta}{\sin^2 2\theta} = \csc^2\theta - \sec^2\theta$

13. $\frac{2\cos 2\theta + 1}{2\cos 2\theta - 1} = \frac{3 - \tan^2\theta}{1 - 3\tan^2\theta}$

14. $\frac{(1 + \tan\theta)^2}{2} = \frac{1 + \sin 2\theta}{1 + \cos 2\theta}$

15. $\tan 4\theta = \frac{4\tan\theta(1 - \tan^2\theta)}{1 - 6\tan^2\theta + \tan^4\theta}$

16. $\tan 3\theta = \frac{\tan\theta(3 - \tan^2\theta)}{1 - 3\tan^2\theta}$

17. $\sin 4\theta = 4\sin\theta\cos^3\theta - 4\sin^3\theta\cos\theta$

18. $\sin 3\theta = 3 \sin \theta - 4 \sin^3 \theta$

19. $\cos 3\theta = 4 \cos^3 \theta - 3 \cos \theta$

20. $\cos 4\theta = 1 - 8 \cos^2 \theta + 8 \cos^4 \theta$

21. $\sec 2\theta - 1 = \tan 2\theta \tan \theta$

22. $1 - \cos 2\theta = \sin 2\theta \tan \theta$

23. $1 + \cos \theta = \dfrac{1 + \cos \theta + \sin \theta \cot \frac{\theta}{2}}{2}$

24. $\cos 2\theta = \dfrac{\cot^2 \theta - 1}{\csc^2 \theta}$

25. $\sin^2 2\theta + 4 \cos^4 \theta = 4 \cos^2 \theta$

26. $\dfrac{\csc^2 \frac{\theta}{2}}{\left(1 + \cot \frac{\theta}{2}\right)^2} = \dfrac{1}{1 + \sin \theta}$

27. $\dfrac{2}{1 + \cos 2\theta} = \sec^2 \theta$

28. $2 \sin 2\theta - \dfrac{\sin 2\theta}{\cos^2 \theta} = 2 \tan \theta \cos 2\theta$

29. $\dfrac{\sin^2 2\theta}{2 + 2 \cos 2\theta} = \sin^2 \theta$

30. $\dfrac{\cos^2 \theta}{\cos 2\theta - \sin \theta} = \dfrac{1 - \sin \theta}{1 - 2 \sin \theta}$

31. $4 \sin^2 \theta \cos^2 \theta = 1 - \cos^2 2\theta$

32. $2 \cos^2 \frac{\theta}{2} - \cos \theta = 1$

33. $\sin 2\theta \cos \frac{\theta}{2} + \cos 2\theta \sin \frac{\theta}{2} = \pm \sqrt{\dfrac{1 - \cos 5\theta}{2}}$

34. $\cos \theta \cos \frac{\theta}{2} - \sin \theta \sin \frac{\theta}{2} = \pm \sqrt{\dfrac{1 + \cos 3\theta}{2}}$

Express each function given in Exercises 35–49 in terms of (a) the same-named function of a positive acute angle and (b) a function of an angle between 0° and 45° or between 0 and $\pi/4$ radians, the latter value being permitted in each case.

35. $\cos 218° 42'$
36. $\sin (-213° 12')$
37. $\tan 987°$
38. $\cot (-893° 12')$
39. $\sin 7895°$
40. $\cos 2174°$
41. $\sin 13\pi/3$
42. $\cos 17\pi/3$
43. $\tan 17\pi/3$
44. $\cot 19\pi/4$
45. $\cos 13\pi/4$
46. $\sin (-23\pi/3)$
47. $\tan (-17\pi/4)$
48. $\cot (-31\pi/3)$
49. $\cos (-19\pi/3)$

Solve the equations in Exercises 50–63 for all values of θ such that $0 \leqq \theta < 2\pi$.

50. $\sin \theta + \cos \theta = 0$

51. $\sin 2\theta - \sin \theta = 0$

52. $\sin 2\theta = \cos^2 \theta - \sin^2 \theta$

53. $6 \cos^2 \theta + \cos \theta = 2$

54. $\sin 5\theta + \sin 3\theta = 0$

55. $\cos 3\theta - \cos \theta = 0$

56. $\cos 2\theta = 2 - 2 \cos^2 \frac{\theta}{2}$

57. $3 \sin^2 \theta - 2 \cos \theta - 2 = 0$

58. $\sec^2 \theta - \tan \theta = 1$

59. $\dfrac{\tan 2\theta + \tan \theta}{1 - \tan 2\theta \tan \theta} = \sqrt{3}$

60. $2\cos^2 3\theta + \sin 3\theta - 1 = 0$

61. $2(\sin\theta - \cos\theta) = \sqrt{2}$

62. $\sin 2\theta + \sin\theta = 1 + 2\cos\theta$

63. $\tan\dfrac{\theta}{2} + \sin 2\theta = \csc\theta$

Prove each of the following:

64. $\text{Arctan } 1 = 2 \text{ Arctan } \frac{1}{3} + \text{Arctan } \frac{1}{7}$

65. $\text{Arctan } 1 = 4 \text{ Arctan } \frac{1}{5} - \text{Arctan } \frac{1}{239}$

66. $\text{Arcsin } 1 = \text{Arcsin } \dfrac{\sqrt{3}}{2} + \text{Arcsin } \dfrac{1}{2}$

67. $\text{Arcsin } 1 = \text{Arcsin } \dfrac{1}{3} + \text{Arcsin } \dfrac{2\sqrt{2}}{3}$

CHAPTER 13

SYSTEMS OF EQUATIONS INVOLVING QUADRATICS

13–1 Introduction. In Chapter 7 we discussed systems of linear equations. That discussion involved the definitions of *systems of equations*, *solutions* of systems of equations, and both the *geometric* and *algebraic* methods of finding solutions. All these concepts will be used in the discussions of this chapter.

A term ax^my^n, where m and n are positive integers (or zero) and $a \neq 0$, is said to be of degree $m + n$ in x and y. A sum of terms of this form is a *polynomial in x and y*, and the *degree* of the polynomial is the degree of the term of highest degree.

EXAMPLE. $2x + 3y^2 - 4xy + 7x^2y$ is a polynomial of degree 3 in x and y.

In this chapter we shall consider various cases of solving pairs of equations in which at least one of the equations is of the second degree. We shall discuss the geometric solution in certain special cases for the purpose of giving additional meaning to the solutions of systems of equations of second degree. The geometric solution of all systems of equations of second degree is beyond the scope of this text, but a brief discussion of the geometry of the general equation of second degree in x and y will explain why we shall study only certain special cases.

13–2 Graph of a quadratic equation in x and y. The general quadratic equation in the two variables x and y is of the form

$$Ax^2 + Bxy + Cy^2 + Dx + Ey + F = 0, \tag{1}$$

where A, B, C, D, E, and F are constants with A, B, C not all zero.

It is shown in analytic geometry that if any real values of x and y satisfy (1), then the graph of equation (1) will, apart from certain exceptional cases, be a *conic section*, that is, one of the curves in which a plane cuts a right circular cone. Moreover, it is also shown that if the coordinate axes are properly chosen with respect to the curve, Eq. (1) will reduce to one of the following standard forms:

A. $ax + by + c = 0$ (a and b not both zero). The graph of this is a straight line, as seen in Chapter 7.

B. $y = ax^2 + bx + c$ ($a \neq 0$). The graph of this is the *parabola* which was discussed in Chapter 8.

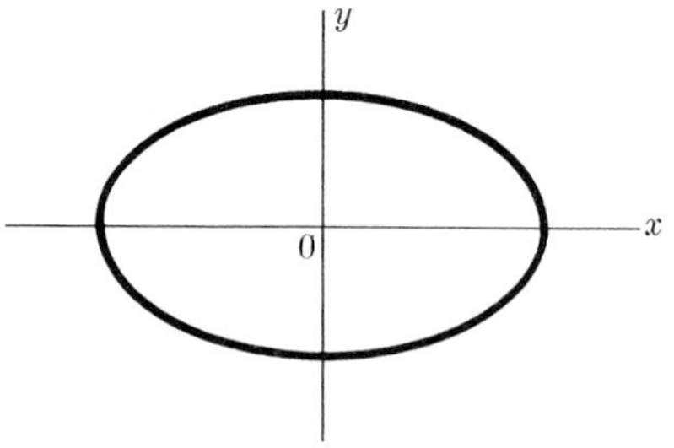

FIGURE 13–1

C. $x^2/a^2 + y^2/b^2 = 1$. The graph of this equation is an *ellipse*, including a *circle* as a special case when $a = b$. The actual drawing of such a curve will be illustrated by an example.

EXAMPLE 1. Draw the graph of $9x^2 + 25y^2 = 225$.

Solution. First divide the given equation by 225 to obtain a 1 as the right member. An equation of this type written in the form C is said to be in *standard form,* and in this instance the standard form is

$$\frac{x^2}{25} + \frac{y^2}{9} = 1.$$

From either form it is clear that if $y = 0$, $x = \pm 5$ and if $x = 0$, $y = \pm 3$. The four points $(5, 0)$, $(-5, 0)$, $(0, 3)$, and $(0, -3)$ are the points where the graph crosses the coordinate axes, and the distances of the points from the origin, each with its proper sign, are called the *intercepts* of the curve. Moreover, if $y^2 > 9$, then x^2 is negative and the values of x are imaginary and, if $x^2 > 25$, then y^2 is negative and the values of y are imaginary. Thus all the points of the graph are inside the rectangle bounded by the lines $x = 5$, $y = -3$, $x = -5$, and $y = 3$. Assigning admissible values to x and solving for the corresponding values of y we obtain the following table of values:

x:	-5	-4	-3	0	3	4	5
y:	0	$\pm\frac{9}{5}$	$\pm\frac{12}{5}$	± 3	$\pm\frac{12}{5}$	$\pm\frac{9}{5}$	0

To obtain the desired graph we plot the above points and draw a smooth curve through them, as in Fig. 13–1.

D. $x^2/a^2 + y^2/b^2 = 0$. The only real values of x and y satisfying this equation are $(0, 0)$ and therefore the graph consists of one point, the origin. Since the equation is similar to that of an ellipse, the graph is referred to as a *point ellipse.*

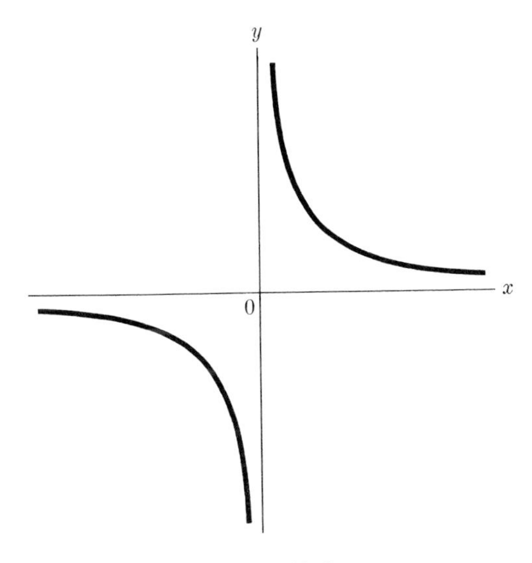

FIGURE 13-2

E. $x^2/a^2 + y^2/b^2 = -1$. Only imaginary values of x and y satisfy this equation so there is no graph of it.

F. $xy = c$. The graph of this equation is a *hyperbola* for all nonzero real values of c. Again we shall illustrate the drawing of such a hyperbola by an example.

EXAMPLE 2. Draw the graph of $xy = 6$.

Solution. Since the product is positive the values of x and y must have the same sign, that is, when x is positive y must also be positive and when x is negative then y is also negative. Moreover, neither x nor y can be zero, so that the graph never touches the coordinate axes. Assigning values to x and solving for the corresponding values of y we obtain the values:

x:	-6	-3	-2	-1	1	2	3	6
y:	-1	-2	-3	-6	6	3	2	1

Again the graph is obtained by plotting the above points and then joining them with a smooth curve, remembering that the curve can never cross a coordinate axis (Fig. 13-2).

Note: If c is negative then x and y must have opposite signs.

G. $x^2/a^2 - y^2/b^2 = 1$. The graph of this equation is also a *hyperbola* but, as will be seen, the curve is located differently with respect to

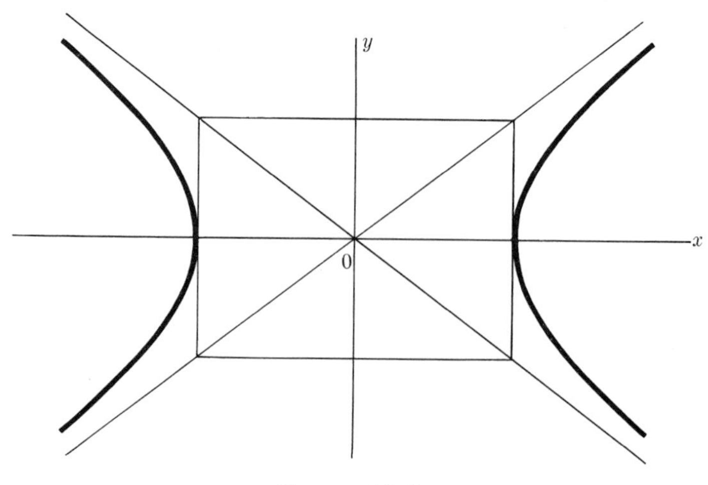

FIGURE 13–3

the coordinate axes. To better understand the graph of this hyperbola consider the following example.

EXAMPLE 3. Draw the graph of the equation $36x^2 - 64y^2 = 2304$.

Solution. Reducing the given equation to standard form we have $x^2/64 - y^2/36 = 1$. It is clear that if $y = 0$, then $x = \pm 8$ and if $y^2 > 0$ then $x^2 > 64$, so that there are no points on the graph for x between -8 and $+8$. If we assign admissible values to x and solve for the corresponding values of y we obtain

x:	-12	-10	-8	8	10	12
y:	$\pm 3\sqrt{5}$	$\pm\frac{9}{2}$	0	0	$\pm\frac{9}{2}$	$\pm 3\sqrt{5}$

In addition to plotting the above points it will also be helpful to draw the rectangle bounded by the lines $x = 8$, $y = -6$, $x = -8$, and $y = 6$. The diagonals of this rectangle are helpful as guide lines in drawing the graph (Fig. 13–3).

H. $x^2/a^2 - y^2/b^2 = 0$. The graph of this equation is a pair of straight lines through the origin.

EXAMPLE 4. The equation $4x^2 - 9y^2 = 0$ is of the type H if both sides of the equation are divided by 36. We may, however, write the equation as

$$(2x + 3y)(2x - 3y) = 0$$

so that either

$$2x + 3y = 0 \quad \text{or} \quad 2x - 3y = 0.$$

Each of these equations has a straight line graph; the two straight lines obtained constitute the graph of the original equation.

Exercise Group 13–1

Draw the graph of each of the following equations.

1. $y = x^2 - 3x + 4$
2. $4x^2 + 9y^2 = 36$
3. $4x^2 - 16y^2 = 16$
4. $xy = 4$
5. $xy = -6$
6. $9y^2 - 16x^2 = 144$
7. $9x^2 + 16y^2 = 144$
8. $y = 2x - x^2$
9. $4x^2 + 4y^2 = 36$
10. $9x^2 - 9y^2 = 36$
11. $9x^2 + 4y^2 = 16$
12. $4x^2 - 9y^2 = 16$
13. $2xy = 4$
14. $9x^2 - 4y^2 = 0$
15. $16y^2 - 25x^2 = 0$

13–3 One linear equation and one second degree equation. The algebraic solution of a pair of equations of which one is linear and the other is of the second degree can be applied equally well whether the second degree equation is limited to one of the standard forms considered above or is of the general type.

Example 1. Determine the points of intersection of the curves represented by the equations

$$\begin{cases} 7x + 6y = 10, \\ 6x^2 - 19x - 6y = 38. \end{cases}$$

Geometric solution. The graph of the first equation is the straight line in Fig. 13–4. The second equation can be put in the form

$$y = x^2 - \tfrac{19}{6}x - \tfrac{19}{3}.$$

By the methods of Section 8–4, we know that the graph is a parabola with vertex at $[\frac{19}{12}, -(\frac{19}{12})^2 - \frac{19}{3}]$ or, approximately, (1.58, —8.84). We then compute the following table of values:

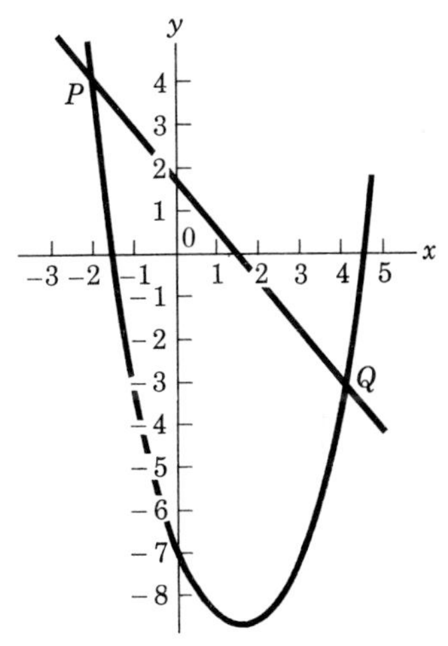

Figure 13–4

x:	—2	—1	0	1	2	3	4	5
y:	4	—2.17	—6.3	—8.5	—8.7	—6.9	—3	2.83

and draw the graph. From the figure it appears that the points of intersection, P and Q, have the coordinates (—2, 4) and (4, —3) respectively.

Algebraic solution. From the first equation, we have

$$6y = 10 - 7x.$$

Substituting this in the second equation, we obtain

$$6x^2 - 19x - 10 + 7x = 38, \quad \text{or} \quad 6x^2 - 12x - 48 = 0.$$

Then $x^2 - 2x - 8 = 0$, $(x-4)(x+2) = 0$, and $x = 4, -2$. Substitution in the first equation gives the corresponding values $y = -3$ and $y = 4$. The two solutions are then $x = 4$, $y = -3$ and $x = -2$, $y = 4$.

EXAMPLE 2. Solve for x and y: $\begin{cases} 5xy = 2x + 2y, \\ 2x + 2y = 5. \end{cases}$

Solution. The second equation gives

$$x = -y + \tfrac{5}{2}.$$

Substitution of this in the first equation gives

$$\begin{aligned} 5(\tfrac{5}{2} - y)y &= 2(\tfrac{5}{2} - y) + 2y, \\ \tfrac{25}{2}y - 5y^2 &= 5 - 2y + 2y, \\ 10y^2 - 25y + 10 &= 0, \quad \text{or} \quad 2y^2 - 5y + 2 = 0. \end{aligned}$$

Then $(2y-1)(y-2) = 0$, and $y = \frac{1}{2}, 2$. The values of x are then found from the second equation. Thus the two pairs of values (x, y) which satisfy the equations are $(2, \frac{1}{2})$ and $(\frac{1}{2}, 2)$.

The method for solving a pair of equations of which one is linear and the other is quadratic is now clear:

1. *Solve the linear equation for one of the unknowns in terms of the other.*
2. *Substitute this in the second degree equation and solve for the second unknown.*
3. *Substitute in the linear equation the values found in Step 2 to find the corresponding values of the first unknown.*

EXAMPLE 3. Solve for x and y:

$$\begin{cases} 9x^2 - 16y^2 = 144, \\ x - 2y = 4. \end{cases}$$

Geometric solution. Construct the graph of each equation and note where the two graphs intersect. The graph of the first equation cuts the x-axis at $x = \pm 4$, and y is imaginary for any value of x between -4 and 4. The graph consists of the two curved branches in Fig. 13–5, and is a *hyperbola*.

The graph of the second equation is a straight line through the points (4, 0) and (0, −2). This line intersects the hyperbola in the points P and Q, whose coordinates are approximately (4, 0) and (−10, −7).

Algebraic solution. As in the preceding examples, we solve the linear equation for x and substitute the resulting expression in the second degree equation. This gives

$$9(4 + 2y)^2 - 16y^2 = 144,$$

which reduces to

$$20y^2 + 144y = 0.$$

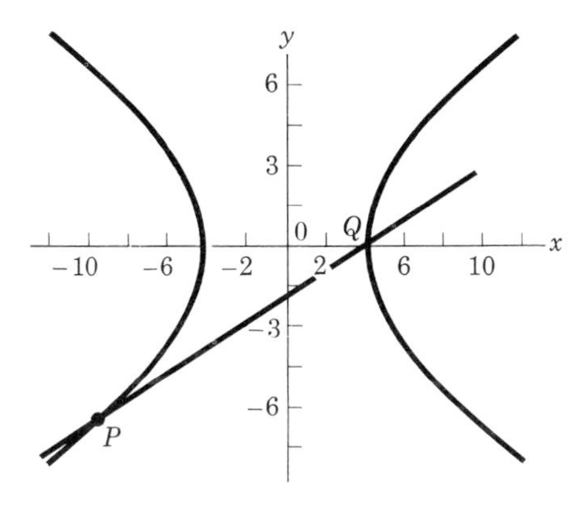

FIGURE 13–5

This can be solved by factoring to give

$$y = 0, \quad -\tfrac{36}{5}.$$

Placing these values in the *linear* equation gives $x = 4$ when $y = 0$ and $x = -\frac{52}{5}$ when $y = -\frac{36}{5}$, so that the two solutions of the equations are seen to be $(4, 0)$ and $(-\frac{52}{5}, -\frac{36}{5})$, which are then the actual coordinates of the points of intersection of the line and the hyperbola.

EXAMPLE 4. Solve for x and y: $\begin{cases} x^2 + 4y^2 - 8y + 2x - 3 = 0, \\ 3y - 2x = 12. \end{cases}$

Solution. From the second equation, we obtain

$$y = 4 + \tfrac{2}{3}x.$$

Substitution of this in the first equation gives

$$x^2 + 4(4 + \tfrac{2}{3}x)^2 - 8(4 + \tfrac{2}{3}x) + 2x - 3 = 0,$$

which reduces to

$$25x^2 + 162x + 261 = 0,$$

or

$$(25x + 87)(x + 3) = 0.$$

Hence $x = -3, -\frac{87}{25}$, and the two solutions are

$$x = -3, \qquad y = 2; \qquad x = -\tfrac{87}{25}, \qquad y = \tfrac{42}{25}.$$

Exercise Group 13–2

In each of the following pairs of equations in Exercises 1–6, draw the graphs of both equations on the same coordinate axes and find the points of intersection. Solve algebraically for x and y and compare results.

1. $x^2 + y^2 = 169,\quad 5x - 6y = 30.$
2. $9x^2 + 16y^2 = 144,\quad 3x - 4y = 12.$
3. $x^2 - y^2 = 9,\quad x - 2y = 3.$
4. $xy = 15,\quad 2x - y = 1.$
5. $x^2 = 2y,\quad 3x - y = 5.$
6. $y = 4x^2 - 8x + 2,\quad 3x - y = 5.$

In Exercises 7–24, solve the system of equations for x and y algebraically.

7. $x^2 + xy + y^2 = 61,\quad x + y = 9.$
8. $y = 9 - 3x,\quad x^2 = 10 - xy.$
9. $x^2 + xy + 2y^2 = 2,\quad 2x - y = 1.$
10. $6x - 6y = 7,\quad 3xy = -1.$
11. $x^2 + y^2 = 74,\quad x - y = 12.$
12. $x^2 - y^2 = 9,\quad 2x + y = 4.$
13. $x^2 - xy + y^2 = 3,\quad x + 2y = 1.$
14. $xy = 5,\quad 2x + 3y = 11.$
15. $2x^2 - 3y^2 = 2,\quad 2y + x = 3.$
16. $3x^2 + 5x - y + 4 = 0,\quad 2x + y = 2.$
17. $x^2 + y^2 - xy = 268,\quad x - y = 18.$
18. $x - 3y + 9 = 0,\quad xy - y^2 + 4 = 0.$
19. $x + 2y = 4,\quad \dfrac{x + y}{x - y} - 3y = 0.$
20. $4x^2 + 3xy = 4,\quad x + 3y - 4 = 0.$
21. $\dfrac{x^2}{16} + \dfrac{y^2}{9} = 1,\quad \dfrac{x}{4} + \dfrac{y}{3} = 1.$
22. $\dfrac{x^2}{a^2} + \dfrac{y^2}{b^2} = 1,\quad \dfrac{x}{a} + \dfrac{y}{b} = 1.$
23. $\dfrac{x^2}{25} - \dfrac{y^2}{16} = 1,\quad \dfrac{x}{5} - \dfrac{y}{4} = 0.$
24. $\dfrac{x^2}{a^2} - \dfrac{y^2}{b^2} = 1,\quad \dfrac{x}{a} - \dfrac{y}{b} = 0.$

25. Find two numbers for which the sum is 2 and the product is 2.

26. Find two positive numbers such that their quotient is 4, and the quotient of their product by their difference is $\frac{20}{3}$.

27. Find the dimensions of a rectangle whose perimeter is 50 ft and whose area is 150 ft^2.

28. The hypotenuse of a right triangle exceeds one side by 2 in., and the third side is 6 in. Find the sides of the triangle.

29. To enclose a rectangular field 68,200 ft^2 in area, 1460 ft of fence are required. Find the dimensions of the field.

30. The perimeter of a right triangle is 70 ft, and its area is 210 ft^2. Find the three sides.

31. The radii of two spheres differ by 18 in., and the difference of the spherical surfaces is equal to the area of a sphere whose radius is 48 in. Find the radii (surface of a sphere $= 4\pi R^2$).

32. An integer less than 100 is equal to four times the sum of its digits, and the sum of the squares of the digits is 20. Find the number. (*Hint:* If t and u are the tens and units digits, respectively, of an integer, then the integer has the form $10t + u$.)

33. The area of a rectangle is 1008 ft^2, and the diagonal is 65 ft. Find the lengths of the sides.

13–4 Two equations of the form $ax^2 + by^2 = c$. An equation of the form $ax^2 + by^2 = c$ may be considered as *linear in* x^2 *and* y^2. By this it is meant that if the substitution $u = x^2$ and $v = y^2$ is made, then the resulting equations are linear in u and v. However, once this fact is recognized it is not necessary to make the actual substitution; the given system of equations can be solved for x^2 and y^2 by the method of Section 7–6, and then x and y can be found.

EXAMPLE. Solve for x and y: $\begin{cases} x^2 + y^2 = 25, \\ x^2 - y^2 = 7. \end{cases}$

Solution: By adding corresponding members of the two equations, we get

$$2x^2 = 32, \qquad x^2 = 16.$$

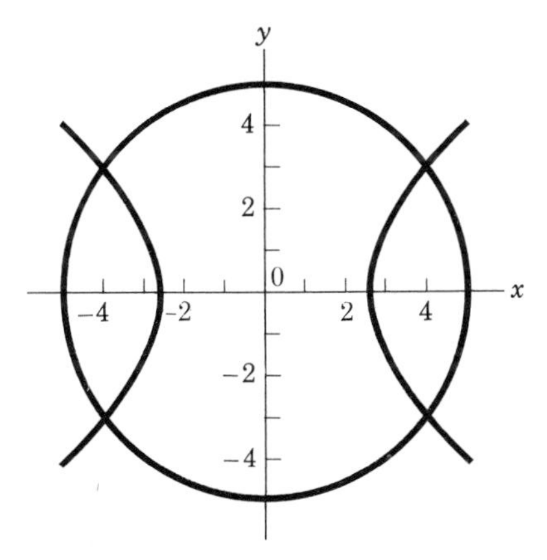

FIGURE 13–6

Substitution of this value of x^2 in the first equation gives

$$16 + y^2 = 25, \qquad y^2 = 9.$$

The four solutions for x and y are

$$x = 4,\ y = -3; \qquad x = -4,\ y = -3,$$
$$x = 4,\ y = 3; \qquad x = -4,\ y = 3;$$

as can be verified by substitution in the given equations.

Graphical solution. If the graph of the first equation is constructed by finding pairs of values (x, y) which satisfy the equation and plotting the corresponding points, the circle shown in Fig. 13–6 is obtained. In a similar manner, the hyperbola shown in the figure is obtained as the graph of the second equation. The circle and hyperbola are seen to intersect in the four points $(4, 3)$, $(-4, 3)$, $(-4, -3)$, $(4, -3)$.

Exercise Group 13–3

In each of the following pairs of equations in Exercises 1–3, draw the graph of both equations on the same coordinate axes and find the points of intersection; also solve algebraically for x and y.

1. $3x^2 + y^2 = 37,\quad 9x^2 - 2y^2 = -14.$
2. $x^2 - 4y^2 = 16,\quad x^2 + y^2 = 16.$
3. $8x^2 + 3y^2 = 59,\quad 7x^2 + y^2 = 37.$

Solve each of the following systems of equations for x and y, algebraically.

4. $2x^2 + 3y^2 = 5,\quad 4y^2 - 7x^2 + 3 = 0.$
5. $4y^2 - 8x^2 + 13 = 0,\quad 7x^2 + 3y^2 - 27 = 0.$
6. $x^2 + y^2 = 25,\quad x^2 + 2y^2 = 34.$
7. $7x^2 - 4y^2 + 21 = 0,\quad 2x^2 + y^2 = 99.$
8. $ax^2 + by^2 = c,\quad bx^2 - ay^2 = 0.$
9. $3x^2 - 5y^2 = 11,\quad 5x^2 + 7y^2 = 13.$
10. $\dfrac{x^2}{a^2} + \dfrac{y^2}{a^2} = 2,\quad b^2x^2 + a^2y^2 = 2a^2b^2.$
11. $3y^2 + 2x^2 = 11,\quad 2y^2 = x^2 + 30.$
12. $3x^2 + 4y^2 = 7,\quad 7x^2 + 12y^2 = 3.$
13. $\frac{2}{3}x^2 - 5y^2 = 0,\quad \frac{5}{21}x^2 + \frac{17}{14}y^2 = 2.$
14. $\frac{1}{4}x^2 + 2y^2 = 6,\quad -\frac{1}{3}x^2 - y^2 = \frac{1}{3}.$
15. $-\frac{2}{5}x^2 + \frac{1}{7}y^2 = -1,\quad \frac{7}{3}x^2 - \frac{12}{7}y^2 = -\frac{1}{3}.$

16. $\frac{1}{5}x^2 + y^2 = \frac{28}{5}$,
$\frac{3}{7}x^2 - y^2 = 16\frac{2}{7}$.

17. $\dfrac{x^2}{4a^2} + \dfrac{y^2}{b^2} = 1$,
$\dfrac{x^2}{a^2} - \dfrac{y^2}{b^2} = 1$.

18. $\frac{2}{3}x^2 - \frac{3}{5}y^2 = 18$,
$\frac{5}{6}x^2 + \frac{7}{10}y^2 = 50$.

19. $\dfrac{x^2}{16} - \dfrac{y^2}{25} = 1$,
$\dfrac{x^2}{25} + \dfrac{y^2}{16} = 1$.

20. $\dfrac{x^2}{25} - \dfrac{y^2}{9} = 1$,
$\dfrac{y^2}{25} - \dfrac{x^2}{36} = 1$.

21. $x^2 - 25y^2 = 20$,
$2x^2 + 25y^2 = 88$.

22. $4x^2 - 3y^2 = 43$,
$3x^2 + y^2 = 3$.

23. $(x + y)^2 + (x - y)^2 = 85$,
$3(x + y)^2 - 2(x - y)^2 = 10$.

13–5 Two quadratic equations, with one homogeneous. *A homogeneous quadratic equation in x and y* is an equation of the form

$$ax^2 + bxy + cy^2 = 0,$$

in which only second degree terms in x and y appear. If a system of two quadratic equations, of which one is homogeneous, is to be solved, the homogeneous equation can always be reduced to two linear equations, either by solving for one of the variables in terms of the other, or by factoring the left member and setting each factor equal to zero. Each of these linear equations, taken with the other given equation of the system of two quadratic equations, gives a pair of equations of which one is linear and one is quadratic. Each of the resulting pairs of equations can be solved by the method of Section 13–3, and there will be in general four solutions of the original system.

EXAMPLE. Solve the following system of equations completely:

$$\begin{cases} x^2 - 5xy + 6y^2 = 0, \\ xy - y^2 = 2. \end{cases}$$

Solution. The first equation is homogeneous. Upon factoring the left member, we have $(x - 3y)(x - 2y) = 0$, which yields the two linear equations

$$x - 3y = 0 \quad \text{and} \quad x - 2y = 0.$$

Each of these is taken with the second given equation, and we obtain the following systems of equations:

$$\begin{cases} xy - y^2 = 2, \\ x - 3y = 0. \end{cases} \qquad \begin{cases} xy - y^2 = 2, \\ x - 2y = 0. \end{cases}$$

These systems are of the type of Section 13–3. Any solution of either system will be a solution of the given system. By the method given in Section 13–3, we find the four solutions,

$$(3, 1), \qquad (-3, -1), \qquad (2\sqrt{2}, \sqrt{2}), \qquad (-2\sqrt{2}, -\sqrt{2}),$$

where the first two are the solutions of the first system above, and the second two are the solutions of the second system.

While there are in general four solutions for the kind of system of equations considered in this section, there may in special cases turn out to be fewer than four solutions.

Exercise Group 13–4

In Exercises 1–20, solve each system of equations for x and y.

1. $x^2 - 2xy = 0,$
   $2x^2 + xy + y^2 = 44.$
2. $6x^2 - xy - y^2 = 0,$
   $y^2 - 3x^2 + 8x + y = 11.$
3. $x^2 - 7xy + 12y^2 = 0,$
   $xy + 3y - 2x = 21.$
4. $16x^2 - 9y^2 = 0,$
   $xy - 2x + 3y = 6.$
5. $x^2 - 5xy + 6y^2 = 0,$
   $x^2 + 3xy - 9y^2 = 9.$
6. $3x^2 - 7xy + 2y^2 = 0,$
   $3x^2 + xy + y^2 = 15.$
7. $2x^2 - 11xy + 5y^2 = 0,$
   $3xy - y^2 = 2.$
8. $12y^2 + xy - 6x^2 = 0,$
   $xy = 24.$
9. $3x^2 + 5xy - 2y^2 = 0,$
   $5y^2 = 8xy + 21.$
10. $3x^2 + xy - 2y^2 = 0,$
    $7x^2 - 3xy = 10.$
11. $14x^2 + xy - 4y^2 = 0,$
    $x^2 - y^2 = xy + 5.$
12. $8x^2 + 10xy - 3y^2 = 0,$
    $2x^2 + xy = 12.$
13. $6x^2 + xy - 2y^2 = 0,$
    $8x^2 + 3xy = 14.$
14. $3x^2 - 8xy - 3y^2 = 0,$
    $2x^2 - 4xy - y^2 = 5.$
15. $x^2 - 8xy + 7y^2 = 0,$
    $2x^2 - 4xy + 5y^2 = 75.$
16. $2x^2 - 4xy - 6y^2 = 0,$
    $x^2 + y^2 - 3y = 2.$
17. $6x^2 - 7xy + 2y^2 = 0,$
    $3x^2 - y^2 + x = 5.$
18. $3x^2 + 17xy + 10y^2 = 0,$
    $3x^2 + 5y^2 - x = 7.$
19. $15x^2 + 22xy - 5y^2 = 0,$
    $x^2 - y^2 = 1.$
20. $6x^2 - xy - 35y^2 = 0,$
    $2xy + 5y = 10.$

13-6 Two equations of the form $ax^2 + bxy + cy^2 = d$. A system of two equations of the form

$$ax^2 + bxy + cy^2 = d$$

can always be solved by the method of the preceding section, upon eliminating the constant terms from the two equations to obtain a quadratic equation which is homogeneous in x and y. The homogeneous equation thus obtained is then solved together with either of the given equations. There will be, in general, four solutions.

EXAMPLE 1. Solve the system of equations,

$$\begin{cases} 2x^2 - xy + y^2 = 16, \\ x^2 - xy + 2y^2 = 44. \end{cases}$$

Solution. To eliminate the constant, we multiply both members of the first equation by 11, the members of the second equation by -4, and add corresponding members of the equations obtained. We obtain the equation $18x^2 - 15xy + 3y^2 = 0$. If both members are then divided by 3, the resulting left member can be factored, and the equation becomes

$$(3x - y)(2x - y) = 0.$$

Using the first of the given equations with the one just obtained, we see that the given system is equivalent to the two following ones:

$$\begin{cases} 2x^2 - xy + y^2 = 16, \\ 3x - y = 0. \end{cases} \qquad \begin{cases} 2x^2 - xy + y^2 = 16, \\ 2x - y = 0. \end{cases}$$

By the method of Section 13-3 the solutions of these systems are, respectively,

$$(\sqrt{2}, 3\sqrt{2}), \qquad (-\sqrt{2}, -3\sqrt{2}) \qquad \text{and} \qquad (2, 4), \qquad (-2, -4),$$

which are the four solutions of the original system.

Special methods often apply to systems of equations of special types. The following example illustrates one such type, with an appropriate method of solution.

EXAMPLE 2. Solve the system of equations,

$$\begin{cases} x^2 + y^2 = 25, \\ xy = 12. \end{cases}$$

Solution. If the second equation of the system is multiplied by 2 and subtracted from the first we get $x^2 - 2xy + y^2 = 1$, which can be written as $(x - y)^2 = 1$. This last equation is equivalent to the two equations $x - y = 1$

and $x - y = -1$. Thus the solutions of the given system may be found by solving the two systems

$$\begin{cases} xy = 12, \\ x - y = 1, \end{cases} \quad \text{and} \quad \begin{cases} xy = 12, \\ x - y = -1. \end{cases}$$

These latter systems are solved by the methods of Section 13–3 and the results are

$$(4, 3); \quad (-3, -4); \quad (-4, -3); \quad (3, 4).$$

The methods developed in this chapter are adequate for the systems of equations which are most frequently encountered. However, the subject has not been exhaustively treated. The solution of a pair of general equations of the second degree,

$$ax^2 + bxy + cy^2 + dx + ey + f = 0,$$
$$Ax^2 + Bxy + Cy^2 + Dx + Ey + F = 0,$$

can be shown* to depend on the solution of a fourth degree equation in one variable.

Exercise Group 13–5

In Exercises 1–20, solve each system of equations for x and y.

1. $x^2 + 3xy = 28,$ $xy + 4y^2 = 8.$
2. $2x^2 - 2xy = 15,$ $2y^2 - xy = 5.$
3. $x^2 + xy + 10y^2 = 22,$ $xy - 2y^2 + 6 = 0.$
4. $x^2 - xy - 4y^2 = 10,$ $x^2 - 3y^2 = 5.$
5. $y^2 + 2xy = 3,$ $8x^2 + y^2 = 9.$
6. $3x^2 - 5xy + 2y^2 = 5,$ $-xy + 2y^2 = 2.$

(*Hint:* In Exercises 7, 8, 9, and 10 use the method of Example 2.)

7. $x^2 + 4y^2 = 17,$ $xy = 4.$
8. $x^2 + y^2 = 13,$ $xy = 2.$
9. $9x^2 + y^2 = 22,$ $xy = 3.$
10. $4x^2 + 9y^2 = 37,$ $xy = 3.$
11. $2x^2 - 3xy - 3y^2 = 3,$ $4x^2 - 4xy - 5y^2 = 2.$
12. $5x^2 - 7y^2 = 17,$ $2x^2 + xy - 4y^2 = 8.$

---

* For an extended treatment of this topic, the student is referred to *College Algebra* by H. B. Fine, pp. 324–339, Boston: Ginn and Co. (1904), and *Algebra* by G. Chrystal, Vol. I, pp. 400–416, London: A. & C. Black, Ltd. (1926).

13. $xy + 6y^2 = 10,$
$2x^2 + 3xy - 4y^2 = 40.$

14. $x^2 + 2xy = y^2 + 7,$
$x^2 + y^2 + 5 = 3xy.$

15. $4x^2 - 2xy - y^2 = -16,$
$4x^2 + 7xy + 2y^2 = 104.$

16. $x^2 + 3xy + 2y^2 = 15,$
$4x^2 + 5y^2 = 24.$

17. $7xy - 8x^2 = 10,$
$8y^2 - 9xy = 18.$

18. $x^2 + xy = 12,$
$xy - 2y^2 = 1.$

19. $x^2 + y^2 = (x + y + 1)^2,$
$x^2 + y^2 = (x - y + 2)^2.$

20. $x^2 + y^2 + 2x + 2y = 23,$
$xy = 6.$

21. The sum of the squares of two numbers is 10 and the product of the same numbers is 3. What are the numbers?

22. The hypotenuse of a right triangle is 20 ft, and the area is 96 ft^2. What are the lengths of the sides of the triangle?

23. The sum of the squares of two numbers plus five times their product is equal to 445; and the sum of their squares minus their product is equal to 67. Find the two numbers.

24. If the numerator of a simple fraction is increased by 5 and the denominator is decreased by 5, the resulting fraction equals the reciprocal of the original fraction. If 3 is added to the numerator and 6 is added to the denominator, the fraction is doubled. Find the fraction.

Review Exercises

In each of the pairs of equations in Exercises 1–6, draw the graphs of both equations on the same coordinate axes and find the points of intersection. Solve algebraically for x and y and compare results.

1. $x - y = 2,$
$y = x^2 - 3x - 2.$

2. $2x - 5y + 2 = 0,$
$4x^2 + 25y^2 = 100.$

3. $xy = 8,$
$x^2 + y^2 = 25.$

4. $4x^2 - 9y^2 = 19,$
$25x^2 + 9y^2 = 706.$

5. $16x^2 + 25y^2 = 3300,$
$4x^2 + y^2 = 300.$

6. $y = 2x - x^2,$
$2y = x^2 - 4x.$

In Exercises 7–28, solve each of the systems of equations for x and y algebraically.

7. $x - 2y + 4 = 0,$
$x^2 + 8x - 2y + 14 = 0.$

8. $2x + 3y = 5,$
$4x^2 + 9y^2 = 25.$

9. $2x - 3y + 5 = 0,$
$4x^2 - 3y^2 = 1.$

10. $xy = 7,$
$2x - 3y = 4.$

11. $4x^2 + 9y^2 = 144,$
$9y^2 - 4x^2 = 144.$

12. $16x^2 + 20y^2 = 252,$
$25x^2 - 16y^2 = 252.$

13. $4x^2 + 9y^2 = 144,$
$4x^2 + 12y^2 = 81.$

14. $x^2 + 4y^2 = 4,$
$4xy = 21.$

15. $9x^2 + 4y^2 = 36,$
$12xy = 11.$

16. $x^2 + xy + y^2 = 3,$
$2x^2 - 13xy - 7y^2 = 0.$

17. $3x^2 - 7xy + 2y^2 = 0,$
$x^2 + y^2 = xy + x - y.$

18. $3x^2 + 4xy + y^2 = 0,$
$4x^2 - y^2 + x + 5y = 7.$

19. $6x^2 + xy - 15y^2 = 0,$
$x^2 + 2xy + 3y^2 + x = y.$

20. $6x^2 - 11xy - 10y^2 = 0,$
$3x^2 - 2y^2 + xy = y.$

21. $4x^2 - 9y^2 = 0,$
$xy - 5y = 0.$

22. $2x^2 + 2xy - 5y^2 = 7,$
$x^2 + 2xy - y^2 = 7.$

23. $x^2 - xy + 3y^2 = 3,$
$x^2 + xy - 2 = 0.$

24. $x^2 - xy - y^2 = 2,$
$x^2 + 4xy - 6y^2 = 6.$

25. $3x^2 + xy + y^2 = 5,$
$27x^2 + 5xy + 12y^2 = 50.$

26. $3x^2 - xy + 4y^2 = 7,$
$x^2 - xy + 2y^2 = 2.$

27. $2x^2 + 3xy - 4y^2 = 5,$
$x^2 + xy - 3y^2 = 3.$

28. $x^2 + 4y^2 = 13,$
$xy = 3.$

CHAPTER 14

PROGRESSIONS

14–1 Sequences. Any collection of numbers of which one is designated as the first, another as the second, another as the third, and so on, indefinitely, is called a sequence of numbers. As an example we may give the sequence of odd, positive integers

$$1, 3, 5, 7, \ldots \tag{1}$$

where the three dots indicate that the succession continues indefinitely. The first number, or *term*, of the sequence is 1, and the second term is 3. It is clear that the third term is $2 \cdot 3 - 1 = 5$, and the fourth term is $2 \cdot 4 - 1 = 7$. We see that if the nth term is desired, that is, the term in nth position, it is given by $2n - 1$. Thus the 20th term is $2 \cdot 20 - 1 = 39$. In fact, if $f(n)$ designates the nth term of the sequence (1) we have

$$f(n) = 2n - 1.$$

The terms of a sequence may, in general, be considered to be the values of a function whose domain is the set of positive integers. It is customary to write the terms in a sequence as

$$a_1, a_2, a_3, \ldots, a_n, \ldots$$

so that a_n may be identified with the $f(n)$ above. For the sequence (1),

$$a_1 = 1, \qquad a_2 = 3, \qquad a_{20} = 39, \qquad a_{47} = 93.$$

EXAMPLE 1. Find the first four terms of the sequence for which $a_n = 2n^2 - 4$.

Solution. We have

$$a_1 = 2(1)^2 - 4 = -2, \qquad a_2 = 2(2)^2 - 4 = 4,$$
$$a_3 = 2(3)^2 - 4 = 14, \qquad a_4 = 2(4)^2 - 4 = 28.$$

It should be emphasized that if a few terms at the beginning of a sequence are given, the value of a_n or $f(n)$ is not uniquely determined. For example, if

$$a_n = n^4 - 10n^3 + 35n^2 - 48n + 23, \tag{2}$$

we get $a_1 = 1$, $a_2 = 3$, $a_3 = 5$, $a_4 = 7$, as in the sequence of odd, positive integers (1). However, $a_5 = 33$, which is not the fifth odd integer. On the other hand, if one were asked to give a_n for the sequence (1), $a_n = 2n - 1$ would be a simpler answer than (2).

EXAMPLE 2. Find a_n for the sequence 1, 4, 7, 10, ...

Solution. It is easily verified that $a_n = 3n - 2$ will suffice.

EXERCISE GROUP 14–1

In Exercises 1–12, write the first four terms of the sequence for which a_n is given; also find the indicated term.

1. $a_n = 2n + 4$; a_{80}
2. $a_n = 5n - 3$; a_{76}
3. $a_n = \dfrac{1}{2n}$; a_{43}
4. $a_n = \dfrac{1}{3n + 1}$; a_{38}
5. $a_n = \dfrac{2n - 1}{2n + 1}$; a_{123}
6. $a_n = \dfrac{3n}{2n + 3}$; a_{96}
7. $a_n = \dfrac{1}{n^2}$; a_{71}
8. $a_n = \dfrac{n}{n^2 + 1}$; a_{48}
9. $a_n = \dfrac{1}{2^n}$; a_{11}
10. $a_n = \dfrac{2^n}{3^n - 1}$; a_7
11. $a_n = \sin \dfrac{n\pi}{6}$; a_{14}
12. $a_n = \cos \dfrac{(2n - 1)\pi}{4}$; a_{10}

In each of the following sequences, find an expression for a_n.

13. 3, 5, 7, 9, ...
14. 2, 5, 8, 11, ...
15. $1, \frac{1}{2}, \frac{1}{3}, \frac{1}{4}, \ldots$
16. $\frac{1}{3}, \frac{1}{7}, \frac{1}{11}, \frac{1}{15}, \ldots$
17. $\frac{1}{4}, \frac{1}{9}, \frac{1}{16}, \frac{1}{25}, \ldots$
18. $\frac{2}{3}, \frac{3}{4}, \frac{4}{5}, \frac{5}{6}, \ldots$
19. $\dfrac{2}{3 \cdot 4}, \dfrac{3}{4 \cdot 5}, \dfrac{4}{5 \cdot 6}, \dfrac{5}{6 \cdot 7}, \ldots$
20. 2, 4, 8, 16, ...
21. $2, \dfrac{3}{1 \cdot 2}, \dfrac{4}{1 \cdot 2 \cdot 3}, \dfrac{5}{1 \cdot 2 \cdot 3 \cdot 4}, \ldots$
22. $\dfrac{1}{2}, \dfrac{1 \cdot 2}{5}, \dfrac{1 \cdot 2 \cdot 3}{8}, \dfrac{1 \cdot 2 \cdot 3 \cdot 4}{11}, \ldots$

14–2 Arithmetic progressions. It can be shown that, neglecting air resistance, a falling body which starts from rest will travel 16 ft the first second, 48 ft the next second, 80 ft the third second, 112 ft the fourth second, and so on. How far will the object fall in 10 sec? during the tenth second? We could compute the distance fallen in each second, and add as many of these distances as necessary, but this would be tedious and would give the solution to this one problem only. We shall seek a general method which will apply to all similar problems.

Consider the distances given above,

$$16, 48, 80, 112, \ldots$$

We note that each number after the first is obtained from the preceding one by adding the same number 32, called the *common difference.* Such a sequence is called an *arithmetic progression.*

DEFINITION 14–1. *An arithmetic progression is a sequence of numbers in which each one after the first is obtained from the preceding one by adding a fixed number, called the common difference.*

Let the common difference of an arithmetic progression be designated by d, the first term by a_1, and the nth term by a_n. The terms, up to and including the nth term, can be written

$$a_1, a_1 + d, a_1 + 2d, \ldots, a_1 + (n - 1)d.$$

The formula for a_n is now clear, and may be written

$$a_n = a_1 + (n - 1)d. \tag{3}$$

Let S_n designate the sum of the first n terms of an arithmetic progression. The values of S_n for $n = 1, 2, 3, \ldots$ also form a sequence, but we are usually interested in S_n for a particular value of n. Let us write S_n as

$$S_n = a_1 + (a_1 + d) + (a_1 + 2d) + \cdots \\ + [a_1 + (n - 2)d] + [a_1 + (n - 1)d]. \tag{4}$$

If the terms in the right member are written in reversed order, we have

$$S_n = [a_1 + (n - 1)d] + [a_1 + (n - 2)d] + \cdots + (a_1 + d) + a_1. \tag{5}$$

If Eqs. (4) and (5) are added, the sum of corresponding terms is the same, and there are n terms; hence

$$2S_n = n[2a_1 + (n - 1)d],$$

or

$$S_n = \frac{n}{2}[2a_1 + (n - 1)d].$$

Formula (3) may be used to give $2a_1 + (n - 1)d = a_1 + a_n$. Thus, two formulas for S_n are obtained:

$$S_n = \frac{n}{2}[2a_1 + (n - 1)d] = \frac{n}{2}(a_1 + a_n). \tag{6}$$

To summarize these results, we note that the five quantities a_1, a_n, d, n, S_n of an arithmetic progression (A.P.) are related by the equations

$$\boxed{a_n = a_1 + (n - 1)d,}$$

$$\boxed{S_n = \frac{n}{2}(a_1 + a_n),}$$

$$\boxed{S_n = \frac{n}{2}[2a_1 + (n - 1)d].}$$

These formulas involve two independent relations, and can therefore be used to determine the remaining two quantities whenever the other three are known.

It is possible now to answer the questions raised above about the falling body. To determine how far it will fall in 10 sec, use the formula

$$S_n = \frac{n}{2}[2a_1 + (n - 1)d],$$

with $n = 10$, $a_1 = 16$, and $d = 32$. This gives $S_{10} = 1600$ ft. To determine how far it will fall during the tenth second, use

$$a_n = a_1 + (n - 1)d,$$

with the same values for a_1, n, and d. This gives $a_{10} = 304$ ft.

EXAMPLE. Determine the 97th term and the sum of the first 150 terms of the arithmetic progression (A.P.) 5, 2, -1, ...

Solution. The first term is 5, hence $a_1 = 5$. The second term minus the first term gives $d = -3$. To find the 97th term, we apply Eq. (3) with $n = 97$, and find

$$\begin{aligned} a_{97} &= 5 + (97 - 1)(-3) = 5 + 96(-3) \\ &= 5 - 288 = -283. \end{aligned}$$

For the second part of the problem S_{150} must be found. Since a_{150} has not been given and is not required, it is convenient here to use the first expression for S_n in Eq. (6). Thus

$$\begin{aligned} S_{150} = \tfrac{150}{2}[2 \cdot 5 + (150 - 1)(-3)] &= 75[10 - 447] = 75(-437) \\ &= -32775. \end{aligned}$$

The terms of an arithmetic progression between a_1 and a_n are called *arithmetic means.* Thus, the insertion of m arithmetic means between two numbers requires the finding of an arithmetic progression of $(m + 2)$ terms. For example, if five arithmetic means are to be inserted between 2 and 20, the progression will have seven terms and will be

$$2, a_2, a_3, a_4, a_5, a_6, 20,$$

where the arithmetic means $a_2, \ldots, a_6$ are to be found. To find these means, Eq. (3) is employed with

$$a_7 = 20, \qquad n = 7, \qquad a_1 = 2,$$

so that

$$20 = 2 + (7 - 1)d; \qquad 6d = 18; \qquad \text{and} \qquad d = 3.$$

Then from the definition of an A.P., we have as the desired arithmetic means:

$$a_2 = 2 + d = 5, \quad a_3 = a_2 + d = 5 + 3 = 8, \quad a_4 = 8 + 3 = 11,$$
$$a_5 = 14, \quad a_6 = 17.$$

Exercise Group 14–2

In Exercises 1–6, write the first three terms of an arithmetic progression for which:

1. $a_1 = 10, d = 2$
2. $a_1 = 11, d = -2$
3. $a_1 = 7, d = \frac{3}{4}$
4. $a_1 = -5, d = 2$
5. $a_1 = \frac{1}{3}, d = -\frac{2}{3}$
6. $a_1 = c, d = e$

In each of Exercises 7–12, write the specified term and find the sum of the terms of the indicated arithmetic progression.

7. Given the first three terms: 2, 5, 8; find the 23rd term and the sum of the first 23 terms.
8. Given the first three terms: $-3, -6, -9$; find the 19th term and the sum of the first 19 terms.
9. Given the first three terms: $5, 5\frac{1}{8}, 5\frac{1}{4}$; find the 101st term and the sum of the first 101 terms.
10. Given the first three terms: 10, 8, 6; find the 48th term and the sum of the first 48 terms.
11. Given the first three terms: 8, 5, 2; find the 15th term and the sum of the first 15 terms.
12. Given the first three terms: $c, c + e, c + 2e$; find the nth term and the sum of the first n terms.

In each of Exercises 13–17, determine the arithmetic mean of the given numbers, i.e., insert one arithmetic mean between them.

13. 10, 36 14. 11, 19 15. $\frac{2}{3}$, $\frac{3}{2}$ 16. $-\frac{2}{5}$, $\frac{9}{7}$ 17. c, d

18. Insert five arithmetic means between 3 and 15.
19. Insert seven arithmetic means between -3 and -19.
20. Insert six arithmetic means between 2 and -10.
21. Insert five arithmetic means between $\frac{2}{3}$ and $\frac{67}{6}$.

In each of Exercises 22–37, find the values of the missing elements among a_1, d, a_n, n, and S_n.

22. $a_1 = 10$, $d = 2$, $n = 17$
23. $a_n = -5$, $d = -\frac{1}{2}$, $n = 33$
24. $a_1 = 13$, $a_n = -56$, $n = 24$
25. $S_n = -792$, $a_1 = 24$, $n = 72$
26. $d = 3$, $a_n = 66$, $n = 18$
27. $S_n = 2070$, $a_1 = 5$, $n = 36$
28. $a_1 = 13$, $a_n = 93$, $d = 2$
29. $S_n = -564$, $a_1 = 11$, $d = -3$
30. $a_1 = 33$, $a_n = -45$, $d = -3$
31. $S_n = 891$, $a_1 = 7$, $d = 2$
32. $a_1 = 2$, $d = 5$, $S_n = 1428$
33. $a_1 = 3$, $d = -2$, $S_n = -140$
34. $a_1 = -9$, $d = 4$, $n = 25$
35. $a_n = 99$, $d = 4$, $S_n = 1274$
36. $a_n = 24$, $d = \frac{1}{2}$, $S_n = 574$
37. $a_1 = -8$, $n = 10$, $S_n = 100$

38. Find S_{50} if $a_3 = 5$, $a_{73} = 82$.
39. Find a_{30} if $a_7 = \frac{19}{3}$, $a_{50} = \frac{148}{3}$.
40. Find $f(1) + f(2) + f(3) + \cdots + f(25)$ if $f(x) = 2x + 3$.
41. Find $f(-\frac{3}{2}) + f(1) + f(\frac{7}{2}) + \cdots + f(16)$ if $f(x) = -x + 2$.
42. Determine the first term and the common difference of an A.P. whose 12th term is 25 and 45th term is 91.
43. Determine the 27th term of an A.P. whose 7th term is 11 and whose common difference is $\frac{5}{2}$.
44. Find the sum of all the even integers from 10 to 2974 inclusive.
45. Find the sum of all the odd integers from 7 to 7291 inclusive.
46. A person saved fifty cents more each month than in the preceding one, and in 15 yr all of his savings amounted to \$10,305. How much did he save the first month? How much the last month?
47. A man accepts a position at a salary of \$3000 for the first year with an increase of \$100 per year each year thereafter. How many years will he have to work for his total earnings to equal \$60,000?
48. The sum of the first four terms of an A.P. is 20 and their product is 384. What are the numbers? (*Hint:* Let $x - 3y$, $x - y$, $x + y$, and $x + 3y$ represent the numbers.)
49. A man contracts to drill a 600-ft well at \$2.50 for the first foot and for each foot thereafter 1¢ more than for the preceding one. How much does he receive for drilling the well?
50. If a body falls 16.1 ft during the first second, 3 times as far during the next second, 5 times as far during the third second, etc., how far will it fall during the 12th second? How far in t seconds?

14–3 Geometric progressions. In Section 11–13 the amount of \$1 invested at compound interest for a period of years was determined. An extension of this topic might lead us to ask the following, as an illustration. If \$1 is invested each year at 3% interest compounded annually, what will be the total amount immediately after the eighteenth dollar has been invested? Such a series of equal payments made periodically is called an *annuity* and the value sought here is called the *amount* of the annuity. The amount of each dollar can be considered as a separate problem and can be treated as in Chapter 11. The sum of all these values is the desired amount immediately after the investment of the eighteenth dollar. Hence the value is

$$(1.03)^{17} + (1.03)^{16} + (1.03)^{15} + \cdots + 1$$

(there is no interest on the last dollar). This sum can be computed term by term and the results added, but a preferable method is to have a formula that works directly. Such a formula will be developed.

The terms of the above sum are seen to have a *common ratio*, that is, the quotient of any term except the first by the next preceding term is the same, specifically $(1.03)^{-1}$. Any sequence of numbers which has a common ratio in this sense is called a *geometric progression* (G.P.). Let this common ratio be designated by r, the first term by a_1, the number of terms by n, the nth term by a_n, and the sum of n terms by S_n. Thus the sum of a general geometric progression can be written as

$$S_n = a_1 + a_1r + a_1r^2 + \cdots + a_1r^{n-1}. \tag{7}$$

The nth term, which has been designated by a_n, is thus seen to be a_1r^{n-1}, and we have the formula

$$a_n = a_1r^{n-1}. \tag{8}$$

Let us multiply both members of Eq. (7) by r and subtract the result, term by term, from the corresponding terms of (7); this gives

$$S_n - rS_n = a_1 - a_1r^n,$$

from which, by solving for S_n, we obtain as a formula for the sum of n terms:

$$S_n = \frac{a_1 - a_1r^n}{1 - r}. \tag{9}$$

If the value for a_n given by Eq. (8) is used in Eq. (9), another formula for S_n is obtained:

$$S_n = \frac{a_1 - ra_n}{1 - r}. \tag{10}$$

To summarize the above results, we note that in any geometric progression there are five quantities a_1, r, a_n, n, S_n which are related by the three equations

$$a_n = a_1 r^{n-1},$$

$$S_n = \frac{a_1 - a_1 r^n}{1 - r},$$

$$S_n = \frac{a_1 - r a_n}{1 - r}.$$

Two of these equations are independent, so that if any three of the five quantities are given the other two can be found from the above relations.

We can now answer the question raised at the beginning of this section. Let us rewrite the sum in reverse order; we may then set $a_1 = 1$, $r = 1.03$, $n = 18$, and by use of Eq. (9) we obtain

$$S_{18} = \frac{1 - 1(1.03)^{18}}{1 - 1.03} = \frac{(1.03)^{18} - 1}{0.03}.$$

Using logarithms to evaluate the power $(1.03)^{18}$, we find that

$$S_{18} = \$23.40.$$

Example. Determine the fifth term and the sum of the first ten terms of the geometric progression

$$2, \quad -\tfrac{3}{2}, \quad \tfrac{9}{8}, \quad -\cdots$$

Solution. The terms have the common ratio $r = -\frac{3}{4}$, and $a_1 = 2$. Hence the 5th term is given by

$$a_5 = 2\left(-\frac{3}{4}\right)^4 = \frac{2 \cdot 3^4}{4^4} = \frac{81}{128}.$$

For the second part of the problem, $n = 10$, $a_1 = 2$, $r = -\frac{3}{4}$, and from Eq. (9) we have

$$S_{10} = \frac{2 - 2(-\frac{3}{4})^{10}}{1 - (-\frac{3}{4})} = \frac{2 - 2(-\frac{3}{4})^{10}}{\frac{7}{4}} = \frac{4 \cdot 2}{7}\left(1 - \frac{3^{10}}{4^{10}}\right)$$

$$= \frac{4^{10} - 3^{10}}{7 \cdot 2 \cdot 4^8} = \frac{989{,}527}{917{,}504}.$$

The terms of a geometric progression between a_1 and a_n are called *geometric means*. For example, if three geometric means are inserted between 3 and 48, we have a geometric progression of five terms:

$$3, a_2, a_3, a_4, 48.$$

Eq. (8) gives (since $a_5 = 48$)

$$48 = 3 \cdot r^4, \qquad r^4 = 16, \qquad r = \pm 2.$$

Hence the desired geometric means are

$$a_2 = 3 \cdot 2 = 6, \qquad a_3 = 6 \cdot 2 = 12, \qquad a_4 = 12 \cdot 2 = 24,$$

or a second set,

$$a_2 = -6, \qquad a_3 = 12, \qquad a_4 = -24.$$

Exercise Group 14–3

Write the first three terms of a G.P. for which:

1. $a_1 = 7, r = 2$ 2. $a_1 = -3, r = 3$ 3. $a_1 = \frac{2}{3}, r = \frac{3}{2}$
4. $a_1 = 5, r = -\frac{2}{3}$ 5. $a_1 = -3, r = -\frac{5}{3}$ 6. $a_1 = c, r = e$

Write the specified term and the sum of the G.P. in Exercises 7–12.

7. Given the first three terms: 2, 6, 18; find the 17th term and the sum of 17 terms.
8. Given the first three terms: -3, -6, -12; find the 9th term and the sum of 9 terms.
9. Given the first three terms: 8, 4, 2; find the 15th term and the sum of 15 terms.
10. Given the first three terms: 27, -9, 3; find the 12th term and the sum of 12 terms.
11. Given the first three terms: $-\frac{1}{3}$, $\frac{2}{3}$, $-\frac{4}{3}$; find the 7th term and the sum of 7 terms.
12. Given the first three terms: p, pq, pq^2; find the nth term and the sum of n terms.

13. Insert five geometric means between 2 and $\frac{1}{32}$.
14. Insert four geometric means between 32 and 10^{-5}.
15. Insert six geometric means between 10 and 100.
16. Insert three geometric means between 5 and 1015.
17. Insert three geometric means between $\frac{9}{4}$ and $\frac{4}{9}$.
18. Insert five geometric means between $\frac{32}{9}$ and $\frac{81}{2}$.
19. Insert six geometric means between 14 and $-\frac{7}{64}$.
20. Insert four geometric means between a and b.

In Exercises 21–28, determine the values of the missing elements among a_1, r, a_n, n, S_n.

21. $a_1 = 512,\ r = \frac{1}{2},\ a_n = \frac{1}{2}$
22. $a_1 = 2,\ r = 2,\ n = 7$
23. $S_n = 765,\ a_1 = 3,\ a_n = 384$
24. $a_1 = 5,\ r = 3,\ a_n = 3645$
25. $a_n = 405,\ a_1 = \frac{5}{9},\ S_n = \frac{2735}{9}$
26. $S_n = -425,\ r = -2,\ a_n = -640$
27. $a_1 = \dfrac{\sqrt{2}}{3},\ r = \dfrac{3}{\sqrt{2}},\ n = 8$
28. $a_1 = 25,\ r = 0.4,\ S_n = \frac{5187}{125}$

29. Find the sum of eight terms of the progression $1 + 2,\ 3 + 2^2,\ 5 + 2^3, \ldots$

30. Find the sum of ten terms of the progression $3 - 1,\ 4 - \frac{1}{2},\ 5 - \frac{1}{4}, \ldots$

31. A man invests \$1000 at the end of each year. If the investments yield 3% interest compounded annually, how much are his investments worth at the end of 20 yr?

32. How long would it take the investments in Exercise 31 to amount to \$15,617.80?

33. If your father had deposited \$100 in an account for you on your first birthday and \$100 on each birthday thereafter, and if the account earned interest at the rate of 3% compounded annually, how much would be in your account on your 18th birthday?

34. A golf ball is dropped from a height of 6 ft. On each rebound it rises $\frac{2}{3}$ of the height from which it last fell. What distance has it traveled at the instant it strikes the ground for the 7th time?

14–4 Geometric progressions with infinitely many terms. Let us consider the geometric progression

$$1, \frac{1}{3}, \frac{1}{9}, \frac{1}{27}, \ldots, \frac{1}{3^{n-1}}, \ldots,$$

in which $r = \frac{1}{3}$. Here $a_n = 1/3^{n-1}$, and it is clear that the larger the value of n the smaller the value of a_n. In fact, if n can increase without bound, the value of a_n can be made smaller than any preassigned value by taking n large enough. In particular, if the preassigned value is 10^{-9}, then in order that $a_n < 10^{-9}$, we must have

$$\frac{1}{3^{n-1}} < \frac{1}{10^9}.$$

Since the numerators of the fractions are equal, it follows that the smaller fraction must have the larger denominator. Hence, it follows that

$$3^{n-1} > 10^9,$$

and taking the logarithm of both sides (also making use of the properties of logarithms), we have

$$(n - 1) \log 3 > 9 \log 10 = 9.$$

If we now solve this last relation for n we have

$$n - 1 > \frac{9}{\log 3} \qquad \text{and} \qquad n > \frac{9}{0.4771} + 1 = 19.9.$$

Thus we see that whenever $n \geqq 20$, $a_n < 10^{-9}$.

The indicated sum of the terms of a geometric progression in which n can increase without bound is called an infinite geometric series, or simply a *geometric series.*

Consider now the geometric series

$$1 + \frac{1}{3} + \frac{1}{9} + \frac{1}{27} + \cdots + \frac{1}{3^{n-1}} + \cdots$$

Let S_n designate the sum of the first n terms of this series:

$$S_n = 1 + \frac{1}{3} + \frac{1}{9} + \cdots + \frac{1}{3^{n-1}}.$$

This is a *finite* sum and is called the nth *partial sum* of the series. By Eq. (9) we find the value of S_n to be

$$S_n = \frac{1}{1 - \frac{1}{3}} - \frac{1 \cdot (\frac{1}{3})^n}{1 - \frac{1}{3}}.$$

Only the second term of S_n contains n, and as n increases the value of this term decreases and becomes closer and closer to zero. Hence as n increases, the value of S_n gets closer and closer to the first term $1/(1 - \frac{1}{3})$. This fact is expressed in the statement

$$\lim_{n \to \infty} S_n = \frac{1}{1 - \frac{1}{3}} = \frac{1}{\frac{2}{3}} = \frac{3}{2}.$$

The left member is read "limit of S_n as n becomes infinite." *The value of this limit is defined as the sum or value of the geometric series.*

In the general case, let us designate the geometric series by S:

$$S = a_1 + a_1 r + a_1 r^2 + \cdots + a_1 r^{n-1} + \cdots \tag{11}$$

We again define S_n as the *finite, partial sum* of the first n terms:

$$S_n = a_1 + a_1 r + a_1 r^2 + \cdots + a_1 r^{n-1}$$

and apply Eq. (9) to find this sum:

$$S_n = \frac{a_1}{1 - r} - \frac{a_1 r^n}{1 - r}.$$

If $|r| < 1$, that is, if $-1 < r < 1$, the value of the second term in S_n will decrease numerically, and approach zero as n increases indefinitely. Hence if $-1 < r < 1$, the value of S_n gets closer and closer to the number $a_1/(1 - r)$, and

$$\boxed{S = \lim_{n \to \infty} S_n = \frac{a_1}{1 - r}.} \tag{12}$$

The series is then said to converge and to have the value $S = a_1/(1 - r)$. When $|r| \geqq 1$, which means when either $r \geqq 1$ or $r \leqq -1$, the partial sums S_n do not approach any value; in this event the series does not converge and is said to *diverge*. We collect these results in the following statement.

THEOREM 14–1. *The geometric series* (11) *converges when and only when* $|r| < 1$, *that is,* $-1 < r < 1$, *and when convergent it has the value* $S = a_1/(1 - r)$.

By use of this theorem, the sum of the geometric series treated earlier in this section is $S = 1/(1 - \frac{1}{3}) = \frac{3}{2}$.

EXERCISE GROUP 14–4

In Exercises 1–10, find the sum of the infinite geometric series.

1. $5 + \frac{1}{2} + \frac{1}{20} + \cdots$
2. $2 - \frac{1}{2} + \frac{1}{8} - \cdots$
3. $10 - 1 + 0.1 - \cdots$
4. $a - 0.1a + 0.01a - \cdots$
5. $1.665 - 1.11 + 0.74 - \cdots$
6. $2.025 + 1.35 + 0.9 + \cdots$
7. $7 + \frac{7}{3} + \frac{7}{9} + \cdots$
8. $\frac{2}{3} - \frac{1}{3} + \frac{1}{6} - \cdots$
9. $\frac{3}{2} - 1 + \frac{2}{3} - \cdots$
10. $6.60 - 2.64 + 1.056 - \cdots$

In Exercises 11–18, find the sum of the infinite geometric series, assuming that x is such that the series converges.

11. $1 - x + x^2 - x^3 + \cdots$
12. $1 + x^2 + x^4 + x^6 + \cdots$
13. $x + x^3 + x^5 + x^7 + \cdots$
14. $\dfrac{\sqrt{x}}{2} - \dfrac{x}{4} + \dfrac{\sqrt{x^3}}{8} - \cdots$
15. $(x + 3) + 2(x + 3)^2 + 4(x + 3)^3 + \cdots$
16. $(x^2 - 2) - 0.1(x^2 - 2)^2 + 0.01(x^2 - 2)^3 - \cdots$
17. $1 + \dfrac{1}{1 - x} + \dfrac{1}{(1 - x)^2} + \cdots$
18. $\dfrac{1}{1 + x} + \dfrac{x}{(1 + x)^2} + \dfrac{x^2}{(1 + x)^3} + \cdots$

19. Find the sum of the infinite series $(1 + \frac{1}{2}) + (\frac{1}{3} + \frac{1}{4}) + (\frac{1}{9} + \frac{1}{8}) + \cdots$ (*Hint:* Consider as $[1 + \frac{1}{3} + \frac{1}{9} + \cdots] + [\frac{1}{2} + \frac{1}{4} + \frac{1}{8} + \cdots]$.)

20. Find the sum of the infinite series

$$(2 - \tfrac{1}{4}) + (\tfrac{1}{2} - \tfrac{1}{12}) + (\tfrac{1}{8} - \tfrac{1}{36}) + \cdots$$

21. A golf ball is dropped from a height of 6 ft. Its center rebounds each time $\frac{2}{3}$ of the height from which it last fell. Find the limit of the distance traveled by the center of the ball in coming to rest.

22. Find the limit of the time the center of the ball of Exercise 21 will travel. [*Hint:* Recall that in Exercise 8 of Exercise Group 5–6 we found that s (the distance a body falls) $= 16t^2$ (t = time of falling in seconds). Hence, $t = \frac{1}{4}\sqrt{s}$.]

Prove that:

23. $1 + \sin^2 x + \sin^4 x + \cdots = \sec^2 x.$

24. $1 + \cos^2 x + \cos^4 x + \cdots = \csc^2 x.$

25. $1 - \tan^2 x + \tan^4 x - \cdots = \cos^2 x.$

26. $1 - \cot^2 x + \cot^4 x - \cdots = \sin^2 x.$

27. $1 + \cos 2x + \cos^2 2x + \cdots = \csc 2x \cot x.$

28. $1 - \cos 4x + \cos^2 4x + \cdots = \csc 4x \tan 2x.$

29. $1 + \sin 2x + \sin^2 2x + \cdots = \dfrac{1}{2}\sec^2\left(\dfrac{\pi}{4} + x\right).$

30. $1 + \cos x + \cos^2 x + \cdots = \dfrac{1}{2}\csc^2\left(\dfrac{x}{2}\right).$

14–5 Repeating decimals. An interesting application of convergent geometric series occurs in the case of *repeating infinite decimals*, that is, decimals in which, after some decimal place, a fixed group of digits repeats indefinitely. Thus the repeating decimal 0.333 . . . can be written as

$$0.3 + 0.03 + 0.003 + \cdots,$$

which is a geometric series with $r = 0.1$. Hence, by (12), the value is

$$S = \frac{a_1}{1 - r} = \frac{0.3}{1 - 0.1} = \frac{0.3}{0.9} = \frac{1}{3}.$$

The general result, of which an example has just been presented, is expressed in the following theorem.

THEOREM 14–2. *Every repeating decimal represents a rational number.*

Proof. A repeating decimal can be expressed as the sum of a finite decimal and an infinite repeating part. The infinite repeating part is a geometric series with $0 < r \leqq 0.1$, hence can be written as a quotient of two finite decimals, and is therefore equal to a rational number. The finite decimal part is also a rational number. The sum of the two parts is thus a rational number also, and the theorem is proved.

EXAMPLE 1. Express $a = 3.0342342\ldots$ as a rational number.

Solution. Write the decimal in the form

$$a = 3 + (0.0342 + 0.0000342 + 0.0000000342 + \cdots)$$

The part in parentheses is a geometric series with $a_1 = 0.0342$ and $r = 0.001$. Hence by Eq. (12) its value is

$$\frac{0.0342}{1 - 0.001} = \frac{0.0342}{0.999} = \frac{342}{9990} = \frac{19}{555} \qquad \text{and} \qquad a = 3 + \tfrac{19}{555} = \tfrac{1684}{555}.$$

This result can be checked by long division.

For the sake of completeness we present the converse of Theorem 14–2 above.

THEOREM 14–3. *Any rational number can be expressed as a repeating decimal.*

Proof. By definition, a rational number can be expressed in the form p/q, where p and q are integers. It is enough to prove the theorem for a positive proper fraction, that is, a fraction in which p and q are positive, and p is smaller than q. If the division of p by q is carried out, the remainder at each step will be either a positive integer smaller than q, or zero. Hence there are q possible remainders, and a remainder will be repeated after at most q steps in the division. At this step the digits in the quotient start repeating, and the quotient will be a repeating decimal.

Note that a number such as $0.783 = 0.783000\ldots$ may be thought of as a repeating decimal in which the digit zero repeats.

EXAMPLE 2. $\frac{3}{7} = 0.428571428571428571\ldots$

```
   0.428571 . . .
7)3.0
  2 8
   20
   14
    60
    56
     40
     35
      50
      49
       10
        7
        3
```

In the division of Example 2, the first remainder is 2, the second is 6, the third is 4, the fourth is 5, the fifth is 1, and the sixth is 3, which was the starting number. In this example, the six possible remainders were obtained before 3 was repeated.

EXAMPLE 3. $\frac{2}{5} = 0.400000\ldots$, which is a repeating decimal with the digit zero repeating indefinitely.

EXERCISE GROUP 14–5

Reduce each of the following repeating decimals to a rational fraction in lowest terms.

1. 0.222 . . . 2. 0.0202020 . . . 3. 0.141414 . . .
4. 1.31313 . . . 5. 63.6363 . . . 6. 0.027027027 . . .
7. 0.101010 . . . 8. 9.99 . . . 9. 0.063063063 . . .
10. 0.8333 . . . 11. 0.181818 . . . 12. 0.729729729 . . .
13. 7.454545 . . . 14. 0.153846153846153846 . . .
15. 0.714285714285714285 . . .

REVIEW EXERCISES

1. Find the 17th term and the sum of the first 17 terms of the progression 3, 5, 7, . . .
2. Find the 91st term and the sum of the first 91 terms of the progression $-2, -5, -8, \ldots$
3. Find the 77th term and the sum of the first 77 terms of the progression 3, 6, 12, . . .
4. Find the 37th term and the sum of the first 37 terms of the progression $2, -3, \frac{9}{2}, \ldots$
5. Insert five arithmetic means between 2 and 20.
6. Insert seven arithmetic means between -5 and -21.
7. Insert four geometric means between 5 and 1215.
8. Insert three geometric means between 3 and $\frac{16}{27}$.

In each of Exercises 9–18, find the values of the missing elements among a_1, a_n, n, S_n, and d or r.

9. $a_1 = 2, d = 3, n = 15$. 10. $a_1 = -3, a_n = 29, d = 2$.
11. $S_n = 39, a_1 = 15, n = 13$, (use d).
12. $a_n = -47, d = -3, S_n = -357$.
13. $a_n = -39, S_n = -391, d = -2$.
14. $a_1 = 256, r = \frac{1}{2}, n = 7$.
15. $S_n = -364, a_1 = 2, a_n = -486$, (use r).
16. $a_1 = 3, r = 2, a_n = 384$. 17. $a_1 = \frac{1}{16}, r = -2, a_n = 4$.
18. $S_n = -\frac{182}{27}, a_1 = \frac{1}{27}, a_n = -9$, (use r).

Find the nth term and the sum of n terms of the progressions in Exercises 19 and 20.

19. $1, \sin\theta, \sin^2\theta, \ldots$ 20. $\sin^2\theta, 1, \csc^2\theta, \ldots$
21. Show that $1/(1 - \sin\theta), \frac{1}{2}, 1/(1 - \csc\theta), \ldots$ is an arithmetic progression.

CHAPTER 15

THE SOLUTION OF OBLIQUE TRIANGLES

15–1 Introduction. In Chapter 9 various types of problems which arise in surveying, navigation, and physics were considered. The solutions of these problems were effected by solving appropriate right triangles. In less restricted situations similar problems could be solved if methods were available for solving *oblique* triangles, that is, triangles which contain no right angle. Such methods will be developed in the present chapter.

The formulas to be developed express certain relations among the sides and angles of a triangle; some of them have an importance apart from their use in the solution of triangles. Although the formulas are designed for use with oblique triangles, they do apply to right triangles as well. We shall, accordingly, not exclude right triangles when referring to oblique triangles, unless such exclusion is specifically mentioned.

15–2 The Law of Sines. In the derivation of the various formulas which apply to oblique triangles, a *standard lettering* will be used. The vertices will be A, B, and C, the corresponding angles will be named similarly, and the side of the triangle opposite any vertex will be labeled with the similar lower-case letter.

Let ABC be either triangle in Fig. 15–1. The altitude h is drawn from B to AC, with D as the foot of this altitude. From right triangle ABD in Fig. 15–1(a) we have

$$h = c \sin (180^\circ - A),$$

which becomes, since $\sin (180^\circ - A) = \sin A$,

$$h = c \sin A. \tag{1}$$

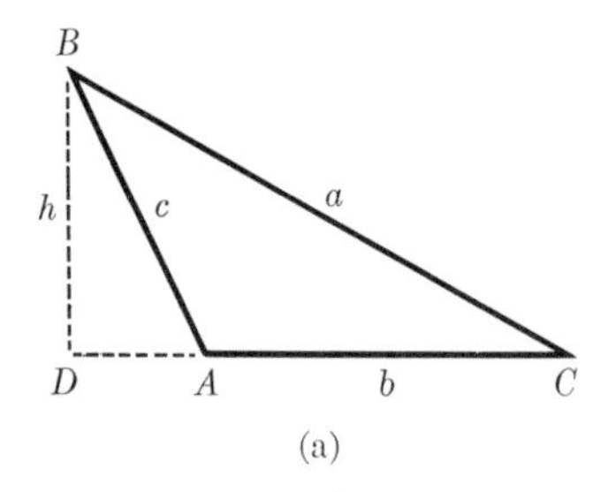

(a)

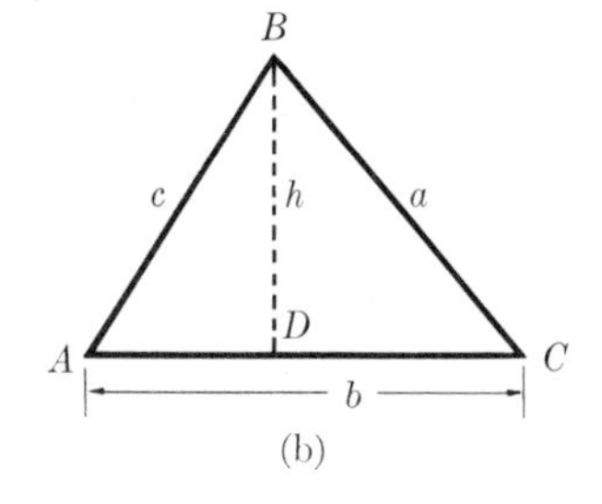

(b)

FIGURE 15–1

For the triangle ABD of Fig. 15-1(b), Eq. (1) follows directly. From right triangle CBD in either figure we also have

$$h = a \sin C. \tag{2}$$

By equating the values of h in Eqs. (1) and (2) we have at once

$$a \sin C = c \sin A,$$

which in turn, upon division of both members by $\sin A \sin C$, gives

$$\frac{a}{\sin A} = \frac{c}{\sin C}. \tag{3}$$

A similar derivation (or a relettering of the triangle) yields the equation

$$\frac{a}{\sin A} = \frac{b}{\sin B}, \tag{4}$$

and a combination of (3) and (4) gives the *Law of Sines:*

$$\boxed{\frac{a}{\sin A} = \frac{b}{\sin B} = \frac{c}{\sin C}.} \tag{5}$$

It is helpful to state this relation in words.

THE LAW OF SINES. *In a triangle the ratio of any side to the sine of the opposite angle is constant.*

If one of the angles in a triangle is a right angle, the Law of Sines still applies, and in fact reduces to formulas obtained in Section 9-3.

15-3 The Law of Cosines. Any triangle with standard lettering may be placed on a coordinate system as in Fig. 15-2. Since angle A is in standard position, the definitions of $\cos A$ and $\sin A$ give, if u and v are the coordinates of B, $\cos A = u/c$, $\sin A = v/c$. Hence, $u = c \cos A$, $v = c \sin A$.

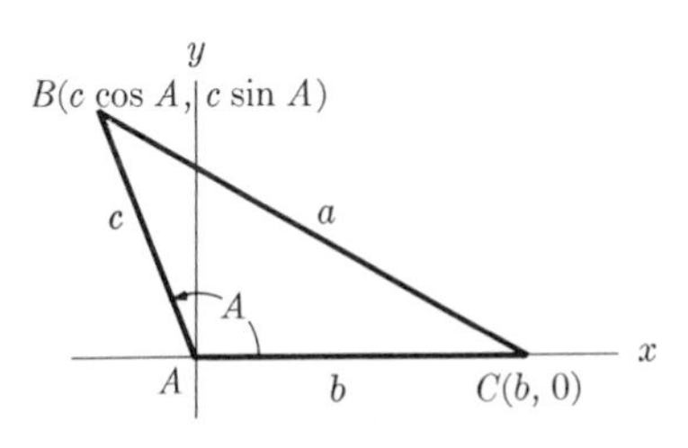

FIGURE 15-2

We now apply the distance formula of Section 5–4 to finding the square of the length BC, and we have

$$\begin{aligned} a^2 &= (b - c\cos A)^2 + (c\sin A)^2 \\ &= b^2 - 2bc\cos A + c^2\cos^2 A + c^2\sin^2 A \\ &= b^2 + c^2 - 2bc\cos A \qquad (\text{since } \cos^2 A + \sin^2 A = 1). \end{aligned}$$

We have thus obtained one form of the *Law of Cosines*,

$$\boxed{a^2 = b^2 + c^2 - 2bc\cos A.} \tag{6}$$

By relettering the triangles, we may at once write down the other forms of the Law of Cosines,

$$\boxed{b^2 = a^2 + c^2 - 2ac\cos B,} \tag{7}$$

$$\boxed{c^2 = a^2 + b^2 - 2ab\cos C.} \tag{8}$$

The three equations (6), (7), and (8) are all contained in the following statement.

THE LAW OF COSINES. *In a triangle the square of any side is equal to the sum of the squares of the other two sides minus twice the product of these sides and the cosine of the angle included between them.*

In the case of a right triangle the Law of Cosines reduces either to the theorem of Pythagoras, or to one of the formulas of Section 9–3. It should be realized that the Law of Cosines has important applications apart from the solution of triangles.

EXAMPLE. Prove that if $(\cos A)/b = (\cos B)/a$, the triangle is either isosceles or a right triangle.

Solution. We may solve Eqs. (6) and (7) to give

$$\cos A = \frac{b^2 + c^2 - a^2}{2bc}, \qquad \cos B = \frac{a^2 + c^2 - b^2}{2ac}.$$

Substitution of these in the given equation yields

$$\frac{b^2 + c^2 - a^2}{2b^2c} = \frac{a^2 + c^2 - b^2}{2a^2c}.$$

Multiplying both members by $2c$, and then clearing of fractions, we have

$$a^2b^2 + a^2c^2 - a^4 = a^2b^2 + b^2c^2 - b^4,$$

which may be written as

$$a^2c^2 - b^2c^2 = a^4 - b^4,$$

and, on partial factorization, as

$$c^2(a^2 - b^2) = (a^2 + b^2)(a^2 - b^2).$$

One possibility is $a^2 - b^2 = 0$, in which case $a = b$ and the triangle is isosceles. If $a^2 - b^2 \neq 0$, we may divide both members of the above equation by $a^2 - b^2$, and we obtain

$$c^2 = a^2 + b^2,$$

from which it follows that the triangle is a right triangle (with $C = 90°$).

Exercise Group 15-1

In the following exercises, the standard lettering of an oblique triangle is used.

1. Use the Law of Sines to prove that $\cos B = a/2b$ if $A = 2B$.
2. Prove the following relations from either triangle of Fig. 15-1:

$$b \cos A + a \cos B = c, \qquad c \cos B + b \cos C = a,$$
$$a \cos C + c \cos A = b.$$

3. Derive the Law of Cosines by eliminating $\cos B$ from the first two equations of Exercise 2, and then eliminating $\cos C$ from the resulting equation and the third equation of Exercise 2.
4. Show that $(a - b)^2 = c^2 - ab$ if $C = 60°$.
5. Show that $(a + b)^2 = c^2 + ab$ if $C = 120°$.
6. Show that $a^2 = b^2 + bc$ if $A = 2B$ and $B \neq C$.
7. By using the identity $\cos \frac{1}{2}A = \sqrt{\frac{1}{2}(1 + \cos A)}$, derive the formula

$$\cos \tfrac{1}{2}A = \tfrac{1}{2}\sqrt{\frac{(b + c)^2 - a^2}{bc}}.$$

8. By a method similar to that of Exercise 7, derive the formula

$$\sin \tfrac{1}{2}A = \tfrac{1}{2}\sqrt{\frac{a^2 - (b - c)^2}{bc}}.$$

9. In an isosceles triangle in which the equal sides are designated by a and the angle included between them by θ, use the Law of Cosines to show that the third side x is given by $x = 2a \sin \theta/2$.
10. Use the Law of Cosines to prove that the square of the length of the median drawn from A is given by $\frac{1}{2}(b^2 + c^2) - \frac{1}{4}a^2$.

11. Use the Law of Sines to prove that the bisector of an angle of a triangle divides the opposite side into parts which are proportional to the adjacent sides.

12. Prove that $(\cos A)/a + (\cos B)/b + (\cos C)/c = (a^2 + b^2 + c^2)/2abc$.

13. Prove that

$$(b^2/a) \cos A + (c^2/b) \cos B + (a^2/c) \cos C = (a^4 + b^4 + c^4)/2abc.$$

15–4 On solving oblique triangles. The three angles and the three sides of any triangle are called the *parts* of the triangle. If three parts of a triangle, including at least one side are known, the remaining parts may in general be found, by methods which will be presented. *To solve a triangle shall mean to find those parts of the triangle which are not known.* It is convenient to consider the following four cases in the discussion of the methods of solving an oblique triangle.

A. *Two angles and one side are known.*

B. *Two sides and the angle opposite one of them are known.*

C. *Two sides and the included angle are known.*

D. *The three sides are known.*

It is clear, in regard to Case A, that if any two angles of a triangle are known, the third one can be found immediately by using the fact that the sum of the angles of a triangle is 180°.

Case B is known as the *ambiguous case*, for, under certain conditions two triangles, distinct in the sense of not being congruent, exist with the same three given parts. In fact, this case is the only one of the four for which there is no corresponding theorem in plane geometry expressing a condition for congruence of triangles.

In each of Cases C and D solutions using the highly important Law of Cosines will be stressed, and additional methods suited to logarithmic computation will be presented in Section 15–7.

15–5 Applications of the Law of Sines. *Case* A. *Two angles and one side.* We may assume in this case that the three angles of the triangle are known, in addition to a side. The Law of Sines may then be used to find in turn each of the remaining sides. To find either unknown side we use the Law of Sines with the ratio which involves that side and the one which involves the given side.

EXAMPLE. Solve the triangle ABC if

$$A = 23^\circ\, 09', \qquad B = 108^\circ\, 43', \qquad c = 123.2.$$

Solution. Angle C can be found at once:

$$C = 180^\circ - (23^\circ\, 09' + 108^\circ\, 43') = 48^\circ\, 08'.$$

Let us find side a. Using the Law of Sines with the ratios which involve a and c, we have

$$\frac{a}{\sin A} = \frac{c}{\sin C},$$

which may be solved for a to give

$$a = \frac{c}{\sin C} \cdot \sin A. \tag{9}$$

We shall use logarithms to evaluate a. Equating logarithms of both members of (9) we have

$$\log a = (\log c - \log \sin C) + \log \sin A.$$

The logarithmic computation follows:

$$\begin{aligned}
\log c = \log 123.2 &= 12.0906 - 10 \quad (-)\\
\log \sin C = \log \sin 48^\circ\, 08' &= \underline{9.8720 - 10}\\
\log (c/\sin C) &= 2.2186 \quad (+)\\
\log \sin A = \log \sin 23^\circ\, 09' &= \underline{9.5945 - 10}\\
\log a &= 11.8131 - 10\\
a &= 65.03.
\end{aligned}$$

To find side b we have an equation similar to (9), involving b and c, namely,

$$b = \frac{c}{\sin C} \cdot \sin B,$$

and the corresponding logarithmic equation,

$$\log b = \log (c/\sin C) + \log \sin B.$$

Using the value of $\log (c/\sin C)$ from the above computation, we have

$$\begin{aligned}
\log (c/\sin C) &= 2.2186 \quad (+)\\
\log \sin B = \log \sin 71^\circ\, 17' &= \underline{9.9764 - 10}\\
\log b &= 12.1950 - 10\\
b &= 157.7.
\end{aligned}$$

Exercise Group 15-2

In Exercises 1-8, solve the triangle ABC having the given parts.

1. $A = 12^\circ$, $C = 47^\circ$, $b = 15$
2. $B = 63^\circ$, $A = 33^\circ$, $c = 22$
3. $C = 52^\circ$, $B = 75^\circ$, $a = 2.01$
4. $B = 17^\circ\, 53'$, $C = 82^\circ\, 36'$, $a = 9.3$
5. $C = 126^\circ\, 09'$, $A = 33^\circ\, 12'$, $b = 3.5$
6. $A = 117^\circ\, 45'$, $B = 26^\circ\, 55'$, $c = 0.03$
7. $a = 32$, $A = 39^\circ\, 17'$, $B = 41^\circ\, 33'$
8. $b = 23$, $B = 127^\circ\, 15'$, $C = 13^\circ\, 29'$

9. A pilot flies with an airspeed of 250 mph on a heading of 136°. The wind is blowing from the direction 255°. If the resulting course is 130°, find the velocity of the wind and the groundspeed of the plane.

10. A tree standing (vertically) on a slope inclined at an angle of 5° to the horizontal casts a shadow 23 ft in length up the slope. If the angle of elevation of the sun is 63°, find the height of the tree.

11. Two points A and B on the bank of a river are 30 ft apart. A point C across the river is located so that angle CAB is 70° and angle ABC is 80°. How wide is the river?

12. A pilot maintains an airspeed of 300 mph on a heading of 330°. The wind is blowing from the northeast (from direction 45°) and the course flown by the pilot is 325° 12′. Find the velocity of the wind and the groundspeed of the plane.

13. An aircraft carrier is sailing at 25 knots on a course of 26° 35′. A plane takes off and flies a course of 301° 30′ to a point P. The pilot then flies on course 113° 10′ until he reaches the carrier again, which has continued to sail with its original velocity during the elapsed time of 5 hr. How far did the pilot fly?

14. A body is acted upon by a force of 978 lb and by a force of unknown magnitude which makes an angle of 154° 13′ with the direction of the first force. The direction of the resultant force can be measured and is found to make an angle of 69° 12′ with the direction of the first force. Find the magnitude of the resultant, and also of the second force.

15. A pilot, who is flying on a straight course of 43°, observes a flashing beacon in the direction 76°, and after flying 30 mi he observes that the beacon is in the direction 110° 30′. How far is he from the beacon on his second observation?

16. An engineer in town A must be in town B, which is 1256 mi east of A, in 12 hr. He decides to go by way of C to visit a branch plant. The direction from A to C is 59° 30′ and the direction from C to B is 120°. If he averages 300 mph in his plane, how much time will he have for his visit at the branch plant at C?

Case B. *The ambiguous case.* We shall assume for the discussion of the case in which two sides and the angle opposite one of them are known, that the known parts of the triangle are A, a, and b. *If angle A is obtuse,*

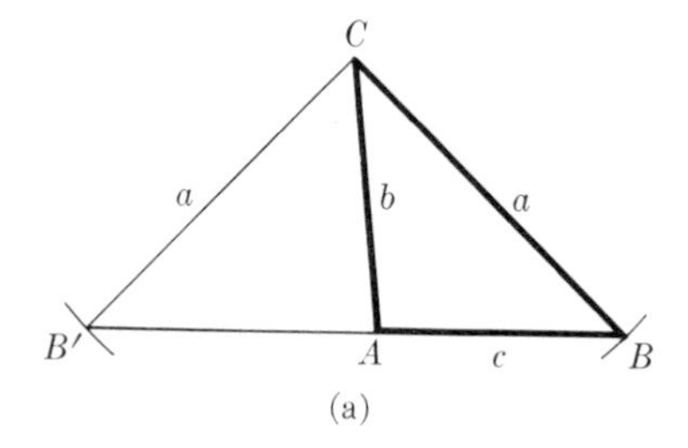

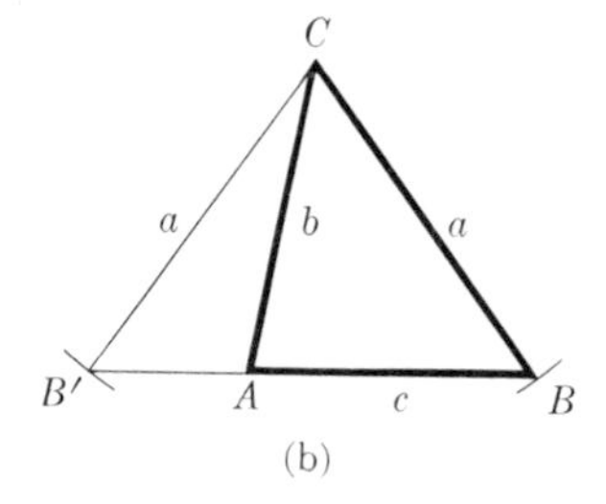

FIGURE 15–3

side a must be larger than side b in order for a triangle to exist, and in that case there is exactly one triangle (Fig. 15–3(a)). A similar statement applies if A is a right angle.

If A is an acute angle, and $a > b$, again only one triangle exists, as in Fig. 15–3(b).

If A is an acute angle, and $a < b$, one of three possibilities may occur. As extended from vertex C, (1) a line of length a may be too short to reach AB, so that no triangle exists, or (2) the line of length a may be precisely the distance from C to the opposite side and one triangle, a right triangle, exists, or (3) a line of length a drawn from C may intersect the side opposite C in two points B and B', forming triangles $AB'C$ and ABC, each of which contains the given parts. The three possibilities are indicated in Fig. 15–4.

Criteria may be established to determine which possibility occurs in a given situation. However, this determination may be effectively made during the process of attempting a solution, as will appear in the examples.

The general method of solution in Case B is to use the Law of Sines to find the unknown angle opposite a given side, then to find the third angle, and finally to find the third side by the Law of Sines again.

EXAMPLE 1. Solve the triangle ABC if $A = 30°$, $a = 3.4$, $b = 7$.

Solution. From the Law of Sines (Section 15–2) we find

$$\sin B = \frac{b \sin A}{a}.$$

Hence, *if a triangle exists*, we must have

$$\sin B = \frac{7 \sin 30°}{3.4} = \frac{3.5}{3.4} > 1.$$

However, a value of $\sin B$ which is greater than 1 is clearly impossible, so that no solution exists.

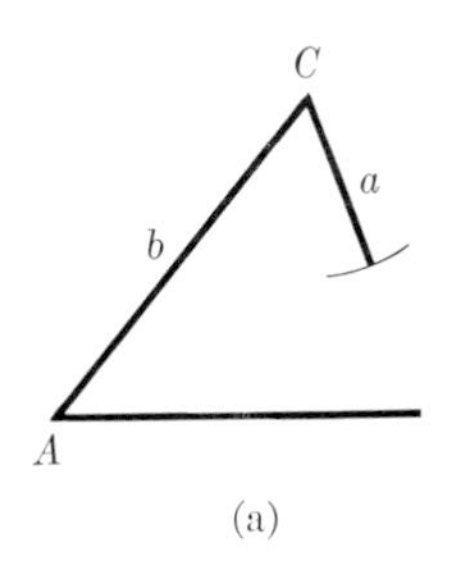

(a)

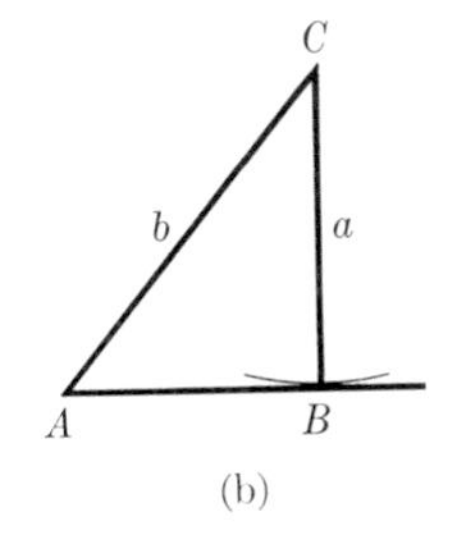

(b)

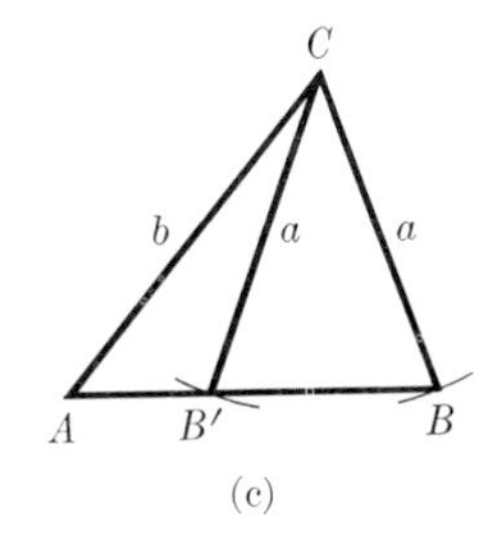

(c)

FIGURE 15–4

If the attempt to compute $\sin B$ in Example 1 is made by use of logarithms, the indication that no solution exists will be the emergence of a value of $\log \sin B$ which is greater than zero. For, since the sine of any angle must be not greater than 1, the logarithm of the sine must be not greater than zero.

EXAMPLE 2. Solve the triangle ABC for which

$$C = 38^\circ\, 17', \qquad a = 2.304, \qquad c = 1.520.$$

Solution. To find angle A we employ the Law of Sines in the form

$$\sin A = \frac{a \sin C}{c},$$

which becomes, in logarithmic form,

$$\log \sin A = \log a + \log \sin C - \log c.$$

The logarithmic computation follows:

$$\begin{aligned}
\log a = \log 2.304 &= 0.3625 \\
\log \sin C = \log \sin 38^\circ\, 17' &= \underline{9.7921 - 10} \quad (+) \\
\log (a \sin C) &= 10.1546 - 10 \\
\log c = \log 1.520 &= \underline{0.1818 } \quad (-) \\
\log \sin A &= 9.9728 - 10.
\end{aligned}$$

There are thus two possible values of angle A, which will be called A and A',

$$A = 69^\circ\, 56', \qquad \text{and} \qquad A' = 110^\circ\, 04'.$$

The corresponding values of the third angle are then

$$B = 71^\circ\, 47', \qquad \text{and} \qquad B' = 31^\circ\, 39'.$$

Finally, to find the remaining side we use the Law of Sines in the form (as in Case A),

$$b = \frac{a \sin B}{\sin A},$$

together with logarithmic computation for each of the possible triangles,

$$\begin{aligned}
\log 2.304 &= 0.3625 \\
\log \sin 71^\circ\, 47' &= \underline{9.9777 - 10} \quad (+) \\
& 10.3402 - 10 \\
\log \sin 69^\circ\, 56' &= \underline{9.9728 - 10} \quad (-) \\
\log b &= 0.3674 \\
b &= 2.330
\end{aligned}$$

$$\begin{aligned}
\log 2.304 &= 0.3625 \\
\log \sin 31^\circ\, 39' &= \underline{9.7199 - 10} \quad (+) \\
& 10.0824 - 10 \\
\log \sin 110^\circ\, 04' &= \underline{9.9728 - 10} \quad (-) \\
\log b' &= 0.1096 \\
b' &= 1.288
\end{aligned}$$

EXAMPLE 3. There can be only one triangle ABC with $A = 18°$, $a = 4.6$, $b = 3.1$, since the side a opposite the known angle A is the larger of the two given sides. If this were overlooked, and the attempt made to solve the triangle, the same conclusion would appear. Thus, angle B is found to be $12° 00'$ to the nearest $10'$; the supplement B' of B gives no triangle, since $A + B' > 180°$. Finally, angle C is $150°$, and side c turns out to be 7.44.

These examples indicate that whenever the Law of Sines is used to find an angle, two supplementary values are possible initially for the angle. Other considerations will then determine whether one of these possibilities must be discarded.

EXERCISE GROUP 15-3

In Exercises 1–12, solve the triangle ABC having the given parts.

1. $A = 48°$, $a = 2$, $b = 3$
2. $B = 123°$, $b = 20$, $c = 7$
3. $C = 40°$, $b = 30$, $c = 20$
4. $b = 0.09$, $c = 0.07$, $C = 44°$
5. $c = 0.1$, $a = 0.2$, $A = 65°$
6. $b = 3$, $a = 5$, $A = 70°$
7. $c = 200$, $b = 150$, $B = 75°$
8. $a = 2$, $c = 1.4$, $C = 60°$
9. $c = 0.098$, $a = 0.23$, $A = 64° 34'$
10. $b = 3.2$, $a = 5.2$, $A = 69° 43'$
11. $a = 280$, $b = 190$, $B = 38° 19'$
12. $B = 13° 19'$, $b = 80$, $a = 190$

13. A and B are two points on opposite sides of a body of water. A third point C is located so that AC and BC are found to be 319 ft and 263 ft, respectively, and the angle BAC is 43°. Compute the distance AB to the degree of accuracy the data justify.

14. A pilot wishes to fly from A to B, which is in the direction 50°. The wind is blowing 20 mph from the direction 290° and the airspeed will be 120 mph. Find the heading that the pilot must fly to reach the point B, and the average groundspeed for the flight.

15. The longer side of a parallelogram is 167.3 ft and the shorter side is 98.27 ft. The longer diagonal makes an angle of $29° 35'$ with the longer side. Find the length of the longer diagonal, and the angle which the two given sides make with each other.

16. Two forces F_1 and F_2 have magnitudes of 198.7 and 193.6 lb, respectively, and their resultant F_3 makes an angle of $37° 14'$ with F_2. Assuming that the direction of F_2 is horizontal, find the direction of F_1 and the magnitude of F_3.

17. A force F_1 has a magnitude of 1892 lb, and a second force F_2 has a magnitude of 2795 lb and is in the direction $59° 38'$. The resultant F_3 of the two forces is in the direction $45° 42'$. Find the magnitude of the resultant F_3 and the direction of F_1.

18. A pilot leaves an airport at A and flies a course of 241° for a distance of 298.5 mi when he finds himself in a very heavy fog bank with a compass that is out of order. He attempts to turn back, but is unable to judge his direction accurately. He flies for approximately 175 mi on a straight course when the fog thins out enough for him to observe a double track railroad and he realizes that he is directly west of his starting point, and heading in a northeasterly direction. What course has he been flying, and how far is he from the airport at A?

19. The mean distance of the planet Mars from the sun (center to center) is 1.524 Astronomical Units. One *Astronomical Unit* is the mean distance from the Earth to the sun, and is 92.9×10^6 mi. On a certain date it was observed that the line joining the Earth to Mars (center to center) made an angle of 59° 32′ with the line joining the Earth to the sun (center to center). How far was it from the Earth to Mars on that date?

15–6 Applications of the Law of Cosines. In Case C, as defined in Section 15–4, two sides and the included angle are known and the Law of Cosines may be used to find the third side. A second angle may be found by the Law of Sines (or by the Law of Cosines again as in Example 3). If the Law of Sines is used, there may be ambiguity regarding the angle. In general, *the order of magnitude of the angles of a triangle is the same as the order of magnitude of the sides*, the smallest angle being opposite the smallest side. Moreover, the two smallest angles in a triangle must be acute. Hence, we shall find the smaller of the two unknown angles, by finding the angle opposite the smaller of the corresponding sides, and are assured that this angle must be acute.

EXAMPLE 1. Solve the triangle ABC if $a = 4$, $b = 6$, $C = 60°$.

Solution. Using the Law of Cosines in the form

$$c^2 = a^2 + b^2 - 2ab\cos C,$$

we have

$$c^2 = 16 + 36 - 2(4)(6)(\tfrac{1}{2}) = 28, \qquad c = \sqrt{28} = 5.29.$$

Since A is the smaller of the unknown angles, we use the Law of Sines in the form

$$\sin A = \frac{a \sin C}{c},$$

and have

$$\sin A = \frac{4 \times 0.866}{5.29} = 0.6548, \qquad A = 41°.$$

Finally, $B = 180° - (60° + 41°) = 79°$.

The method of Example 1 for finding the third side of a triangle becomes rather involved if the given sides are four or five place numbers, and the angle is other than one of the special angles. For such cases another method, to which logarithms can be applied, will be developed in Section 15–7. There are times, however, when we are not concerned with obtaining a numerical value for the third side, but we wish to express that side as a function of the opposite angle.

EXAMPLE 2. Express the length of a chord of a circle as a function of the central angle θ.

Solution. Using the Law of Cosines, we have from Fig. 15–5,

$$\begin{aligned} c^2 &= r^2 + r^2 - 2r \cdot r \cos \theta \\ &= 2r^2 - 2r^2 \cos \theta \\ &= 2r^2(1 - \cos \theta), \end{aligned}$$

and

$$c = r\sqrt{2(1 - \cos \theta)}.$$

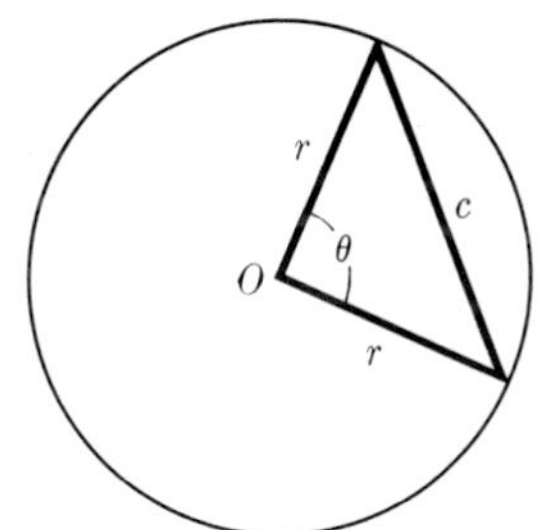

FIGURE 15–5

When the three sides of a triangle are known (Case D), an angle may be found with the formula obtained by solving one of the forms of the Law of Cosines for the cosine which appears.

EXAMPLE 3. Solve the triangle ABC if $a = 8$, $b = 17$, $c = 13$.

Solution. Equation (6) of Section 15–3 may be solved for $\cos A$ as

$$\cos A = \frac{b^2 + c^2 - a^2}{2bc}.$$

Then

$$\cos A = \frac{289 + 169 - 64}{2(17)(13)} = \frac{394}{442} = 0.8914, \qquad \text{and} \quad A = 27°.$$

Similarly,

$$\begin{aligned} \cos B &= \frac{a^2 + c^2 - b^2}{2ac} \\ &= \frac{64 + 169 - 289}{2(8)(13)} = -\frac{56}{208} = -0.2692, \quad \text{and} \quad B = 106°. \end{aligned}$$

Finally,

$$\begin{aligned} \cos C &= \frac{a^2 + b^2 - c^2}{2ab} \\ &= \frac{64 + 289 - 169}{2(8)(17)} = \frac{184}{272} = 0.6765, \qquad \text{and} \quad C = 47°. \end{aligned}$$

As a check, we verify that $A + B + C = 180°$.

Exercise Group 15–4

In Exercises 1–20, use the Law of Cosines to solve the triangle ABC having the given parts.

1. $a = 4.0,\ b = 5.0,\ C = 135^\circ$
2. $b = 6,\ c = 7,\ A = 60^\circ$
3. $a = 150,\ c = 320,\ B = 59^\circ\ 20'$
4. $a = 210,\ b = 430,\ C = 120^\circ$
5. $b = 10,\ c = 50,\ A = 150^\circ$
6. $a = 7.0,\ c = 24,\ B = 72^\circ$
7. $a = 21,\ b = 16,\ C = 132^\circ$
8. $b = 12,\ c = 31,\ A = 40^\circ$
9. $c = 0.12,\ a = 0.15,\ B = 29^\circ$
10. $a = 0.35,\ b = 0.13,\ C = 40^\circ$
11. $a = 2,\ b = 3,\ c = 4$
12. $a = 10,\ b = 8,\ c = 7$
13. $a = 12,\ b = 14,\ c = 16$
14. $a = 11,\ b = 13,\ c = 17$
15. $a = 2.0,\ b = 0.6,\ c = 1.5$
16. $a = 1.0,\ b = 1.6,\ c = 2.0$
17. $a = 0.7,\ b = 0.9,\ c = 1.0$
18. $a = 5,\ b = 8,\ c = 7$
19. $a = 1.3,\ b = 0.5,\ c = 1.0$
20. $a = 1.6,\ b = 1.1,\ c = 0.7$

21. The exact distance between two points A and B, which are on opposite sides of a building, is desired. A third point C is located so that AC is 130 ft and BC is 210 ft; the angle ACB is found to be $68^\circ\ 20'$. Compute distance AB.

22. A pilot desires to fly a heading of 220° at an airspeed of 100 mph. If the wind is blowing from the north at 17 mph, find the course and the groundspeed.

23. Two ships leave port at the same time; one sails on a course of 49° at a speed of 15 knots while the second sails on a course of 169° at a speed of 12 knots. How far apart are they after 3 hr and what is the direction from the first to the second?

24. Two forces F_1 and F_2 have magnitudes of 10 and 15 lb, respectively, and are directed in such a way that their resultant F_3 has a magnitude of 20 lb. Find the angles that the directions of the three forces make with each other.

25. Three airports A, B, and C are located so that A is 300 mi directly east of B, the distance AC is 250 mi, and the distance BC is 120 mi. What course would a plane fly in going from B to C? in going from C to A?

26. The adjacent sides of a parallelogram are 15 and 11 in., respectively, while the shorter diagonal is 13 in. What is the length of the longer diagonal? (Solve by using only the Law of Cosines.)

15–7 The Law of Tangents and the half-angle formulas. A disadvantage in the use of the Law of Cosines to solve a triangle in which two sides and the included angle are known is that this method does not lend itself well to logarithmic computation. Hence, if the numbers involved have more than three significant figures, the method is inefficient. On the other hand, the formulas to be developed here are particularly well adapted for use with logarithms.

Starting with the Law of Sines in the form

$$\frac{a}{b} = \frac{\sin A}{\sin B}, \tag{10}$$

we subtract 1 from each member, and have

$$\frac{a}{b} - 1 = \frac{\sin A}{\sin B} - 1,$$

so that

$$\frac{a-b}{b} = \frac{\sin A - \sin B}{\sin B}. \tag{11}$$

Similarly, by adding 1 to each member of (10), we obtain

$$\frac{a+b}{b} = \frac{\sin A + \sin B}{\sin B}. \tag{12}$$

Division of the members of (11) by the corresponding members of (12) gives

$$\frac{a-b}{a+b} = \frac{\sin A - \sin B}{\sin A + \sin B}.$$

Application of the factor formulas of Section 12–7 to the numerator and denominator of the right member yields

$$\frac{a-b}{a+b} = \frac{2 \sin \frac{1}{2}(A - B) \cos \frac{1}{2}(A + B)}{2 \sin \frac{1}{2}(A + B) \cos \frac{1}{2}(A - B)},$$

which becomes, upon dividing numerator and denominator of the fraction on the right by $\cos \frac{1}{2}(A - B) \cos \frac{1}{2}(A + B)$,

$$\boxed{\frac{a-b}{a+b} = \frac{\tan \frac{1}{2}(A - B)}{\tan \frac{1}{2}(A + B)}.} \tag{13}$$

Formula (13) is known as the *Law of Tangents.* Similar formulas can immediately be written involving a and c, or b and c.

In solving Case C by the Law of Tangents, formula (13) is used in the form involving the two known sides, let us say a and b. Then, since angle C is given, the sum $A + B$ can be found as $180° - C$, and (13) enables the finding of $A - B$. Then with the sum and difference of A and B known, the angles A and B themselves can be found. With the angles known, the third side can be found by the Law of Sines.

EXAMPLE 1. Solve the triangle ABC if

$$a = 18.32, \qquad b = 27.09, \qquad C = 58° 42'.$$

Solution. Since $a < b$, it is convenient to use the Law of Tangents in the form

$$\frac{b-a}{b+a} = \frac{\tan \frac{1}{2}(B - A)}{\tan \frac{1}{2}(B + A)}. \tag{14}$$

We have $B + A = 180° - C = 121° 18'$, and hence

$$\tfrac{1}{2}(B + A) = 60° 39'. \tag{15}$$

Furthermore, $b - a = 8.77$, $b + a = 45.41$. Solving (14) for $\tan \frac{1}{2}(B - A)$, and substituting the known values, we find

$$\tan \tfrac{1}{2}(B - A) = \frac{8.77 \tan 60° 39'}{45.41},$$

which yields the logarithmic equation

$$\log \tan \tfrac{1}{2}(B - A) = \log 8.77 + \log \tan 60° 39' - \log 45.41.$$

The logarithmic computation follows:

$$\begin{aligned} \log 8.77 &= 0.9430 \\ \log \tan 60° 39' &= 0.2500 \quad (+) \\ \log (\text{Num}) &= 11.1930 - 10 \\ \log 45.41 &= 1.6572 \quad (-) \\ \log \tan \tfrac{1}{2}(B - A) &= 9.5358 - 10 \end{aligned}$$

$$\tfrac{1}{2}(B - A) = 18° 57'. \tag{16}$$

Addition of (15) and (16) then gives $B = 79° 36'$, and subtraction of (16) from (15) gives $A = 41° 42'$. Side c may now be found by the Law of Sines as $c = 23.53$.

Formulas may be derived from the Law of Cosines which can be used to solve logarithmically a triangle in which the three sides are given (Case D). These formulas are expressed in terms of the *semiperimeter* s of the triangle; thus, we have

$$2s = a + b + c.$$

The following relations will be needed, and are easily verified:

$$b + c - a = 2(s - a), \qquad a - b + c = 2(s - b), \qquad a + b - c = 2(s - c). \tag{17}$$

We shall use the half-angle formulas (Section 12–6),

$$\sin \frac{A}{2} = \sqrt{\frac{1 - \cos A}{2}}, \qquad \cos \frac{A}{2} = \sqrt{\frac{1 + \cos A}{2}}, \tag{18}$$

with the positive values of the square roots taken since $A/2 < 90°$. From the Law of Cosines, we have (see Example 3 in Section 15–6)

$$\cos A = \frac{b^2 + c^2 - a^2}{2bc}.$$

Hence we find

$$1 - \cos A = 1 - \frac{b^2 + c^2 - a^2}{2bc} = \frac{a^2 - b^2 + 2bc - c^2}{2bc}$$

$$= \frac{a^2 - (b - c)^2}{2bc} = \frac{(a - b + c)(a + b - c)}{2bc}.$$

Applying (17) here, we obtain

$$1 - \cos A = \frac{2(s - b) \cdot 2(s - c)}{2bc},$$

which, with (18), gives

$$\sin \frac{A}{2} = \sqrt{\frac{(s - b)(s - c)}{bc}}. \tag{19}$$

An entirely similar procedure gives

$$\cos \frac{A}{2} = \sqrt{\frac{s(s - a)}{bc}}. \tag{20}$$

Division of $\sin A/2$ by $\cos A/2$ then yields

$$\tan \frac{A}{2} = \sqrt{\frac{(s - b)(s - c)}{s(s - a)}},$$

which can be expressed in the form

$$\tan \frac{A}{2} = \frac{1}{s - a}\sqrt{\frac{(s - a)(s - b)(s - c)}{s}}. \tag{21}$$

Formulas (19), (20), and (21), together with the corresponding ones for angles B and C, are the *half-angle formulas* for a triangle. Let r be the radius of the circle inscribed in triangle ABC. It can be shown (see Exercise 31 in Exercise Group 15-5) that

$$\boxed{r = \sqrt{\frac{(s - a)(s - b)(s - c)}{s}}.} \tag{22}$$

The half-angle formulas for the tangent may now be written in the form

$$\boxed{\tan \frac{A}{2} = \frac{r}{s - a}, \quad \tan \frac{B}{2} = \frac{r}{s - b}, \quad \tan \frac{C}{2} = \frac{r}{s - c}.} \tag{23}$$

Whenever three sides of a triangle are known, the half-angle formulas may be used to find any or all angles. Formulas (23), in conjunction with (22), will generally be found to be the most useful for this purpose.

EXAMPLE 2. Solve the triangle ABC if

$$a = 103.2, \qquad b = 97.40, \qquad c = 158.8.$$

Solution. The semiperimeter of the triangle is

$$s = \tfrac{1}{2}(a + b + c) = 179.7.$$

From (22) we obtain, with the appropriate numbers,

$$\log r = \tfrac{1}{2}(\log 76.5 + \log 82.3 + \log 20.9 - \log 179.7).$$

To compute $\log r$ we have

$$\begin{aligned} \log 76.5 &= 1.8837 \\ \log 82.3 &= 1.9154 \quad (+) \\ \log 20.9 &= \underline{1.3201} \\ & 5.1192 \\ \log 179.7 &= \underline{2.2546} \quad (-) \\ \log r^2 &= 2.8646 \quad (\div 2) \\ \log r &= 1.4323. \end{aligned}$$

The value of r itself is not required. From (23) we find

$$\log \tan \frac{A}{2} = \log r - \log (s - a),$$

and similar equations involving $B/2$ and $C/2$. The computation follows:

$$\begin{aligned} \log r &= 1.4323 \\ \log 76.5 &= \underline{1.8837} \quad (-) \\ \log \tan A/2 &= 9.5486 - 10 \\ A/2 &= 19^\circ\, 29' \\ A &= 38^\circ\, 58' \end{aligned} \qquad \begin{aligned} \log r &= 1.4323 \\ \log 82.3 &= \underline{1.9154} \quad (-) \\ \log \tan B/2 &= 9.5169 - 10 \\ B/2 &= 18^\circ\, 12' \\ B &= 36^\circ\, 24' \end{aligned}$$

$$\begin{aligned} \log r &= 1.4323 \\ \log 20.9 &= \underline{1.3201} \quad (-) \\ \log \tan C/2 &= 0.1122 \\ C/2 &= 52^\circ\, 19' \\ C &= 104^\circ\, 38'. \end{aligned}$$

It should be noted that the third angle can be found very simply after two angles are found. However, very little additional work is required to obtain the third angle as was done above, and a check is provided for the computation by verifying that $A + B + C = 180^\circ$.

Exercise Group 15-5

In Exercises 1-20, solve the triangle ABC with the given parts.

1. $a = 123.4$, $b = 234.5$, $C = 125° 13'$
2. $b = 23.14$, $c = 34.52$, $A = 73° 46'$
3. $a = 2.936$, $b = 4.389$, $C = 42° 12'$
4. $b = 834.1$, $c = 542.6$, $A = 69° 31'$
5. $c = 0.2345$, $a = 0.3426$, $B = 123° 14'$
6. $a = 0.03176$, $b = 0.02347$, $C = 137° 43'$
7. $b = 23.92$, $c = 31.86$, $A = 143° 15'$
8. $c = 42830$, $a = 213900$, $B = 86° 19'$
9. $c = 834900$, $b = 316500$, $A = 95° 16'$
10. $b = 0.3174$, $a = 0.2143$, $C = 78° 43'$
11. $a = 1342$, $b = 3412$, $c = 4123$
12. $a = 1423$, $b = 1235$, $c = 2341$
13. $a = 231.4$, $b = 314.2$, $c = 412.0$
14. $a = 43.12$, $b = 31.24$, $c = 42.13$
15. $a = 0.01234$, $b = 0.003461$, $c = 0.008943$
16. $a = 0.03216$, $b = 0.05264$, $c = 0.02437$
17. $a = 0.3198$, $b = 0.5176$, $c = 0.2352$
18. $a = 0.3128$, $b = 0.4936$, $c = 0.2545$
19. $a = 4.791$, $b = 3.969$, $c = 4.015$
20. $a = 6.392$, $b = 5.947$, $c = 4.932$

21. A pilot must fly from A to B, which is a distance of 300 mi in the direction $S\ 23° 31'\ E$. The wind is blowing from the west at 25 mph. Find the heading and the average airspeed the pilot must maintain to complete the trip in exactly 2 hr.

22. Find the resultant F_3 of two forces F_1 and F_2, if the magnitude of F_1 is 175.8 lb and its direction is horizontal, while the magnitude of F_2 is 217.3 lb and its direction makes an angle of 43° 12′ with the direction of F_1.

23. A force F_1 has a magnitude of 216.2 lb and is directed vertically. A second force F_2 has a magnitude of 163.8 lb and its direction makes an angle of 144° 43′ with the direction of F_1. Find the magnitude and direction of the resultant F_3 of the two forces F_1 and F_2.

24. An aircraft carrier is steaming at 25 knots on a course of 119° 28′ and continues on this course at the given speed. An airplane takes off and flies on a course of 352° 30′ at a speed of 300 nautical miles per hour. How far is the plane from the carrier after 2 hr, and what is the direction from the plane to the carrier?

25. It is desired to find the distance between two points A and B as accurately as possible. The two points are on opposite sides of a small body of water. A third point C is located so that angle ACB is 72° 18′, and the distances AC and BC are measured and found to be 492.3 ft and 348.6 ft, respectively. Compute the distance AB as accurately as the data justify.

26. Two forces F_1 and F_2 are applied at the same point and have magnitudes of 523 lb and 216 lb, respectively. Their resultant has a magnitude of 417 lb. Find the directions of the force F_2 and the resultant with respect to F_1.

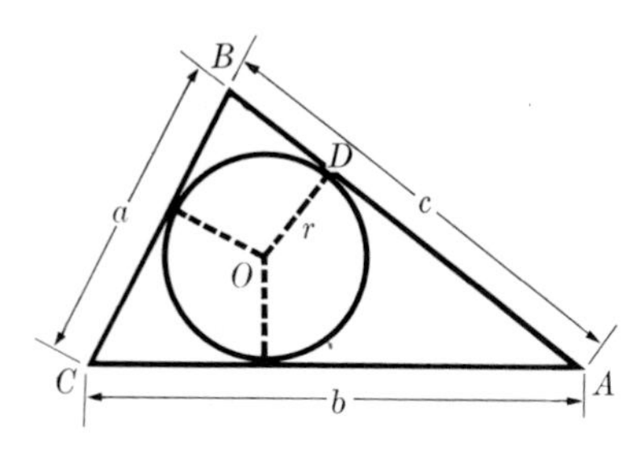

FIGURE 15–6

27. B is 1392 mi directly east of A, and C is north of the line joining A and B. The distance from A to C is 895.5 mi, and the distance from B to C is 756 mi. Find the direction from A to C, and also from B to C.

28. An airplane maintains an airspeed of 300 mph and a course of 180°. There is a northwesterly wind of 25 mph, and the plane has an average groundspeed of 317 mph. What heading does the plane fly, and what is the exact direction of the wind?

29. An airplane takes off from an airfield A and flies in a northeasterly direction with an average groundspeed of 176.4 mph. At the same instant a second plane takes off from an airfield B, which is 300 mi due east of A, and flies in a northwesterly direction with an average groundspeed of 217.3 mph. If they meet one hour and ten minutes after taking off, find the course each was flying.

30. Three friends A, B, and C have their own airplanes and plan to meet at a point equidistant from all three. A lives 1200 mi due east of B; C lives north of the line joining A and B, and is 800 mi from A and 1000 mi from B. What is the direction each must fly to reach the point agreed upon?

31. In Fig. 15–6, $\tan A/2 = r/AD$, where r is the radius of the inscribed circle. Show that $AD = s - a$. Then use formula (21) to derive the expression for r in formula (22).

15–8 Area of a triangle. The basic theorem from plane geometry on the area of a triangle states: *The area of a triangle is equal to one-half the product of any side of the triangle and the altitude drawn to that side.* With this result several different formulas may be obtained for the area of a triangle, each being particularly suited to one of the cases of the oblique triangle. We shall use the letter K to denote the area.

Referring to Fig. 15–1 of Section 15–2, we see that in either triangle the length of the altitude h is given by $h = c \sin A$. Hence, since $K = \frac{1}{2}bh$, we have

$$\boxed{K = \tfrac{1}{2}bc \sin A.} \tag{24}$$

Similar formulas involving the other angles of the triangle may be written at once. In words, the formula becomes: *The area of a triangle is equal to one-half the product of any two sides and the sine of the included angle.* This statement indicates the applicability of formula (24) to Case C.

We may derive a second formula for K as follows. By the Law of Sines we have

$$\frac{b}{c} = \frac{\sin B}{\sin C}, \qquad \text{and} \qquad b = \frac{c \sin B}{\sin C}.$$

Substitution of the latter in (24) gives the formula

$$\boxed{K = \frac{1}{2}\frac{c^2 \sin A \sin B}{\sin C}.} \tag{25}$$

Whenever two angles of a triangle are known, the third angle can be found directly. Hence, formula (25), or one of the two other similar forms, applies to Case A.

Finally, we obtain a formula for K in terms of the sides a, b, c. In Fig. 15–6, in which r is the radius of the inscribed circle, the area of triangle BOC is $\frac{1}{2}ra$, the area of AOC is $\frac{1}{2}rb$, and the area of AOB is $\frac{1}{2}rc$. Hence, the area K of triangle ABC is

$$K = \tfrac{1}{2}ra + \tfrac{1}{2}rb + \tfrac{1}{2}rc = r[\tfrac{1}{2}(a + b + c)],$$

or,

$$\boxed{K = rs,} \tag{26}$$

where s is the semiperimeter, and the value of r is given by (22).

Example 1. Find the area of triangle ABC if

$$A = 23^\circ\,09', \qquad B = 108^\circ\,43', \qquad c = 123.2.$$

Solution. We find $C = 48^\circ\,08'$. Then by formula (25) we have

$$K = \frac{1}{2}\frac{(123.2)^2 \sin 23^\circ\,09' \sin 108^\circ\,43'}{\sin 48^\circ\,08'}.$$

Logarithmic computation is well suited to this expression, and gives the value $K = 15180$.

Example 2. Find the area of the triangle ABC if

$$a = 4, \qquad b = 6, \qquad C = 120^\circ.$$

Solution. The area of the triangle is found from the formula

$$K = \tfrac{1}{2}ab \sin C$$

to be

$$K = \tfrac{1}{2}(4)(6) \sin 120° = \tfrac{1}{2}(4)(6)\left(\frac{\sqrt{3}}{2}\right) = 6\sqrt{3}.$$

EXAMPLE 3. Find the area of the triangle ABC if

$$a = 103.2, \qquad b = 97.40, \qquad c = 158.8.$$

Solution. This is the triangle in Example 2 of Section 15–7, where the values of $\log r$ and $\log s$ were found to be

$$\log r = 1.4323, \qquad \log s = 2.2546.$$

From (26) we obtain the relation

$$\log K = \log r + \log s.$$

We then find

$$\log K = 1.4323 + 2.2546 = 3.6869, \qquad K = 4863.$$

EXERCISE GROUP 15–6

In Exercises 1–16, find the area of the triangle having the given parts.

1. $A = 26° 32'$, $C = 43° 16'$, $b = 23.41$
2. $C = 132° 13'$, $B = 24° 19'$, $a = 0.01356$
3. $A = 38° 42'$, $B = 97° 13'$, $c = 31.76$
4. $B = 23° 16'$, $A = 59° 35'$, $c = 0.8914$
5. $c = 0.09826$, $a = 0.2346$, $A = 64° 34'$
6. $a = 263$, $b = 319$, $A = 43°$
7. $b = 0.03396$, $c = 0.03147$, $B = 68° 17'$
8. $c = 283.1$, $b = 136.5$, $C = 97° 33'$
9. $a = 2.936$, $b = 4.389$, $C = 42° 12'$
10. $c = 0.2345$, $a = 0.3426$, $B = 123° 14'$
11. $b = 0.2834$, $c = 0.8293$, $A = 97° 38'$
12. $c = 8.391$, $b = 91.73$, $A = 13° 14'$
13. $a = 0.3198$, $b = 0.5176$, $c = 0.2352$
14. $a = 4.791$, $b = 3.969$, $c = 4.015$
15. $a = 83.46$, $b = 38.64$, $c = 62.79$
16. $a = 39.77$, $b = 183.2$, $c = 158.1$

17. Two sides of a parallelogram are 2.143 in. and 4.261 in., and the longer diagonal is 5.316 in. Find the area of the parallelogram.

18. A triangular lot has frontages of 87 ft and 147 ft on two streets which intersect at an angle of 96°. Find the area of the lot.

19. A triangular park has frontages of 697 ft, 493 ft, and 562 ft on the three streets which bound it. Find the area of the park.

20. Find the area of a regular pentagon (five equal sides and five equal angles), the length of a side being 43.26 ft.

21. Three points A, B, and C are located so that the distance AB is 30 ft, angle CAB is 70°, and angle ABC is 80°. Find the area of triangle ABC.

22. Find the area of a regular hexagon (six equal sides and six equal angles), which is inscribed in a circle of radius 21.43 in.

23. A triangular field has an area of 10 acres (435,600 ft^2). The longest side runs along a river and needs no fence. How much fence will be required for the other two sides if the angles at the vertices of the field are 31°, 68°, and 81°?

24. A quadrangular plot of ground has two sides of 62.83 ft and 132.8 ft which are perpendicular to each other. The other sides have lengths of 83.72 ft and 139.5 ft. Find the area of the plot.

CHAPTER 16

COMPLEX NUMBERS

16–1 Introduction. Complex numbers were introduced and treated briefly in Section 4–11. In the present chapter we undertake a more systematic treatment of this topic.

The need for complex numbers arises when the attempt is made, in the study of algebra, to solve certain quadratic equations, such as the equation

$$x^2 + x + 1 = 0.$$

When a solution is attempted, it becomes evident that the system of real numbers is inadequate. An extension of the real number system, by the addition of complex numbers as defined below, then provides a system of numbers sufficient for the purposes of algebra. Complex numbers, as they will be defined, include the real numbers, and the definitions of addition, subtraction, multiplication, and division, for complex numbers will be such that they will generalize the corresponding ones for real numbers.

DEFINITION 16–1. *A complex number is any number of the form $a + bi$, where a and b are real numbers and i is a number such that $i^2 = -1$. The number a is called the real part of the complex number, and b is called the imaginary part.*

For example, $2 - 3i$ is a complex number with $a = 2$ as the real part, and $b = -3$ as the imaginary part. A number such as $-2i$, with real part zero, is called a *pure imaginary* number. Any real number can be considered a complex number with imaginary part zero.

DEFINITION 16–2. *A complex number $a + bi$ is zero if and only if $a = 0$ and $b = 0$, that is, if and only if the real part and the imaginary part are both zero.*

DEFINITION 16–3. *Two complex numbers $a_1 + b_1i$ and $a_2 + b_2i$ are equal if and only if $a_1 = a_2$ and $b_1 = b_2$, that is, if and only if the real parts are equal and the imaginary parts are equal.*

EXAMPLE 1. Find the values of x and y if

$$(x + 3y - 1) + (2x - y)i = 0.$$

Solution. By Definition 16–2 we must have

$$x + 3y - 1 = 0, \qquad 2x - y = 0.$$

The solution of this pair of simultaneous linear equations gives the desired values $x = \frac{1}{7}$, $y = \frac{2}{7}$.

EXAMPLE 2. Solve for x and y if

$$(x^2 - y) + (2x - y)i = (y - x) + i.$$

Solution. By Definition 16–3, we must have

$$x^2 - y = y - x,$$
$$2x - y = 1.$$

Substitution in the first equation of the value $y = 2x - 1$, as obtained from the second equation, yields the quadratic equation

$$x^2 - 3x + 2 = 0.$$

The solution of this equation gives $x = 1$ or 2; the corresponding values of y may be obtained from the second of the above pair of equations as $y = 1$ when $x = 1$, and $y = 3$ when $x = 2$. The two solutions are then $x = 1$, $y = 1$, and $x = 2$, $y = 3$.

16–2 Graphical representation of complex numbers. The points of a rectangular Cartesian coordinate system may be used to represent graphically any concept defined by a pair of real numbers. In particular, a complex number $a + bi$ depends on two real numbers a and b, and may be represented in this manner. Accordingly, *we shall represent the complex number $a + bi$ by the point P with abscissa a and ordinate b.* It follows at once that a real number is represented by a point on the x-axis, and a pure imaginary number by a point on the y-axis. It is helpful and instructive to represent the number $a + bi$ at times also by the vector $\overline{OP}$ (see Fig. 16–1), directed from the origin to the point (a, b). We shall use both the *vector and point representations* of a complex number as thus defined.

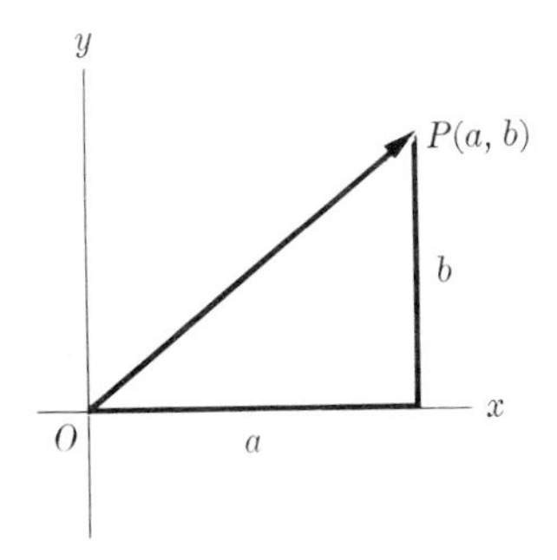

FIGURE 16–1

DEFINITION 16–4. *The conjugate of the complex number $a + bi$ is defined as the complex number $a - bi$.*

It is clear that the conjugate of $a - bi$ is then $a - (-b)i = a + bi$. Hence two conjugate complex numbers differ only in the signs of their imaginary parts. Since the imaginary part of a complex number is the y-coordinate of its point representation, two conjugate complex numbers are the images of each other in the x-axis. For example, $-1 + 2i$ and $-1 - 2i$ are conjugate complex numbers; each is the image of the other in the x-axis, with the first point in Q_2 and the second point in Q_3.

DEFINITION 16–5. *The absolute value or modulus of the complex number $a + bi$ is the length of the vector $\overline{OP}$ in Fig.* 16–1, *or the polar distance of P.*

We shall denote the modulus of $a + bi$ by $|a + bi|$ or by r. It is then clear from the figure, with the use of the Pythagorean Theorem, that

$$\boxed{r = |a + bi| = \sqrt{a^2 + b^2},} \tag{1}$$

for any complex number. It follows from (1) that *the modulus of a complex number is always positive, or zero.*

DEFINITION 16–6. *The amplitude or argument of the complex number $a + bi$ is the angle that OP in Fig.* 16–1 *makes with the positive x-axis.*

We shall denote the argument of $a + bi$ by $\arg (a + bi)$, and usually by θ. It follows that

$$\boxed{\theta = \arg (a + bi) = \arctan b/a = \arcsin b/r,} \tag{2}$$

the two latter expressions being given in order to specify the correct quadrant for the angle θ.

EXAMPLE. Find the modulus and argument of the complex number $1 - \sqrt{3}\, i$.

Solution. By (1) we have, for the modulus,

$$r = |1 - \sqrt{3}\, i| = \sqrt{1 + (-\sqrt{3})^2} = \sqrt{1 + 3} = 2,$$

and by (2) the argument is

$$\theta = \arg (1 - \sqrt{3}\, i) = \arctan (-\sqrt{3}) = \arcsin (-\sqrt{3}/2).$$

Since $\tan \theta < 0$ and $\sin \theta < 0$, the argument θ must be an angle in Q_4, and one value is 300°. Another possible value is −60°.

It follows from Definition 16–6 that the argument of a complex number is infinitely many-valued; in fact, *the difference between any two arguments of the same complex number is a multiple of* $360°$ *or of* 2π.

Exercise Group 16–1

In Exercises 1–16, plot the point that represents the complex number, and the point that represents its conjugate. Draw the vectors that represent the number and its conjugate.

1. $5 + 12i$ 2. $3 - 4i$ 3. $24 - 7i$ 4. $-24 + 7i$
5. $-5 - 12i$ 6. $12 - 5i$ 7. $3i$ 8. 4
9. $-5i$ 10. -6 11. $-12 + 5i$ 12. $-7 - 24i$
13. $-1 + i\sqrt{3}$ 14. $3 - 3i$ 15. $\frac{5}{2}(\sqrt{3} + i)$ 16. $4(\frac{1}{3} + i)$

Find the modulus and the argument of the complex number, and also of its conjugate, in each of Exercises 17–36.

17. $\sqrt{3} + i$ 18. $1 + i$ 19. $1 - \sqrt{3}\,i$ 20. $-1 + \sqrt{3}\,i$
21. $-1 - i$ 22. 3 23. $4i$ 24. $-3i$
25. -7 26. $-5 - 5i$ 27. $-\sqrt{3} - 3i$ 28. $-2\sqrt{3} + 6i$
29. $5 + 7i$ 30. $-8 + 5i$ 31. $0.5 - \frac{1}{2}\sqrt{3}\,i$ 32. $1.2 + 0.5i$
33. $3(\cos 135° + i \sin 135°)$ 34. $4(\sin 30° + i \sin 30°)$
35. $0.7 - 2.4i$ 36. $\cos(-17°) + i \sin(-17°)$

In each of Exercises 37–45, determine the values of x and y for which the statement is true.

37. $3 + 4i = 2x + 5 - yi$ 38. $xi - 4y = 7 - 5i$
39. $2x + 3 = (y + 3)i$ 40. $2 + 3ax = 5bi - 2yi$
41. $(a - y) + (b - x)i = 0$ 42. $(7a + cy) - (5d - bx)i = 0$
43. $7a - 5di = bxi - cy$ 44. $3a - 2x = (4b - 5y)i$
45. $2xi + 3 = (y + 3)i + 2y$

46. Prove that the absolute values of two conjugate complex numbers are equal.

16–3 Addition and subtraction of complex numbers. The algebraic addition of complex numbers involves the addition of the real parts and the imaginary parts of the numbers, respectively.

Definition 16–7. $(a + bi) \pm (c + di)$ *is defined as the complex number* $(a \pm c) + (b \pm d)i$.

Thus, the real part of the sum is equal to the sum of the real parts of the numbers, and the imaginary part of the sum is equal to the sum of the imaginary parts of the numbers. Moreover, if the numbers are real, so that $b = d = 0$, the sum is $a + c$ and the difference is $a - c$.

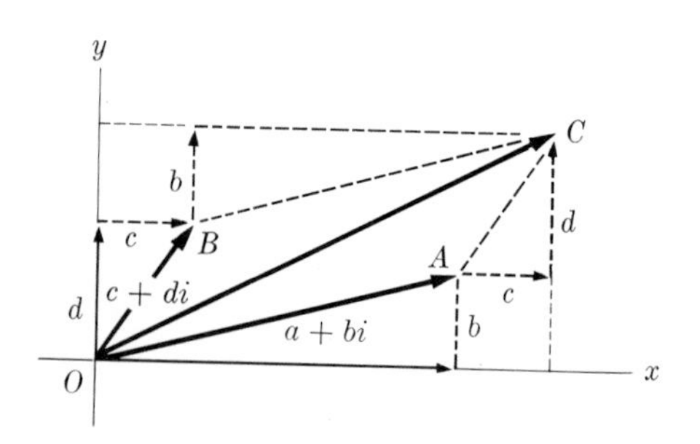

FIGURE 16–2

EXAMPLE 1. Determine the sum and difference of the complex numbers $3 + 2i$ and $5 + i$.

Solution. From the above definition we have

for the sum: $(3 + 2i) + (5 + i) = (3 + 5) + (2 + 1)i = 8 + 3i;$
for the difference: $(3 + 2i) - (5 + i) = (3 - 5) + (2 - 1)i = -2 + i.$

In the graphical representation of complex numbers, as defined in Section 16–2, an interesting interpretation of addition and subtraction arises. By Definition 16–7, the real part of the sum of $a + bi$ and $c + di$ is $a + c$, while the imaginary part is $b + d$. On the other hand, if $\overline{OC}$ is the diagonal of the parallelogram $OACB$ in Fig. 16–2, it follows that $a + c$ is the abscissa of C and $b + d$ is the ordinate. Since $\overline{OC}$ is the sum of the vectors $\overline{OA}$ and $\overline{OB}$, we conclude that *the sum of the complex numbers $a + bi$ and $c + di$ can be represented by the vector sum of the vectors $a + bi$ and $c + di$ as defined in Section* 9–7.

The negative of a vector is given by a vector with the same length and opposite direction. *The difference of two complex numbers is then given graphically by the sum of the first vector and the negative of the second vector.*

EXAMPLE 2. Find the sum and difference of the numbers $3 + 2i$ and $5 + i$ graphically.

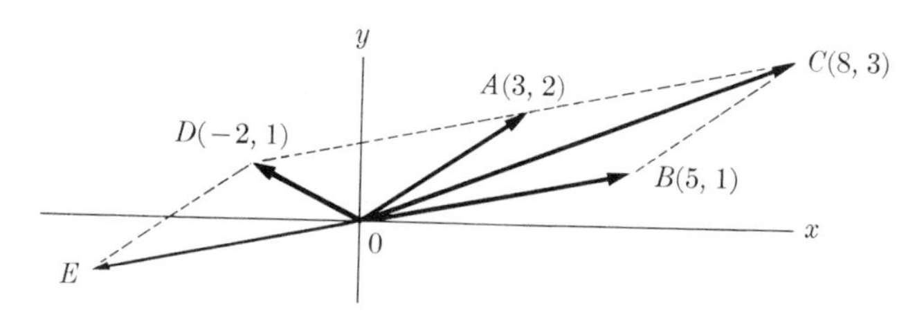

FIGURE 16–3

Solution. In Fig. 16–3 the vector $\overline{OA}$ represents the number $3 + 2i$, and $\overline{OB}$ represents $5 + i$. The sum of these vectors is given by $\overline{OC}$, which is seen to be the complex number $8 + 3i$.

The difference $(3 + 2i) - (5 + i)$ is given by $\overline{OA} + (-\overline{OB}) = \overline{OA} + \overline{OE}$, which is the vector $\overline{OD}$, or $-2 + i$.

Exercise Group 16–2

In each of Exercises 1–20, find the complex number which is equal to the sum of the given complex numbers, and find also the complex number which is the first given number minus the second. Work each exercise both graphically and algebraically.

1. $3 + 4i,\ 5 + 12i$
2. $3 - 4i,\ -5 + 12i$
3. $-4i,\ -12 + 5i$
4. $-5,\ 12 - 5i$
5. $(3 - 2i) + (4 - 2i),\ 5 - 4i$
6. $-2 - 3i,\ -3 + 4i$
7. $(2 + 3i) + (-5 - i),\ 3 + 2i$
8. $3 - 2i,\ (1 - 2i) - (3 + i)$
9. $1 + 2i,\ (3 + 4i) + (5 - 6i)$
10. $(1 + 2i) + 3,\ 4i - (5 + 6i)$
11. $(2 + 3i) + (2 - 3i),\ 4 - 5i$
12. $(2 + 3i) - (2 - 3i),\ 5 - 4i$
13. $(3 - 2i) + (4 + 2i),\ 5 - 4i$
14. $2 - 3i,\ (4 - 5i) - (3 + 4i)$
15. $-1 + \dfrac{i\sqrt{3}}{2},\ 3\sqrt{3} + 3i$
16. $3 - 4i,\ -5 + 5i$
17. $\frac{1}{2}(3 + 4i\sqrt{3}),\ -5i$
18. $\frac{5}{2}(-1 + i\sqrt{3}),\ -\frac{7}{2}(1 + i\sqrt{3})$

16–4 Trigonometric form of complex numbers. From Fig. 16–4, and similar ones with θ in different quadrants, or simply from the definitions of $\cos\theta$ and $\sin\theta$ as given in Section 6–6, we find

$$a = r\cos\theta, \qquad b = r\sin\theta,$$

where r is the absolute value, and θ is the argument of $a + bi$. Hence, for the complex number $a + bi$ we have

$$a + bi = r\cos\theta + (r\sin\theta)i = r(\cos\theta + i\sin\theta).$$

Definition 16–8. *The expression $r(\cos\theta + i\sin\theta)$, where r is the absolute value and θ is the amplitude of a complex number, is called the trigonometric form of that number.*

Thus, any complex number can be written in trigonometric form, and in this form the angle θ is of course subject to the multiple-valuedness of the amplitude. At times a particular choice of θ may be more convenient than others, but any choice may be used in writing the trigonometric form.

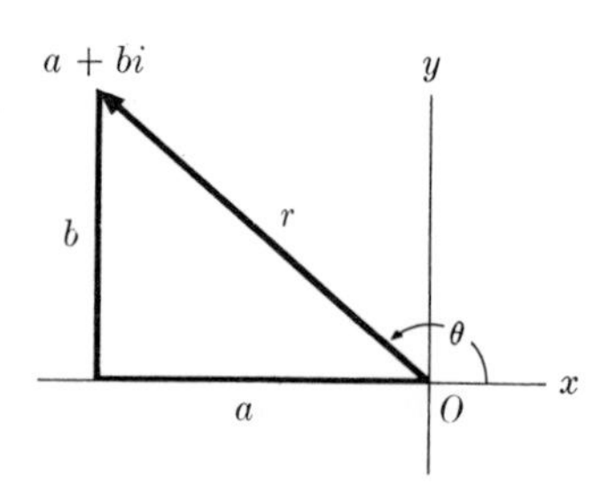

FIGURE 16–4

EXAMPLE 1. Write the number $1 - \sqrt{3}\,i$ in trigonometric form.

Solution. In the example of Section 16–2 we found for the given number that $r = 2$, $\theta = 300°$. One trigonometric form of the number is then

$$1 - \sqrt{3}\,i = 2(\cos 300° + i \sin 300°).$$

Note that the trigonometric form of a complex number is essentially in the form $a + bi$. Thus in the example, the real part is $a = 2 \cos 300° = 1$, and the imaginary part is $b = 2 \sin 300° = -\sqrt{3}$.

EXAMPLE 2. Express the number $2(\cos 10° + i \sin 20°)$ in trigonometric form.

Solution. The number as given is not in trigonometric form because different angles appear. From the table of natural functions we find

$$2(\cos 10° + i \sin 20°) = 2(0.9848 + 0.3420i) = 1.9696 + 0.6840i.$$

To find r we use Eq. (1) and have

$$r = \sqrt{(1.9696)^2 + (0.6840)^2} = \sqrt{4.3472} = 2.0850.$$

For the amplitude θ we have

$$\theta = \arctan \frac{0.6840}{1.9696} = \arctan 0.3473 = 19°\,09',$$

so that the trigonometric form of the number is actually

$$2.0850(\cos 19°\,09' + i \sin 19°\,09').$$

EXAMPLE 3. Express the number $3(\cos 120° - i \sin 120°)$ in trigonometric form.

Solution. The given number is not in trigonometric form because of the minus sign. The real part is $3 \cos 120°$ and the imaginary part is $-3 \sin 120°$.

The modulus is then

$$r = \sqrt{9 \cos^2 120° + 9 \sin^2 120°} = 3,$$

and for the amplitude θ we have

$$\theta = \arctan\left(\frac{-3 \sin 120°}{3 \cos 120°}\right) = \arctan(-\tan 120°) = 240°,$$

since an angle in Q_3 is required. The desired form is then

$$3(\cos 120° - i \sin 120°) = 3(\cos 240° + i \sin 240°).$$

Exercise Group 16–3

Express the number in each of Exercises 1–20 in trigonometric form.

1. $1 + i$
2. $1 + \sqrt{3}\, i$
3. $1 - i$
4. $\sqrt{3} - i$
5. $-1 + i$
6. $-3 + \sqrt{3}\, i$
7. $-2 - 2i$
8. $-\sqrt{3} + i$
9. 2
10. $-5i$
11. $1.2 + 0.5i$
12. $3 + 4i$
13. $\cos 182° + i \sin 358°$
14. $10(\cos 293° 40' - i \sin 293° 40')$
15. $5(-\cos 25° 35' + i \sin 25° 35')$
16. $0.7 - 2.4i$
17. $-1.2 + 0.5i$
18. $5 - 12i$
19. $-24 + 7i$
20. $-7 - i\sqrt{15}$

16–5 Multiplication and division of complex numbers. The operations of multiplication and division of complex numbers are defined in terms of the corresponding ones for real numbers, and in such a way that if the complex numbers are real, the definitions reduce to those for real numbers.

Definition 16–9. *The product of $a + bi$ and $c + di$ is defined as the complex number $(ac - bd) + (bc + ad)i$.*

The value of the product given in this definition is equal to the direct product of the complex numbers $a + bi$ and $c + di$ by the rules for real numbers, with simplification of the result by use of the relation $i^2 = -1$. This statement indicates the procedure usually used for multiplying complex numbers.

Example 1. Determine the product $(2 + 3i)(3 + 5i)$.

Solution. Direct multiplication gives

$$6 + 9i + 10i + 15i^2 = 6 + 19i - 15 = -9 + 19i,$$

which is also in accord with the definition.

DEFINITION 16–10. *The quotient* $(a + bi) \div (c + di)$ *is defined as*

$$\frac{a + bi}{c + di} = \frac{(ac + bd) + (bc - ad)i}{c^2 + d^2}.$$

This definition is equivalent to multiplying numerator and denominator of the fraction on the left by $c - di$, and simplifying.

EXAMPLE 2. Reduce the quotient $(2 + 3i) \div (3 + 5i)$ to a complex number of the form $a + bi$.

Solution. Writing the quotient as a fraction, and multiplying numerator and denominator of the fraction by $3 - 5i$, which is the conjugate of the denominator, we have

$$\frac{2 + 3i}{3 + 5i} = \frac{2 + 3i}{3 + 5i} \cdot \frac{3 - 5i}{3 - 5i} = \frac{6 + 9i - 10i - 15i^2}{9 + 25}$$
$$= \frac{21 - i}{34} = \frac{21}{34} + \frac{-1}{34} i.$$

Multiplication and division of complex numbers become very simple for numbers in trigonometric form. In fact, this simplicity accounts for much of the advantage in using the trigonometric form. Thus, we have for the product of two complex numbers in trigonometric form,

$$r_1(\cos \theta_1 + i \sin \theta_1) \cdot r_2(\cos \theta_2 + i \sin \theta_2)$$
$$= r_1 r_2[(\cos \theta_1 \cos \theta_2 - \sin \theta_1 \sin \theta_2) + i(\sin \theta_1 \cos \theta_2 + \cos \theta_1 \sin \theta_2)].$$

We may apply the addition formulas (11) and (10) of Section 12–3 to the quantities in parentheses, and obtain

$$r_1(\cos \theta_1 + i \sin \theta_1) \cdot r_2(\cos \theta_2 + i \sin \theta_2) = r_1 r_2[\cos (\theta_1 + \theta_2) + i \sin (\theta_1 + \theta_2)]. \tag{3}$$

Hence, *the product of two complex numbers is a complex number whose absolute value is the product of the two absolute values, and for which an amplitude is the sum of the two amplitudes.*

Similarly, we have for the division of two complex numbers in trigonometric form

$$\frac{r_1(\cos \theta_1 + i \sin \theta_1)}{r_2(\cos \theta_2 + i \sin \theta_2)} = \frac{r_1(\cos \theta_1 + i \sin \theta_1)}{r_2(\cos \theta_2 + i \sin \theta_2)} \cdot \frac{(\cos \theta_2 - i \sin \theta_2)}{(\cos \theta_2 - i \sin \theta_2)}$$
$$= \frac{r_1}{r_2} \cdot \frac{(\cos \theta_1 \cos \theta_2 + \sin \theta_1 \sin \theta_2) + i\,(\sin \theta_1 \cos \theta_2 - \cos \theta_1 \sin \theta_2)}{\cos^2 \theta_2 + \sin^2 \theta_2}.$$

If we apply to this expression the appropriate addition formulas of Section 12–3 and the squares identity (7) of Section 12–1, we obtain

$$\frac{r_1(\cos\theta_1 + i\sin\theta_1)}{r_2(\cos\theta_2 + i\sin\theta_2)} = \frac{r_1}{r_2}[\cos(\theta_1 - \theta_2) + i\sin(\theta_1 - \theta_2)].$$

Thus, *the quotient of one complex number by another is a complex number whose absolute value is the quotient of the two absolute values in the same order, and for which an amplitude is the amplitude of the dividend minus the amplitude of the divisor.*

EXAMPLE 3. Use the trigonometric form in finding the product of the numbers $1 - \sqrt{3}\,i$ and $1 + i$, and the quotient of the first by the second.

Solution. The trigonometric forms of these numbers are found to be $1 - \sqrt{3}\,i = 2(\cos 300° + i\sin 300°)$, $1 + i = \sqrt{2}(\cos 45° + i\sin 45°)$. The above rules then give

$$\begin{aligned}(1 - \sqrt{3}\,i)(1 + i) &= 2(\cos 300° + i\sin 300°)\cdot\sqrt{2}(\cos 45° + i\sin 45°)\\ &= 2\sqrt{2}(\cos 345° + i\sin 345°);\end{aligned}$$

$$\frac{1 - \sqrt{3}\,i}{1 + i} = \frac{2(\cos 300° + i\sin 300°)}{\sqrt{2}(\cos 45° + i\sin 45°)} = \sqrt{2}(\cos 255° + i\sin 255°).$$

These results can, if necessary, be continued further by substituting the values of the trigonometric functions which appear.

EXERCISE GROUP 16–4

Perform the indicated operation in each of Exercises 1–17.

1. $(3 + 4i)(5 - 12i)$
2. $(i - 1)(3 + 7i)$
3. $i^2(6 - 8i)(i^7 + i^8)$
4. $i^3(-8i^3 + 6i^2)$
5. $(15i^2 - 5i^3)(2 + i^5)$
6. $(i^5 - i^8)(i^3 + i^{10})$
7. $(i - 2)^2(1 + 3i)$
8. $(2 + 3i)^2(3 - 2i)^2$
9. $(-3 + i\sqrt{3})^2(\sqrt{3} - i)^2$
10. $\dfrac{3 - 4i}{4 + 3i}$
11. $\dfrac{2 + 5i}{5 - 3i}$
12. $\dfrac{5i + 8}{9i + 7}$
13. $\dfrac{i(7 - 8i)}{11i - 15}$
14. $\dfrac{(2 - i)(1 + i)}{5i - 6}$
15. $\dfrac{(2 + 3i)(1 - i)}{1 + i - i^2}$
16. $\dfrac{3 - 2i}{i(5i + 2)}$
17. $\dfrac{12 - 9i}{(2 + 3i)(4 - 5i)}$

Express each of the complex numbers in Exercises 18–29 in trigonometric form, and then perform the indicated operations.

18. $(1 - i)(\sqrt{3} + i)$
19. $(-1 + i)(1 - \sqrt{3}\, i)$
20. $(-5 - 5i)(-2\sqrt{3} + 2i)$
21. $(-\sqrt{3} + 3i)(3 - 3i)$
22. $\dfrac{1 + i}{\sqrt{3} - i}$
23. $\dfrac{3 - \sqrt{3}\, i}{5 - 5i}$
24. $\dfrac{i(12 + 4\sqrt{3}\, i)}{3(-7 + 7i)}$
25. $\dfrac{3(-\sqrt{3} + i)}{5i(4 - 4i)}$
26. $\dfrac{(3 + 4i)(5 - 12i)}{(-8 + 15i)(24 - 7i)}$
27. $\dfrac{(-5i)(-5\sqrt{3} + 15i)}{7(\sqrt{3} - \sqrt{22}\, i)}$
28. $\dfrac{-i(\sqrt{7} - 3i)}{\sqrt{5} + 2\sqrt{5}\, i}$
29. $\dfrac{(-\sqrt{11} + 5i)(\sqrt{13} - 6i)}{(-2 - 2\sqrt{3}\, i)(7 + \sqrt{15}\, i)}$

16–6 De Moivre's Theorem. The rule of the preceding section for the multiplication of complex numbers in trigonometric form can be used in the derivation of an important theorem for the raising of complex numbers to powers.

Let us set $r_1 = r_2 = r$ and $\theta_1 = \theta_2 = \theta$ in Eq. (3) of Section 16–5; we obtain the relation

$$[r(\cos\theta + i\sin\theta)]^2 = r^2(\cos 2\theta + i\sin 2\theta). \tag{4}$$

If we now multiply each member of this equation by $r(\cos\theta + i\sin\theta)$, we have

$$[r(\cos\theta + i\sin\theta)]^3 = r^3(\cos 2\theta + i\sin 2\theta)\cdot(\cos\theta + i\sin\theta).$$

When Eq. (3) is applied to the right member, this equation becomes

$$[r(\cos\theta + i\sin\theta)]^3 = r^3(\cos 3\theta + i\sin 3\theta).$$

On the basis of the formulas obtained, it would seem reasonable to expect that a similar formula holds for any positive integral exponent. Such is indeed the case, and in fact a more general theorem holds, for any rational exponent. The statement of this theorem follows.

De Moivre's Theorem.* The relation

$$\boxed{[r(\cos\theta + i\sin\theta)]^n = r^n(\cos n\theta + i\sin n\theta)} \tag{5}$$

---

* For a proof of this theorem the reader is referred to *College Algebra and Plane Trigonometry* by A. Spitzbart and Ross H. Bardell, p. 282. Reading, Mass.: Addison-Wesley Publishing Co., Inc. (1955).

holds if n is any integer. If n is a rational number p/q in lowest terms, with $q > 1$, the right member of (5) gives one of the q values of the left member.

EXAMPLE. Evaluate the quantity $(1 - i)^7$.

Solution. With the use of De Moivre's Theorem we have

$$\begin{aligned}(1 - i)^7 &= [2^{1/2}(\cos 315° + i \sin 315°)]^7 = 2^{7/2}(\cos 2205° + i \sin 2205°)\\ &= 2^{7/2}(\cos 45° + i \sin 45°) = 2^{7/2}\left(\frac{\sqrt{2}}{2} + \frac{\sqrt{2}}{2}i\right) = 8 + 8i.\end{aligned}$$

16–7 Roots of complex numbers. It can be shown (by rather advanced methods for which we are not prepared at this point) that *any complex number A has exactly n nth roots,* that is, two square roots, three cube roots, four fourth roots, etc. De Moivre's Theorem may be used to find all of them, that is, to find the n distinct values of $A^{1/n}$.

If θ is an argument of A, then $\theta + 2k\pi$, where k is any integer, is also an argument of A, since the argument of any complex number may be increased by any multiple of 2π. We may then write A in trigonometric form as

$$A = r[\cos(\theta + 2k\pi) + i \sin(\theta + 2k\pi)],$$

where r is the modulus of A. Applying De Moivre's Theorem with exponent $1/n$ to this expression, we obtain

$$\{r[\cos(\theta + 2k\pi) + i \sin(\theta + 2k\pi)]\}^{1/n} = r^{1/n}\left(\cos\frac{\theta + 2k\pi}{n} + i \sin\frac{\theta + 2k\pi}{n}\right),$$

where k is any integer. The n distinct roots of A may be obtained by letting $k = 0, 1, 2, \ldots, n - 1$ in turn. Any other integral value of k will differ from one of these by a multiple of n, so that the corresponding values of $(\theta + 2k\pi)/n$ will differ by a multiple of 2π, and the same nth root will result. We shall state explicitly the result that has been proved.

THEOREM 16–1. *The n nth roots of the number $r(\cos\theta + i \sin\theta)$, where n is a positive integer, are given by*

$$[r(\cos\theta + i \sin\theta)]^{1/n} = r^{1/n}\left[\cos\frac{\theta + 2k\pi}{n} + i \sin\frac{\theta + 2k\pi}{n}\right],$$

$$k = 0, 1, 2, \ldots, n - 1.$$

EXAMPLE 1. Find the cube roots of $\sqrt{3} + i$.

Solution. The absolute value of $\sqrt{3} + i$ is 2, and one argument is $\pi/6$. We then have

$$\sqrt{3} + i = 2\left(\cos\frac{\pi}{6} + i \sin\frac{\pi}{6}\right),$$

and by Theorem 16–1 we obtain

$$\begin{aligned}
(\sqrt{3}+i)^{1/3} &= \left[2\left(\cos\frac{\pi}{6}+i\sin\frac{\pi}{6}\right)\right]^{1/3} \\
&= 2^{1/3}\left[\cos\frac{1}{3}\left(\frac{\pi}{6}+2k\pi\right)+i\sin\frac{1}{3}\left(\frac{\pi}{6}+2k\pi\right)\right] \\
&= 2^{1/3}\left[\cos\left(\frac{\pi}{18}+\frac{2k\pi}{3}\right)+i\sin\left(\frac{\pi}{18}+\frac{2k\pi}{3}\right)\right] \\
&= 2^{1/3}\left(\cos\frac{\pi}{18}+i\sin\frac{\pi}{18}\right) \qquad \text{for } k=0, \\
&= 2^{1/3}\left(\cos\frac{13\pi}{18}+i\sin\frac{13\pi}{18}\right) \qquad \text{for } k=1, \\
&= 2^{1/3}\left(\cos\frac{25\pi}{18}+i\sin\frac{25\pi}{18}\right) \qquad \text{for } k=2.
\end{aligned}$$

If $k = 3$, the argument $\pi/18 + 2k\pi/3$ becomes $\pi/18 + 2\pi$, which gives the same root as for $k = 0$.

This method of finding roots of complex numbers applies equally well to finding the nth roots of real numbers.

EXAMPLE 2. Find the fourth roots of -16.

Solution. One argument of -16 is π radians. Hence, applying Theorem 16–1 in the same manner as above, we have

$$\begin{aligned}
(-16)^{1/4} &= [16(\cos\pi+i\sin\pi)]^{1/4} \\
&= 2[\cos\tfrac{1}{4}(\pi+2k\pi)+i\sin\tfrac{1}{4}(\pi+2k\pi)] \\
&= 2\left[\cos\left(\frac{\pi}{4}+\frac{k\pi}{2}\right)+i\sin\left(\frac{\pi}{4}+\frac{k\pi}{2}\right)\right] \\
&= 2\left(\cos\frac{\pi}{4}+i\sin\frac{\pi}{4}\right) = \sqrt{2}+i\sqrt{2} \qquad \text{for } k=0, \\
&= 2\left(\cos\frac{3\pi}{4}+i\sin\frac{3\pi}{4}\right) = -\sqrt{2}+i\sqrt{2} \qquad \text{for } k=1, \\
&= 2\left(\cos\frac{5\pi}{4}+i\sin\frac{5\pi}{4}\right) = -\sqrt{2}-i\sqrt{2} \qquad \text{for } k=2, \\
&= 2\left(\cos\frac{7\pi}{4}+i\sin\frac{7\pi}{4}\right) = \sqrt{2}-i\sqrt{2} \qquad \text{for } k=3.
\end{aligned}$$

It is easy to see that, in general, successive nth roots of a complex number differ in argument by $2\pi/n$, but have the same absolute value. We may then state the following result.

THEOREM 16–2. *The n nth roots of the complex number with absolute value r and argument θ lie equally spaced on the circumference of a circle with center at the origin and radius $r^{1/n}$, one of them having the argument θ/n.*

EXERCISE GROUP 16–5

Perform the indicated operations in Exercises 1–16.

1. $(1-\sqrt{3}\,i)^5$
2. $(-1-i)^4$
3. $(-\sqrt{3}+i)^3$
4. $(\sqrt{3}-3i)^6$
5. $(-i)^7$
6. $(-5+5i)^2$
7. $\left[\dfrac{-1-i\sqrt{3}}{2}\right]^{-11}$
8. $\left[\dfrac{1-i}{\sqrt{2}}\right]^{-13}$
9. $\left[\dfrac{\sqrt{3}-i}{2}\right]^{-9}$
10. $\dfrac{i^9(-\sqrt{3}+i)^5}{32}$
11. $\left[\dfrac{1-i}{\sqrt{2}}\right]^7\left[\dfrac{-\sqrt{3}-i}{2}\right]^8$
12. $(1-i)^2(1-\sqrt{3}\,i)^{-5}$
13. $(\cos 312^\circ - i\sin 48^\circ)^{-4}$
14. $(\cos 225^\circ - i\sin 315^\circ)^{-2}$
15. $(\sin 210^\circ + i\sin 300^\circ)^2$
16. $(\cos 132^\circ - i\sin 132^\circ)^3$

Find the indicated roots in Exercises 17–28.

17. The cube roots of 1
18. The fourth roots of 16
19. The fifth roots of -32
20. The cube roots of -8
21. The cube roots of i
22. The fourth roots of $-i$
23. The fourth roots of $\dfrac{1-i\sqrt{3}}{2}$
24. The fifth roots of $1-i$
25. The cube roots of $3-\sqrt{3}\,i$
26. The square roots of $3+4i$
27. The sixth roots of $24-7i$
28. The ninth roots of $-5-12i$

REVIEW EXERCISES

In Exercises 1–8, perform the indicated operations by the methods of Examples 1 and 2 of Section 16–5, and express the result in the form $a+bi$.

1. $(2+3i)(3-4i)$
2. $(4-5i)(3+7i)$
3. $(32+i)(4-i)$
4. $(1-i)(3i+7)$
5. $(2-3i)/(5-4i)$
6. $(3i-7)/(5+6i)$
7. $(4-3i)/(4+5i)$
8. $(3-4i)/(3+7i)$

In Exercises 9–14, express each of the complex numbers in trigonometric form, and then perform the indicated operations.

9. $\dfrac{(0.3-0.4i)(-2.4+0.7i)}{(1.2i-0.5)i}$
10. $\dfrac{(\sqrt{13}-\sqrt{3}\,i)(i-1)}{(\sqrt{7}+3i)}$

11. $\dfrac{(\sqrt{17} + 2\sqrt{2}\,i)(-3\sqrt{2} + \sqrt{7}\,i)}{(\sqrt{31} - \sqrt{5}\,i)(-\sqrt{26} - \sqrt{10}\,i)}$

12. $\dfrac{i^2(\sqrt{19} - \sqrt{6}\,i)}{(i - 2)(1 + 3i)}$

13. $\dfrac{i(6 - 8i)(i\sqrt{2} + 7\sqrt{2})}{(-i - 4\sqrt{3})(1 - 4\sqrt{5}\,i)}$

14. $\dfrac{i^3(-8i^3 + 6i^2)}{(4\sqrt{5} - 2\sqrt{5}\,i)(2\sqrt{5} - 4\sqrt{5}\,i)}$

In the following exercises, find the indicated roots.

15. The fifth roots of 32

16. The cube roots of -8

17. The seventh roots of 7

18. The eighth roots of -32

19. The cube roots of $-6 - 6i$

20. The fourth roots of $2 + 2i$

ANSWERS TO ODD-NUMBERED EXERCISES

ANSWERS TO ODD-NUMBERED EXERCISES

Exercise Group 1–1

1. 17 3. 29 5. 23 7. 76 9. 100
11. 615 13. 4144 15. 23 17. 76 19. 92
21. 45 23. 310 25. 121 27. 48 29. 243

Exercise Group 1–2

1. (a) 8, (b) 46 3. (a) -58, (b) 84 5. (a) 8, (b) -86
7. (a) -26, (b) -12 9. (a) -61, (b) 9 11. (a) -33, (b) -111
13. (a) 15, (b) 59 15. (a) -78, (b) 46 17. 8
19. 15 21. 16 23. -34
25. -3 27. 30 29. 47
31. 11 33. -79 35. 37

Exercise Group 1–3

1. 15 3. 63 5. 84 7. 168 9. -756
11. 1944 13. 193,545 15. -19 17. 5 19. 1
21. -9 23. -61 25. -46 27. 60 29. 22
31. 18 33. 37 35. -24

Exercise Group 1–4

1. $3x - y$, $13x - 5y$ 3. $21x + 22y + 11z$, $21x + 4y - 11z$
5. $14ab + 7abc - 35bc$, $38ab - 23abc + 5bc$
7. $14m + 25x + 14v - 19z$, $38m - 5x + 14v + 21z$
9. $x - 5y$ 11. $-2x + 6y$ 13. $-4m + 7n - 7p$
15. $-9a - 3b$ 17. $bc - ac$ 19. $2a - b - d$
21. $3x - y$ 23. $-11x + 14y + 3z$ 25. $b - a$
27. $4b - 3a$ 29. $z - 2x - 3y$ 31. $10z - x$
33. $b + c + 2x$ 35. $6y - 3z - 2w$ 37. $ax + bx - (ay + by)$
39. $cx - dx - (dy - cy)$ 41. $3au + 3bu - (av - bv)$
43. $3ax - 5bx - (10by - 6ay)$ 45. $bu - bv - (2hv - 2hu)$

Exercise Group 1–5

1. 9 3. 64 5. 216 7. 243 9. $3^5 = 243$
11. 10^{13} 13. 7^{15} 15. 1000 17. $2^{15} \cdot 3^{10}$ 19. $2^{15} \cdot 7^6$
21. $2^{14} \cdot 3^{16}$ 23. $2^{11} \cdot 3^2 \cdot 5^7$ 25. $3x^9$ 27. $2^4 \cdot 3^6 a^6 b^{12}$
29. $a^{13}b^{12}$ 31. $-2^5 \cdot 5^4 a^{17} b^{10}$ 33. $108a^{5h}$ 35. $a^{3k}b^{3k}$
37. $a^{5k}b^{4k}$ 39. $3^{2d}a^{2bd}c^{2dx}$ 41. $3^n a^{2hn} b^{2kn}$ 43. $2^{k+3}a^{2k+3h}$

Exercise Group 1–6

1. $6x^2 - 15x$ 3. $-2ax + a^2y$ 5. $6y^2 - 3ay$ 7. $-3x^3y + 3xy^3 + 3xy$
9. $6a^6 - 3a^3b - 6a^2b^4$ 11. $-35x^5y^2z + 25x^5y^3z^2 + 10x^4yz^3$
13. $6x - 9x^2 + 12x^3$ 15. $x^2 + x - 20$ 17. $4x^2 - 20x + 25$
19. $15x^2 + xy - 28y^2$ 21. $4y^2 - 12yz + 9z^2$ 23. $4x^2 - b^2$
25. $x^3 - 8y^3$ 27. $x^3 + 6x^2 + 11x + 6$ 29. $4x^2 - 9y^2$
31. $6x^2 - 17xy + 12y^2$ 33. $a^2x^4 + 2abx^2y^3 + b^2y^6$
35. $x^5 - 10x^4 + 17x^3 + 33x^2 - 32x - 21$
37. $x^{10} - 3x^8 - x^7 + x^6 - 2x^4 - 3x^2 - 4x - 1$
39. $a^{16} - 1$ 41. $a^{m+2} - 2a^{m+1} + 2a^m + a^{m-1} + 4a^{m-2}$
43. $x^{3n} + y^{3k}$ 45. $x^{3n} - y^{3k}$ 47. 0

Exercise Group 1–7

1. $2^5 = 32$ 3. $\frac{1}{5^5} = \frac{1}{3125}$ 5. $\frac{2^4}{3^5} = \frac{16}{243}$ 7. $\frac{1}{10^4}$ 9. $\frac{1}{3^5 \cdot 10^5}$
11. $\frac{x^8}{3}$ 13. $\frac{x^7}{3^3}$ 15. $\frac{y^5}{x^5}$ 17. $\frac{2y^6z^6}{3x^4}$ 19. $\frac{5^2a^4x^7}{2^5b^6}$
21. $\frac{x^4y^{10}}{a^7b^3c^2}$ 23. $\frac{a^2c^8}{3^4b^6x^6}$ 25. $2^{9-y}a^{8-x}b^{10-z}$
27. $\frac{2^{y+z-x}b^{10-z}}{a^{y-x}}$ 29. $\frac{2^{9+x-z}b^{z-y}}{a^{8+x-y}}$ 31. $\frac{a^{y-x}b^{z-y}}{10^{z-x}}$

Exercise Group 1–8

1. 5, 2 3. 8, 7 5. 19, 15 7. 27, 2
9. 23, 28 11. $x - 3$, 0 13. $x + 3$, 0 15. $3a + 4b$, 0
17. $a^2 - 3a + 1$, 0 19. $3x^2 + 4x + 13$, 0
21. $2x^2 - x - 6$, -11 23. $x^4 - 3x^3 + 9x^2 - 27x + 81$, 0
25. $-x^4 - 2x^3 - 4x^2 - 8x - 16$, 0 27. $7a^2 + 5a + 4$, 0
29. $2b + 3$, $3b - 1$ 31. $6a + 5$, 1
33. $a^2 + ab + b^2$, 0 35. $x^{3m} - x^{2m}y^n + x^my^{2n} - y^{3n}$, 0
37. $2x^{2n} + 3x^n - 4$, 0

Review Exercises for Chapter 1

1. 110 3. 593 5. -391 7. $7x - 2y$
9. $a - 3b - 3x + 2y$ 11. a^7b^{10} 13. $2^7a^{18}b^{17}$
15. $20a^3b + 15a^4b - 10a^5b^2$ 17. $6a^4 + 5a^3y - 6a^2y^2$
19. $3x^3 - 5ax^2 + 3a^2x - a^3$ 21. $\frac{1}{b^5}$ 23. $\frac{3y^4z^2}{4xu^3}$
25. $(x - 1)^n(x + 1)$ 27. $-2a - \frac{7}{5}$, $\frac{34}{5}a - \frac{14}{5}$
29. $x^2 - 1$, $4x - 14$

Exercise Group 2–1

1. $2 \cdot 3 \cdot 7 \cdot 11$ 3. $2 \cdot 5 \cdot 7 \cdot 97$ 5. $2^2 \cdot 3^2 \cdot 47$ 7. $2^3 \cdot 3 \cdot 7 \cdot 11$
9. $5 \cdot 7^3$ 11. $2^8 \cdot 3^2$ 13. $3^2 \cdot 11^2$ 15. $2^3 \cdot 3^4 \cdot 11^2$
17. $5 \cdot 7^2 \cdot 11^3$ 19. $2^2 \cdot 3^3 \cdot 7^2 \cdot 19$ 21. $3 \cdot 5^2 \cdot 7^3 \cdot 17$ 23. $3 \cdot 5^2 \cdot 7^2 \cdot 13$
25. $3^2 \cdot 1549$ 27. 53, 59, 61, 67, 71, 73, 79, 83, 89, 97

Exercise Group 2–2

1. $6a - 15b$ 3. $6ab - 10ac$ 5. $ax^2 - 2bx^2 + 3cx^2$ 7. $ax + ay$
9. $6a^2b - 9b^3$ 11. $15a^5b^3 - 21a^2b^6$
13. $2x^2 + xy - 3y^2$ 15. $a^2x^2 + 2abxy + b^2y^2$
17. $x^2 + ax + bx + ab$ 19. $x^2 + ax - bx - ab$
21. $10x^2 + 19x - 15$ 23. $3a(x - 2ay)$
25. $2ab(5b - 3ax)$ 27. $x(-4b + x - ax^2)$
29. $x^2(x^2 - 3x - 2)$ 31. $27axy(2y - 3a)$
33. $(u - v)(3a + 5b)$ 35. $(a + b)(x^2 + y^2)$
37. $(a + b + c)y$ 39. $(x + y)(m + n)$
41. $(n + y)(2a - 3b)$ 43. $(6x - 13)(x^3 - 7)$
45. $(x + y + z)(a + b)$

Exercise Group 2–3

1. $c^2 - b^2$ 3. $a^2x^2 - y^2$ 5. $4 - 25x^2$ 7. $v^2 - b^2u^2$
9. $x^{2a} - y^{2b}$ 11. $x^{4a} - 1$ 13. $y^6 - y^4$ 15. $9a^4 - 49k^2$
17. $9x^2 - 25y^2 - 50yz - 25z^2$ 19. $x^2 - y^2 - 2yz - z^2$
21. $a^2 - 2ad + d^2 - b^2 + 2bc - c^2$ 23. 6391 25. 39,975
27. 8051 29. 3,999,919 31. $(4 + 3y)(4 - 3y)$
33. $(3a + 4b)(3a - 4b)$ 35. $(5u + 8v)(5u - 8v)$ 37. $(1 + 6x)(1 - 6x)$
39. $(12 + 5c)(12 - 5c)$ 41. $(3y + \frac{1}{3})(3y - \frac{1}{3})$ 43. $(a^3b + 2c^4)(a^3b - 2c^4)$
45. $(8a + 9b^2)(8a - 9b^2)$ 47. $3(x - y)(3x - y)$
49. $(7x^2 - 2a - b)(7x^2 + 2a + b)$ 51. $4ab$
53. $(7x - y - 2a + b)(7x - y + 2a - b)$
55. $(2y - 13x)(6y - 11x)$

Exercise Group 2–4

1. $a^2 + 2ab + b^2$ 3. $x^2 + 2cxy + c^2y^2$ 5. $b^2 - 2bc + c^2$
7. $a^2x^2 - 2abxy + b^2y^2$ 9. $0.04u^2 + 0.12uv + 0.09v^2$
11. $a^2 - 2ab + b^2 - 2ac + 2bc + c^2$ 13. $a^2 - 2ab + 2ac + b^2 - 2bc + c^2$
15. $x^2 - 4x + 2ax + 4 - 4a + a^2$ 17. $x^2 - 6xy + 2xz + 9y^2 - 6yz + z^2$
19. $a^2 + 2ab + b^2 + 2ac + 2bc + 2ad + 2bd + c^2 + 2cd + d^2$
21. $x^2 + 2xy + y^2$ 23. 6241 25. 9801
27. 89,401 29. 1,004,004 31. $(2x + 5y)^2$
33. $(6u + 5v)^2$ 35. $(3x - 2y)^2$ 37. $(11y - 2z)^2$
39. $(\frac{1}{2}a - \frac{1}{3}x)^2$ 41. $(\frac{1}{4}c + 3d)^2$ 43. $(17y - 13x)^2$
45. $(2u - 15v)^2$ 47. $(x - y - 5)^2$ 49. $(17a - 16b)^2$
51. $(24x - 8y - 5z)^2$ 53. $(16a + 15b)^2$

Exercise Group 2–5

1. $x^2 + 12x + 35$
3. $x^2 + 6x - 55$
5. $x^2 + 9xy + 14y^2$
7. $x^2 + 2xy - 15y^2$
9. $4x^2 - 8xy - 21y^2$
11. $9x^2 - 45xy + 56y^2$
13. $a^2x^2 + 4axy - 21y^2$
15. $10u^2 - 13uv - 3v^2$
17. $6a^4 + a^2b - 35b^2$
19. $21a^2 - 92ab^2 + 55b^4$
21. $2a^2 + 4ab + 2b^2 + 13a + 13b + 21$
23. $10x^2 + 19xy + 19xz + 6y^2 + 12yz + 6z^2$
25. $33a^2 + 131ab + 131ac - 52b^2 - 104bc - 52c^2$
27. $14a^2 - ab - ac - 33b^2 - 66bc - 33c^2$
29. $(x + 7)(x + 2)$
31. $(a - 5)(a + 2)$
33. $(\mathrm{p} - 9)(\mathrm{p} + 2)$
35. $-(x + 5)(x - 3)$
37. $-(x + 7)(x - 3)$
39. $-(x + 7)(x - 2)$
41. $(x + 4)(4x - 5)$
43. $-(x - 5)(2x + 3)$
45. $(2x - 5)(5x - 2)$
47. $(7x - 2)(2x + 7)$
49. $(2x - 5)(5x + 2)$
51. $(8y - 7)(y + 2)$
53. $(2r + 3)(7r - 5)$
55. $(12x - 5)(4x + 3)$
57. $(2 + 3y)(7 - 10y)$
59. $(7t - 5)(t - 2)$
61. $(2a - 5b)(3a + 7b)$
63. $(4 - 7a)(3 + 5a)$

Exercise Group 2–6

1. $a^3 + 8$
3. $a^3 - 8b^3$
5. $8u^3 + \frac{1}{8}$
7. $8x^6 + 27$
9. $a^3x^9 + b^9y^3$
11. $a^3 + (b + c)^3$
13. $a^3 - 8(b - c)^3$
15. $(a + 2b)(a^2 - 2ab + 4b^2)$
17. $(2x + 3y)(4x^2 - 6xy + 9y^2)$
19. $(t - \frac{1}{2}s)(t^2 + \frac{1}{2}ts + \frac{1}{4}s^2)$
21. $(4x - 3ab)(16x^2 + 12abx + 9a^2b^2)$
23. $(\frac{1}{3}a - c)(\frac{1}{9}a^2 + \frac{1}{3}ac + c^2)$
25. $(\frac{1}{2}a + \frac{1}{3}x)(\frac{1}{4}a^2 - \frac{1}{6}ax + \frac{1}{9}x^2)$
27. $(0.1 - x)(0.01 + 0.1x + x^2)$
29. $\left(\frac{1}{10}ax + 2u\right)\left(\frac{a^2x^2}{100} - \frac{aux}{5} + 4u^2\right)$
31. $(a + b - c)[(a + b)^2 + (a + b)c + c^2]$
33. $[3(u + v) + 5w][9(u + v)^2 - 15(u + v)w + 25w^2]$
35. $(0.2u + v - 0.1w)[0.04u^2 - 0.2u(v - 0.1w) + (v - 0.1w)^2]$
37. $[5(a - b) - (2c - 3d)][25(a - b)^2 + 5(a - b)(2c - 3d) + (2c - 3d)^2]$

Exercise Group 2–7

1. $-3x^3y + 3xy^3 + 3xy$
3. $14x^3y^2z + 4xy^2z^3 - 6x^3yz^2$
5. $b^m + b^{n+m} - b^{2m}$
7. $4a^2 - 9b^2$
9. $v^2 - b^2u^2$
11. $x^{2m} - y^{2m}$
13. $4a^2 + 36ab + 81b^2$
15. $16d^4e^4 + 24d^2e^2f^2 + 9f^4$
17. $a^2 + 2ab + b^2 + 2ac + 2bc + c^2$
19. $6x^2 + 31xy + 35y^2$
21. $4x^4 + 16x^2y^3 + 15y^6$
23. $a^2 + 2ab + b^2 + ac + bc - 2c^2$
25. $a^2 - x^2 - 2xy - y^2$
27. $x^2 + 4xy + 6xz + 4y^2 + 12yz + 9z^2$
29. $8x^3 + 27y^3$
31. $x^2 + 2xy + y^2 - z^2$
33. $a^2 + 2ab + b^2 - 6a - 6b + 9$
35. $4x^2 + 12xy + 9y^2 - 20xz - 30yz + 25z^2$
37. $4u^2 + 28uy + 49y^2 - 9v^2 - 30vx - 25x^2$

Exercise Group 2–8

1. $x^2(x+3)(x-3)$
3. $x^3(x-5)$
5. $2(a+6x)(a-x)$
7. $9x^2y^2(z+1)(z-1)$
9. $(5-x)(3+x)$
11. $(6-x)(1-x)$
13. $2(1-6x)(1+6x)$
15. $(x-y)(a+b+2)$
17. $4xy(6+x)(3-x)$
19. $6(a+b-2)^2$
21. $5xy(2x+7y)(3x-y)$
23. $(x+1)(x-1)(x^2+4)(x+2)(x-2)$
25. $(x-5)(x+2)(x-2)(x-1)$
27. $2x^2y^2(7x-2y)^2$
29. $(17a^2+9b^2)(a+2b)(a-2b)$
31. $(5x+y)(5x-y)(x+2y)(x-2y)$
33. $(x^3+4)(x+1)(x^2-x+1)$

Exercise Group 2–9

1. $(x-y)(1-3z)$
3. $(a-b)(x+y)$
5. $(3a-5b)(x+2y)$
7. $(b+2h)(u+v)$
9. $(3c-4k)(w-x)$
11. $(a-2)(a-1)(a+1)$
13. $(u+2)(u^2+1)$
15. $(u-2x+y)(u+2x-y)$
17. $(x+y)(m+n)$
19. $(x+y)(2a-3b)$
21. $(x+y+z)(a+b)$
23. $(3u+3x-1)(3u-3x+1)$
25. $(4a+b-5c)(4a+b+5c)$
27. $(x+y-4z)(x+y+4z)$
29. $(a+3b)(x+2y)$
31. $(a+3)(1+a^2)$
33. $(2u-3v-a-b)(2u-3v+a+b)$
35. $(3x-3y-1)(x-y-3)$
37. $(x-2y)(x-y-2)$
39. $(a+b)(x+2)^2$
41. $(x+2)(x+4)(x^2+5x+8)$

Review Exercises for Chapter 2

1. $9a^2-4b^2$
3. $a^2x^2+2abxy+b^2y^2$
5. $4a^2x^2+12abxy^2+9b^2y^4$
7. $4x^2+12xy+9y^2-16z^2$
9. $a^2x^2+b^2y^2+c^2+2abxy+2acx+2bcy$
11. $4a^2x^2+9b^2y^2+c^2z^2-12abxy+4acxz-6bcyz$
13. $4a^2+9b^2+16c^2+12ab-16ac-24bc$
15. $2a^2+6ab-9ac+4b^2-12bc+9c^2$
17. $x^3+6x^2+12x+8$
19. $8x^3+36x^2y+54xy^2+27y^3$
21. $8x^3-27y^3$
23. x^3-125
25. $(3x+5y)(3x-5y)$
27. $(a-b+x+y)(a-b-x-y)$
29. $(7a+2b)^2$
31. $(5-x+y)^2$
33. $(a-b)(a+b-4)$
35. $(x+y-3)(x-y+3)$
37. $(p-q+r)(p-q-r)$
39. $-(7a-5b)(3a-11b)$
41. $(7y-3x)(2y+5x)$
43. $9(a-b-2)^2$
45. $(3u-2v-4x+5y)(3u-2v+4x-5y)$
47. $(3x-2y)(9x^2+6xy+4y^2)$
49. $(a+b+4)(a+b+1)$

Exercise Group 3–1

1. Not equal 3. Equal 5. Equal 7. Equal
9. Not equal 11. $\frac{6}{5}$ 13. $-\frac{7}{11}$ 15. $-\frac{81}{14}$
17. $-\frac{11}{29}$ 19. $\frac{27}{7}$ 21. $\frac{107}{27}$ 23. $\dfrac{2x}{7y^2}$
25. $\dfrac{3a+b}{a+3b}$ 27. $\dfrac{a(x+y)}{x-y}$ 29. $\dfrac{y+x}{-a}$ 31. $\dfrac{3a+4b}{3a^2-5b^2}$
33. $-\dfrac{x+y}{2x+y}$ 35. $\dfrac{x+2}{x+4}$ 37. $-\dfrac{x^2+9y^2}{x+3y}$ 39. -1
41. $\dfrac{1}{b-a}$ 43. $\dfrac{(a^2+x)(x+y)}{a-b}$ 45. $\dfrac{a+b}{c+d}$
47. $\dfrac{a-b+c}{a+b-c}$ 49. $\dfrac{3x+11}{3x+5}$ 51. $\dfrac{a^2-2ab+4b^2}{a^2-4}$
53. $\dfrac{4x^2+6bx+9b^2}{2x-3b}$ 55. $\dfrac{a^2-2a+3}{3a-5}$

Exercise Group 3–2

1. 160 3. 288 5. 588 7. 2310 9. $210a^2b^2$
11. $360x^3y^5z^2$ 13. $27{,}720a^4b^3c^4d^2$ 15. $36(x-1)^2(x+1)$
17. $30(x+3)(x-2)$ 19. $(x+2)(x-3)(x+4)$
21. $(3a+4)(a+1)(2a-3)$ 23. $(3x-5)(5x+2)(5x-2)(x+3)$
25. $(a+b)(a-b)(a^2-ab+b^2)(a^2+ab+b^2)$
27. $(x+5)(x+3)(x-2)$ 29. $(x-3)(x+4)(x-5)$
31. $(5x+2)(3x-2)(2x+5)$ 33. $(x^4-y^4)(x^2-xy+y^2)$

Exercise Group 3–3

1. $\frac{6}{7}$ 3. $\frac{2}{3}$ 5. $\frac{2}{11}$ 7. -1 9. -1 11. $\frac{1}{7}$
13. $\dfrac{x^2+y^2}{x^2-y^2}$ 15. $\dfrac{x}{x+y}$ 17. $\dfrac{a^2+b^2}{ab(a-c)}$ 19. $\dfrac{6(2a-1)}{a-2}$
21. $\dfrac{6x^2-5}{2x-3}$ 23. $\dfrac{3x-1}{(x-2)(x+3)}$ 25. $\dfrac{2(x+4)}{(x+2)(x+6)}$
27. $-\dfrac{(a+b)(a+4b)}{(a+3b)(a^2-4b^2)}$ 29. $\dfrac{10a}{4a^2-9}$ 31. $\dfrac{x^2-2x}{x^2-1}$
33. $\dfrac{2x^3+3x^2+x-1}{x^2-1}$ 35. $\dfrac{2x^2-13}{(x+1)(x+2)(x-3)}$
37. $\dfrac{3a(a^3-4a+2)}{(2a-1)^2}$ 39. $\dfrac{2}{a+b}$ 41. $-\dfrac{2}{a-1}$
43. $\dfrac{22x^2-16x+3}{x(3x-1)(2x-1)}$ 45. $\dfrac{x^2+6x-6}{(x+1)(x+2)(3-x)}$

Exercise Group 3–4

1. $\frac{5}{12}$ 3. $\frac{1}{12}$ 5. $-\frac{1}{20}$ 7. $-\frac{9}{4}$ 9. $\frac{1}{102}$

11. $\frac{119}{13}$ 13. $\frac{3a^2}{10b^2}$ 15. $-\frac{a}{2}$ 17. $\frac{(a-1)^2}{(a+1)^2}$ 19. $\frac{x-4}{x-2}$

21. $\frac{a}{b}$ 23. $\frac{-3}{2(x+y)}$ 25. $\frac{ab(x+y)}{c}$

27. $\frac{(x+2)(x-11)}{(x-3)(x-1)}$ 29. $\frac{y(3y+2)}{(1-y)^2}$ 31. $\frac{x+9}{x+5}$

33. $\frac{2x+1}{2x+3}$ 35. $\frac{2(a-1)^2}{15(4a-1)}$ 37. $\frac{2a-3}{3a-2}$

39. $\frac{3(x-3)}{x+3}$ 41. a

Exercise Group 3–5

1. $\frac{15}{34}$ 3. $\frac{21}{355}$ 5. $-\frac{714}{95}$ 7. (a) $\frac{1}{4}$, (b) $-\frac{13}{8}$, (c) $-\frac{34}{113}$

9. $\frac{44}{53}$ 11. $\frac{472}{45}$ 13. $\frac{a}{c}$ 15. $\frac{a-2}{a+2}$

17. $\frac{(x^2+1)^2}{x^2(x+1)^2}$ 19. $\frac{x+2}{x}$ 21. $a-1$ 23. $\frac{a-b}{a+b}$

25. $\frac{-1}{x^2-5x+7}$ 27. $\frac{8(x+1)}{(x-1)(x+3)^3}$

Review Exercises for Chapter 3

1. $\frac{6(a^2-1)}{2a-3}$ 3. $\frac{cu-cv-ux+uy}{cu(v-y)}$ 5. $\frac{2x^2+9xy-33y^2}{(x+3y)(x-3y)}$

7. $\frac{3}{2-a}$ 9. $\frac{11x+7}{(x-2)(x-3)(x+3)(x+5)}$

11. $\frac{2(x+1)^2}{21(4x+1)}$ 13. $\frac{(a-b)(a-2b)}{(a+b)(a+2b)}$ 15. x

17. $\frac{a^2+b^2}{ab}$ 19. $\frac{1-2a}{1-a}$ 21. -1 23. $-\frac{4740}{41}$

Exercise Group 4–1

1. $\frac{1}{64}$ 3. $\frac{1}{16}$ 5. 1 7. $\frac{1}{32}$ 9. 4

11. $\frac{3}{x^5}$ 13. $\frac{1}{8x^3}$ 15. 2 17. 1 19. $\frac{5}{y^3}$

21. $\frac{1}{y^2}$ 23. $\frac{4}{x^5}$ 25. $\frac{5y^2}{x^3}$ 27. $\frac{2}{x^2y^3}$ 29. $3+\frac{1}{y^2}$

31. $y+x$ 33. y^2-x^2 35. $\frac{xy}{y+x}$ 37. 1

39. $12a^2b^3c^{-3}d^{-1}$ 41. $a^{-2}b^3x^{-2}y^3$ 43. $5^{-1}x^{-2}y^{-3}$
45. $2 \cdot 3^{-1}x^{-7}y^{-3}z^4$ 47. $(3x + 2y)^{-1}$ 49. $(2x + y)(x - 5y)^{-1}$
51. a^8 53. y^{3x} 55. c^{7b} 57. x^4 59. z^3 61. 5
63. 5^2 65. x^{20} 67. a^{18} 69. x^{6a} 71. x^{6ab} 73. a^{48}
75. $2^{15}3^{10}$ 77. a^{10bc^2} 79. $2^{xz}a^{2z}3^{yz}b^{3z}$ 81. $2^{3c}3^{2c}a^{2cx}b^{3cy}$
83. $\frac{a^7}{b^7}$ 85. $\frac{a^{12}}{b^{18}}$ 87. $\frac{32x^{10}}{243y^{20}}$ 89. $\frac{-32a^5}{243b^{10}}$ 91. $\frac{(-1)^a}{3^ab^{2a}}$
93. $\frac{b}{a}$ 95. $4a^6$ 97. 10^4 99. $2^6 \cdot 3 \cdot 5^3$ 101. $\frac{2}{3^8xy}$
103. $\frac{324b^{26}}{c^{24}}$ 105. $\frac{2a^{16}b^3}{3}$ 107. $\frac{6 - 11a + 14a^2 - 5a^3}{a^7}$

Exercise Group 4–2

1. 2 3. 3 5. $\frac{1}{4}$ 7. 2 9. $\frac{1}{16}$ 11. $\frac{1}{4}$
13. $\frac{1}{2}$ 15. $\frac{1}{7}$ 17. -1 19. $-\frac{1}{3}$ 21. 0.1 23. 27
25. 25 27. $\frac{1}{32}$ 29. $\frac{1}{256}$ 31. 125 33. $\frac{1}{81}$ 35. 10
37. $\frac{3}{2xy^2}$ 39. $\frac{2b^2}{a^3}$ 41. $\frac{4x^4}{y^2}$ 43. $\frac{64a^2}{729b}$
45. $\frac{2a^2b^2}{5}$ 47. x^3 49. $\frac{4b^4}{3c^5}$ 51. $\frac{27b^{15}}{125a^9}$
53. $\frac{3^{4/3}a}{2^{4/3}b^{7/3}}$ 55. $a^{2/5}b^{2/7} - a^{4/5}b^{6/7}$ 57. $a^{1/3} + b^{1/3}$ 59. $a^{17/12}$
61. $16^{2/3}$ 63. $x^{17/12}$ 65. a^5b^2 67. $1/a^2$ 69. $\frac{21}{4}$ 71. -415

Exercise Group 4–3

1. $5\sqrt{2}$ 3. $3\sqrt[3]{2}$ 5. $2\sqrt[4]{2}$ 7. $-5\sqrt[3]{3}$ 9. $-2\sqrt[3]{2}$
11. $6b\sqrt{2ab}$ 13. $2ab\sqrt[4]{ab^2}$ 15. $2abc^2\sqrt[5]{2ab}$ 17. $b\sqrt{a^2 + c^2}$
19. $2x\sqrt[3]{2 + 3x^2}$ 21. $x\sqrt[3]{27 + 64y^3}$ 23. $2\sqrt[4]{a^4 + 16b^4}$ 25. $2a\sqrt[4]{2a - b^4}$
27. $(a^2 - 4)\sqrt{a + 3}$ 29. $(a + b)\sqrt{2}$ 31. $(a + 3b)\sqrt{ab}$
33. $(a - b)\sqrt{(a^2 + ab + b^2)(a + b)}$ 35. $(a + 2)\sqrt{(a - 2)(a - 1)}$
37. $(a^2 + b^2)\sqrt{(a^4 - a^2b^2 + b^4)(a^2 - b^2)}$
39. $2x^2y^2\sqrt[k]{xy^{k-1} - 4}$ 41. $3^{4k}5^{3k}x^k\sqrt{3^{2k}5^{2k}x + 1}$

Exercise Group 4–4

1. $\frac{\sqrt{70}}{14}$ 3. $\frac{a^3\sqrt{26ax}}{6x}$ 5. $\frac{2}{3}$ 7. 3
9. $\frac{\sqrt{6}}{3}$ 11. $\frac{\sqrt[3]{6}}{2}$ 13. $\frac{\sqrt[3]{75}}{10}$ 15. $\frac{a\sqrt[7]{ab^6c^4}}{c}$
17. $3\sqrt[3]{4a^2b}$ 19. $\frac{x^2}{2y}\sqrt[k]{2^{k-1}x^2y^3}$ 21. $\frac{\sqrt{30}}{6}$ 23. $\frac{\sqrt[3]{ab(a^2 + b^2)}}{ab}$

25. $\pm \dfrac{3a - 4b}{6ab}\sqrt{3ab}$, whichever is positive

27. $\dfrac{3\sqrt[3]{b^3 - 2a^3}}{2ab}$ 29. $\dfrac{1}{ab}\sqrt[3]{(b - a^2)ab^2}$

Exercise Group 4–5

1. $\sqrt{2}$ 3. $\sqrt[3]{5}$ 5. $\sqrt{2}$ 7. $\sqrt{2}$ 9. $2a\sqrt{2ab}$

11. $\sqrt[4]{9x^2y^3}$ 13. $ab^2\sqrt{2a}$ 15. $y\sqrt[4]{6x^3}$ 17. $\dfrac{b\sqrt{6abc}}{3c}$ 19. $\dfrac{\sqrt{6abcd}}{3c^2d}$

21. $\sqrt{a + b}$ 23. $c\sqrt[4]{4c(a + b)^2}$ 25. $\dfrac{\sqrt{x(x^2 - 1)}}{x}$

27. $\dfrac{\sqrt{2a(a^2 + 3)}}{a}$ 29. $\dfrac{\sqrt[3]{2u^2(u - 5)^2}}{u}$

Exercise Group 4–6

1. $\dfrac{\sqrt{6}}{3}$ 3. $\dfrac{\sqrt[3]{18}}{3}$ 5. $\dfrac{\sqrt{ab}}{b}$ 7. $\dfrac{\sqrt[3]{ab^2}}{b}$

9. $\dfrac{x\sqrt[4]{8a}}{4}$ 11. $\dfrac{2\sqrt[5]{2a}}{a}$ 13. $\dfrac{v\sqrt{uw}}{wz}$ 15. $\dfrac{xy^2\sqrt{xyz}}{z}$

17. $\dfrac{y\sqrt{x(x + y)}}{x + y}$ 19. $\dfrac{\sqrt[3]{a^2b^2(a^2 - b^2)}}{ab}$ 21. $\dfrac{(x - y)\sqrt{xy(x - y)}}{xy}$

23. $\sqrt[3]{u^2(u - v)}$, if $u - v$ is positive 25. $\dfrac{3\sqrt[3]{y^2(8y^4 + 3)}}{4xy^2}$

27. $\sqrt{2(a + b)}$ 29. $\dfrac{x^2y^3\sqrt[n]{xy^5z^2}}{z^2}$ 31. $\sqrt[3]{a^3 + b^3}$

33. $4x\sqrt{2x + 3y^2}$ 35. $\dfrac{3\sqrt[3]{xy^3 - 2}}{y}$ 37. $\dfrac{\sqrt[3]{x^2y^2(x^3 - 27y^3)}}{xy}$

39. $\sqrt[3]{2(x + y)}$ 41. $\dfrac{\sqrt{3(x^2 + y)}}{x}$ 43. $\dfrac{2ab^{2k}}{9c}\sqrt[3]{36ac}$

Exercise Group 4–7

1. $5\sqrt{5}$ 3. $2\sqrt[3]{3}$ 5. $4\sqrt{2}$ 7. $4\sqrt{2}$ 9. $\sqrt[3]{2} + 2\sqrt[3]{3}$

11. $\dfrac{3\sqrt{10}}{8}$ 13. $\dfrac{7\sqrt{3}}{3}$ 15. $\frac{22}{15}\sqrt[3]{12} - \frac{10}{9}\sqrt[3]{3}$

17. $3(1 + 2b)\sqrt{2a}$ 19. $(2b + 3a)\sqrt[3]{3a^2b^2}$

21. $\dfrac{(a^2y + abx)\sqrt{bc}}{b^2y} + \dfrac{ac\sqrt{b}}{bx}$ 23. $\dfrac{a^2bc - ab^2 + c^3}{abc^2}\sqrt[3]{abc}$

25. $yz(2 - xy^2z)\sqrt{xyz}$ 27. $\dfrac{7\sqrt{15a}}{5a}$

29. $\dfrac{-3 + \sqrt{3}}{3}$ 31. $\dfrac{-4 - \sqrt{10}}{3}$ 33. $\dfrac{-3b - 3\sqrt{b^2 + 8b}}{4}$

Exercise Group 4–8

1. $\sqrt{15}$ 3. $9\sqrt{6}$ 5. $5\sqrt[3]{2}$ 7. 6 9. $4\sqrt[3]{9}$
11. $2ab^2\sqrt[3]{3a}$ 13. $6x^2\sqrt[6]{x^3y^2}$ 15. $18x^5$ 17. $a^2 + b^2$
19. $\sqrt{ab} - \sqrt{ac}$ 21. $-5\sqrt{6}$ 23. $31 - 4\sqrt{21}$ 25. $a - 4b$
27. $2\sqrt{6} - 3\sqrt{10} - \sqrt{15} - 9$
29. $b^2c + (ab - bc)\sqrt{bc} - bc\sqrt{ac} + c^2\sqrt{ab} - abc$
31. $-\frac{41}{49}$ 33. $\dfrac{4 - 2\sqrt{3}}{3}$ 35. $\dfrac{p}{r}$
37. $x^2 + 1 - 4\sqrt{x^2 - 3}$ 39. $3 + 2\sqrt{3x - x^2}$
41. $2\sqrt[6]{54}$ 43. $28 - 4\sqrt{10}$ 45. 8 47. 0
49. $20 + 14\sqrt{3}$ 51. $-\frac{2}{3}$

Exercise Group 4–9

1. $\dfrac{\sqrt{15}}{3}$ 3. $\dfrac{\sqrt{5x}}{x}$ 5. $\sqrt{2}$ 7. $\dfrac{\sqrt{42}}{3}$ 9. $\dfrac{3x\sqrt{10}}{5}$
11. $\dfrac{2\sqrt[3]{2x^2}}{x}$ 13. $\dfrac{\sqrt{6x}}{3}$ 15. $\dfrac{\sqrt[3]{9x^2}}{3}$ 17. $\dfrac{\sqrt[6]{72x^5}}{2x^2}$
19. $\dfrac{45\sqrt{2} - 18\sqrt{10}}{2}$ 21. $2 - \sqrt{3}$ 23. $\dfrac{\sqrt{21} - \sqrt{15}}{2}$
25. $5 - 2\sqrt{6}$ 27. $\dfrac{36 - 7\sqrt{15}}{33}$ 29. $\dfrac{(ax + y^2)\sqrt{xy} - axy - xy^2}{a^2x - y^3}$
31. $\dfrac{\sqrt{a - 1} - (a - 1)}{2 - a}$ 33. $\sqrt[6]{250}$ 35. $\dfrac{\sqrt[12]{3456}}{2}$ 37. $\dfrac{\sqrt[6]{432}}{2}$

Exercise Group 4–10

1. $-i$ 3. i 5. $-i$ 7. $7i$ 9. $11i$
11. $2i\sqrt{2}$ 13. $7i\sqrt{3}$ 15. $7i\sqrt{2}$ 17. $i\sqrt{59}$ 19. $2\sqrt{30}$
21. $9i\sqrt{2}$ 23. $\dfrac{34i\sqrt{30}}{15}$ 25. 0 27. -21 29. 0

Review Exercises for Chapter 4

1. $\frac{9}{8}$ 3. 8 5. $\frac{4}{121}$ 7. $\dfrac{25}{4a^{10}by^6}$ 9. $\dfrac{1}{a^8}$
11. $x^{3/50}$ 13. $\dfrac{3y + 2x}{x^2}$ 15. 32 17. $\frac{77}{25}$ 19. $3x\sqrt{1 + 3x}$
21. $\dfrac{(y + 2x)\sqrt{xy}}{xy}$ 23. $9\sqrt{2}$ 25. $a\sqrt[6]{108}$ 27. $2\sqrt[6]{a^3b^2}$
29. $\dfrac{\sqrt[6]{648a^5}}{3a}$ 31. $2(y + z)\sqrt{xy + xz}$ 33. $\dfrac{\sqrt{6ab} + 5\sqrt{3ac}}{2b - 25c}$
35. $36 - 2i\sqrt{6}$

Exercise Group 5–1

5. (a) On a straight line 3 units to the left of the y-axis
   (b) On a straight line 2 units above the x-axis
7. 9
9. -13
11. On a straight line $1\frac{1}{2}$ units above the x-axis
13. $(\frac{11}{2}, 4)$, $(\frac{11}{2}, -4)$
15. One solution, (5, 2)
17. (1, 8), (1, -2), (6, 8), (6, -2)

Exercise Group 5–2

1. $(-1, -\frac{5}{2})$, $\sqrt{145}$
3. $(2, \frac{15}{2})$, $5\sqrt{5}$
5. $(-\frac{11}{2}, \frac{1}{2})$, $\sqrt{314}$
7. $\left(\frac{a+c}{2}, \frac{b+d}{2}\right)$, $\sqrt{(a-c)^2+(b-d)^2}$
9. $\left(\frac{a-c}{2}, \frac{a-c}{2}\right)$, $(a+c)\sqrt{2}$

Exercise Group 5–3

1. $A = s^2$
3. $A = \frac{\pi d^2}{4}$
5. $y = \sqrt{5}\,x$
7. $f(0) = 6, f(-2) = 16, f(3) = 6, f(a) = a^2 - 3a + 6$
9. $H(2) = 7, [H(-1)]^2 = 25, H\left[\frac{x}{z}\right] = \frac{3x^2 + 2z^2}{xz}$
11. 2
13. $-8x - 14$
15. $f(-x) = -2x - 1, f(x+1) = 2x + 1, f(x+h) = 2x + 2h - 1,$
    $\frac{1}{h}[f(x+h) - f(x)] = 2$
17. $f(-x) = -x^3 + x, f(x+1) = x^3 + 3x^2 + 2x,$
    $f(x+h) = x^3 + 3hx^2 + (3h^2 - 1)x + h^3 - h,$
    $\frac{1}{h}[f(x+h) - f(x)] = 3x^2 + 3hx + h^2 - 1$
23. 0
25. $x^2 - x$
27. $\frac{\sqrt{3}\,c}{4}$
29. $\frac{16+\pi}{8}w^2$
31. $A = \frac{\sqrt{3}}{4}s^2$
33. $H = \frac{\sqrt{3}\,x}{2}$
35. (a) $g(1) = 2, g(3) = 4,$ (b) $x = 2$
37. $f(2) = 12, f(4) = 48$
39. $f(2) = 2, f(4) = 12$

Exercise Group 5–6

1. $y = \frac{2x}{5}, \frac{14}{5}$
3. $u = \frac{8}{v}, \frac{8}{3}$
5. $v = \frac{5u}{4}, \frac{45}{2}$
7. $S = 4\pi r^2$
9. $S = 6x^2$
11. $V = \frac{7A}{9}$
13. The force is four times as large

Exercise Group 5–7

1. $y = \frac{x^2z}{8}, \frac{45}{4}$ 3. $u = \frac{40v^2}{9w^3}, \frac{125}{9}$ 5. $W = \frac{18uv^2}{t^3}, \frac{405}{32}$

7. $Y = -\frac{64xz^2}{u^3v}, -\frac{147}{5}$ 9. \$100,774

11. Reduced 90.2% 13. 3.01 in. 15. 15 hp

Review Exercises for Chapter 5

1. $f(-3) = 18, f(5) = 50$ 3. $f(-3) = -28, f(5) = -60$

5. $f(-1) = 16, f(0) = 15, f(3) = 0, f(-a) = 15 + 2a - a^2$ 7. $\frac{16}{11}$

13. 13 15. 16 17. $(\frac{13}{2}, 4), \sqrt{965}$

19. $\left(\frac{a+b}{2}, \frac{c+d}{2}\right), \sqrt{(a-b)^2 + (d-c)^2}$ 23. $\frac{1}{16}$ in.

25. 11,616,000 ft·lb 27. $V = 4x(6 - x)(8 - x)$ 29. $A = 2x(10 - x)$

Exercise Group 6–1

1. 90° 3. 135° 5. −210° 7. 12°
9. 540° 11. 15° 13. −270° 15. $67\frac{1}{2}°$
17. 315° 19. 420° 21. 74° 29′ 04″ 23. 42° 58′ 19″
25. 0° 34′ 23″ 27. 401° 04′ 15″ 29. 122° 02′ 24″ 31. −408° 31′ 09″

33. $\frac{7\pi}{6}$ 35. $\frac{7\pi}{4}$ 37. $\frac{9\pi}{4}$ 39. $\frac{5\pi}{3}$ 41. 4π 43. $\frac{3\pi}{5}$

45. 0.756 47. 1.92 49. 3.70 51. 1.98 53. −3.73 55. 2.40

Exercise Group 6–2

1. $\left(\frac{\sqrt{3}}{2}, \frac{1}{2}\right)$ 3. $\left(\frac{\sqrt{2}}{2}, -\frac{\sqrt{2}}{2}\right)$ 5. $\left(\frac{\sqrt{2}}{2}, \frac{\sqrt{2}}{2}\right)$ 7. $\left(-\frac{\sqrt{3}}{2}, -\frac{1}{2}\right)$

9. Q_2, 52° 11. Q_2, 39° 13. Q_4, 41° 30′

15. Q_2, 88° 51′ 17. $y = -4$ 19. $x = -\sqrt{51}$

21. $x = \pm 2$ 23. $x = \pm 3\sqrt{2},\ y = \pm\sqrt{2}$ 25. $y = \frac{3}{2},\ r = \frac{5}{2}$

27. Q_3 29. Q_4 31. Q_2 33. Q_4 35. Q_4

Exercise Group 6–3

In this set of answers, the values of the trigonometric functions will be given in the order $\sin\theta$, $\cos\theta$, $\tan\theta$, $\cot\theta$, $\sec\theta$, $\csc\theta$.

1. $\frac{4}{5}, -\frac{3}{5}, -\frac{4}{3}, -\frac{3}{4}, -\frac{5}{3}, \frac{5}{4}$

3. $-\frac{2\sqrt{5}}{5}, -\frac{\sqrt{5}}{5}, 2, \frac{1}{2}, -\sqrt{5}, -\frac{\sqrt{5}}{2}$

5. $-\frac{24}{25}, \frac{7}{25}, -\frac{24}{7}, -\frac{7}{24}, \frac{25}{7}, -\frac{25}{24}$

7. $\pm\dfrac{\sqrt{15}}{4}, \dfrac{1}{4}, \pm\sqrt{15}, \pm\dfrac{\sqrt{15}}{15}, 4, \pm\dfrac{4\sqrt{15}}{15}$

9. $\dfrac{1}{2}, \dfrac{\sqrt{3}}{2}, \dfrac{\sqrt{3}}{3}, \sqrt{3}, \dfrac{2\sqrt{3}}{3}, 2$

11. $\pm\dfrac{1}{\sqrt{2}}, \mp\dfrac{1}{\sqrt{2}}, -1, -1, \mp\sqrt{2}, \pm\sqrt{2}$

13. $\frac{4}{5}, -\frac{3}{5}, -\frac{4}{3}, -\frac{3}{4}, -\frac{5}{3}, \frac{5}{4}$

15. $\dfrac{2\sqrt{2}}{3}, \dfrac{1}{3}, 2\sqrt{2}, \dfrac{\sqrt{2}}{4}, 3, \dfrac{3\sqrt{2}}{4}$

17. $-\frac{4}{5}, \frac{3}{5}, -\frac{4}{3}, -\frac{3}{4}, \frac{5}{3}, -\frac{5}{4}$

19. $-\frac{12}{13}, -\frac{5}{13}, \frac{12}{5}, \frac{5}{12}, -\frac{13}{5}, -\frac{13}{12}$

21. $\pm\frac{7}{25}, \mp\frac{24}{25}, -\frac{7}{24}, -\frac{24}{7}, \mp\frac{25}{24}, \pm\frac{25}{7}$

23. $\frac{3}{5}, \pm\frac{4}{5}, \pm\frac{3}{4}, \pm\frac{4}{3}, \pm\frac{5}{4}, \frac{5}{3}$

25. $\dfrac{\sqrt{3}}{2}, -\dfrac{1}{2}, -\sqrt{3}, -\dfrac{\sqrt{3}}{3}, -2, \dfrac{2\sqrt{3}}{3}$

27. $-\frac{4}{5}, \frac{3}{5}, -\frac{4}{3}, -\frac{3}{4}, \frac{5}{3}, -\frac{5}{4}$

29. $-\frac{24}{25}, -\frac{7}{25}, \frac{24}{7}, \frac{7}{24}, -\frac{25}{7}, -\frac{25}{24}$

31. $\pm\dfrac{2\sqrt{2}}{3}, \dfrac{1}{3}, \pm2\sqrt{2}, \pm\dfrac{\sqrt{2}}{4}, 3, \pm\dfrac{3\sqrt{2}}{4}$

33. $\pm\dfrac{\sqrt{35}}{6}, -\dfrac{1}{6}, \mp\sqrt{35}, \mp\dfrac{\sqrt{35}}{35}, -6, \pm\dfrac{6\sqrt{35}}{35}$

35. $\pm\dfrac{\sqrt{26}}{26}, \mp\dfrac{5\sqrt{26}}{26}, -\dfrac{1}{5}, -5, \mp\dfrac{\sqrt{26}}{5}, \pm\sqrt{26}$

Exercise Group 6–4

In this set of answers for Exercises 1 through 19, the values of the trigonometric functions will be given in the order $\sin\theta$, $\cos\theta$, $\tan\theta$, $\cot\theta$, $\sec\theta$, $\csc\theta$.

1. $\dfrac{1}{2}, \dfrac{\sqrt{3}}{2}, \dfrac{\sqrt{3}}{3}, \sqrt{3}, \dfrac{2\sqrt{3}}{3}, 2$

3. $\dfrac{\sqrt{3}}{2}, -\dfrac{1}{2}, -\sqrt{3}, -\dfrac{\sqrt{3}}{3}, -2, \dfrac{2\sqrt{3}}{3}$

5. $\dfrac{\sqrt{2}}{2}, -\dfrac{\sqrt{2}}{2}, -1, -1, -\sqrt{2}, \sqrt{2}$

7. 0, 1, 0, —, 1, —

9. -1, 0, —, 0, —, -1

11. 0, 1, 0, —, 1, —

13. $-\dfrac{\sqrt{3}}{2}, \dfrac{1}{2}, -\sqrt{3}, -\dfrac{\sqrt{3}}{3}, 2, -\dfrac{2\sqrt{3}}{3}$

15. $-\dfrac{1}{2}, \dfrac{\sqrt{3}}{2}, -\dfrac{\sqrt{3}}{3}, -\sqrt{3}, \dfrac{2\sqrt{3}}{3}, -2$

17. $\dfrac{\sqrt{3}}{2}, -\dfrac{1}{2}, -\sqrt{3}, -\dfrac{\sqrt{3}}{3}, -2, \dfrac{2\sqrt{3}}{3}$

19. $-\dfrac{\sqrt{3}}{2}, -\dfrac{1}{2}, \sqrt{3}, \dfrac{\sqrt{3}}{3}, -2, -\dfrac{2\sqrt{3}}{3}$

Exercise Group 6–5

1. 0.3411 3. 0.7050 5. 1.258 7. 2.356 9. 0.0465
11. 1.688 13. 0.9932 15. 3.204 17. −1.836 19. −1.963
21. −0.8090 23. 1.122 25. 0.9325 27. −0.5150 29. 4.134
31. 6.314 33. −0.9929 35. −1.022 37. 71° 30′ 39. 76° 40′
41. 19° 40′ 43. 22° 10′ 45. 63° 30′ 47. 11° 30′ 49. 10° 30′
51. 9° 20′ 53. 89° 40′ 55. 9° 40′ 57. 3° 20′ 59. 1°
61. 264° 63. 95° 30′ 65. 102° 40′ 67. 138° 20′ 69. 149°
71. 220° 30′ 73. cos 71° 28′ 75. cot 16° 31′ 77. csc 22° 02′ 79. sin 51° 13′
81. tan 76° 12′ 83. sec 21° 38′

Review Exercises for Chapter 6

1. $\frac{5\pi}{4}$ 3. $\frac{28\pi}{15}$ 5. 165° 7. 118° 01′ 47″

9. $\sin\theta = \pm\frac{\sqrt{5}}{3}$, $\tan\theta = \mp\frac{\sqrt{5}}{2}$, $\cot\theta = \mp\frac{2\sqrt{5}}{5}$, $\sec\theta = -\frac{3}{2}$, $\csc\theta = \pm\frac{3\sqrt{5}}{5}$

11. $\sin\theta = \frac{1}{3}$, $\cos\theta = \pm\frac{2\sqrt{2}}{3}$, $\tan\theta = \pm\frac{\sqrt{2}}{4}$, $\cot\theta = \pm 2\sqrt{2}$, $\sec\theta = \pm\frac{3\sqrt{2}}{4}$

13. $\sin\theta = \frac{\pm 1}{\sqrt{1+b^2}}$, $\cos\theta = \frac{\pm b}{\sqrt{1+b^2}}$, $\tan\theta = \frac{1}{b}$, $\sec\theta = \pm\frac{\sqrt{1+b^2}}{b}$, $\csc\theta = \pm\sqrt{1+b^2}$

In the remaining answers, the values of the trigonometric functions are given in the order $\sin\theta$, $\cos\theta$, $\tan\theta$, $\cot\theta$, $\sec\theta$, $\csc\theta$.

15. $-\frac{1}{\sqrt{2}}, \frac{1}{\sqrt{2}}, -1, -1, \sqrt{2}, -\sqrt{2}$ 17. $\frac{1}{\sqrt{2}}, -\frac{1}{\sqrt{2}}, -1, -1, -\sqrt{2}, \sqrt{2}$

19. $-\frac{1}{2}, -\frac{\sqrt{3}}{2}, \frac{1}{\sqrt{3}}, \sqrt{3}, -\frac{2}{\sqrt{3}}, -2$

21. 0, −1, 0, —, −1, —

23. $\frac{1}{2}, -\frac{\sqrt{3}}{2}, -\frac{1}{\sqrt{3}}, -\sqrt{3}, -\frac{2}{\sqrt{3}}, 2$

25. $\frac{\sqrt{3}}{2}, \frac{1}{2}, \sqrt{3}, \frac{1}{\sqrt{3}}, 2, \frac{2}{\sqrt{3}}$

Exercise Group 7–1

1. $f(0) = 5, m = 2$ 3. $f(0) = 7, m = -3$ 5. $f(0) = 5, f(-\frac{5}{3}) = 0$
7. $\frac{8}{3}$ 9. $\frac{19}{105}$ 11. $\frac{1}{2}$ 13. $\frac{2}{213}$ 15. $\frac{100}{13}$ 17. $\frac{24}{5}$
19. $\frac{c}{a-b}$ 21. $a + b$ 23. $\frac{5}{8}$

Exercise Group 7–2

1. 8 3. $-\frac{1}{12}$ 5. $\frac{3}{2}$ 7. -1
9. No solution 11. $-\frac{7}{4}$ 13. $\frac{5}{8}$ 15. -4
17. 8 19. $\sin x = 1$ 21. $\tan x = -\frac{2}{3}$ 23. $\sec x = -8$
25. $\sin x = 1$ 27. $\cot x = -\frac{3}{4}$

Exercise Group 7–3

1. (a) $1.25x$, (b) $0.25x$ 3. 4.5% 5. 10%
7. \$127.34 9. \$3,906.25 11. $2r$ 13. 7.5 in.
15. 33.1% 17. (a) $50t$, (b) 24.5 19. 43.75 mph
21. 300 mph 23. In 6 hr, 360 mi from start 25. $26\frac{2}{3}$%
27. 50 cm^3 29. 100 cm^3 31. 2 lb 33. $\frac{2}{4}$
35. 7, 10 37. \$33,600

Exercise Group 7–4

1. (2, 3) 3. $(\frac{3}{2}, \frac{2}{3})$ 5. $(-3, -5)$ 7. (15, 8) 9. $(\frac{3}{2}, -\frac{2}{3})$
11. $(-\frac{36}{5}, -\frac{88}{5})$ 13. $(\frac{8}{3}, \frac{3}{2})$ 15. $(-\frac{1}{5}, \frac{1}{4})$
17. $(0.2, -0.3)$ 19. $(-0.4, -0.7)$ 21. $(a + b, a)$
23. $\left(a, -\frac{b}{a}\right)$ 25. $(1 + z, 1 - z)$ 27. $\left(\frac{2a}{5}, -\frac{3a}{7}\right)$
29. $(1.8c^2, -2.3b^2)$ 31. $(-2, 7)$ 33. $(\frac{3}{2}, 0)$

Exercise Group 7–5

1. (7, 3, 0) 3. $(\frac{1}{2}, \frac{1}{3}, 1)$ 5. $(10, -6, 4)$
7. $(-1, 1, -2)$ 9. $(\frac{1}{3}, 2, \frac{1}{3})$ 11. (a, b, c)
13. (a, b, ab) 15. $(2u, -2u, 8u)$ 17. $(1, -2, 3, -4)$

Exercise Group 7–6

1. 69, 34 3. 18 ft/sec, 27 ft/sec 5. $\frac{2}{3}, \frac{3}{4}$
7. \$8,000, 6.25% 9. 4 hr 11. 4 yd, 5 yd
13. $2x^2 + 3x - 4$ 15. $-x^2 + 3x - 4$ 17. \$5,000, \$1,000, \$4,000
19. 120 min, 180 min, 360 min 21. $A = 2, B = -7, C = 6$

Review Exercises for Chapter 7

1. 74 3. 1 5. $-\frac{9}{5}$ 7. $-\frac{11}{7}$
9. $-\frac{9}{5}$ 11. 100 cc 13. 4.5% 15. $(-2, 3)$
17. $(-\frac{16}{15}, \frac{27}{25})$ 19. (a, b) 21. $(1, -2, 3)$ 23. (a, b, c)
25. $(1, -2, 3)$ 27. $\left(\frac{a}{2}, -\frac{a}{2}, b\right)$
29. Airspeed 425 mph, wind velocity 25 mph

Exercise Group 8–1

1. 2, 3 3. −7, 9 5. −3, 7 7. −4, 13 9. 6, −9
11. $3a$, $-7a$ 13. −1, b 15. $p, \dfrac{1}{p}$ 17. 0, 3 19. $\pm\frac{5}{4}$
21. $\pm\dfrac{b}{a}$ 23. $-\frac{5}{3}, -\frac{5}{3}$ 25. $\frac{5}{2}, \frac{5}{2}$ 27. $-\dfrac{2q}{p}, -\dfrac{2q}{p}$ 29. $-\frac{3}{2}$, 1
31. $\frac{4}{3}, -\frac{1}{2}$ 33. $1, -\frac{5}{7}$ 35. $\frac{2}{5}, -\frac{1}{3}$ 37. $-7, \frac{23}{2}$ 39. $\frac{7}{2}, -\frac{2}{5}$
41. $2, -\frac{43}{2}$

Exercise Group 8–2

1. $1, -\frac{2}{3}$ 3. $1 \pm \sqrt{6}$ 5. $\frac{1}{2}(-a \pm \sqrt{a^2 + 24})$
7. $\pm\frac{1}{7}(4i\sqrt{7})$ 9. $0, -\frac{5}{9}$ 11. $\frac{1}{4}(5 \pm i\sqrt{31})$
13. $\dfrac{1}{a}(1 \pm \sqrt{1 - 7a^2})$ 15. $\frac{1}{6}(u \pm \sqrt{u^2 - 24})$ 17. $\dfrac{1}{2c}(-b \pm \sqrt{b^2 - 4ac})$
19. $a \pm \sqrt{a^2 - c}$ 21. $\dfrac{7 \pm \sqrt{69 + 20a}}{2(a + 1)}$

Exercise Group 8–3

1. $-1, \frac{2}{3}$ 3. $-1 \pm \sqrt{6}$ 5. $\frac{1}{2}(a \pm \sqrt{a^2 + 24})$
7. $\frac{1}{7}(1 \pm i\sqrt{34})$ 9. $i \pm 1$ 11. $\frac{4}{3}, \frac{5}{7}$
13. $\frac{3}{2}, \frac{2}{3}$ 15. $\sqrt{3} \pm 1$ 17. $\frac{1}{4}(5 \pm \sqrt{65})$
19. $\frac{1}{2}(-1 \pm \sqrt{5})$ 21. $\frac{1}{10}(-3 \pm i\sqrt{131})$ 23. $p, \dfrac{1}{p}$
25. $-\dfrac{a}{2}, -b$ 27. $\dfrac{b \pm \sqrt{b^2 - 4ac + 4c}}{2(a - 1)}$
29. $\frac{1}{2}(-1 \pm \sqrt{5})(a + b)$ 31. $11 \pm 7i$
33. −49, −53 35. $-3, \frac{33}{7}$ 37. $\dfrac{a + b}{a - b}, \dfrac{b - a}{a + b}$
39. $\dfrac{a}{a + 1}, \dfrac{a}{a - 1}$ 41. $-\frac{13}{3}$, 13 43. $-a, \dfrac{1}{a}$

Exercise Group 8–4

3. $(\frac{3}{4}, -\frac{41}{8})$ 5. (2, −6) 7. $(-\frac{1}{2}, \frac{9}{4})$ 9. (−1, −1)
11. $(\frac{1}{2}, -\frac{7}{2})$ 13. (−3, −4) 15. $(\frac{11}{2}, -\frac{121}{20})$ 17. (−1, −7)
19. $(-\frac{2}{3}, \frac{11}{3})$ 21. $(\frac{1}{2}, \frac{1}{4})$ 23. $(-\frac{1}{4}, \frac{1}{8})$ 25. $(-\frac{1}{4}, -\frac{3}{2})$

Exercise Group 8–5

1. 49 ft, $\frac{7}{4}$ sec, 48 ft 3. $k = \pm 4$ 5. −4
7. 1250 yd^2 9. \$10 11. $\frac{1}{4}(7 \pm \sqrt{49 - s}), \frac{7}{4}, \frac{7}{2}$
13. 1 ft 15. 5 in. square
17. $300 + 200\sqrt{2} = 582.74$ in^2 19. 15×36
21. 3 in. on each side

Exercise Group 8–6

1. 1, roots real, unequal, rational
3. −44, roots imaginary and unequal
5. 180, roots real, unequal, irrational
7. 9, roots real, unequal, rational
9. −3, roots imaginary and unequal
11. 0, roots real, equal, rational
13. 113, roots real, unequal, irrational
15. 0, roots real, equal, rational
17. 1.97, roots real, unequal, irrational
19. $\pm\sqrt{3}$
21. $\frac{9}{20}$
23. $\dfrac{-5 \pm \sqrt{85}}{2}$

Exercise Group 8–7

1. $\frac{3}{2}, \frac{7}{2}$
3. $-\frac{5}{3}, -\frac{7}{3}$
5. $\dfrac{b}{c}, -\dfrac{a}{c}$
7. $\dfrac{c}{d}, -\dfrac{b}{d}$
9. $i, 1$
11. $x^2 + x - 6 = 0$
13. $2x^2 - x - 10 = 0$
15. $x^2 + x + 1 = 0$
17. $12x^2 + 11x + 2 = 0$
19. $x^2 - 4x - 1 = 0$
21. $bx^2 - 2ax + a = 0$
23. $0, \frac{1}{5}$
25. $\frac{1}{3}$
27. $\frac{15}{29}$
29. 36

Exercise Group 8–8

1. $\pm 1, \pm 3$
3. $-1, -2, \dfrac{1 \pm i\sqrt{3}}{2}, 1 \pm i\sqrt{3}$
5. $1, 2, -1 \pm i\sqrt{3}, \frac{1}{2}(-1 \pm i\sqrt{3})$
7. $\pm\sqrt{3}, \pm\frac{1}{2}\sqrt{14}$
9. $-1, -\frac{1}{2}$
11. $\pm 2, \pm i\sqrt{10}$
13. $-1, 2, -3, 4$
15. $\dfrac{-9 \pm \sqrt{141}}{6}, \dfrac{-3 \pm \sqrt{5}}{2}$
17. $-3, -2, 0, 1$
19. $-\frac{3}{2}, -\frac{1}{3}$
21. $x = \dfrac{\pi}{2}$
23. $\tan x = \frac{1}{3}$
25. $\sin x = \pm\dfrac{\sqrt{10}}{5}$; $x = \dfrac{\pi}{3}, \dfrac{2\pi}{3}, \dfrac{4\pi}{3}, \dfrac{5\pi}{3}$

Exercise Group 8–9

1. 7
3. No solution
5. 27
7. 6
9. 8
11. 8
13. No solution
15. $\frac{1}{2}$
17. $0, -\frac{4}{5}$
19. $\pm i\sqrt{3}$
21. $\frac{659}{17}$
23. $4, \frac{36}{17}$
25. 2
27. $\frac{2}{5}\sqrt{26}$
29. ± 1
31. 81
33. 14
35. $x = \dfrac{\pi}{6}, \dfrac{5\pi}{6}$
37. $\tan x = -\frac{4}{3}$

Review Exercises for Chapter 8

1. $0.1(13 \pm \sqrt{229})$
3. $\frac{1}{4}(-3 \pm i\sqrt{31})$
5. $\frac{1}{3}(1 \pm i\sqrt{23})$
7. $\dfrac{1}{3a}(b \pm \sqrt{b^2 - 9a^2})$
9. $\dfrac{1}{4a}(c \pm \sqrt{c^2 - 8a^2})$
11. $\dfrac{1}{2b}(1 - c \pm \sqrt{(c-1)^2 - 4ab})$
13. $\frac{1}{4}(-3 \pm i\sqrt{31})$

15. $0.1(-3 \pm \sqrt{269})$ 17. $0.1(3 \pm i\sqrt{131})$

19. $\dfrac{b - 3 \pm \sqrt{(b-3)^2 + 24(c-2)}}{2(c-2)}$

21. $\dfrac{b \pm \sqrt{b^2 - 4ad + 4ac}}{2a}$

23. $\dfrac{2 - b \pm \sqrt{(b-2)^2 + 4a(c+13)}}{2a}$

25. $\frac{7}{3}, -\frac{5}{2}$ 27. $2, -\frac{4}{3}$ 29. $a, -\dfrac{c}{b}$ 31. $0, -12$

33. $\frac{1}{25}(-14 \pm 2\sqrt{399})$ 35. $\frac{1}{2}(3 \pm 4i)$

37. Roots real, unequal, irrational; $S = -\frac{5}{3}$, $P = -\frac{7}{3}$

39. Roots imaginary and unequal; $S = -\frac{1}{3}$, $P = \frac{10}{9}$

41. Roots imaginary and unequal; $S = 5$, $P = 9$

43. $-2, -1, 1 \pm i\sqrt{3}, \frac{1}{2}(1 \pm i\sqrt{3})$

45. $\pm 3, \pm 5i$ 47. $\pm 1, \pm \dfrac{i\sqrt{21}}{3}$ 49. $\frac{11}{2}$ 51. $\frac{1}{6}$

Exercise Group 9–1

1. $s = 6$ ft, $A = 9$ ft^2 3. $s = 11.5$ in., $A = 28.75$ in^2

5. $s = \dfrac{35\pi}{6}$ ft $= 18.33$ ft, $A = \dfrac{245\pi}{12}$ ft^2 $= 64.14$ ft^2

7. $s = 15\pi$ cm $= 47.12$ cm, $A = 1125\pi$ cm^2 $= 3534.3$ cm^2

9. $s = 220\pi$ cm $= 691.2$ cm, $A = 19360\pi$ cm^2 $= 60{,}820$ cm^2

11. $s = 11.87$ yd, $A = 474.8$ yd^2 13. $s = 0.28$ in., $A = 0.007$ in^2

15. $s = 185.9$ ft, $A = 19{,}800$ ft^2

17. $s = 0.005096$ ft, $A = 10.19 \times 10^{-6}$ ft^2

19. 3 rad, 171° 53′, 121.5 in^2 21. 2.029 rad, 116° 15′, 11,180 cm^2

23. 0.3752 rad, 21° 30′, 12.40 ft^2 25. 4.205 rad, 240° 56′, 38.88 ft^2

27. 0.25 rad, 14° 19′, 3.125 m^2 29. 0.6316 rad, 36° 11′, 893.8 in^2

31. 70.4 rad/sec 33. 775 ft/sec

35. 15° 37. 0.64 mi/sec

39. 52.36 ft/sec, 40π rad/sec

Exercise Group 9–2

1. 0.5185 3. 2.029 5. 0.1002 7. 3.081 9. 0.1369

11. 0.9408 13. −0.5488 15. −0.1189 17. 1.350 19. −1.372

21. 1.486 23. 1.248 25. 39° 37′ 27. 12° 26′ 29. 30° 46′

31. 96° 05′ 33. 131° 04′ 35. 122° 35′ 37. 20° 43′ 39. 84° 10′

41. 30° 32′ 43. 100° 53′ 45. 93° 23′ 47. 5° 27′

Exercise Group 9–3

1. $B = 16° 48'$, $a = 79.61$, $b = 24.03$

3. $A = 20° 22'$, $b = 102.9$, $c = 109.8$

5. $A = 57° 34'$, $a = 3.353$, $c = 3.972$
7. $B = 47° 37'$, $a = 356.1$, $c = 528.3$
9. $A = 31° 45'$, $a = 47.02$, $b = 75.99$
11. $A = 29° 35'$, $B = 60° 25'$, $c = 2.684$
13. $A = 84° 57'$, $B = 5° 03'$, $a = 0.1831$
15. $A = 28° 54'$, $B = 61° 06'$, $b = 781.7$
17. $B = 68° 26'$, $b = 80.33$, $c = 86.37$
19. $A = 30° 19'$, $B = 59° 41'$, $c = 494.5$
21. $A = 58° 17'$, $b = 15.43$, $c = 29.34$
23. $A = 31° 43'$, $a = 0.1832$, $c = 0.3485$
25. $A = 22° 46'$, $B = 67° 14'$, $c = 0.3217$
27. $B = 26° 55'$, $a = 7.966$, $b = 4.044$
29. $A = 28° 52'$, $B = 61° 08'$, $b = 0.3825$
31. For 1°, $AB = BC = CD = 0.0175$;
for 3°, $AB = 0.0523$ and $BC = CD = 0.0524$;
for 5°, $AB = 0.0872$, $BC = 0.0873$, $CD = 0.0875$

Exercise Group 9–4

1. 23.46, 23.5
3. 0.003452, 0.00345
5. 2179000, 2180000
7. 0.9615, 0.962
9. 2.325, 2.33
11. 0.01234, 0.0123
13. ± 0.05 cm
15. ± 0.5 ft
17. ± 0.0005 ft^3
19. ± 0.00005 yd
21. ± 0.5 in^3
23. 2.45
25. 56.6
27. 991
29. $130{,}000 = 1.3 \times 10^5$
31. 9.753
33. 51°
35. 60°
37. 10° 53′
39. 8° 30′
41. 71°
43. 42°
45. $A = 47°$, $B = 43°$, $b = 3.1$
47. $A = 40°$, $B = 50°$, $a = 2.4$
49. $A = 62° 50'$, $B = 27° 10'$, $c = 8.23$
51. $A = 48°$, $a = 37$, $b = 33$
53. $A = 61°$, $B = 29°$, $a = 4.2$

Exercise Group 9–5

1. 84.4 ft
3. 140 mph
5. 58 naut mi, 294°
7. $d = 1507$ mi, $\theta = 234°$
9. 554 ft
11. $d = 6.3$ mi
13. $h = 20.4$ ft
15. 8009 ft, 1268 ft
17. 128 in.
19. 2894 mi, 50.51 mi

Exercise Group 9–6

1. $H = 127.4$, $V = 120.0$
3. $H = 180.0$, $V = 254.8$
5. $H = 56.79$, $V = 113.6$
7. $H = 184.5$, $V = 106.5$
9. $H = M \cos \theta$, $V = M \sin \theta$
11. $R = 316.2$, in direction 251° 34′
13. $R = 41.4$, in direction 135°
15. $R = 77.96$, in direction 189° 54′
17. 242 mph, 219° 20′
19. Heading of 56° 50′, 251 mph
21. 262 lb
23. $T = C = 100$ lb
25. $T = 76.53$ lb, $C = 100$ lb
27. $T = 50\sqrt{5}$ lb, $C = 50$ lb
29. $F_{30} = 500\sqrt{3}$ lb, $F_{60} = 500$ lb

Review Exercises for Chapter 9

1. $A = 67°, b = 14, c = 35$ 3. $A = 45°, B = 45°, a = 2.3$
5. 90 mph 7. Hor. comp. = 188 lb, vert. comp. = 201 lb
9. 98 ft

Exercise Group 10–1

1. $A = 1, P = 2\pi$ 3. $A = 1, P = 2\pi$ 5. $A = \frac{1}{2}, P = 2\pi$
7. $A = \frac{5}{2}, P = 2\pi$ 9. $A = \frac{3}{5}, P = 2\pi$

Exercise Group 10–3

1. $(0, 2), (\pi, -2)$ 3. $\left(-\frac{\pi}{2}, 2\right), \left(\frac{\pi}{2}, -2\right)$
5. $(-2\pi, 3), (0, -3)$ 7. $(0, 2), (\pi, -2)$
9. $(\pi, 3), (0, -3)$ 11. $(\pi, 1), (2\pi, -1)$
13. $\left(-\frac{\pi}{6}, 1\right), \left(\frac{5\pi}{6}, -1\right)$ 15. $\left(\frac{\pi}{3}, 1\right), \left(\frac{2\pi}{3}, -1\right)$
17. $\left(\frac{\pi}{3}, 1\right), \left(\frac{2\pi}{3}, -1\right)$

Review Exercises for Chapter 10

1. $P = \pi$ 3. $P = \frac{2\pi}{3}, A = \frac{1}{2}$ 5. $P = \frac{\pi}{3}$
7. $P = \pi, A = 3$ 9. $P = \frac{\pi}{2}$ 11. $P = 3\pi$
13. $P = 2\pi, A = 2$ 15. $P = \pi, A = \frac{1}{2}$ 17. $P = \pi, A = 3$
19. $P = 2\pi, (A = \sqrt{5})$ 21. $P = 12\pi$

Exercise Group 11–1

1. $\frac{\pi}{4} + 2n\pi, \frac{3\pi}{4} + 2n\pi$ 3. $\frac{\pi}{6} + 2n\pi, \frac{11\pi}{6} + 2n\pi$ 5. $\frac{\pi}{4} + n\pi$
7. $\frac{7\pi}{6} + 2n\pi, \frac{11\pi}{6} + 2n\pi$ 9. $\frac{3\pi}{4} + n\pi$ 11. $\frac{4\pi}{3} + 2n\pi, \frac{5\pi}{3} + 2n\pi$
13. $n\pi$ 15. $\frac{\pi}{2} + n\pi$ 17. $x = \frac{1}{2} \arcsin 3y$ 19. $x = \frac{\pi}{4} + \operatorname{arcsec} 2y$
21. $x = -\frac{1}{2} + \frac{1}{2} \arcsin y$ 23. $x = 2 \tan y$ 25. $x = \sin\left(y - \frac{\pi}{2}\right)$
27. $x = 1 + \tan(y + \pi)$ 37. Inverse period $= 2\pi$, no inverse amplitude
39. Inverse period $= 4\pi$, inverse amplitude $= 2$
41. Inverse period $= 6\pi$, inverse amplitude $= 2$
43. Inverse period $= 2\pi$, inverse amplitude $= 1$
45. Inverse period $= 2\pi$, inverse amplitude $= 1$
47. Inverse period $= 6\pi$, inverse amplitude $= \frac{1}{2}$

Exercise Group 11–2

1. $45°$ 3. $60°$ 5. $30°$ 7. $56° 50'$ 9. $42° 30'$
11. $-41° 50'$ 13. $-73°$ 15. $-18° 20'$ 17. $-30°$
19. $\frac{\pi}{6}$ 21. $-\frac{\pi}{4}$ 23. $-\frac{\pi}{3}$ 25. 0 27. $\frac{\pi}{2}$
29. $\frac{\pi}{2}$ 31. $\frac{2\pi}{3}$ 33. π 35. $-\frac{\pi}{18}$ 37. $\frac{3}{5}$
39. $\frac{1}{2}$ 41. 0 43. $-\frac{5}{13}$ 45. $\frac{\sqrt{5}}{2}$ 47. $\frac{\sqrt{5}}{3}$
49. $\frac{\sqrt{3}}{2}$ 51. 0

Exercise Group 11–3

1. $10^{0.7781}$ 3. $10^{1.6232}$ 5. $10^{-0.1761}$
7. $10^{0.1963}$ 9. $10^{2.4592}$ 11. $10^{3.8309}$
13. $10^{0.0333}$ 15. $10^{0.2216}$ 17. $10^{1.7993}$
19. $10^{2.6353}$ 21. $10^{-0.3899}$ 23. $10^{0.1896}$
25. $10^{3.2508}$ 27. $10^{1.2596}$ 29. $10^{0.9286}$
31. $10^{0.8228}$ 33. $10^{0.5797}$ 35. $10^{0.5325}$

Exercise Group 11–4

1. $\log_2 16 = 4$ 3. $\log_5 \frac{1}{25} = -2$ 5. $\log_{27} 3 = \frac{1}{3}$
7. $\log_{81} 9 = \frac{1}{2}$ 9. $\log_{17} 1 = 0$ 11. $\log_{1/3} 9 = -2$
13. $3^5 = 243$ 15. $7^3 = 343$ 17. $(1.5)^3 = 3.375$
19. $32^{7/5} = 128$ 21. $9^{0.5} = 3$ 23. $16^{-0.25} = 0.5$
25. $y = 4$ 27. $y = -2$ 29. $y = -3$
31. $y = 4$ 33. $y = 1.5$ 35. $x = 0.01$
37. $x = \frac{1}{32}$ 39. $x = 7^{2/3}$ 41. $x = \frac{1}{256}$
43. $b = 9$ 45. $b = a$ 47. $b = 5$
49. $b = 2^{3/4}$ 51. $b = \sqrt{3}$ 53. $b = a$

Exercise Group 11–6

1. 1.1461 3. 1.6232 5. 2.8504 7. 4.9930 9. 0.1963
11. 0.1649 13. 9.2430 − 10 15. 0.8355 17. 2.4608
19. 0.6394 21. 3.0178 23. 9.5738 − 10 25. 8560
27. 3.85 29. 0.922 31. 397 33. 0.000608
35. 11.5 37. 891 39. 2.03 41. 0.867
49. $y = 5x^3$ 51. $y = 7(10^{2x})$ 53. $y = 10^{kx+1}$ 55. $y = 25x^{3/2}$

Exercise Group 11–7

1. 2.4972 3. 1.9230 5. 9.3923 − 10 7. 4.7660
9. 6.2611 − 10 11. 8.8126 − 10 13. 551.4 15. 75.06
17. 0.01575 19. 0.002653 21. 0.00004206 23. 0.0000009504
25. 0.4979 27. 0.2953 29. 0.2227 31. 0.06004
33. 0.004576 35. 0.03705

Exercise Group 11–8

1. 351.9
3. 0.3441
5. 0.2053
7. 3.538
9. 111.0
11. 0.03973
13. 0.3238
15. 1.838
17. 0.4717
19. 0.008304
21. 2.527
23. 5,519,000
25. 10.54
27. 0.02829
29. 2.194×10^{-11}
31. 3.155×10^{-7}

Exercise Group 11–9

1. 9.5963 — 10
3. 0.5780
5. 0.1000
7. 0.7428
9. 0.1610
11. 9.8439 — 10
13. 68° 27′
15. 62° 17′
17. 37° 06′
19. 2° 06′
21. 2° 25′
23. 51° 17′
25. $B = 53° 42'$, $b = 236.3$, $c = 293.1$
27. $A = 13° 05'$, $B = 76° 55'$, $c = 1.382$
29. $B = 13° 24'$, $a = 102.1$, $c = 105.0$
31. $A = 35° 55'$, $b = 4.345$, $c = 5.365$
33. $A = 76° 33'$, $a = 9.812$, $c = 10.09$
35. 36.64 mph
37. $T_1 = 2176$ lb, $T_2 = 1974$ lb
39. 9.2 mi
41. 870.8 lb

Exercise Group 11–10

1. 1.650
3. 0.4943
5. 36.42
7. 6711
9. 1.209
11. 0.6241
13. 1724
15. 20.05
17. 23.15
19. $170
21. $2451
23. 4.7%

Exercise Group 11–11

1. 4.990
3. 3.782
5. —2.921
7. —1.053
9. 76.10
11. 4.014
13. 8.361
15. 1.217

Review Exercises for Chapter 11

1. $y = 4$
3. $x = \frac{1}{5}$
5. $b = 2$
17. $y = 2(10^{3x})$
19. $y = 10^{(5x+3)/2}$
21. 0.2057
23. 2.121
25. 3.642×10^{-12}
27. 0.7761
29. 0.2507
31. 7.501
33. 0.607
35. 0.959
37. 0.039
39. $x = \frac{1}{2} \arccos \frac{y}{2}$
41. $x = \frac{1}{2} \sin y$
43. $x = \frac{1}{b} \arctan \frac{y}{a}$
45. $\frac{\pi}{6}$
47. 0.5498 rad
49. 0.7694 rad
51. $-\frac{5}{12}$
53. $\frac{3}{5}$
55. $\frac{2\sqrt{3}}{3}$

Exercise Group 12–1

49. $\sec \theta$
51. $\cos \theta$
53. $a \sin^3 \theta$
55. $x = \arctan 1$
57. $x = \arccos 0$
59. $x = \arctan 0$, $x = \arctan 1$
61. $x = \arccos 1$
63. $x = \arcsin \frac{1}{2}$, $x = \arcsin (-1)$

Exercise Group 12–2

In Exercises 1, 3, and 5, the answers are given in the order sin $(A + B)$, sin $(A - B)$, cos $(A + B)$, cos $(A - B)$, tan $(A + B)$, and tan $(A - B)$.

1. $\frac{33}{65}, -\frac{63}{65}, -\frac{56}{65}, \frac{16}{65}, -\frac{33}{56}, -\frac{63}{16}$
3. $\frac{117}{125}, \frac{3}{5}, \frac{44}{125}, -\frac{4}{5}, \frac{117}{44}, -\frac{3}{4}$
5. $\frac{56}{65}, -\frac{16}{65}, \frac{33}{65}, \frac{63}{65}, \frac{56}{33}, -\frac{16}{33}$
7. $\dfrac{\sqrt{6} - \sqrt{2}}{4}$
9. $\dfrac{\sqrt{3}}{2}$
11. $-2 - \sqrt{3}$
13. 0
15. $\sqrt{3}$
17. $-\dfrac{\sqrt{2}}{2}$
41. 1

Exercise Group 12–3

1. $\sin 15°$
3. $\frac{1}{2} \sin 2\theta$
5. $\cos 4A$
7. $\sin^2 2\theta$
9. $\sin^2 \theta$
11. $\tan 2\theta$
13. $\frac{24}{25}, -\frac{7}{25}, -\frac{24}{7}$
15. $\frac{24}{25}, -\frac{7}{25}, -\frac{24}{7}$
17. $-\frac{120}{169}, -\frac{119}{169}, \frac{120}{119}$
19. $\dfrac{4\sqrt{5}}{9}, \dfrac{1}{9}, 4\sqrt{5}$
21. $\dfrac{5\sqrt{11}}{18}, \dfrac{7}{18}, \dfrac{5\sqrt{11}}{7}$
23. $\dfrac{1}{2}, -\dfrac{\sqrt{3}}{2}, -\dfrac{\sqrt{3}}{3}$
25. 1, 0, —
27. $\dfrac{3\sqrt{10}}{10}, -\dfrac{\sqrt{10}}{10}, -3$
29. $\dfrac{5\sqrt{34}}{34}, -\dfrac{3\sqrt{34}}{34}, -\dfrac{5}{3}$
31. $\dfrac{3\sqrt{13}}{13}, \dfrac{2\sqrt{13}}{13}, \dfrac{3}{2}$
33. $\frac{3}{5}$
35. $\frac{24}{25}$
37. $\dfrac{1 - x^2}{1 + x^2}$
39. $\dfrac{1 - \sqrt{1 - x^2}}{x}$
41. $\dfrac{x^2 - 1}{x^2 + 1}$
59. $\sin \theta = \dfrac{2t}{1 + t^2}, \cos \theta = \dfrac{1 - t^2}{1 + t^2}$

Exercise Group 12–4

1. $2 \sin 30° \cos 20°$
3. $2 \sin 41° \cos 91°$
5. $-2 \sin 17\frac{1}{2}° \sin 2\frac{1}{2}°$
7. $2 \sin 2\theta \cos 4\theta$
9. $-2 \sin 7\theta \sin 3\theta$
11. $\frac{1}{2} \sin 60° - \frac{1}{2} \sin 20°$
13. $\frac{1}{2} \cos 136° + \frac{1}{2} \cos 64°$
15. $\frac{1}{2} \sin 3\theta + \frac{1}{2} \sin \theta$
17. $\frac{1}{2} \cos 4\theta + \frac{1}{2} \cos 2\theta$
19. $\frac{1}{2} \sin 15A - \frac{1}{2} \sin A$
21. $\frac{1}{2} \cos 36C + \frac{1}{2} \cos 2C$

Exercise Group 12–5

1. $\theta = \dfrac{\pi}{6}, \dfrac{5\pi}{6}$
3. $\theta = \dfrac{\pi}{6}, \dfrac{5\pi}{6}, \dfrac{7\pi}{6}, \dfrac{11\pi}{6}$
5. $\theta = 0, \dfrac{2\pi}{3}, \pi, \dfrac{4\pi}{3}$
7. $\theta = 0, \pi$
9. $\theta = \dfrac{2\pi}{3}$
11. $\theta = \dfrac{2\pi}{3}, \pi, \dfrac{4\pi}{3}$
13. $\theta = \dfrac{\pi}{4}, \dfrac{3\pi}{4}, \dfrac{5\pi}{4}, \dfrac{7\pi}{4}$
15. $\theta = \dfrac{\pi}{6}, \dfrac{5\pi}{6}, \dfrac{3\pi}{2}$
17. $\theta = \dfrac{\pi}{3}, \dfrac{5\pi}{3}$
19. $\theta = \dfrac{\pi}{6}, \dfrac{2\pi}{3}, \dfrac{5\pi}{6}, \dfrac{4\pi}{3}$
21. $\theta = \dfrac{\pi}{2}, \dfrac{3\pi}{2}$
23. $\theta = 0, \dfrac{2\pi}{3}, \dfrac{4\pi}{3}$
25. $\theta = \dfrac{\pi}{4}, \dfrac{5\pi}{4}$
27. $\theta = 0, \dfrac{\pi}{3}, \dfrac{2\pi}{3}, \pi, \dfrac{4\pi}{3}, \dfrac{5\pi}{3}, \dfrac{\pi}{9}, \dfrac{5\pi}{9}, \dfrac{7\pi}{9}, \dfrac{11\pi}{9}, \dfrac{13\pi}{9}, \dfrac{17\pi}{9}$
29. $\theta = \dfrac{\pi}{2}, \dfrac{7\pi}{6}, \dfrac{11\pi}{6}, \dfrac{\pi}{12}, \dfrac{\pi}{4}, \dfrac{5\pi}{12}, \dfrac{7\pi}{12}, \dfrac{3\pi}{4}, \dfrac{11\pi}{12}, \dfrac{13\pi}{12}, \dfrac{5\pi}{4}, \dfrac{17\pi}{12}, \dfrac{19\pi}{12}, \dfrac{7\pi}{4}, \dfrac{23\pi}{12}$

9. $\left(\frac{1+\sqrt{10}}{3}, -1+\sqrt{10}\right), \left(\frac{1-\sqrt{10}}{3}, -1-\sqrt{10}\right),$
$\left(\frac{-1+\sqrt{10}}{3}, 1+\sqrt{10}\right), \left(\frac{-1-\sqrt{10}}{3}, 1-\sqrt{10}\right)$

11. $\left(\frac{3\sqrt{2}}{2}, -2\sqrt{2}\right), \left(-\frac{3\sqrt{2}}{2}, 2\sqrt{2}\right), \left(\frac{3i}{2}, i\right), \left(-\frac{3i}{2}, -i\right)$

13. (4, 1), (—4, —1), (7, —2), (—7, 2)

15. (2, 4), (—2, —4), (6, —20), (—6, 20)

17. (5, 6), (—5, —6), (2, 3), (—2, —3)

19. $(-\frac{2}{3}, \frac{1}{2}), (-\frac{3}{2}, -2)$ 21. 1, 3; —1, —3 23. 7, 9; —7, —9

Review Exercises for Chapter 13

1. (4, 2), (0, —2)

3. $\left(\frac{3+\sqrt{41}}{2}, \frac{-3+\sqrt{41}}{2}\right), \left(\frac{3-\sqrt{41}}{2}, \frac{-3-\sqrt{41}}{2}\right),$
$\left(\frac{-3+\sqrt{41}}{2}, \frac{3+\sqrt{41}}{2}\right), \left(\frac{-3-\sqrt{41}}{2}, \frac{3-\sqrt{41}}{2}\right)$

5. $(5\sqrt{2}, 10), (5\sqrt{2}, -10), (-5\sqrt{2}, 10), (-5\sqrt{2}, -10)$

7. $(-2, 1), (-5, -\frac{1}{2})$ 9. $(-1, 1), (\frac{7}{2}, 4)$ 11. (0, 4), (0, —4)

13. $\left(\frac{3\sqrt{37}}{2}, i\sqrt{21}\right), \left(\frac{3\sqrt{37}}{2}, -i\sqrt{21}\right), \left(\frac{-3\sqrt{37}}{2}, i\sqrt{21}\right),$
$\left(\frac{-3\sqrt{37}}{2}, -i\sqrt{21}\right)$

15. $\left(\frac{5+\sqrt{47}}{6}, \frac{-5+\sqrt{47}}{4}\right), \left(\frac{5-\sqrt{47}}{6}, \frac{-5-\sqrt{47}}{4}\right),$
$\left(\frac{-5+\sqrt{47}}{6}, \frac{5+\sqrt{47}}{4}\right), \left(\frac{-5-\sqrt{47}}{6}, \frac{5-\sqrt{47}}{4}\right)$

17. $(0, 0), (\frac{2}{3}, \frac{1}{3}), (-\frac{2}{7}, -\frac{6}{7})$ 19. $(0, 0), (-\frac{1}{11}, -\frac{2}{33}), (-\frac{20}{11}, \frac{12}{11})$

21. $(0, 0), (5, \frac{10}{3}), (5, -\frac{10}{3})$

23. $(1, 1), (-1, -1), \left(\frac{6}{\sqrt{15}}, -\frac{1}{\sqrt{15}}\right), \left(-\frac{6}{\sqrt{15}}, \frac{1}{\sqrt{15}}\right)$

25. $\left(\frac{\sqrt{3}}{3}, \sqrt{3}\right), \left(-\frac{\sqrt{3}}{3}, -\sqrt{3}\right), \left(\frac{2\sqrt{55}}{11}, -\frac{\sqrt{55}}{11}\right), \left(-\frac{2\sqrt{55}}{11}, \frac{\sqrt{55}}{11}\right)$

27. $(3, -1), (-3, 1), (i, -i), (-i, i)$

29. $(-2, 2), \left(\frac{1+i\sqrt{15}}{2}, \frac{-1+i\sqrt{15}}{2}\right), \left(\frac{1-i\sqrt{15}}{2}, \frac{-1-i\sqrt{15}}{2}\right)$

Exercise Group 14–1

1. 6, 8, 10, 12; 164
3. $\frac{1}{2}, \frac{1}{4}, \frac{1}{6}, \frac{1}{8}; \frac{1}{86}$
5. $\frac{1}{3}, \frac{3}{5}, \frac{5}{7}, \frac{7}{9}; \frac{245}{247}$
7. $1, \frac{1}{4}, \frac{1}{9}, \frac{1}{16}; \frac{1}{5041}$
9. $\frac{1}{2}, \frac{1}{4}, \frac{1}{8}, \frac{1}{16}; \frac{1}{2048}$
11. $\frac{1}{2}, \frac{\sqrt{3}}{2}, 1, \frac{\sqrt{3}}{2}; \frac{\sqrt{3}}{2}$
13. $a_n = 2n + 1$
15. $a_n = \frac{1}{n}$
17. $a_n = \frac{1}{(n+1)^2}$
19. $a_n = \frac{n+1}{(n+2)(n+3)}$
21. $a_n = \frac{n+1}{1 \cdot 2 \cdot 3 \cdots n}$

Exercise Group 14–2

1. 10, 12, 14
3. $7, \frac{31}{4}, \frac{17}{2}$
5. $\frac{1}{3}, -\frac{1}{3}, -1$
7. $a_{23} = 68, S_{23} = 805$
9. $a_{101} = \frac{35}{2}, S_{101} = \frac{4545}{4}$
11. $a_{15} = -34, S_{15} = -195$
13. 23
15. $\frac{13}{12}$
17. $\frac{c+d}{2}$
19. $-5, -7, -9, -11, -13, -15, -17$
21. $\frac{29}{12}, \frac{25}{6}, \frac{71}{12}, \frac{23}{3}, \frac{113}{12}$
23. $a_1 = 11, S_{33} = 99$
25. $d = -\frac{70}{71}, a_{72} = -46$
27. $d = 3, a_{36} = 110$
29. $n = 24, a_{24} = -58$
31. $n = 27, a_{27} = 59$
33. $n = 14, a_{14} = -23$
35. $a_1 = -1, n = 26$
37. $d = 4, a_{10} = 28$
39. $\frac{88}{3}$
41. -42
43. $a_{27} = 61$
45. 13,293,307
47. 16 yr
49. \$3,297

Exercise Group 14–3

1. 7, 14, 28
3. $\frac{2}{3}, 1, \frac{3}{2}$
5. $-3, 5, -\frac{25}{3}$
7. $a_{17} = 2 \cdot 3^{16}, S_{17} = 3^{17} - 1$
9. $a_{15} = \frac{1}{2^{11}}, S_{15} = 16 - \frac{1}{2^{11}}$
11. $a_7 = -\frac{64}{3}, S_7 = -\frac{43}{3}$
13. $\pm 1, \frac{1}{2}, \pm\frac{1}{4}, \frac{1}{8}, \pm\frac{1}{16}$
15. $10^{8/7}, 10^{9/7}, 10^{10/7}, 10^{11/7}, 10^{12/7}, 10^{13/7}$
17. $\pm\frac{3}{2}, 1, \pm\frac{2}{3}$
19. $-7, \frac{7}{2}, -\frac{7}{4}, \frac{7}{8}, -\frac{7}{16}, \frac{7}{32}$
21. $n = 11, S_{11} = \frac{2047}{2}$
23. $n = 8, r = 2$
25. $n = 7, r = -3$
27. $a_8 = \frac{729}{8}, S_8 = \frac{2805 + 935\sqrt{2}}{24}$
29. 574
31. \$26,870
33. \$2,341

Exercise Group 14–4

1. $\frac{50}{9}$ 3. $\frac{100}{11}$ 5. 0.999 7. $\frac{21}{2}$ 9. $\frac{9}{10}$
11. $\dfrac{1}{1+x}$ 13. $\dfrac{x}{1-x^2}$ 15. $-\dfrac{x+3}{2x+5}$ 17. $\dfrac{x-1}{x}$ 19. $\frac{5}{2}$
21. 30 ft

Exercise Group 14–5

1. $\frac{2}{9}$ 3. $\frac{14}{99}$ 5. $\frac{700}{11}$ 7. $\frac{10}{99}$
9. $\frac{7}{111}$ 11. $\frac{2}{11}$ 13. $\frac{82}{11}$ 15. $\frac{5}{7}$

Review Exercises for Chapter 14

1. $a_{17} = 35$, $S_{17} = 323$ 3. $a_{77} = 3 \cdot 2^{76}$, $S_{77} = 3(2^{77} - 1)$
5. 5, 8, 11, 14, 17 7. 15, 45, 135, 405
9. $a_{15} = 44$, $S_{15} = 345$ 11. $d = -2$, $a_{13} = -9$
13. $n = 17$, $a_1 = -7$; $n = 23$, $a_1 = 5$
15. $r = -3$, $n = 6$ 17. $n = 7$, $S_7 = \frac{43}{16}$
19. $a_n = \sin^{n-1}\theta$, $S_n = \dfrac{1 - \sin^n \theta}{1 - \sin \theta}$

Exercise Group 15–2

1. $B = 121°$, $a = 3.6$, $c = 13$ 3. $A = 53°$, $b = 2.4$, $c = 2.0$
5. $B = 20° 39'$, $a = 5.4$, $c = 8.0$ 7. $C = 99° 10'$, $b = 34$, $c = 50$
9. Groundspeed = 270 mph, velocity of wind is 32 mph 11. 56 ft
13. 1720 naut mi 15. 29 mi

Exercise Group 15–3

1. No solution
3. $B = 75°$, $A = 65°$, $a = 28$; $B = 105°$, $A = 35°$, $a = 18$
5. $C = 27°$, $B = 88°$, $b = 0.22$ 7. No solution
9. $C = 23°$, $B = 92°$, $b = 0.25$
11. $A = 66° 0'$, $C = 75° 40'$, $c = 297$; $A = 114° 0'$, $C = 27° 40'$, $c = 142$
13. $AB = 381$ ft or 85.7 ft 15. 198.7 ft, $\theta = 86° 46'$ or $93° 14'$
17. 4481 lb, 24° 52′; 944.0 lb, 246° 32′ 19. 1.764 astronomical units

Exercise Group 15–4

1. $c = 8.3$, $B = 25° 10'$, $A = 19° 50'$
3. $b = 276$, $A = 27° 50'$, $C = 92° 40'$

5. $a = 59$, $B = 4° 50'$, $C = 25° 10'$
7. $c = 34$, $A = 28°$, $B = 20°$
9. $b = 0.074$, $A = 99°$, $C = 52°$
11. $A = 29°$, $B = 47°$, $C = 104°$
13. $A = 47°$, $B = 58°$, $C = 75°$
15. $A = 141°$, $B = 11°$, $C = 28°$
17. $A = 43°$, $B = 61°$, $C = 76°$
19. $A = 116°$, $B = 20°$, $C = 44°$
21. 202 ft
23. 70 mi, 203°
25. 35° 40′, 113°; 144° 20′, 67°

Exercise Group 15–5

1. $A = 18° 16'$, $B = 36° 32'$, $c = 321.6$
3. $A = 41° 41'$, $B = 96° 07'$, $c = 2.965$
5. $A = 34° 10'$, $C = 22° 36'$, $b = 0.5102$
7. $B = 15° 40'$, $C = 21° 04'$, $a = 53.04$
9. $B = 20° 02'$, $C = 64° 42'$, $a = 919{,}400$
11. $A = 17° 26'$, $B = 49° 40'$, $C = 112° 54'$
13. $A = 33° 54'$, $B = 49° 12'$, $C = 96° 54'$
15. $A = 167° 26'$, $B = 3° 30'$, $C = 9° 04'$
17. $A = 24° 50'$, $B = 137° 10'$, $C = 18°$
19. $A = 73° 44'$, $B = 52° 42'$, $C = 53° 34'$
21. Heading 165° 50′, average airspeed = 142 mph
23. 48° 55′ with F_1, 125.5 lb
25. 509.3 ft
27. A to C, 60° 20′; B to C, 305° 50′
29. 1st plane 42° 38′, 2nd plane 326° 32′

Exercise Group 15–6

1. 89.40
3. 449.6
5. 0.01151
7. 0.0004229
9. 4.328
11. 0.1164
13. 0.02557
15. 1151
17. 8.706 in^2
19. 137,300 ft^2
21. 833 ft^2
23. 1960 ft of fence

Exercise Group 16–1

17. $2, \frac{\pi}{6}; 2, -\frac{\pi}{6}$
19. $2, -\frac{\pi}{3}; 2, \frac{\pi}{3}$
21. $\sqrt{2}, -\frac{3\pi}{4}; \sqrt{2}, \frac{3\pi}{4}$
23. $4, \frac{\pi}{2}; 4, -\frac{\pi}{2}$
25. $7, \pi; 7, \pi$
27. $2\sqrt{3}, -\frac{2\pi}{3}; 2\sqrt{3}, \frac{2\pi}{3}$
29. $\sqrt{74}$, 54° 28′; $\sqrt{74}$, −54° 28′
31. 1, −60°; 1, 60°
33. 3, 135°; 3, −135°
35. 2.5, −73° 44′; 2.5, 73° 44′
37. $x = -1$, $y = -4$
39. $x = -\frac{3}{2}$, $y = -3$
41. $x = b$, $y = a$
43. $x = -\frac{5d}{b}$, $y = -\frac{7a}{c}$
45. $x = \frac{9}{4}$, $y = \frac{3}{2}$

Exercise Group 16–2

1. $8 + 16i, -2 - 8i$ 3. $-12 + i, 12 - 9i$ 5. $12 - 8i, 2$
7. $4i, -6$ 9. $9, -7 + 4i$ 11. $8 - 5i, 5i$
13. $12 - 4i, 2 + 4i$
15. $(3\sqrt{3} - 1) + \left(3 + \frac{\sqrt{3}}{2}\right)i, -(1 + 3\sqrt{3}) + \left(\frac{\sqrt{3}}{2} - 3\right)i$
17. $1.5 + (2\sqrt{3} - 5)i, 1.5 + (2\sqrt{3} + 5)i$

Exercise Group 16–3

1. $\sqrt{2}\,(\cos 45° + i \sin 45°)$ 3. $\sqrt{2}\,(\cos 315° + i \sin 315°)$
5. $\sqrt{2}\,(\cos 135° + i \sin 135°)$ 7. $2\sqrt{2}\,(\cos 225° + i \sin 225°)$
9. $2(\cos 0° + i \sin 0°)$ 11. $1.3(\cos 22°\, 37' + i \sin 22°\, 37')$
13. $\cos 182° + i \sin 182°$ 15. $5(\cos 154°\, 25' + i \sin 154°\, 25')$
17. $1.3(\cos 157°\, 23' + i \sin 157°\, 23')$ 19. $25(\cos 163°\, 44' + i \sin 163°\, 44')$

Exercise Group 16–4

1. $63 - 16i$ 3. $2 + 14i$ 5. $-35 - 5i$
7. $15 + 5i$ 9. $-24 - 24\sqrt{3}\, i$ 11. $-\frac{5}{34} + \frac{31}{34}i$
13. $-\frac{43}{346} - \frac{193}{346}i$ 15. $\frac{11}{5} - \frac{3}{5}i$ 17. $\frac{258}{533} - \frac{231}{533}i$
19. $2\sqrt{2}(\cos 75° + i \sin 75°)$ 21. $6\sqrt{6}(\cos 75° + i \sin 75°)$
23. $\frac{\sqrt{6}}{5}\,(\cos 15° + i \sin 15°)$ 25. $\frac{3\sqrt{2}}{20}\,(\cos 105° + i \sin 105°)$
27. $\frac{10\sqrt{3}}{7}\,(\cos 99°\, 44' + i \sin 99°\, 44')$ 29. $\frac{21}{16}(\cos 155°\, 37' + i \sin 155°\, 37')$

Exercise Group 16–5

1. $16 + 16i\sqrt{3}$ 3. $8i$ 5. i
7. $-\frac{1}{2} - \frac{1}{2}i\sqrt{3}$ 9. $-i$ 11. $0.2588 - 0.9659i$
13. $-0.9781 - 0.2079i$ 15. $-\frac{1}{2} + \frac{\sqrt{3}}{2}i$
17. $1, \frac{1}{2}(-1 + i\sqrt{3}), \frac{1}{2}(-1 - i\sqrt{3})$
19. $2(\cos 36° + i \sin 36°), 2(\cos 108° + i \sin 108°), -2,$
$2(\cos 252° + i \sin 252°), 2(\cos 324° + i \sin 324°)$
21. $\frac{1}{2}(\sqrt{3} + i), \frac{1}{2}(-\sqrt{3} + i), -i$
23. $\cos 75° + i \sin 75°, \cos 165° + i \sin 165°, \cos 255° + i \sin 255°,$
$\cos 345° + i \sin 345°$
25. $\sqrt[6]{12}\,(\cos 110° + i \sin 110°), \sqrt[6]{12}\,(\cos 230° + i \sin 230°),$
$\sqrt[6]{12}\,(\cos 350° + i \sin 350°)$

27. $\sqrt[3]{5}$ (cos 57° 17′ + i sin 57° 17′), $\sqrt[3]{5}$ (cos 117° 17′ + i sin 117° 17′),
$\sqrt[3]{5}$ (cos 177° 17′ + i sin 177° 17′), $\sqrt[3]{5}$ (cos 237° 17′ + i sin 237° 17′),
$\sqrt[3]{5}$ (cos 297° 17′ + i sin 297° 17′), $\sqrt[3]{5}$ (cos 357° 17′ + i sin 357° 17′)

Review Exercises for Chapter 16

1. $18 + i$
3. $129 - 28i$
5. $\frac{22}{41} - \frac{7}{41}i$
7. $\frac{1}{41} - \frac{32}{41}i$
9. $\frac{25}{26}$(cos 267° 59′ + i sin 267° 59′)
11. $\frac{25}{36}$(cos 352° 35′ + i sin 352° 35′)
13. $\frac{100}{63}$(cos 300° 24′ + i sin 300° 24′)
15. 2, 2(cos 72° + i sin 72°), 2(cos 144° + i sin 144°),
2(cos 216° + i sin 216°), 2(cos 288° + i sin 288°)
17. $\sqrt[7]{7}$, $\sqrt[7]{7}$(cos $51\frac{3}{7}$° + i sin $51\frac{3}{7}$°), $\sqrt[7]{7}$ (cos $102\frac{6}{7}$° + i sin $102\frac{6}{7}$°),
$\sqrt[7]{7}$ (cos $154\frac{2}{7}$° + i sin $154\frac{2}{7}$°), $\sqrt[7]{7}$ (cos $205\frac{5}{7}$° + i sin $205\frac{5}{7}$°),
$\sqrt[7]{7}$ (cos $257\frac{1}{7}$° + i sin $257\frac{1}{7}$°), $\sqrt[7]{7}$ (cos $308\frac{4}{7}$° + i sin $308\frac{4}{7}$°)
19. $\sqrt[6]{72}$ (cos 75° + i sin 75°), $\sqrt[6]{72}$ (cos 195° + i sin 195°),
$\sqrt[6]{72}$ (cos 315° + i sin 315°) = $\sqrt[3]{3}\,(1 - i)$

APPENDIX

Table 1

Powers and Roots

No.	*Sq.*	*Sq. Root*	*Cube*	*Cube Root*	*No.*	*Sq.*	*Sq. Root*	*Cube*	*Cube Root*
1	1	1.000	1	1.000	51	2,601	7.141	132,651	3.708
2	4	1.414	8	1.260	52	2,704	7.211	140,608	3.733
3	9	1.732	27	1.442	53	2,809	7.280	148,877	3.756
4	16	2.000	64	1.587	54	2,916	7.348	157,464	3.780
5	25	2.236	125	1.710	55	3,025	7.416	166,375	3.803
6	36	2.449	216	1.817	56	3,136	7.483	175,616	3.826
7	49	2.646	343	1.913	57	3,249	7.550	185,193	3.849
8	64	2.828	512	2.000	58	3,364	7.616	195,112	3.871
9	81	3.000	729	2.080	59	3,481	7.681	205,379	3.893
10	100	3.162	1,000	2.154	60	3,600	7.746	216,000	3.915
11	121	3.317	1,331	2.224	61	3,721	7.810	226,981	3.936
12	144	3.464	1,728	2.289	62	3,844	7.874	238,328	3.958
13	169	3.606	2,197	2.351	63	3,969	7.937	250,047	3.979
14	196	3.742	2,744	2.410	64	4,096	8.000	262,144	4.000
15	225	3.873	3,375	2.466	65	4,225	8.062	274,625	4.021
16	256	4.000	4,096	2.520	66	4,356	8.124	287,496	4.041
17	289	4.123	4,913	2.571	67	4,489	8.185	300,763	4.062
18	324	4.243	5,832	2.621	68	4,624	8.246	314,432	4.082
19	361	4.359	6,859	2.668	69	4,761	8.307	328,509	4.102
20	400	4.472	8,000	2.714	70	4,900	8.367	343,000	4.121
21	441	4.583	9,261	2.759	71	5,041	8.426	357,911	4.141
22	484	4.690	10,648	2.802	72	5,184	8.485	373,248	4.160
23	529	4.796	12,167	2.844	73	5,329	8.544	389,017	4.179
24	576	4.899	13,824	2.884	74	5,476	8.602	405,224	4.198
25	625	5.000	15,625	2.924	75	5,625	8.660	421,875	4.217
26	676	5.099	17,576	2.962	76	5,776	8.718	438,976	4.236
27	729	5.196	19,683	3.000	77	5,929	8.775	456,533	4.254
28	784	5.292	21,952	3.037	78	6,084	8.832	474,552	4.273
29	841	5.385	24,389	3.072	79	6,241	8.888	493,039	4.291
30	900	5.477	27,000	3.107	80	6,400	8.944	512,000	4.309
31	961	5.568	29,791	3.141	81	6,561	9.000	531,441	4.327
32	1,024	5.657	32,768	3.175	82	6,724	9.055	551,368	4.344
33	1,089	5.745	35,937	3.208	83	6,889	9.110	571,787	4.362
34	1,156	5.831	39,304	3.240	84	7,056	9.165	592,704	4.380
35	1,225	5.916	42,875	3.271	85	7,225	9.220	614,125	4.397
36	1,296	6.000	46,656	3.302	86	7,396	9.274	636,056	4.414
37	1,369	6.083	50,653	3.332	87	7,569	9.327	658,503	4.431
38	1,444	6.164	54,872	3.362	88	7,744	9.381	681,472	4.448
39	1,521	6.245	59,319	3.391	89	7,921	9.434	704,969	4.465
40	1,600	6.325	64,000	3.420	90	8,100	9.487	729,000	4.481
41	1,681	6.403	68,921	3.448	91	8,281	9.539	753,571	4.498
42	1,764	6.481	74,088	3.476	92	8,464	9.592	778,688	4.514
43	1,849	6.557	79,507	3.503	93	8,649	9.644	804,357	4.531
44	1,936	6.633	85,184	3.530	94	8,836	9.695	830,584	4.547
45	2,025	6.708	91,125	3.557	95	9,025	9.747	857,375	4.563
46	2,116	6.782	97,336	3.583	96	9,216	9.798	884,736	4.579
47	2,209	6.856	103,823	3.609	97	9,409	9.849	912,673	4.595
48	2,304	6.928	110,592	3.634	98	9,604	9.899	941,192	4.610
49	2,401	7.000	117,649	3.659	99	9,801	9.950	970,299	4.626
50	2,500	7.071	125,000	3.684	100	10,000	10.000	1,000,000	4.642

Table 2

Four-place Values of Functions and Radians

Degrees	Radians	Sin	Cos	Tan	Cot	Sec	Csc		
0° 00′	.0000	.0000	1.0000	.0000	——	1.000	——	1.5708	**90° 00′**
10	029	029	000	029	343.8	000	343.8	679	50
20	058	058	000	058	171.9	000	171.9	650	40
30	.0087	.0087	1.0000	.0087	114.6	1.000	114.6	1.5621	30
40	116	116	.9999	116	85.94	000	85.95	592	20
50	145	145	999	145	68.75	000	68.76	563	10
1° 00′	.0175	.0175	.9998	.0175	57.29	1.000	57.30	1.5533	**89° 00′**
10	204	204	998	204	49.10	000	49.11	504	50
20	233	233	997	233	42.96	000	42.98	475	40
30	.0262	.0262	.9997	.0262	38.19	1.000	38.20	1.5446	30
40	291	291	996	291	34.37	000	34.38	417	20
50	320	320	995	320	31.24	001	31.26	388	10
2° 00′	.0349	.0349	.9994	.0349	28.64	1.001	28.65	1.5359	**88° 00′**
10	378	378	993	378	26.43	001	26.45	330	50
20	407	407	992	407	24.54	001	24.56	301	40
30	.0436	.0436	.9990	.0437	22.90	1.001	22.93	1.5272	30
40	465	465	989	466	21.47	001	21.49	243	20
50	495	494	988	495	20.21	001	20.23	213	10
3° 00′	.0524	.0523	.9986	.0524	19.08	1.001	19.11	1.5184	**87° 00′**
10	553	552	985	553	18.07	002	18.10	155	50
20	582	581	983	582	17.17	002	17.20	126	40
30	.0611	.0610	.9981	.0612	16.35	1.002	16.38	1.5097	30
40	640	640	980	641	15.60	002	15.64	068	20
50	669	669	978	670	14.92	002	14.96	039	10
4° 00′	.0698	.0698	.9976	.0699	14.30	1.002	14.34	1.5010	**86° 00′**
10	727	727	974	729	13.73	003	13.76	981	50
20	756	756	971	758	13.20	003	13.23	952	40
30	.0785	.0785	.9969	.0787	12.71	1.003	12.75	1.4923	30
40	814	814	967	816	12.25	003	12.29	893	20
50	844	843	964	846	11.83	004	11.87	864	10
5° 00′	.0873	.0872	.9962	.0875	11.43	1.004	11.47	1.4835	**85° 00′**
10	902	901	959	904	11.06	004	11.10	806	50
20	931	929	957	934	10.71	004	10.76	777	40
30	.0960	.0958	.9954	.0963	10.39	1.005	10.43	1.4748	30
40	989	987	951	992	10.08	005	10.13	719	20
50	.1018	.1016	948	.1022	9.788	005	9.839	690	10
6° 00′	.1047	.1045	.9945	.1051	9.514	1.006	9.567	1.4661	**84° 00′**
10	076	074	942	080	9.255	006	9.309	632	50
20	105	103	939	110	9.010	006	9.065	603	40
30	.1134	.1132	.9936	.1139	8.777	1.006	8.834	1.4573	30
40	164	161	932	169	8.556	007	8.614	544	20
50	193	190	929	198	8.345	007	8.405	515	10
7° 00′	.1222	.1219	.9925	.1228	8.144	1.008	8.206	1.4486	**83° 00′**
10	251	248	922	257	7.953	008	8.016	457	50
20	280	276	918	287	7.770	008	7.834	428	40
30	.1309	.1305	.9914	.1317	7.596	1.009	7.661	1.4399	30
40	338	334	911	346	7.429	009	7.496	370	20
50	367	363	907	376	7.269	009	7.337	341	10
8° 00′	.1396	.1392	.9903	.1405	7.115	1.010	7.185	1.4312	**82° 00′**
10	425	421	899	435	6.968	010	7.040	283	50
20	454	449	894	465	6.827	011	6.900	254	40
30	.1484	.1478	.9890	.1495	6.691	1.011	6.765	1.4224	30
40	513	507	886	524	6.561	012	6.636	195	20
50	542	536	881	554	6.435	012	6.512	166	10
9° 00′	.1571	.1564	.9877	.1584	6.314	1.012	6.392	1.4137	**81° 00′**
		Cos	Sin	Cot	Tan	Csc	Sec	Radians	Degrees

TABLE 2

FOUR-PLACE VALUES OF FUNCTIONS AND RADIANS

DEGREES	RADIANS	Sin	Cos	Tan	Cot	Sec	Csc		
9° 00′	.1571	.1564	.9877	.1584	6.314	1.012	6.392	1.4137	81° 00′
10	600	593	872	614	197	013	277	108	50
20	629	622	868	644	084	013	166	079	40
30	.1658	.1650	.9863	.1673	5.976	1.014	6.059	1.4050	30
40	687	679	858	703	871	014	5.955	1.4021	20
50	716	708	853	733	769	015	855	992	10
10° 00′	.1745	.1736	.9848	.1763	5.671	1.015	5.759	1.3963	80° 00′
10	774	765	843	793	576	016	665	934	50
20	804	794	838	823	485	016	575	904	40
30	.1833	.1822	.9833	.1853	5.396	1.017	5.487	1.3875	30
40	862	851	827	883	309	018	403	846	20
50	891	880	822	914	226	018	320	817	10
11° 00′	.1920	.1908	.9816	.1944	5.145	1.019	5.241	1.3788	79° 00′
10	949	937	811	974	066	019	164	759	50
20	978	965	805	.2004	4.989	020	089	730	40
30	.2007	.1994	.9799	.2035	4.915	1.020	5.016	1.3701	30
40	036	.2022	793	065	843	021	4.945	672	20
50	065	051	787	095	773	022	876	643	10
12° 00′	.2094	.2079	.9781	.2126	4.705	1.022	4.810	1.3614	78° 00′
10	123	108	775	156	638	023	745	584	50
20	153	136	769	186	574	024	682	555	40
30	.2182	.2164	.9763	.2217	4.511	1.024	4.620	1.3526	30
40	211	193	757	247	449	025	560	497	20
50	240	221	750	278	390	026	502	468	10
13° 00′	.2269	.2250	.9744	.2309	4.331	1.026	4.445	1.3439	77° 00′
10	298	278	737	339	275	027	390	410	50
20	327	306	730	370	219	028	336	381	40
30	.2356	.2334	.9724	.2401	4.165	1.028	4.284	1.3352	30
40	385	363	717	432	113	029	232	323	20
50	414	391	710	462	061	030	182	294	10
14° 00′	.2443	.2419	.9703	.2493	4.011	1.031	4.134	1.3265	76° 00′
10	473	447	696	524	3.962	031	086	235	50
20	502	476	689	555	914	032	039	206	40
30	.2531	.2504	.9681	.2586	3.867	1.033	3.994	1.3177	30
40	560	532	674	617	821	034	950	148	20
50	589	560	667	648	776	034	906	119	10
15° 00′	.2618	.2588	.9659	.2679	3.732	1.035	3.864	1.3090	75° 00′
10	647	616	652	711	689	036	822	061	50
20	676	644	644	742	647	037	782	032	40
30	.2705	.2672	.9636	.2773	3.606	1.038	3.742	1.3003	30
40	734	700	628	805	566	039	703	974	20
50	763	728	621	836	526	039	665	945	10
16° 00′	.2793	.2756	.9613	.2867	3.487	1.040	3.628	1.2915	74° 00′
10	822	784	605	899	450	041	592	886	50
20	851	812	596	931	412	042	556	857	40
30	.2880	.2840	.9588	.2962	3.376	1.043	3.521	1.2828	30
40	909	868	580	994	340	044	487	799	20
50	938	896	572	.3026	305	045	453	770	10
17° 00′	.2967	.2924	.9563	.3057	3.271	1.046	3.420	1.2741	73° 00′
10	996	952	555	089	237	047	388	712	50
20	.3025	979	546	121	204	048	356	683	40
30	.3054	.3007	.9537	.3153	3.172	1.049	3.326	1.2654	30
40	083	035	528	185	140	049	295	625	20
50	113	062	520	217	108	050	265	595	10
18° 00′	.3142	.3090	.9511	.3249	3.078	1.051	3.236	1.2566	72° 00′
		Cos	Sin	Cot	Tan	Csc	Sec	RADIANS	DEGREES

Table 2

Four-place Values of Functions and Radians

Degrees	Radians	Sin	Cos	Tan	Cot	Sec	Csc		
18° 00′	.3142	.3090	.9511	.3249	3.078	1.051	3.236	1.2566	**72° 00′**
10	171	118	502	281	047	052	207	537	50
20	200	145	492	314	018	053	179	508	40
30	.3229	.3173	.9483	.3346	2.989	1.054	3.152	1.2479	30
40	258	201	474	378	960	056	124	450	20
50	287	228	465	411	932	057	098	421	10
19° 00′	.3316	.3256	.9455	.3443	2.904	1.058	3.072	1.2392	**71° 00′**
10	345	283	446	476	877	059	046	363	50
20	374	311	436	508	850	060	021	334	40
30	.3403	.3338	.9426	.3541	2.824	1.061	2.996	1.2305	30
40	432	365	417	574	798	062	971	275	20
50	462	393	407	607	773	063	947	246	10
20° 00′	.3491	.3420	.9397	.3640	2.747	1.064	2.924	1.2217	**70° 00′**
10	520	448	387	673	723	065	901	188	50
20	549	475	377	706	699	066	878	159	40
30	.3578	.3502	.9367	.3739	2.675	1.068	2.855	1.2130	30
40	607	529	356	772	651	069	833	101	20
50	636	557	346	805	628	070	812	072	10
21° 00′	.3665	.3584	.9336	.3839	2.605	1.071	2.790	1.2043	**69° 00′**
10	694	611	325	872	583	072	769	1.2014	50
20	723	638	315	906	560	074	749	985	40
30	.3752	.3665	.9304	.3939	2.539	1.075	2.729	1.1956	30
40	782	692	293	973	517	076	709	926	20
50	811	719	283	.4006	496	077	689	897	10
22° 00′	.3840	.3746	.9272	.4040	2.475	1.079	2.669	1.1868	**68° 00′**
10	869	773	261	074	455	080	650	839	50
20	898	800	250	108	434	081	632	810	40
30	.3927	.3827	.9239	.4142	2.414	1.082	2.613	1.1781	30
40	956	854	228	176	394	084	595	752	20
50	985	881	216	210	375	085	577	723	10
23° 00′	.4014	.3907	.9205	.4245	2.356	1.086	2.559	1.1694	**67° 00′**
10	043	934	194	279	337	088	542	665	50
20	072	961	182	314	318	089	525	636	40
30	.4102	.3987	.9171	.4348	2.300	1.090	2.508	1.1606	30
40	131	.4014	159	383	282	092	491	577	20
50	160	041	147	417	264	093	475	548	10
24° 00′	.4189	.4067	.9135	.4452	2.246	1.095	2.459	1.1519	**66° 00′**
10	218	094	124	487	229	096	443	490	50
20	247	120	112	522	211	097	427	461	40
30	.4276	.4147	.9100	.4557	2.194	1.099	2.411	1.1432	30
40	305	173	088	592	177	100	396	403	20
50	334	200	075	628	161	102	381	374	10
25° 00′	.4363	.4226	.9063	.4663	2.145	1.103	2.366	1.1345	**65° 00′**
10	392	253	051	699	128	105	352	316	50
20	422	279	038	734	112	106	337	286	40
30	.4451	.4305	.9026	.4770	2.097	1.108	2.323	1.1257	30
40	480	331	013	806	081	109	309	228	20
50	509	358	001	841	066	111	295	199	10
26° 00′	.4538	.4384	.8988	.4877	2.050	1.113	2.281	1.1170	**64° 00′**
10	567	410	975	913	035	114	268	141	50
20	596	436	962	950	020	116	254	112	40
30	.4625	.4462	.8949	.4986	2.006	1.117	2.241	1.1083	30
40	654	488	936	.5022	1.991	119	228	054	20
50	683	514	923	059	977	121	215	1.1025	10
27° 00′	.4712	.4540	.8910	.5095	1.963	1.122	2.203	1.0996	**63° 00′**
		Cos	Sin	Cot	Tan	Csc	Sec	Radians	Degrees

TABLE 2

FOUR-PLACE VALUES OF FUNCTIONS AND RADIANS

Degrees	Radians	Sin	Cos	Tan	Cot	Sec	Csc		
27° 00′	.4712	.4540	.8910	.5095	1.963	1.122	2.203	1.0996	**63° 00′**
10	741	566	897	132	949	124	190	966	50
20	771	592	884	169	935	126	178	937	40
30	.4800	.4617	.8870	.5206	1.921	1.127	2.166	1.0908	30
40	829	643	857	243	907	129	154	879	20
50	858	669	843	280	894	131	142	850	10
28° 00′	.4887	.4695	.8829	.5317	1.881	1.133	2.130	1.0821	**62° 00′**
10	916	720	816	354	868	134	118	792	50
20	945	746	802	392	855	136	107	763	40
30	.4974	.4772	.8788	.5430	1.842	1.138	2.096	1.0734	30
40	.5003	797	774	467	829	140	085	705	20
50	032	823	760	505	816	142	074	676	10
29° 00′	.5061	.4848	.8746	.5543	1.804	1.143	2.063	1.0647	**61° 00′**
10	091	874	732	581	792	145	052	617	50
20	120	899	718	619	780	147	041	588	40
30	.5149	.4924	.8704	.5658	1.767	1.149	2.031	1.0559	30
40	178	950	689	696	756	151	020	530	20
50	207	975	675	735	744	153	010	501	10
30° 00′	.5236	.5000	.8660	.5774	1.732	1.155	2.000	1.0472	**60° 00′**
10	265	025	646	812	720	157	1.990	443	50
20	294	050	631	851	709	159	980	414	40
30	.5323	.5075	.8616	.5890	1.698	1.161	1.970	1.0385	30
40	352	100	601	930	686	163	961	356	20
50	381	125	587	969	.675	165	951	327	10
31° 00′	.5411	.5150	.8572	.6009	1.664	1.167	1.942	1.0297	**59° 00′**
10	440	175	557	048	653	169	932	268	50
20	469	200	542	088	643	171	923	239	40
30	.5498	.5225	.8526	.6128	1.632	1.173	1.914	1.0210	30
40	527	250	511	168	621	175	905	181	20
50	556	275	496	208	611	177	896	152	10
32° 00′	.5585	.5299	.8480	.6249	1.600	1.179	1.887	1.0123	**58° 00′**
10	614	324	465	289	590	181	878	094	50
20	643	348	450	330	580	184	870	065	40
30	.5672	.5373	.8434	.6371	1.570	1.186	1.861	1.0036	30
40	701	398	418	412	560	188	853	1.0007	20
50	730	422	403	453	550	190	844	977	10
33° 00′	.5760	.5446	.8387	.6494	1.540	1.192	1.836	.9948	**57° 00′**
10	789	471	371	536	530	195	828	919	50
20	818	495	355	577	520	197	820	890	40
30	.5847	.5519	.8339	.6619	1.511	1.199	1.812	.9861	30
40	876	544	323	661	501	202	804	832	20
50	905	568	307	703	1.492	204	796	803	10
34° 00′	.5934	.5592	.8290	.6745	1.483	1.206	1.788	.9774	**56° 00′**
10	963	616	274	787	473	209	781	745	50
20	992	640	258	830	464	211	773	716	40
30	.6021	.5664	.8241	.6873	1.455	1.213	1.766	.9687	30
40	050	688	225	916	446	216	758	657	20
50	080	712	208	959	437	218	751	628	10
35° 00′	.6109	.5736	.8192	.7002	1.428	1.221	1.743	.9599	**55° 00′**
10	138	760	175	046	419	223	736	570	50
20	167	783	158	089	411	226	729	541	40
30	.6196	.5807	.8141	.7133	1.402	1.228	1.722	.9512	30
40	225	831	124	177	.393	231	715	483	20
50	254	854	107	221	385	233	708	454	10
36° 00′	.6283	.5878	.8090	.7265	1.376	1.236	1.701	.9425	**54° 00′**
		Cos	**Sin**	**Cot**	**Tan**	**Csc**	**Sec**	Radians	Degrees

Table 2

Four-place Values of Functions and Radians

Degrees	Radians	Sin	Cos	Tan	Cot	Sec	Csc		
36° 00′	.6283	.5878	.8090	.7265	1.376	1.236	1.701	.9425	**54° 00′**
10	312	901	073	310	368	239	695	396	50
20	341	925	056	355	360	241	688	367	40
30	.6370	.5948	.8039	.7400	1.351	1.244	1.681	.9338	30
40	400	972	021	445	343	247	675	308	20
50	429	995	004	490	335	249	668	279	10
37° 00′	.6458	.6018	.7986	.7536	1.327	1.252	1.662	.9250	**53° 00′**
10	487	041	969	581	319	255	655	221	50
20	516	065	951	627	311	258	649	192	40
30	.6545	.6088	.7934	.7673	1.303	1.260	1.643	.9163	30
40	574	111	916	720	295	263	636	134	20
50	603	134	898	766	288	266	630	105	10
38° 00′	.6632	.6157	.7880	.7813	1.280	1.269	1.624	.9076	**52° 00′**
10	661	180	862	860	272	272	618	047	50
20	690	202	844	907	265	275	612	.9018	40
30	.6720	.6225	.7826	.7954	1.257	1.278	1.606	.8988	30
40	749	248	808	.8002	250	281	601	959	20
50	778	271	790	050	242	284	595	930	10
39° 00′	.6807	.6293	.7771	.8098	1.235	1.287	1.589	.8901	**51° 00′**
10	836	316	753	146	228	290	583	872	50
20	865	338	735	195	220	293	578	843	40
30	.6894	.6361	.7716	.8243	1.213	1.296	1.572	.8814	30
40	923	383	698	292	206	299	567	785	20
50	952	406	679	342	199	302	561	756	10
40° 00′	.6981	.6428	.7660	.8391	1.192	1.305	1.556	.8727	**50° 00′**
10	.7010	450	642	441	185	309	550	698	50
20	039	472	623	491	178	312	545	668	40
30	.7069	.6494	.7604	.8541	1.171	1.315	1.540	.8639	30
40	098	517	585	591	164	318	535	610	20
50	127	539	566	642	157	322	529	581	10
41° 00′	.7156	.6561	.7547	.8693	1.150	1.325	1.524	.8552	**49° 00′**
10	185	583	528	744	144	328	519	523	50
20	214	604	509	796	137	332	514	494	40
30	.7243	.6626	.7490	.8847	1.130	1.335	1.509	.8465	30
40	272	648	470	899	124	339	504	436	20
50	301	670	451	952	117	342	499	407	10
42° 00′	.7330	.6691	.7431	.9004	1.111	1.346	1.494	.8378	**48° 00′**
10	359	713	412	057	104	349	490	348	50
20	389	734	392	110	098	353	485	319	40
30	.7418	.6756	.7373	.9163	1.091	1.356	1.480	.8290	30
40	447	777	353	217	085	360	476	261	20
50	476	799	333	271	079	364	471	232	10
43° 00′	.7505	.6820	.7314	.9325	1.072	1.367	1.466	.8203	**47° 00′**
10	534	841	294	380	066	371	462	174	50
20	563	862	274	435	060	375	457	145	40
30	.7592	.6884	.7254	.9490	1.054	1.379	1.453	.8116	30
40	621	905	234	545	048	382	448	087	20
50	650	926	214	601	042	386	444	058	10
44° 00′	.7679	.6947	.7193	.9657	1.036	1.390	1.440	.8029	**46° 00′**
10	709	967	173	713	030	394	435	999	50
20	738	988	153	770	024	398	431	970	40
30	.7767	.7009	.7133	.9827	1.018	1.402	1.427	.7941	30
40	796	030	112	884	012	406	423	912	20
50	825	050	092	942	006	410	418	883	10
45° 00′	.7854	.7071	.7071	1.000	1.000	1.414	1.414	.7854	**45° 00′**
		Cos	Sin	Cot	Tan	Csc	Sec	Radians	Degrees

TABLE 3

FOUR-PLACE LOGARITHMS OF NUMBERS

N	0	1	2	3	4	5	6	7	8	9
10	0000	0043	0086	0128	0170	0212	0253	0294	0334	0374
11	0414	0453	0492	0531	0569	0607	0645	0682	0719	0755
12	0792	0828	0864	0899	0934	0969	1004	1038	1072	1106
13	1139	1173	1206	1239	1271	1303	1335	1367	1399	1430
14	1461	1492	1523	1553	1584	1614	1644	1673	1703	1732
15	1761	1790	1818	1847	1875	1903	1931	1959	1987	2014
16	2041	2068	2095	2122	2148	2175	2201	2227	2253	2279
17	2304	2330	2355	2380	2405	2430	2455	2480	2504	2529
18	2553	2577	2601	2625	2648	2672	2695	2718	2742	2765
19	2788	2810	2833	2856	2878	2900	2923	2945	2967	2989
20	3010	3032	3054	3075	3096	3118	3139	3160	3181	3201
21	3222	3243	3263	3284	3304	3324	3345	3365	3385	3404
22	3424	3444	3464	3483	3502	3522	3541	3560	3579	3598
23	3617	3636	3655	3674	3692	3711	3729	3747	3766	3784
24	3802	3820	3838	3856	3874	3892	3909	3927	3945	3962
25	3979	3997	4014	4031	4048	4065	4082	4099	4116	4133
26	4150	4166	4183	4200	4216	4232	4249	4265	4281	4298
27	4314	4330	4346	4362	4378	4393	4409	4425	4440	4456
28	4472	4487	4502	4518	4533	4548	4564	4579	4594	4609
29	4624	4639	4654	4669	4683	4698	4713	4728	4742	4757
30	4771	4786	4800	4814	4829	4843	4857	4871	4886	4900
31	4914	4928	4942	4955	4969	4983	4997	5011	5024	5038
32	5051	5065	5079	5092	5105	5119	5132	5145	5159	5172
33	5185	5198	5211	5224	5237	5250	5263	5276	5289	5302
34	5315	5328	5340	5353	5366	5378	5391	5403	5416	5428
35	5441	5453	5465	5478	5490	5502	5514	5527	5539	5551
36	5563	5575	5587	5599	5611	5623	5635	5647	5658	5670
37	5682	5694	5705	5717	5729	5740	5752	5763	5775	5786
38	5798	5809	5821	5832	5843	5855	5866	5877	5888	5899
39	5911	5922	5933	5944	5955	5966	5977	5988	5999	6010
40	6021	6031	6042	6053	6064	6075	6085	6096	6107	6117
41	6128	6138	6149	6160	6170	6180	6191	6201	6212	6222
42	6232	6243	6253	6263	6274	6284	6294	6304	6314	6325
43	6335	6345	6355	6365	6375	6385	6395	6405	6415	6425
44	6435	6444	6454	6464	6474	6484	6493	6503	6513	6522
45	6532	6542	6551	6561	6571	6580	6590	6599	6609	6618
46	6628	6637	6646	6656	6665	6675	6684	6693	6702	6712
47	6721	6730	6739	6749	6758	6767	6776	6785	6794	6803
48	6812	6821	6830	6839	6848	6857	6866	6875	6884	6893
49	6902	6911	6920	6928	6937	6946	6955	6964	6972	6981
50	6990	6998	7007	7016	7024	7033	7042	7050	7059	7067
51	7076	7084	7093	7101	7110	7118	7126	7135	7143	7152
52	7160	7168	7177	7185	7193	7202	7210	7218	7226	7235
53	7243	7251	7259	7267	7275	7284	7292	7300	7308	7316
54	7324	7332	7340	7348	7356	7364	7372	7380	7388	7396

TABLE 3

FOUR-PLACE LOGARITHMS OF NUMBERS

N	0	1	2	3	4	5	6	7	8	9
55	7404	7412	7419	7427	7435	7443	7451	7459	7466	7474
56	7482	7490	7497	7505	7513	7520	7528	7536	7543	7551
57	7559	7566	7574	7582	7589	7597	7604	7612	7619	7627
58	7634	7642	7649	7657	7664	7672	7679	7686	7694	7701
59	7709	7716	7723	7731	7738	7745	7752	7760	7767	7774
60	7782	7789	7796	7803	7810	7818	7825	7832	7839	7846
61	7853	7860	7868	7875	7882	7889	7896	7903	7910	7917
62	7924	7931	7938	7945	7952	7959	7966	7973	7980	7987
63	7993	8000	8007	8014	8021	8028	8035	8041	8048	8055
64	8062	8069	8075	8082	8089	8096	8102	8109	8116	8122
65	8129	8136	8142	8149	8156	8162	8169	8176	8182	8189
66	8195	8202	8209	8215	8222	8228	8235	8241	8248	8254
67	8261	8267	8274	8280	8287	8293	8299	8306	8312	8319
68	8325	8331	8338	8344	8351	8357	8363	8370	8376	8382
69	8388	8395	8401	8407	8414	8420	8426	8432	8439	8445
70	8451	8457	8463	8470	8476	8482	8488	8494	8500	8506
71	8513	8519	8525	8531	8537	8543	8549	8555	8561	8567
72	8573	8579	8585	8591	8597	8603	8609	8615	8621	8627
73	8633	8639	8645	8651	8657	8663	8669	8675	8681	8686
74	8692	8698	8704	8710	8716	8722	8727	8733	8739	8745
75	8751	8756	8762	8768	8774	8779	8785	8791	8797	8802
76	8808	8814	8820	8825	8831	8837	8842	8848	8854	8859
77	8865	8871	8876	8882	8887	8893	8899	8904	8910	8915
78	8921	8927	8932	8938	8943	8949	8954	8960	8965	8971
79	8976	8982	8987	8993	8998	9004	9009	9015	9020	9025
80	9031	9036	9042	9047	9053	9058	9063	9069	9074	9079
81	9085	9090	9096	9101	9106	9112	9117	9122	9128	9133
82	9138	9143	9149	9154	9159	9165	9170	9175	9180	9186
83	9191	9196	9201	9206	9212	9217	9222	9227	9232	9238
84	9243	9248	9253	9258	9263	9269	9274	9279	9284	9289
85	9294	9299	9304	9309	9315	9320	9325	9330	9335	9340
86	9345	9350	9355	9360	9365	9370	9375	9380	9385	9390
87	9395	9400	9405	9410	9415	9420	9425	9430	9435	9440
88	9445	9450	9455	9460	9465	9469	9474	9479	9484	9489
89	9494	9499	9504	9509	9513	9518	9523	9528	9533	9538
90	9542	9547	9552	9557	9562	9566	9571	9576	9581	9586
91	9590	9595	9600	9605	9609	9614	9619	9624	9628	9633
92	9638	9643	9647	9652	9657	9661	9666	9671	9675	9680
93	9685	9689	9694	9699	9703	9708	9713	9717	9722	9727
94	9731	9736	9741	9745	9750	9754	9759	9763	9768	9773
95	9777	9782	9786	9791	9795	9800	9805	9809	9814	9818
96	9823	9827	9832	9836	9841	9845	9850	9854	9859	9863
97	9868	9872	9877	9881	9886	9890	9894	9899	9903	9908
98	9912	9917	9921	9926	9930	9934	9939	9943	9948	9952
99	9956	9961	9965	9969	9974	9978	9983	9987	9991	9996

Table 4
Logarithms of Trigonometric Functions

Degrees	Log$_{10}$ Sine	Log$_{10}$ Tangent	Log$_{10}$ Cotangent	Log$_{10}$ Cosine	
0° 00′					90° 00′
10′	.4637 −3	.4637 −3	2.5363	.0000	50′
20′	.7648 −3	.7648 −3	2.2352	.0000	40′
30′	9408 −3	.9409 −3	2.0591	.0000	30′
40′	.0658 −2	.0658 −2	1.9342	.0000	20′
50′	.1627 −2	.1627 −2	1.8373	.0000	10′
1° 00′	.2419 −2	.2419 −2	1.7581	.9999 −1	89° 00′
10′	.3088 −2	.3089 −2	1.6911	.9999 −1	50′
20′	.3668 −2	.3669 −2	1.6331	.9999 −1	40′
30′	.4179 −2	.4181 −2	1.5819	.9999 −1	30′
40′	.4637 −2	.4638 −2	1.5362	.9998 −1	20′
50′	.5050 −2	.5053 −2	1.4947	.9998 −1	10′
2° 00′	.5428 −2	.5431 −2	1.4569	.9997 −1	88° 00′
10′	.5776 −2	.5779 −2	1.4221	.9997 −1	50′
20′	.6097 −2	.6101 −2	1.3899	.9996 −1	40′
30′	.6397 −2	.6401 −2	1.3599	.9996 −1	30′
40′	.6677 −2	.6682 −2	1.3318	.9995 −1	20′
50′	.6940 −2	.6945 −2	1.3055	.9995 −1	10′
3° 00′	.7188 −2	.7194 −2	1.2806	.9994 −1	87° 00′
10′	.7423 −2	.7429 −2	1.2571	.9993 −1	50′
20′	.7645 −2	.7652 −2	1.2348	.9993 −1	40′
30′	.7857 −2	.7865 −2	1.2135	.9992 −1	30′
40′	.8059 −2	.8067 −2	1.1933	.9991 −1	20′
50′	.8251 −2	.8261 −2	1.1739	.9990 −1	10′
4° 00′	.8436 −2	.8446 −2	1.1554	.9989 −1	86° 00′
10′	.8613 −2	.8624 −2	1.1376	.9989 −1	50′
20′	.8783 −2	.8795 −2	1.1205	.9988 −1	40′
30′	.8946 −2	.8960 −2	1.1040	.9987 −1	30′
40′	.9104 −2	.9118 −2	1.0882	.9986 −1	20′
50′	.9256 −2	.9272 −2	1.0728	.9985 −1	10′
5° 00′	.9403 −2	.9420 −2	1.0580	.9983 −1	85° 00′
10′	.9545 −2	.9563 −2	1.0437	.9982 −1	50′
20′	.9682 −2	.9701 −2	1.0299	.9981 −1	40′
30′	.9816 −2	.9836 −2	1.0164	.9980 −1	30′
40′	.9945 −2	.9966 −2	1.0034	.9979 −1	20′
50′	.0070 −1	.0093 −1	.9907	.9977 −1	10′
6° 00′	.0192 −1	.0216 −1	.9784	.9976 −1	84° 00′
10′	.0311 −1	.0336 −1	.9664	.9975 −1	50′
20′	.0426 −1	.0453 −1	.9547	.9973 −1	40′
30′	.0539 −1	.0567 −1	.9433	.9972 −1	30′
40′	.0648 −1	.0678 −1	.9322	.9971 −1	20′
50′	.0755 −1	.0786 −1	.9214	.9969 −1	10′
7° 00′	.0859 −1	.0891 −1	.9109	.9968 −1	83° 00′
10′	.0961 −1	.0995 −1	.9005	.9966 −1	50′
20′	.1060 −1	.1096 −1	.8904	.9964 −1	40′
30′	.1157 −1	.1194 −1	.8806	.9963 −1	30′
40′	.1252 −1	.1291 −1	.8709	.9961 −1	20′
50′	.1345 −1	.1385 −1	.8615	.9959 −1	10′
8° 00′	.1436 −1	.1478 −1	.8522	.9958 −1	82° 00′
10′	.1525 −1	.1569 −1	.8431	.9956 −1	50′
20′	.1612 −1	.1658 −1	.8342	.9954 −1	40′
30′	.1697 −1	.1745 −1	.8255	.9952 −1	30′
40′	.1781 −1	.1831 −1	.8169	.9950 −1	20′
50′	.1863 −1	.1915 −1	.8085	.9948 −1	10′
9° 00′	.1943 −1	.1997 −1	.8003	.9946 −1	81° 00′
	Log$_{10}$ Cosine	Log$_{10}$ Cotangent	Log$_{10}$ Tangent	Log$_{10}$ Sine	Degrees

TABLE 4
LOGARITHMS OF TRIGONOMETRIC FUNCTIONS

Degrees	Log₁₀ Sine	Log₁₀ Tangent	Log₁₀ Cotangent	Log₁₀ Cosine	
9° 00′	.1943 − 1	.1997 − 1	.8003	.9946 − 1	81° 00′
10′	.2022 − 1	.2078 − 1	.7922	.9944 − 1	50′
20′	.2100 − 1	.2158 − 1	.7842	.9942 − 1	40′
30′	.2176 − 1	.2236 − 1	.7764	.9940 − 1	30′
40′	.2251 − 1	.2313 − 1	.7687	.9938 − 1	20′
50′	.2324 − 1	.2389 − 1	.7611	.9936 − 1	10′
10° 00′	.2397 − 1	.2463 − 1	.7537	.9934 − 1	80° 00′
10′	.2468 − 1	.2536 − 1	.7464	.9931 − 1	50′
20′	.2538 − 1	.2609 − 1	.7391	.9929 − 1	40′
30′	.2606 − 1	.2680 − 1	.7320	.9927 − 1	30′
40′	.2674 − 1	.2750 − 1	.7250	.9924 − 1	20′
50′	.2740 − 1	.2819 − 1	.7181	.9922 − 1	10′
11° 00′	.2806 − 1	.2887 − 1	.7113	.9919 − 1	79° 00′
10′	.2870 − 1	.2953 − 1	.7047	.9917 − 1	50′
20′	.2934 − 1	.3020 − 1	.6980	.9914 − 1	40′
30′	.2997 − 1	.3085 − 1	.6915	.9912 − 1	30′
40′	.3058 − 1	.3149 − 1	.6851	.9909 − 1	20′
50′	.3119 − 1	.3212 − 1	.6788	.9907 − 1	10′
12° 00′	.3179 − 1	.3275 − 1	.6725	.9904 − 1	78° 00′
10′	.3238 − 1	.3336 − 1	.6664	.9901 − 1	50′
20′	.3296 − 1	.3397 − 1	.6603	.9899 − 1	40′
30′	.3353 − 1	.3458 − 1	.6542	.9896 − 1	30′
40′	.3410 − 1	.3517 − 1	.6483	.9893 − 1	20′
50′	.3466 − 1	.3576 − 1	.6424	.9890 − 1	10′
13° 00′	.3521 − 1	.3634 − 1	.6366	.9887 − 1	77° 00′
10′	.3575 − 1	.3691 − 1	.6309	.9884 − 1	50′
20′	.3629 − 1	.3748 − 1	.6252	.9881 − 1	40′
30′	.3682 − 1	.3804 − 1	.6196	.9878 − 1	30′
40′	.3734 − 1	.3859 − 1	.6141	.9875 − 1	20′
50′	.3786 − 1	.3914 − 1	.6086	.9872 − 1	10′
14° 00′	.3837 − 1	.3968 − 1	.6032	.9869 − 1	76° 00′
10′	.3887 − 1	.4021 − 1	.5979	.9866 − 1	50′
20′	.3937 − 1	.4074 − 1	.5926	.9863 − 1	40′
30′	.3986 − 1	.4127 − 1	.5873	.9859 − 1	30′
40′	.4035 − 1	.4178 − 1	.5822	.9856 − 1	20′
50′	.4083 − 1	.4230 − 1	.5770	.9853 − 1	10′
15° 00′	.4130 − 1	.4281 − 1	.5719	.9849 − 1	75° 00′
10′	.4177 − 1	.4331 − 1	.5669	.9846 − 1	50′
20′	.4223 − 1	.4381 − 1	.5619	.9843 − 1	40′
30′	.4269 − 1	.4430 − 1	.5570	.9839 − 1	30′
40′	.4314 − 1	.4479 − 1	.5521	.9836 − 1	20′
50′	.4359 − 1	.4527 − 1	.5473	.9832 − 1	10′
16° 00′	.4403 − 1	.4575 − 1	.5425	.9828 − 1	74° 00′
10′	.4447 − 1	.4622 − 1	.5378	.9825 − 1	50′
20′	.4491 − 1	.4669 − 1	.5331	.9821 − 1	40′
30′	.4533 − 1	.4716 − 1	.5284	.9817 − 1	30′
40′	.4576 − 1	.4762 − 1	.5238	.9814 − 1	20′
50′	.4618 − 1	.4808 − 1	.5192	.9810 − 1	10′
17° 00′	.4659 − 1	.4853 − 1	.5147	.9806 − 1	73° 00′
10′	.4700 − 1	.4898 − 1	.5102	.9802 − 1	50′
20′	.4741 − 1	.4943 − 1	.5057	.9798 − 1	40′
30′	.4781 − 1	.4987 − 1	.5013	.9794 − 1	30′
40′	.4821 − 1	.5031 − 1	.4969	.9790 − 1	20′
50′	.4861 − 1	.5075 − 1	.4925	.9786 − 1	10′
18° 00′	.4900 − 1	.5118 − 1	.4882	.9782 − 1	72° 00′
	Log₁₀ Cosine	Log₁₀ Cotangent	Log₁₀ Tangent	Log₁₀ Sine	Degrees

TABLE 4
LOGARITHMS OF TRIGONOMETRIC FUNCTIONS

Degrees	Log₁₀ Sine	Log₁₀ Tangent	Log₁₀ Cotangent	Log₁₀ Cosine	
18° 00′	.4900 − 1	.5118 − 1	.4882	.9782 − 1	**72° 00′**
10′	.4939 − 1	.5161 − 1	.4839	.9778 − 1	50′
20′	.4977 − 1	.5203 − 1	.4797	.9774 − 1	40′
30′	.5015 − 1	.5245 − 1	.4755	.9770 − 1	30′
40′	.5052 − 1	.5287 − 1	.4713	.9765 − 1	20′
50′	.5090 − 1	.5329 − 1	.4671	.9761 − 1	10′
19° 00′	.5126 − 1	.5370 − 1	.4630	.9757 − 1	**71° 00′**
10′	.5163 − 1	.5411 − 1	.4589	.9752 − 1	50′
20′	.5199 − 1	.5451 − 1	.4549	.9748 − 1	40′
30′	.5235 − 1	.5491 − 1	.4509	.9743 − 1	30′
40′	.5270 − 1	.5531 − 1	.4469	.9739 − 1	20′
50′	.5306 − 1	.5571 − 1	.4429	.9734 − 1	10′
20° 00′	.5341 − 1	.5611 − 1	.4389	.9730 − 1	**70° 00′**
10′	.5375 − 1	.5650 − 1	.4350	.9725 − 1	50′
20′	.5409 − 1	.5689 − 1	.4311	.9721 − 1	40′
30′	.5443 − 1	.5727 − 1	.4273	.9716 − 1	30′
40′	.5477 − 1	.5766 − 1	.4234	.9711 − 1	20′
50′	.5510 − 1	.5804 − 1	.4196	.9706 − 1	10′
21° 00′	.5543 − 1	.5842 − 1	.4158	.9702 − 1	**69° 00′**
10′	.5576 − 1	.5879 − 1	.4121	.9697 − 1	50′
20′	.5609 − 1	.5917 − 1	.4083	.9692 − 1	40′
30′	.5641 − 1	.5954 − 1	.4046	.9687 − 1	30′
40′	.5673 − 1	.5991 − 1	.4009	.9682 − 1	20′
50′	.5704 − 1	.6028 − 1	.3972	.9677 − 1	10′
22° 00′	.5736 − 1	.6064 − 1	.3936	.9672 − 1	**68° 00′**
10′	.5767 − 1	.6100 − 1	.3900	.9667 − 1	50′
20′	.5798 − 1	.6136 − 1	.3864	.9661 − 1	40′
30′	.5828 − 1	.6172 − 1	.3828	.9656 − 1	30′
40′	.5859 − 1	.6208 − 1	.3792	.9651 − 1	20′
50′	.5889 − 1	.6243 − 1	.3757	.9646 − 1	10′
23° 00′	.5919 − 1	.6279 − 1	.3721	.9640 − 1	**67° 00′**
10′	.5948 − 1	.6314 − 1	.3686	.9635 − 1	50′
20′	.5978 − 1	.6348 − 1	.3652	.9629 − 1	40′
30′	.6007 − 1	.6383 − 1	.3617	.9624 − 1	30′
40′	.6036 − 1	.6417 − 1	.3583	.9618 − 1	20′
50′	.6065 − 1	.6452 − 1	.3548	.9613 − 1	10′
24° 00′	.6093 − 1	.6486 − 1	.3514	.9607 − 1	**66° 00′**
10′	.6121 − 1	.6520 − 1	.3480	.9602 − 1	50′
20′	.6149 − 1	.6553 − 1	.3447	.9596 − 1	40′
30′	.6177 − 1	.6587 − 1	.3413	.9590 − 1	30′
40′	.6205 − 1	.6620 − 1	.3380	.9584 − 1	20′
50′	.6232 − 1	.6654 − 1	.3346	.9579 − 1	10′
25° 00′	.6259 − 1	.6687 − 1	.3313	.9573 − 1	**65° 00′**
10′	.6286 − 1	.6720 − 1	.3280	.9567 − 1	50′
20′	.6313 − 1	.6752 − 1	.3248	.9561 − 1	40′
30′	.6340 − 1	.6785 − 1	.3215	.9555 − 1	30′
40′	.6366 − 1	.6817 − 1	.3183	.9549 − 1	20′
50′	.6392 − 1	.6850 − 1	.3150	.9543 − 1	10′
26° 00′	.6418 − 1	.6882 − 1	.3118	.9537 − 1	**64° 00′**
10′	.6444 − 1	.6914 − 1	.3086	.9530 − 1	50′
20′	.6470 − 1	.6946 − 1	.3054	.9524 − 1	40′
30′	.6495 − 1	.6977 − 1	.3023	.9518 − 1	30′
40′	.6521 − 1	.7009 − 1	.2991	.9512 − 1	20′
50′	.6546 − 1	.7040 − 1	.2960	.9505 − 1	10′
27° 00′	.6570 − 1	.7072 − 1	.2928	.9499 − 1	**63° 00′**
	Log₁₀ Cosine	Log₁₀ Cotangent	Log₁₀ Tangent	Log₁₀ Sine	Degrees

TABLE 4
LOGARITHMS OF TRIGONOMETRIC FUNCTIONS

Degrees	Log_{10} Sine	Log_{10} Tangent	Log_{10} Cotangent	Log_{10} Cosine	
27° 00′	.6570 −1	.7072 −1	.2928	.9499 −1	63° 00′
10′	.6595 −1	.7103 −1	.2897	.9492 −1	50′
20′	.6620 −1	.7134 −1	.2866	.9486 −1	40′
30′	.6644 −1	.7165 −1	.2835	.9479 −1	30′
40′	.6668 −1	.7196 −1	.2804	.9473 −1	20′
50′	.6692 −1	.7226 −1	.2774	.9466 −1	10′
28° 00′	.6716 −1	.7257 −1	.2743	.9459 −1	62° 00′
10′	.6740 −1	.7287 −1	.2713	.9453 −1	50′
20′	.6763 −1	.7317 −1	.2683	.9446 −1	40′
30′	.6787 −1	.7348 −1	.2652	.9439 −1	30′
40′	.6810 −1	.7378 −1	.2622	.9432 −1	20′
50′	.6833 −1	.7408 −1	.2592	.9425 −1	10′
29° 00′	.6856 −1	.7438 −1	.2562	.9418 −1	61° 00′
10′	.6878 −1	.7467 −1	.2533	.9411 −1	50′
20′	.6901 −1	.7497 −1	.2503	.9404 −1	40′
30′	.6923 −1	.7526 −1	.2474	.9397 −1	30′
40′	.6946 −1	.7556 −1	.2444	.9390 −1	20′
50′	.6968 −1	.7585 −1	.2415	.9383 −1	10′
30° 00′	.6990 −1	.7614 −1	.2386	.9375 −1	60° 00′
10′	.7012 −1	.7644 −1	.2356	.9368 −1	50′
20′	.7033 −1	.7673 −1	.2327	.9361 −1	40′
30′	.7055 −1	.7701 −1	.2299	.9353 −1	30′
40′	.7076 −1	.7730 −1	.2270	.9346 −1	20′
50′	.7097 −1	.7759 −1	.2241	.9338 −1	10′
31° 00′	.7118 −1	.7788 −1	.2212	.9331 −1	59° 00′
10′	.7139 −1	.7816 −1	.2184	.9323 −1	50′
20′	.7160 −1	.7845 −1	.2155	.9315 −1	40′
30′	.7181 −1	.7873 −1	.2127	.9308 −1	30′
40′	.7201 −1	.7902 −1	.2098	.9300 −1	20′
50′	.7222 −1	.7930 −1	.2070	.9292 −1	10′
32° 00′	.7242 −1	.7958 −1	.2042	.9284 −1	58° 00′
10′	.7262 −1	.7986 −1	.2014	.9276 −1	50′
20′	.7282 −1	.8014 −1	.1986	.9268 −1	40′
30′	.7302 −1	.8042 −1	.1958	.9260 −1	30′
40′	.7322 −1	.8070 −1	.1930	.9252 −1	20′
50′	.7342 −1	.8097 −1	.1903	.9244 −1	10′
33° 00′	.7361 −1	.8125 −1	.1875	.9236 −1	57° 00′
10′	.7380 −1	.8153 −1	.1847	.9228 −1	50′
20′	.7400 −1	.8180 −1	.1820	.9219 −1	40′
30′	.7419 −1	.8208 −1	.1792	.9211 −1	30′
40′	.7438 −1	.8235 −1	.1765	.9203 −1	20′
50′	.7457 −1	.8263 −1	.1737	.9194 −1	10′
34° 00′	.7476 −1	.8290 −1	.1710	.9186 −1	56° 00′
10′	.7494 −1	.8317 −1	.1683	.9177 −1	50′
20′	.7513 −1	.8344 −1	.1656	.9169 −1	40′
30′	.7531 −1	.8371 −1	.1629	.9160 −1	30′
40′	.7550 −1	.8398 −1	.1602	.9151 −1	20′
50′	.7568 −1	.8425 −1	.1575	.9142 −1	10′
35° 00′	.7586 −1	.8452 −1	.1548	.9134 −1	55° 00′
10′	.7604 −1	.8479 −1	.1521	.9125 −1	50′
20′	.7622 −1	.8506 −1	.1494	.9116 −1	40′
30′	.7640 −1	.8533 −1	.1467	.9107 −1	30′
40′	.7657 −1	.8559 −1	.1441	.9098 −1	20′
50′	.7675 −1	.8586 −1	.1414	.9089 −1	10′
36° 00′	.7692 −1	.8613 −1	.1387	.9080 −1	54° 00′
	Log_{10} Cosine	Log_{10} Cotangent	Log_{10} Tangent	Log_{10} Sine	Degrees

TABLE 4
LOGARITHMS OF TRIGONOMETRIC FUNCTIONS

Degrees	Log10 Sine	Log10 Tangent	Log10 Cotangent	Log10 Cosine	
36° 00′	.7692 −1	.8613 −1	.1387	.9080 −1	54° 00′
10′	.7710 −1	.8639 −1	.1361	.9070 −1	50′
20′	.7727 −1	.8666 −1	.1334	.9061 −1	40′
30′	.7744 −1	.8692 −1	.1308	.9052 −1	30′
40′	.7761 −1	.8718 −1	.1282	.9042 −1	20′
50′	.7778 −1	.8745 −1	.1255	.9033 −1	10′
37° 00′	.7795 −1	.8771 −1	.1229	.9023 −1	53° 00′
10′	.7811 −1	.8797 −1	.1203	.9014 −1	50′
20′	.7828 −1	.8824 −1	.1176	.9004 −1	40′
30′	.7844 −1	.8850 −1	.1150	.8995 −1	30′
40′	.7861 −1	.8876 −1	.1124	.8985 −1	20′
50′	.7877 −1	.8902 −1	.1098	.8975 −1	10′
38° 00′	.7893 −1	.8928 −1	.1072	.8965 −1	52° 00′
10′	.7910 −1	.8954 −1	.1046	.8955 −1	50′
20′	.7926 −1	.8980 −1	.1020	.8945 −1	40′
30′	.7941 −1	.9006 −1	.0994	.8935 −1	30′
40′	.7957 −1	.9032 −1	.0968	.8925 −1	20′
50′	.7973 −1	.9058 −1	.0942	.8915 −1	10′
39° 00′	.7989 −1	.9084 −1	.0916	.8905 −1	51° 00′
10′	.8004 −1	.9110 −1	.0890	.8895 −1	50′
20′	.8020 −1	.9135 −1	.0865	.8884 −1	40′
30′	.8035 −1	.9161 −1	.0839	.8874 −1	30′
40′	.8050 −1	.9187 −1	.0813	.8864 −1	20′
50′	.8066 −1	.9212 −1	.0788	.8853 −1	10′
40° 00′	.8081 −1	.9238 −1	.0762	.8843 −1	50° 00′
10′	.8096 −1	.9264 −1	.0736	.8832 −1	50′
20′	.8111 −1	.9289 −1	.0711	.8821 −1	40′
30′	.8125 −1	.9315 −1	.0685	.8810 −1	30′
40′	.8140 −1	.9341 −1	.0659	.8800 −1	20′
50′	.8155 −1	.9366 −1	.0634	.8789 −1	10′
41° 00′	.8169 −1	.9392 −1	.0608	.8778 −1	49° 00′
10′	.8184 −1	.9417 −1	.0583	.8767 −1	50′
20′	.8198 −1	.9443 −1	.0557	.8756 −1	40′
30′	.8213 −1	.9468 −1	.0532	.8745 −1	30′
40′	.8227 −1	.9494 −1	.0506	.8733 −1	20′
50′	.8241 −1	.9519 −1	.0481	.8722 −1	10′
42° 00′	.8255 −1	.9544 −1	.0456	.8711 −1	48° 00′
10′	.8269 −1	.9570 −1	.0430	.8699 −1	50′
20′	.8283 −1	.9595 −1	.0405	.8688 −1	40′
30′	.8297 −1	.9621 −1	.0379	.8676 −1	30′
40′	.8311 −1	.9646 −1	.0354	.8665 −1	20′
50′	.8324 −1	.9671 −1	.0329	.8653 −1	10′
43° 00′	.8338 −1	.9697 −1	.0303	.8641 −1	47° 00′
10′	.8351 −1	.9722 −1	.0278	.8629 −1	50′
20′	.8365 −1	.9747 −1	.0253	.8618 −1	40′
30′	.8378 −1	.9772 −1	.0228	.8606 −1	30′
40′	.8391 −1	.9798 −1	.0202	.8594 −1	20′
50′	.8405 −1	.9823 −1	.0177	.8582 −1	10′
44° 00′	.8418 −1	.9848 −1	.0152	.8569 −1	46° 00′
10′	.8431 −1	.9874 −1	.0126	.8557 −1	50′
20′	.8444 −1	.9899 −1	.0101	.8545 −1	40′
30′	.8457 −1	.9924 −1	.0076	.8532 −1	30′
40′	.8469 −1	.9949 −1	.0051	.8520 −1	20′
50′	.8482 −1	.9975 −1	.0025	.8507 −1	10′
45° 00′	.8495 −1	.0000	.0000	.8495 −1	45° 00′
	Log10 Cosine	Log10 Cotangent	Log10 Tangent	Log10 Sine	Degrees

INDEX

INDEX

ABCDE698765432